On final
Prob. on Chapter 11 will count
has quiz & as final
Be sure to study

MACHINE DESIGN

McGRAW-HILL SERIES IN MECHANICAL ENGINEERING

ROBERT M. DRAKE, JR., AND STEPHEN J. KLINE, *Consulting Editors*

BEGGS · *Mechanism*

CAMBEL AND JENNINGS · *Gas Dynamics*

DURELLI, PHILLIPS, AND TSAO · *Introduction to the Theoretical and Experimental Analysis of Stress and Strain*

ECKERT AND DRAKE · *Heat and Mass Transfer*

HAM, CRANE, AND ROGERS · *Mechanics of Machinery*

HARTMAN · *Dynamics of Machinery*

HINZE · *Turbulence*

JACOBSEN AND AYRE · *Engineering Vibrations*

PHELAN · *Fundamentals of Mechanical Design*

SABERSKY · *Engineering Thermodynamics*

SHIGLEY · *Kinematic Analysis of Mechanisms*

SHIGLEY · *Machine Design*

STOECKER · *Refrigeration and Air Conditioning*

The Series was established in 1954 under the Consulting Editorship of Richard G. Folsom, who continued in this capacity until he assumed the Presidency of Rensselaer Polytechnic Institute in 1958.

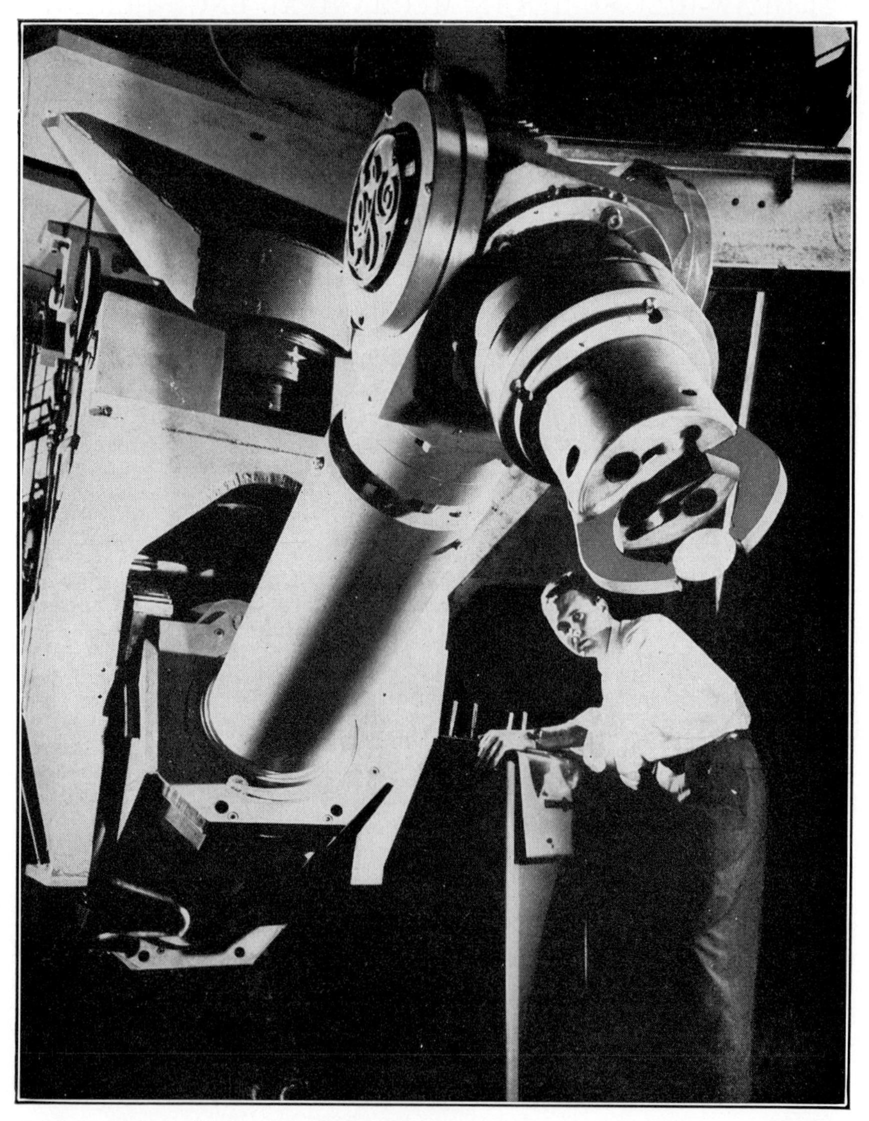

O-Man, a 15-ton remote-controlled mechanical arm designed to operate in radioactive areas, demonstrates its accurate control by picking up an egg. (*Courtesy of the General Electric Company.*)

Machine Design

JOSEPH EDWARD SHIGLEY

Associate Professor
Department of Mechanical Engineering
University of Michigan
Ann Arbor, Michigan

McGRAW-HILL BOOK COMPANY, INC.

New York Toronto London

1956

MACHINE DESIGN

Library of Congress Catalog Card Number 55-11180

IV

THE MAPLE PRESS COMPANY, YORK, PA.

PREFACE

This book is written as a text for students of engineering. For many years machine design has occupied a prominent position in the engineering curriculum. One of the reasons for this is that in the design of machine members the student finds it necessary to select items of information from many different areas of study. Mathematics, chemistry, physics, mechanics, materials, manufacturing processes, engineering drawing, and English are subjects for which a definite use is found in machine design. Thus its study not only serves the important purpose of emphasizing and strengthening these important subjects but also integrates them into the educational program of the engineer and effectively shatters the boundaries of compartmentalization.

In addition, machine design has served an important purpose because of its role as an intermediary between those areas of study which are basically scientific and analytic in content and the more practical engineering courses which are best described as teaching the art of engineering.

While these purposes are sufficiently valuable to justify for machine design a continued position in the curriculum, recent definitions have made it possible for this subject to contribute substantially to the accomplishment of the major goals of engineering education. A recent report of the Committee on Evaluation of Engineering Education of the American Society for Engineering Education states:

> Training for the creative and practical phases of economic design, involving analysis, synthesis, development and engineering research, is the most distinctive feature of professional engineering education.
>
> The technical goal of engineering education is preparation for performance of the functions of analysis and design or of the functions of construction, production or operation with full knowledge of analysis and design of the structure, machine, or process involved.

In accordance with these and other educational goals stated by the committee referred to above, the objectives of this book are:

1. To stimulate and exercise the creative ability of the student.
2. To cause the student to spend a major portion of his time in synthesizing rather than in analyzing.
3. To teach design as a formulation of decisions.

4. As far as is practical in an academic study, to teach *all* the factors which influence the design of a machine.

5. To teach machine design on a more scientific basis; to point out the empiricism and deficiencies in existing methods of analysis; and to plant the seed that methods of analysis are not closed subjects, that they are dynamic, and that someday the student himself may wish to contribute to their improvement.

For many years schools of engineering have been severely criticized for stifling the ingenuity of the student. It is the author's experience that all students of engineering possess a greater or lesser amount of creative ability, that some possess it to a remarkable degree, that it *can* be developed by exercise, and that unless it is developed it may lie dormant for a very long time.

In Chap. 1 the mechanism of creative thinking is developed. Chapter 5 reinforces this mechanism through a precise statement of the various steps involved, together with sufficient hints to start the student on his way. The problems which are associated with Chap. 5 and also those associated with the subsequent chapters in the book are, for the most part, designed to give the student sufficient freedom to permit him to make a choice. Unless the problem is made up with a certain freedom for solution, the student is deprived of the opportunity for exercise of his ingenuity. Having set up the problem so that choices are available, the student is invited to use his imagination and, at the same time, is forced to make decisions.

Throughout the entire book, it is the author's purpose to place the emphasis upon setting up of the problem and evaluation of the solution. The mere substitution of numbers into formulas to obtain answers has little educational value. In general, the solution of design problems first requires the student to choose a method of attack; many of the problems are set up with sufficient background information so that several choices are available. Secondly, he must select the data and information required for the solution. These data may be concealed in an excess of information, or in other cases the problem may require the use of outside sources in order to obtain it. Thirdly, the student must make his own set of simplifying assumptions, after which he may solve the problem. The last step is an evaluation of the solution in the light of the information which is given. Various means are used and emphasized throughout the text to make this step possible.

Two types of problems have been included. The first type is a pure practice problem intended to ground the reader in the methods of analysis being studied. These problems require no decisions and usually have only one answer. The second type of problem is one which permits a choice and requires that decisions be made in order to obtain *a* solution.

Some of these are long and may be used as design-room problems. Others are short enough so that they may be assigned as homework. All of them are marked with an asterisk in order to differentiate them clearly from the purely practice-type problem.

Part 1 (Fundamentals of Machine Design) is intended to be more than a review. It has been the author's experience that a transition period is necessary in the evolution of a student's thinking when he is introduced to machine design. This is partly the fault of an educational system which appears to regiment the attitudes of all but a few of the most individualistic. Thus in Part 1 it is intended that the student be gradually separated from his comfortable and secure attitude; that he be introduced to the concept that problems may have many answers; that the answer depends upon how he, the student, sets up the problem; that the answer depends upon his decisions and his assumptions; and that he alone is responsible for the solution.

The design of shafts, machine frames, and other elements provides an excellent vehicle for teaching fundamentals. These topics are also basic to all machines. For this reason, the design of these elements is included in Part 1 rather than in separate chapters. It is believed that Castigliano's theorem has been neglected too long in the education of a designer. It is a powerful tool for the analysis of complex mechanical structures and accordingly has been included in Part 1.

The various chapters in Part 2 (The Design and Selection of Machine Elements) are independent and may be introduced in any order. Although the author agrees that the design of complete machines has no place in an academic program, yet the design of any single member is dependent upon its relation to the whole machine. It is in accordance with this philosophy that these relationships are injected into the various problems. No problems involving the design of whole machines are included, but because these relations are included in the problems it is believed that the student will have a better understanding of this kind of design.

The author is especially grateful to his close friend and associate for many years, Professor Douglas W. Bradbury, who has read the entire manuscript and offered many helpful suggestions. He participated in discussions with the author over a period of years, and the philosophy of the book, therefore, is a blending of Professor Bradbury's ideas and those of the author.

JOSEPH E. SHIGLEY

CONTENTS

Preface vii

PART 1. FUNDAMENTALS OF MACHINE DESIGN

1. Introduction 3

1-1. Definition of Design. 1-2. Design Decisions. 1-3. The Nature of Creative Thinking. 1-4. The Improvement of Existing Solutions. 1-5. The Analysis of the Problem. 1-6. Shaping and Synthesizing the Parts. 1-7. Design Factors. 1-8. Strength Factors. 1-9. Stiffness Factors. 1-10. Other Design Factors.

2. Stresses in Machine Parts 16

2-1. Factor of Safety. 2-2. Tension, Compression, and Shear. 2-3. Combined Stresses. 2-4. Torsional Stresses. 2-5. Bending Stresses. 2-6. Superposition. 2-7. Hertz Contact Stresses. 2-8. Concentration of Stress.

3. Deflection of Machine Parts 48

3-1. Introduction. 3-2. Elasticity. 3-3. Statically Indeterminate Problems. 3-4. Tensile or Compressive Strain in Two Directions. 3-5. Deflection of Beams. 3-6. Indeterminate Beams. 3-7. Strain Energy in Tension and Compression. 3-8. Strain Energy in Torsion. 3-9. Strain Energy in Bending. 3-10. The Theorem of Castigliano. 3-11. Columns. 3-12. Curved Beams. 3-13. Vibration. 3-14. Thermal Stresses and Strains.

4. Materials and Their Properties 89

4-1. Static Strength. 4-2. Ductility. 4-3. Resilience. 4-4. Toughness. 4-5. Hardness. 4-6. Fatigue. 4-7. Results of Fatigue Tests. 4-8. Designing for Fatigue Conditions. 4-9. Factors Affecting Fatigue Strength. 4-10. Failure Theories. 4-11. Impact Properties. 4-12. Creep and Temperature Properties. 4-13. Numbering Systems. 4-14. Processing Methods—General. 4-15. Casting Processes. 4-16. Powder-metallurgy Process. 4-17. Hot-working Processes. 4-18. Cold-working Processes. 4-19. Equilibrium Diagrams. 4-20. The Heat-treatment of Steel. 4-21. Alloy Steels. 4-22. Cast Steels. 4-23. Stainless Steels. 4-24. Cast Iron. 4-25. Aluminum and Its Alloys. 4-26. Magnesium. 4-27. Copper-base Alloys.

5. Principles of Machine Design 148

5-1. The Specifications. 5-2. The Selection and Arrangement of the Parts. 5-3. Design Factors. 5-4. The Strength Design Factor. 5-5. The Material and Process. 5-6. Methods of Solution. 5-7. Assumptions. 5-8. Recording the Design. 5-9. Cost Reduction.

PART 2. THE DESIGN AND SELECTION OF MACHINE ELEMENTS

6. The Design of Screws, Fasteners, and Joints 181

6-1. Power Screws. 6-2. Preloading of Bolts. 6-3. Selection of the Nut. 6-4. Bolted and Riveted Joints Loaded in Shear. 6-5. Bolted Joints Loaded in Tension. 6-6. Effect of Assumptions. 6-7. Keys and Splines. 6-8. Pins, Cotters, and Retainers. 6-9. Welded Joints. 6-10. Closure.

7. Mechanical Springs 223

7-1. Stresses in Helical Springs. 7-2. Deflection of Helical Springs. 7-3. Extension Springs. 7-4. Compression Springs. 7-5. Fatigue Loading. 7-6. Assumptions and Decisions. 7-7. Helical Torsion Springs. 7-8. Belleville Springs. 7-9. Leaf Springs. 7-10. Critical Frequency of Helical Springs. 7-11. Energy Considerations. 7-12. Spring Materials.

8. Antifriction Bearings 247

8-1. Bearing Types. 8-2. Bearing Theory. 8-3. Bearing Selection. 8-4. Selection of Ball Bearings. 8-5. Selection of Tapered Roller Bearings. 8-6. Thrust Bearings. 8-7. Lubrication. 8-8. Enclosure. 8-9. Shaft and Housing Details.

9. Lubrication and Journal Bearings 270

9-1. Fundamentals. 9-2. Viscosity. 9-3. Statement of the Problem. 9-4. Hydrodynamic Theory. 9-5. Design Factors. 9-6. The Relation of the Variables. 9-7. Pressure-fed Bearings. 9-8. Heat Dissipation of Bearings. 9-9. Practical Range of the Variables. 9-10. The Independent Variables. 9-11. The Dependent Variables. 9-12. Bearing Types. 9-13. Bearing Materials. 9-14. Journal-bearing Design.

10. Spur Gears. 313

10-1. Introduction. 10-2. Conjugate Action. 10-3. Involute Properties. 10-4. Fundamentals. 10-5. Cutting Methods. 10-6. Tooth Systems. 10-7. Loads. 10-8. Discussion of Tooth Loads. 10-9. Preliminary Design Decisions. 10-10. Beam Strength. 10-11. The Buckingham Equation for Dynamic Loads. 10-12. Surface Durability. 10-13. Friction and Heat. 10-14. Gear Materials. 10-15. Gear-blank Design.

11. Helical, Worm, and Bevel Gears. 366

11-1. Parallel Helical Gears. 11-2. Tooth Relationships. 11-3. Helical-gear Bearing Loads. 11-4. Tooth Proportions for Helical Gears. 11-5. Strength of Helical Gears. 11-6. Crossed-helical Gears. 11-7. Strength of Crossed-helical Gears. 11-8. Efficiency of Crossed-helical Gears. 11-9. Worm Gears. 11-10. Strength of Worm-gear Teeth. 11-11. Straight Bevel Gears. 11-12. Beam Strength of Straight-tooth Bevel Gears. 11-13. Dynamic Load and Wear. 11-14. Shaft Loads. 11-15. Spiral Bevel Gears.

12. Clutches, Brakes, and Couplings 402

12-1. Positive-contact Clutches. 12-2. Frictional-contact Rim Clutches and Brakes. 12-3. Frictional-contact Axial Clutches. 12-4. Friction Materials. 12-5. Energy Considerations. 12-6. Miscellaneous Clutches and Brakes. 12-7. Hydraulic Couplings. 12-8. Decisions.

13. Flexible Machine Elements 433

13-1. Belts. 13-2. Flat Belts. 13-3. V Belts. 13-4. General Considerations. 13-5. Roller Chain. 13-6. Rope Drives. 13-7. Wire Rope. 13-8. Flexible Shafts.

14. Miscellaneous Machine Elements 462

14-1. Stresses in Thin-walled Cylinders. 14-2. Stresses in Thick-walled Cylinders. 14-3. Press and Shrink Fits. 14-4. Flat Plates. 14-5. Rectangular Plates. 14-6. Rotating Disks. 14-7. Flywheels. 14-8. Hydraulic Machines.

Appendix 491

Index 511

PART 1

FUNDAMENTALS OF MACHINE DESIGN

CHAPTER 1

INTRODUCTION

1-1. Definition of Design. To design is to make decisions. The Ford automobile and the Chevrolet automobile both represent successful solutions to the same problem. The Ford and the Chevrolet are different from each other; they look different; they have different motors, with different piston sizes and different valve arrangements; in fact, the only parts common or identical in the two cars are those standard parts, such as bolts and nuts, and accessories made by a third manufacturer. Yet each automobile represents a successful solution to the same design problem.

Considering the number of different makes of automobiles now being manufactured and considering that each make represents a solution of the same design problem, we see that a design problem has many solutions. When the variety and quantity of products manufactured in the United States today are considered, such as washing machines, metalworking lathes, electric motors, boats, lawn mowers, bicycles, pumps, fans, and steam turbines, to name a few, it is seen that every design problem has a great many solutions. Why are these solutions different from each other?

A manufacturer makes a decision to use cast-iron gears in a machine. He does this because he has an efficient and well-organized foundry; he can produce good strong gears at a low price. But, because these gears are made of cast iron, which is weaker than steel, they will occupy a larger space in the finished machine. The decision to use cast iron instead of steel makes the gears and the housing in which they operate larger.

An automotive manufacturer makes the decision to use a compression ratio of 7.8 instead of 7.2. The higher compression ratio places more force on the piston, wrist pin, connecting rod, and crankshaft, causing the manufacturer to "heavy up" on these elements or to use stronger materials. The decision to use the higher compression ratio requires that the parts be made of stronger or heavier materials.

A window manufacturer decides to build aluminum windows. Aluminum, having a lower modulus than steel, requires a higher moment of inertia for equal deflection under load. The decision to use aluminum requires that the frames and dividers be increased in width.

A decision, once made, influences all the other decisions in the chain between initiation of the design and marketing of the finished product. The decision to use a cast-iron gear influenced the entire chain of events leading to the finished design. It led to larger bearings which caused the frame to be larger. Because the frame became larger, its dimensions also had to be made larger in order to reduce the deflection.

The manufacturer of the engine with the higher compression ratio found that changes were necessary all the way from the piston to the rear wheels. Therefore, machines are different from each other because each represents an individual interdependent chain of decisions.

To design is to make decisions. The study of machine design is an investigation of the various decisions which determine the mechanical arrangement of parts in a machine and which influence the size, shape, or material of a finished machine part.

1-2. Design Decisions. Quite frequently there is found on the market an inferior product or machine which owes its inferiority to the quality of the decisions made during the design. Poor decisions will result in a poor design. A decision based upon conjecture, poor judgment, or inadequate knowledge will produce an inferior design. As the frontiers of knowledge advance, so will the quality of design decisions improve and, in turn, the resulting machines.

No one expects the model 1975 Buick to be an exact prototype of the 1960 model. New materials, better mechanical arrangements, new production machines, and new methods of analysis, all the result of increased knowledge, will affect the design decisions and bring about a vast improvement of the 1975 model.

Improvement will also come in other ways. It has become customary in the automotive industry to place the engine in the front end of the car with the cylinders lined up in the direction of travel, the crankshaft being below and the cylinder head on top. What would happen if the axis of the engine were to be placed crosswise of the car, or if the axis were to be placed vertical, or if the engine were turned over with the spark plugs on the bottom? Perhaps one of these methods would eliminate a great many parts, or simplify machining operations, or lessen the load on certain parts, or use a less expensive manufacturing process. For year after year new improved models of automobiles and engine lathes, weaving looms and radios, tractors and diesel engines have appeared on the market. The ingenuity and imagination of the design engineer creatively applied to each decision have resulted in this rapid progress of American industry.

Decisions are always compromises. The engineer would always prefer to use the strongest material—but it is expensive, and so he compromises. He would prefer to use a material light in weight—but it has too much deflection; he compromises. He prefers the lowest-priced fuel—but the engine knocks; he compromises. These continual compromises make the designer dissatisfied with the product he has designed. The only way he can remove this feeling of dissatisfaction is by *creating* a new design to eliminate the difficulties of the old. Thus machine design is a study of decisions—decisions which require a broad comprehensive knowledge, a rich background of experience tempered with judgment, and, most important of all, creative imagination!

1-3. The Nature of Creative Thinking. Creation may be defined as a successful step across the border line of knowledge. It is an addition to knowledge—a defining of things which were previously unknown. For the purposes of this book anything new or unheard of in the total experience of the reader will be considered to be "unknown."

Graham Wallas[1] recognizes four successive steps in the inventive act. These four steps are the periods of *preparation*, *incubation*, *illumination*, and *verification*.

Preparation. The preparation stage is a period of conscious, directed labor. It is the vitally necessary first step in the creative act. It is also one of the most difficult of the steps because it requires mental discipline and will of the highest order.

Briefly, the period of preparation is an exploration of all possible solutions to the problem. Initially, these solutions, no matter how absurd they may appear to be, are recorded and investigated from every angle of approach. Various combinations of them are tried. The intent is that the problem be explored to complete exhaustion so that the embryo creator is mentally familiar with the problem and its requirements in the most minute detail.

It is, in fact, a preparation of the mind.

Incubation. The mind is fully prepared when it is completely familiar with all the little byways, when it has traveled these byways to the innermost recesses, and when trial after trial after trial has failed to yield even the faintest wisp of something new. The mind is then in condition to recognize a solution. But between the periods of preparation and illumination there usually exists a period of incubation. During this time the mind may be relaxed or it may be working on other problems. The fact that this period of time exists—sometimes short, sometimes long—has been verified by many observers.

Illumination. The subconscious mind, haunted and worried by a problem, everlastingly seeks a solution by constantly rearranging an array of facts and experiences stored within the recesses of the memory. These facts and experiences are continually changing, forming an endless

[1] Graham Wallas, "The Art of Thought," Harcourt, Brace and Company, Inc., New York, 1926.

variety of shifting and different patterns. When a pattern is found which appears to be workable, that picture is flashed to the conscious mind. In exactly the same way, the engineer is worried and obsessed by his inability to find a new mechanical arrangement of parts. Suddenly into his conscious mind flashes a new and fresh answer, placed there by his subconscious mind from the kaleidoscope of patterns. Such is the period or instant of illumination.

A very common experience which is illustrative of illumination happens occasionally when we search our mind for a name or a certain means of accomplishing an end, but without success. In fact, our struggle to remember apparently has the effect of making the matter even more difficult to recall. But if we let the matter drop, the material which we had battled with in vain flashes into our memory, bringing with it satisfying relief. This is exactly the manner in which the long-sought solution comes to the mind of the inventor.

Sometimes illumination is accidental. Goodyear worked for years on the problem of curing rubber. Quite by accident he dropped a mixture of raw rubber and sulfur on a hot stove. He saw that the rubber had cured, and he realized that he had the answer he had sought for so long. Without the period of preparation, however, Goodyear would not have recognized the significance of the accident.

Verification. Illumination has occurred. The period of verification is that time during which the solution is analyzed and tested and found to be truly a solution. It is reduced to exact form and shape and made communicable to others. This period, too, requires conscious mental action and often a great deal of labor. Verification is the final necessary step in the creative process.

Irritation and Decision. Two additional points regarding creative thinking have sufficient importance to warrant emphasis. They represent what are probably the most important contributions resulting from a three-day symposium on the nature of creative thinking which was held in 1952.[1] The first point was brought out by Dr. F. S. C. Northrop, Yale University philosopher. He states:

> The beginning of creativity consists in being disturbed by something, in having something in the situation confronting you that raises a problem. . . . Creative thinking consists in being sensitive to that disturbance, in staying with it and analyzing it and finally coming up with some kind of speculative answer which is then confirmed by empirical, and preferably experimental, evidence.

Dr. Arthur Holly Compton, Chancellor of Washington University, made the second point. He states:

[1] "The Nature of Creative Thinking," Industrial Research Institute, New York, 1952.

First of all, to my mind the thing which is the essence of creativity is the decision to do something about it when you are irritated. I would agree that irritation is the first step; but the decision to do something about it—that is the essence of creativity. . . . The difference between a good scientist and a scientist that isn't so good is whether he will make himself do the thing that he sees needs to be done. It seems to me that here is perhaps the most important element in creativity. The creative man must have in himself the incentive and the self-discipline to do the thing that he sees needs to be done.

Creative thinking in machine design will, in general, take three forms. They are:

1. The improvement of existing solutions
2. The analysis of the particular problem
3. The shaping and synthesizing of the parts

1-4. The Improvement of Existing Solutions. Existing methods of solving machine-design problems may take one of three forms. These are:

1. Methods which employ a theory or law
2. Methods which employ experimental evidence
3. Empirical methods

Theory. Mathematics is a human invention and therefore can never perfectly describe nature.[1] The fact that a mathematical equation gives answers for a range of numbers substituted in it without limit does not mean that all the answers have physical significance. The equation for the velocity of a mass gives answers for masses from an atomic order to a solar order, but the equation fails to distinguish between the correct and the incorrect answers. Again, the equation for the velocity of a bicycle gives velocities of, say, 10 ft per day or 700 mph. The mathematics does not automatically introduce the effect of air resistance at velocities of 700 mph, nor does it account for the irregularities and bumps in the road at velocities of 10 ft per day.

Thus our mathematical equations have certain limitations on the range of values which may be used. Many times these limitations remain unstated and must be determined inferentially from some other consideration. The present tendency toward heavier loads, higher speeds, and lighter materials makes it vitally necessary that we be aware of these limitations and that we realize that when the extremes of the range are reached improvement of existing solutions is possible.

[1] P. W. Bridgman, "The Logic of Modern Physics," p. 60, The Macmillan Company, New York, 1946.

A second means of improvement is sometimes possible when we consider the basic assumptions used in deriving the mathematical equations. The collection of mathematical solutions available for use in machine design today is the product of the best minds in history. However, history also tells us that improvement is not only possible but probable. A few examples here will serve to illustrate the main thesis.

Galileo (1564–1642) first analyzed stresses in a cantilever beam.[1] He assumed the stress to be uniformly distributed over the cross-sectional area of the beam. Machines designed by using Galileo's assumption would have been heavy and awkward, for we know that it gave a value of stress three times as high as that calculated according to modern-day assumptions. Mariotte (1620–1684) realized that Galileo's assumption gave poor results. He contributed the assumption we use today, namely, that the stress in a beam varies as the distance from the neutral axis.

In order to make mathematics work for us in the solution of any problem it is necessary to make assumptions. These simplify and limit the scope of the problem. They make it capable of being solved within a reasonable time and with a reasonable amount of effort.

We shall distinguish two kinds of assumptions, *basic assumptions*, which are used in the derivation of the fundamental equations, and *design assumptions*, which are used to simplify a complicated machine part to the point where it can be analyzed by one of the fundamental equations.

It is probable that an alteration of the basic assumptions may sometime make possible an improvement in many solutions. It is certainly true that our position would be sad if we believed that continued improvement were impossible. Mathematics is a very useful engineering tool, but when theory fails to agree with experimental facts the engineer should seek the answer elsewhere.

Experiment. A second method of solving design problems employs experimental procedures. The methods used vary widely. The elaborate testing of full-size machine parts under actual service conditions may be cited as an example of good practice. However, this is not always economical or feasible. It is often necessary to adapt the results of experiments which have been performed upon small-scale models under carefully controlled laboratory conditions to the design of a machine element. When this is done an element of uncertainty is always present.

An example of this is the experimental determination of the coefficient of friction for a brake band. No matter how carefully this coefficient is determined in the laboratory, there is always the possibility that environ-

[1] S. P. Timoshenko, "The History of Strength of Materials," McGraw-Hill Book Company, Inc., New York, 1953.

mental conditions will cause the coefficient to change substantially when the brake band is placed in service.

The uncertainty which is present when employing experimental procedures must be accounted for somewhere in the design. The elimination of this uncertainty or a reduction of its degree will result in improvement in the solutions of design problems.

Recent years have seen a great many improvements in experimental methods. The reader is undoubtedly familiar with many of these so that one example will be sufficient.

Probably the most important contribution to experimental stress analysis is Simon's electric strain gauge which was made at the California Institute of Technology in 1938.[1] Simon's first gauge consisted of 14 ft of No. 40 gauge constantan wire bonded in "zigzag" fashion to the sides of a tension test bar. When a tensile load is placed on the bar, the gauge, which is also in tension, changes its resistance. By subjecting the gauge to a flow of current, a voltage drop is obtained which is proportional to the strain of the bar. After calibration of the gauge, either dynamic or static loads may be imposed and the resulting strains faithfully recorded. This bonded-resistance-type strain gauge is now manufactured in hundreds of sizes and shapes and is in common use in thousands of laboratories. It has made possible countless advances in the field of experimental stress analysis.

Empirical Methods. Empiricism may be defined as a vague sensing of relationships which is obtained by observation and previous experience. Empirical design is thus an extrapolation of a previous design. The well-informed machine designer of today has little use for the old empirical methods of design which were formerly employed so extensively.

However, the word "empirical" has gradually acquired a more respectable meaning. Let us suppose that one of the fundamental equations fails to give answers which completely agree with experiment. It is frequently possible to apply an experimentally determined correction factor to that equation in order to cause it to give correct answers. This is the case, for example, when a stress-concentration factor is applied to a fundamental stress equation. In this sense of the word, almost all machine design as it exists today is empirical. For this reason we speak of solutions as "largely empirical" or "slightly empirical"; in other words, there are various degrees of empiricism. A highly empirical solution is one in which the relationships are poorly understood. On the other hand, if we have a good but not complete understanding of the problem, then we say that it is slightly empirical.

The degree of empiricism used in machine design has been tremendously

[1] Reported by D. S. Clark and G. Datwyler, Stress-Strain Relations under Tension Impact Loadings, *Proc. ASTM*, vol. 38, pp. 98–111, 1938.

reduced during the past 20 or 30 years as a result of the improvements in analytical and experimental techniques.[1] Some empiricism, however, is present in design, and when it is encountered the reader should accept it as a challenge.

Highly empirical methods are used in design because no better method exists, when the economics of the entire problem is considered (see Chap. 13). Rational methods may exist, but if these give results that are no better, then their use may not be justified. When the only satisfactory solutions available are empirical, we must use them; but we should certainly not be satisfied with the solutions so obtained nor ever cease searching for a more satisfactory one!

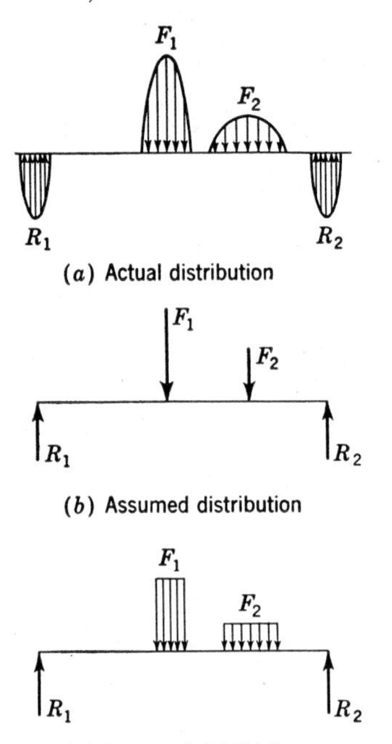

FIG. 1-1. Actual and assumed distribution of load and bearing reactions on a rotating shaft. (a) Actual distribution of load. (b) This distribution might be assumed in order to reduce the time necessary for solution. (c) This distribution might be assumed in order to obtain a fairly reliable result. Note that still other assumptions are possible.

The previous discussion has been included to show the reader that there is just as much opportunity for creative thinking today as in Galileo's time. In fact, as the borders of knowledge are pushed back, a wider horizon is revealed with infinitely more possibilities for imagination in engineering. The reader should learn to evaluate carefully each solution and method he encounters in the normal course of events, paying particular attention to the limitations and disadvantages of each. There are many borderline problems beyond which the usual solutions give poor or unreliable results. Other methods are complex and require involved mathematical steps or tedious experimental work.

1-5. The Analysis of the Problem. Problems usually given in elementary courses are carefully selected to fit the assumptions made in deriving the basic equations. In machine design it is necessary to deal with machine parts of definite size and shape which rarely fit the ideal conditions. For this reason, additional assumptions called *design assumptions* must be made.

[1] John M. Lessells states that the design of machine elements is no longer based on empirical relations. This statement is made only with reference to the strength of the elements. See J. M. Lessells, "Strength and Resistance of Metals," pref., John Wiley & Sons, Inc., New York, 1954.

A design assumption is a decision which the designer must make to simplify the problem so that it can be analyzed by known methods. It is a decision because there are usually several possibilities open.

The nature of the problem and its economics may, for example, indicate that high-quality engineering is neither necessary nor desired. In this case the designer may elect to make a rather crude assumption in order to obtain a result in a relatively short period of time. By crude assumption we mean that we have assumed a particular situation or set of conditions which causes the problem to be easy to solve.

Sometimes the situation demands engineering of the very highest order. In this case our assumptions must be highly refined. They must fit the actual conditions very closely. Figure 1-1 illustrates the difference between a relatively crude assumption and one that is more refined.[1]

A second example is illustrated in Fig. 1-2*a*, in which we see a bar loaded in simple tension as it would be shown in a text on strength of materials. The mechanical means required to apply the load is not shown, but Fig. 1-2*b* shows one means by which the load might be applied. Suppose that the decision is now made that the bar is to be designed on the basis of strength and that the material has been selected. The next step is to make the assumptions necessary to solve the problem. The bar could be designed on the basis of any one of the following assumptions:

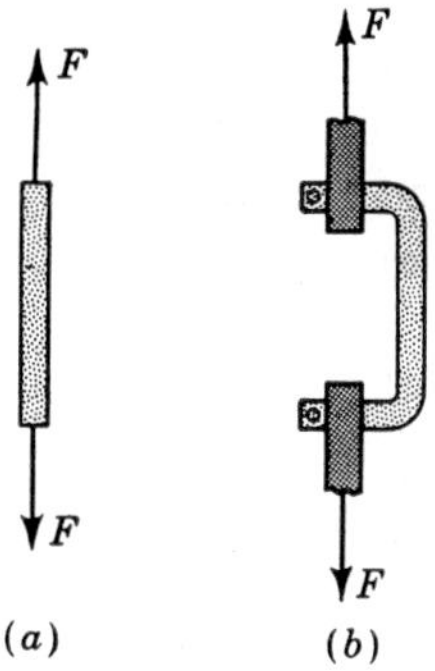

F F F F (*a*) (*b*)

Fig. 1-2. A bar loaded in tension.

1. The stress is uniformly distributed across the area.
2. The stress is uniformly distributed across the area, but stress concentration exists at the corners.
3. The stress is not uniformly distributed across the area but is due to combined tension and bending. Stress concentration is neglected.
4. The same as item 3 except that stress concentration is not neglected.
5. Stresses exist in the body of the bar because of combined bending and tension; stress concentration exists at the corners of the bar and also

[1] Problems in elementary courses are frequently worded, for example, "assume a coefficient of friction of 0.40," or "assuming steel with a modulus of elasticity of 30,000,000 psi." The fact that the word "assume" has been used should not be taken to mean that this is the same kind of assumption which we are defining. The problem could just as well have stated that "the coefficient of friction is 0.40," or "the material is steel with a modulus of elasticity of 30,000,000 psi." As the reader progresses in machine design, he will find that the selection of 0.40 for the coefficient of friction is a *decision* resulting from the designer's selection of certain frictional materials, but it is *not* an assumption. Again, the designer makes the *decision* to use a certain steel, and he finds that its modulus of elasticity is 30,000,000 psi. The *decision* to use steel is *not* an assumption.

at the junction of the bar and the links. The reaction of the bar and the link is concentrated along the center line of the link.

6. The same as item 5 except that the reaction between the bar and the link is uniformly distributed.

7. The same as item 5 and the material has residual stresses which are to be evaluated.

We have enumerated seven different assumptions, any one of which could have been used to design the bar. The reader will undoubtedly be able to find more.

In summary, the analysis of the problem requires assumptions which are necessary in order to make the problem capable of being solved. The degree of the assumptions made depends upon the nature of the particular problem and its economics. The fact that assumptions are necessary, coupled with the fact that they constitute decisions which must be made by the designer, makes it possible for him to exercise creative thinking in obtaining a result.

In engineering courses the student regards the solution of the problem as of fundamental importance; this is rightly so, since only by solving a great many problems can he acquire the necessary techniques and knowledge. In design work, however, the solution represents only the mechanical steps necessary after the problem has been synthesized. It is expected that correct answers will be obtained from the mechanical steps taken, but the quality of these answers will be dependent upon the synthesis and analysis of the problem, which include both the assumptions and decisions made. It is this synthesis and analysis of the problem, and the evaluation of the answer, with which we are concerned in the study of machine design. The mathematical substitution of numbers into an equation to obtain answers is mere routine "horsework" and is to be regarded as a necessary evil in a design office—an evil which is tolerated in the same manner as the task of blueprinting. Operations of this nature can just as well be performed by subordinates.

1-6. Shaping and Synthesizing the Parts. In beginning a design the designer first obtains the specifications for the machine. Many of these specifications will be stated; others will be implied by the use of the machine. If it is a subassembly which is to work into an existing machine, various limitations, such as in space or power, will be imposed. Other limitations will be imposed by the machinery and manufacturing facilities available. Included in the specifications will be information concerning the output and input quantities, the speeds and feeds, temperature limitations, the maximum range, and other quantities. Also included will be dimensional details and weight limitations. By far the great majority of designs made today are redesigns of existing machines, parts of machines, or subassemblies. In redesign work the designer is greatly handicapped by the necessity of using existing machinery. The specifications will also include a statement of the quantity to be manufactured. Usually, without its being stated in the specifications, the designer will be limited to certain materials and manufacturing processes, because of the machinery and the types and skills of the labor available.

Before any portion of the design is placed on the drawing board or on the analysis sheet, it is necessary to make three groups of decisions. The making of these decisions is a creative activity because they may often result in something which is new or different or in a machine which performs its function more economically and with better results. These decisions may be classified as follows:

1. *The Arrangement of the Parts.* The decisions made here will include the answers to many questions. What type of power transmission is to be used—gears, belts, or chains? Which bearing—ball, roller, or journal? What kind of gears—spur, helical, bevel, or worm? Which group of fasteners—bolts, studs, cap screws, or rivets? The lubrication system—grease or oil, pressure or gravity? If it is a gasoline engine—how many cylinders? In-line or V-type? These and hundreds of similar questions must be answered before the preliminary design work can be started. The arrangement chosen should be that one which accomplishes the purpose of the machine in the simplest possible manner. The total number of parts used should be held to the least number. They should be arranged for ease of maintenance and assembly. Each part should have sufficient strength and rigidity. Safety features and appearance are often important and cannot be neglected.

2. *The Processes and Materials Used.* The fact that, no matter how complex it may be, a particular part is possible to manufacture does not justify its inclusion in a machine. The designer should strive for processes and materials which are simple. Any reduction in the degree of skill required in manufacturing is worthwhile. Reduction in the amount of labor required is paramount. Considerable economy will result by striving to design parts that do not require highly specialized and expensive machinery. Parts requiring unskilled labor, such as stampings, die castings, and cold-headed parts, are especially desirable. The use of standard rolled, drawn, and extruded shapes is economical.

3. *The Standard Parts Used.* The use of standard purchased parts, such as springs, seals, bearings, bolts, motors, clutches, and the like, wherever possible, is usually very economical. Manufacturers specializing in these products are set up for large-quantity production, which will generally represent a considerable saving. The use of standard parts is also desirable where maintenance and replacement problems are important, since this class of parts is usually purchasable anywhere.

1-7. Design Factors. Quite frequently in design a particular factor may be found which is directly responsible for the size, shape, or the material of a part. We most often think of the strength of the part as the consideration which governs the final dimensions. This is often true, but just as often we find that strength is not very important and that some other factor, such as rigidity, becomes the governing consideration. Sometimes factors not related to strength or stiffness, such as wear resistance, corrosion resistance, or even the manufacturing processes used, govern the design.

1-8. Strength Factors. The first calculations made to determine the dimensions are generally, but not always, based on strength. Sometimes, as in the case of a rotating shaft, it is necessary to make several different calculations to determine which is the governing strength factor. A shaft, for example, might be loaded both in bending and in torsion; in this case it would be necessary for the designer to determine the diameter, say, for bending and then to check the safety of the calculated diameter for torsion. Strength factors ordinarily encountered in design are bending, torsion, shear, tension, compression, fatigue strength, impact strength, and creep and temperature properties.

1-9. Stiffness Factors. Stiffness is a measure of the amount of sag or deflection of a material under load. A rigid, or stiff, material will have a small deflection under the action of a load, whereas a less rigid material will have a large deflection. Stiffness is very important in many design problems. Springs, for example, must deflect a definite amount for a definite load. Machine tools must be designed very rigid; otherwise the cutting force might cause deflection of the work and produce inaccuracies. In the design of gear shafts, pump rods, and the like, stiffness means good performance of closely adjusted parts. It decreases vibration amplitudes and results in less wear and noise.

1-10. Other Design Factors. There are many other design factors which are fully as important as those mentioned, and these will be considered in detail where they are appropriate. These factors include such items as corrosion resistance, cost, frictional characteristics, and manufacturing considerations.

Sometimes a designer makes decisions for which he apparently has no reason. For example, two parts having no forces on them are to be bolted together. The designer chooses ½-in. bolts. Why, he probably could not say. It might be that ½-in. bolts have a better appearance, that they are in good proportion with the whole machine, or that they make the machine look strong and well built.

The task of designing a die-cast frame for a typewriter is assigned. The frame must be rigid so that it will keep the parts operating in proper relationship to each other. In order to design for rigidity the operating forces must first be determined. But the only forces on a typewriter are the finger pressure on the keys and the impact force of the moving carriage. These are insignificant; the loads caused by shipping and handling will be far greater, but they cannot be calculated.

These are examples of decisions which depend upon the judgment and experience of the designer.

CHAPTER 2

STRESSES IN MACHINE PARTS

In the early stages of design the decisions which determine the tentative mechanical arrangement of the parts are made. Some of these parts may be subjected to the action of external loads. When this is the case, the strength of the part may be an important design factor; the designer will then want to know the values of the internal stresses in order to assure an adequate margin of safety. He will probably apply one of the methods to be outlined in this chapter.

2-1. Factor of Safety.[1] The strength of a machine part is an important design factor whenever the possibility exists that the internal stresses may become high enough to cause the part to fail to perform its required function. In order to assure that the actual stresses will never become as large as the strength of the material used, or that the load will never become as large as the strength of the part, we use a number which is called the *factor of safety*. The factor of safety is defined as follows:

$$\text{f.s.} = \frac{s'}{s} = \frac{\text{strength of material, psi}}{\text{stress in material, psi}} \tag{2-1}$$

or

$$\text{f.s.} = \frac{F'}{F} = \frac{\text{strength of member, lb}}{\text{load on member, lb}} \tag{2-2}$$

Of the two methods of defining factor of safety, Eq. (2-1) is usually preferred because it defines in terms of more elementary material properties. It is necessary to use Eq. (2-2) when the stress is not a linear function of the load. In both equations the strength is that value of the internal stress[2] or external load at which the part fails to function in the machine.

2-2. Tension, Compression, and Shear. In elementary studies we learn that, when a body is subjected to the action of pure tensile, compressive, or shearing forces, an internal stress is obtained as follows:

[1] For a complete discussion of this important concept, see Chap. 5.

[2] In this book stress shall always be taken to mean *unit stress* and is measured in pounds per square inch. The load shall be considered to be an external *force* acting upon a physical edge or boundary and is measured in pounds.

$$s = \frac{F}{A} \tag{2-3}$$

where s = stress, lb per in.^{2}
F = load, lb
A = cross-sectional area, in.^{2}

In the design of various machine members the stress situation is rarely as simple as that expressed by Eq. (2-3). For this reason it is necessary to study the basic assumptions which were used in deriving the equation.

Assumptions. In Fig. 2-1*a* is shown a bar loaded in tension by the forces F through the centroid of the section. The bar is imagined to be cut by the plane A-A, the lower portion removed, and its effect replaced by internal forces acting upon the cut section (Fig. 2-1*b*). The stress is then defined as the magnitude of the internal force per unit area. Stress is thus an artificial concept since it is something which we cannot measure directly, nor feel, nor see. The assumptions used in deriving Eq. (2-3) are:

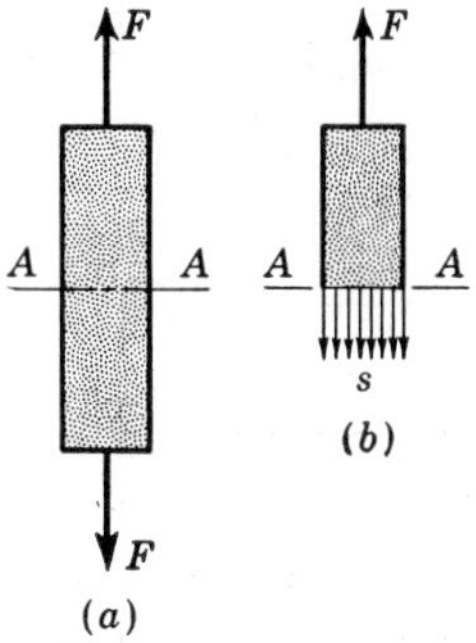

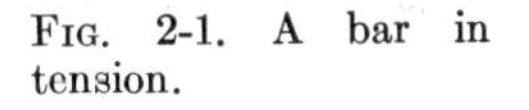

FIG. 2-1. A bar in tension.

1. The load is steady or static. When the load is moving, the inertia of the body will affect the magnitude of the stresses.

2. The body is free from initial stresses. The initial stresses which are built into a bar by cold working, heat-treatment, or assembly operations are frequently of great importance and so should be considered in addition to the stress obtained from Eq. (2-3).

3. The stress is uniformly distributed over the cross section of the bar. This requires that the material be homogeneous and that the section taken be remote from an abrupt change in section and from the point of application of the load. It is very doubtful if the assumption of uniform stress distribution is ever true, and this is particularly applicable to simple shear.

2-3. Combined Stresses. In the design of the various elements of a machine, it frequently happens that a part is acted upon by several external loads of different nature. For example, the loads on a rotating shaft may act in such a manner that the shaft is both bent and twisted. A machine frame may be eccentrically loaded so that it is twisted and compressed. In tightening a nut on a bolt the final torquing of the wrench subjects the bolt to a twisting and tensile action.

Many materials exist which have varying properties of strength. For example, cast iron is weaker in tension than in compression. Brittle materials may be weaker in tension than in shear. These properties of various materials make it necessary to investigate the stress condition for which the material is weakest.

In Fig. 2-2 is shown an element which has been taken from a body under a state of stress. Tensile stresses s_x and s_y act in the x and y directions together with the shearing stresses s_{xy}. The element may be cut by any plane m-n whose normal makes an angle ϕ with the x axis. If one portion of the element is removed (Fig. 2-3), then its action must be replaced by a normal stress s_n acting at right angles to the plane m-n

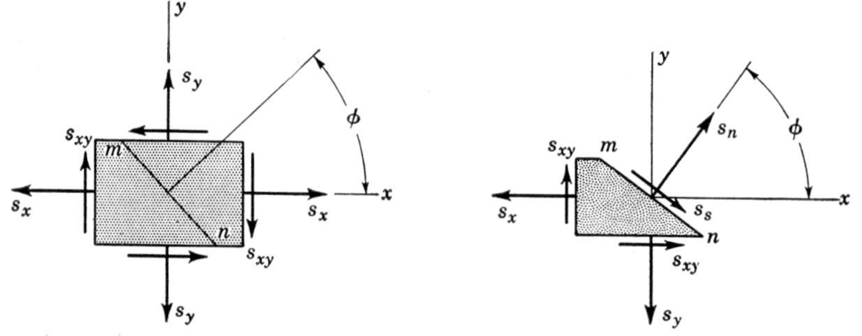

Fig. 2-2. The general condition of two-dimensional stress.

Fig. 2-3

and a shearing stress s_s acting parallel to m-n. From strength of materials, the magnitudes of these stresses are

$$s_n = \frac{s_x + s_y}{2} + \frac{s_x - s_y}{2} \cos 2\phi - s_{xy} \sin 2\phi \tag{2-4}$$

$$s_s = \frac{s_x - s_y}{2} \sin 2\phi + s_{xy} \cos 2\phi \tag{2-5}$$

As the angle 2ϕ is varied from 0 to 360°, two particular values will occur at which the normal stress s_n is either a maximum or a minimum. These values of ϕ may be obtained from the equation

$$\tan 2\phi = -\frac{2s_{xy}}{s_x - s_y} \tag{2-6}$$

In addition, there are two values of 2ϕ at which the shearing stress s_s is a maximum. These may be obtained from the equation

$$\tan 2\phi = \frac{s_x - s_y}{2s_{xy}} \tag{2-7}$$

The two values of 2ϕ obtained from Eq. (2-6) are 180° apart, so that the angle ϕ between the maximum normal stress s_1 and the minimum normal stress s_2 is 90°. The two stresses, s_1 and s_2, are called the *principal stresses,* and the planes are called the *principal planes.* Substitution of both the angles ϕ from Eq. (2-6) into Eq. (2-5) will show that the shearing stress is zero on both the principal planes.

Similarly, the two values of 2ϕ from Eq. (2-7) are 180° apart, and consequently the maximum shearing stress s_s' occurs on planes which are 90° apart.

The values for both the principal stresses and for the maximum shearing stress may be obtained by substituting these values of ϕ in Eqs. (2-4) and (2-5). This gives

$$s_1 \text{ or } s_2 = \frac{s_x + s_y}{2} \pm \sqrt{\left(\frac{s_x - s_y}{2}\right)^2 + s_{xy}^2} \tag{2-8}$$

$$s_s' = \pm \sqrt{\left(\frac{s_x - s_y}{2}\right)^2 + s_{xy}^2} \tag{2-9}$$

Mohr's Circle Diagram. A graphical method for expressing Eqs. (2-4) to (2-9), inclusive, called *Mohr's circle diagram,* is available, and it constitutes a very effective means of visualization.[1] In Fig. 2-4 the stresses

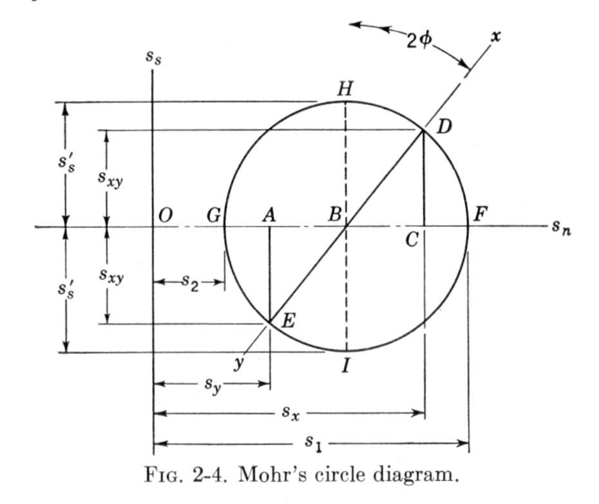

Fig. 2-4. Mohr's circle diagram.

are represented by the coordinates of a point whose location is determined by the values of s_x, s_y, s_{xy}, and ϕ. The value of s_y to a certain scale is laid off as OA on the s_n axis. The value of s_x is similarly laid off as OC. Beginning at point C, the shearing stress s_{xy} is laid off parallel to the s_s axis as CD, and again from point A as AE. Points D and E are now

[1] There are many problems in engineering which may be solved either graphically or mathematically. The graphical solution is much to be preferred. Generally the graphical solution is simple, requiring only arithmetic. When drafting tools are at hand, it is also usually faster. Mathematical errors are very infrequent in graphical solutions, but of even greater importance is the fact that a much more comprehensive grasp of the problem is acquired.

connected by a straight line crossing the s_n axis at B. Point B is the center of Mohr's circle, which is constructed to pass through points D and E. Points D and E now represent the stress situation defined by s_x, s_y, and s_{xy}. It should be noted too that $\phi = 0$ for this situation, so that the line BD represents the x axis, the line BE represents the y axis, and the angle 2ϕ between these lines is 180°. This corresponds to $\phi = 90°$ between the x and y axes on the element.

The principal stresses and maximum shearing stresses are obtained as follows: The maximum normal stress s_1 occurs at point F, and the minimum normal stress s_2 at point G. The maximum shearing stresses occur at points H and I. The sign convention is as follows: Tension is considered as positive and is measured on the s_n axis to the right of the origin. Compression is considered as negative and is measured to the left of the origin. Shearing stresses

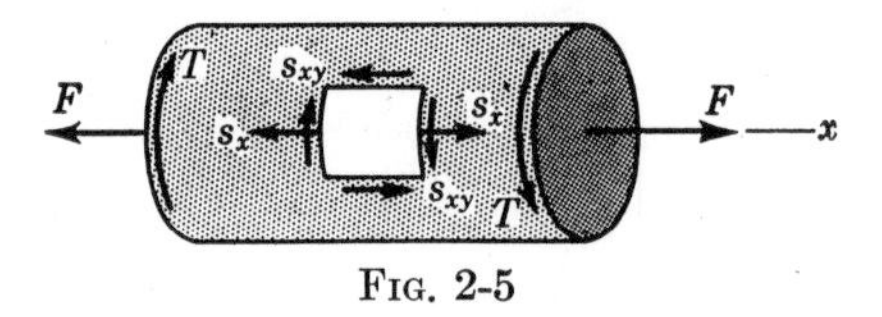

FIG. 2-5

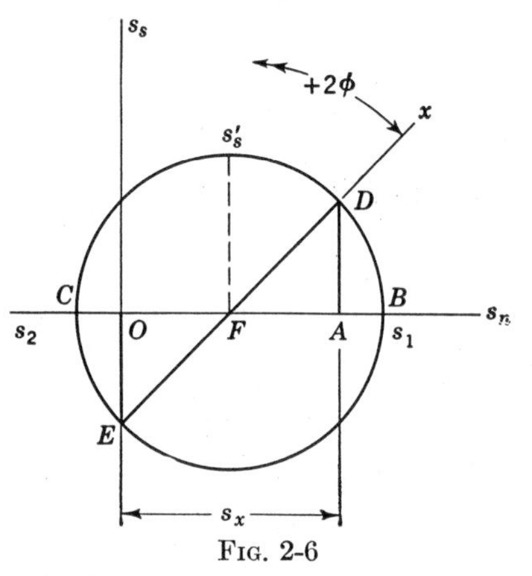

FIG. 2-6

are measured parallel to the s_s axis and are positive above the origin and negative below. In this demonstration we have assumed that $s_x > s_y$.

Shearing Stress Combined with Tensile or Compressive Stress. Of particular importance in machine design is the case in which shearing stress is combined with tensile or compressive stress. An example of this is found in Fig. 2-5, which shows a shaft twisted by torque T and loaded by tensile force F. An element on the surface of the shaft is acted upon by shearing stresses s_{xy} and tensile stresses s_x. To construct Mohr's circle (Fig. 2-6) the value of s_x is laid off on the s_n axis as OA. Parallel to the s_s axis, the distance AD representing the value of s_{xy} is laid off. Now, whenever a positive shearing stress exists, for equilibrium there must also exist a negative shearing stress of equal value. Therefore, since $s_y = 0$, lay off the value of s_{xy} again on the s_s axis in the negative direction. This is represented by OE. Draw the line DE crossing the s_n axis at point F, which is the center of Mohr's circle. The line DE is the zero line for the measurement of the angle 2ϕ (ϕ is always measured counterclockwise on Mohr's circle) and corresponds to the x axis in Fig. 2-5. The principal stresses and the shearing stresses can now be determined directly from the diagram. They are

$$s_1 \text{ or } s_2 = \frac{s_x}{2} \pm \sqrt{\left(\frac{s_x}{2}\right)^2 + s_{xy}^2} \tag{2-10}$$

$$s_s' = \sqrt{\left(\frac{s_x}{2}\right)^2 + s_{xy}^2} \tag{2-11}$$

Tension or Compression in Two Directions. The situation in which $s_{xy} = 0$ and only tension or compression in two directions exists is a special case. The relations may similarly be deduced from Mohr's circle. For this case the principal stresses are

$$s_1 = s_x \qquad \phi = 0° \tag{2-12}$$
$$s_2 = s_y \qquad \phi = 90° \tag{2-13}$$

and the maximum shearing stress is

$$s_s' = \frac{s_x - s_y}{2} \qquad \phi = 45 \text{ or } 135° \tag{2-14}$$

Tension or Compression in a Single Direction. By setting up the condition that $s_y = 0$ and $s_{xy} = 0$ we obtain the special case of tension in a single direction. The principal stresses are

$$s_1 = s_x \qquad \phi = 0° \tag{2-15}$$
$$s_2 = 0 \qquad \phi = 90° \tag{2-16}$$

The maximum shearing stress is

$$s_s' = \frac{s_x}{2} \qquad \phi = 45° \tag{2-17}$$

EXAMPLE 2-1. A solid round shaft is twisted by a torque T which induces a shearing stress of 4,000 psi in the outer fibers. In addition, a compressive load F exists on the shaft, inducing a compressive stress of 6,000 psi in the axial direction. The bar is shown in Fig. 2-7. (*a*) Using Mohr's circle, determine the magnitude and direction of the maximum shearing stress. (*b*) What is the value of the normal stress when the shearing stress is a maximum? (*c*) Determine the values of the normal and shearing stresses when $\phi = 60°$.

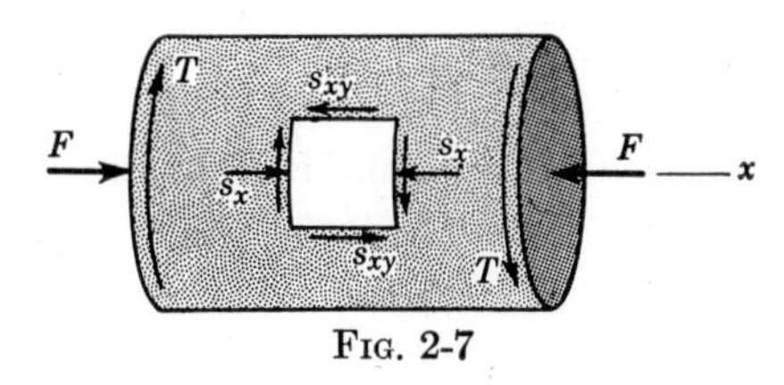

FIG. 2-7

Solution. (*a*) The solution is shown in Fig. 2-8. The compressive stress of 6,000 psi is distance OA. The shearing stress of 4,000 psi is distance AB. The maximum shearing stress occurs at point D. The direction and magnitude are found by scaling the diagram. They are

$$s_s' = 5{,}000 \text{ psi} \qquad \phi = 161°30' \qquad \textit{Ans.}$$

(*b*) The normal stress is represented by distance *OE*. Its value is

$$s_n = 3{,}000 \text{ psi} \qquad Ans.$$

(*c*) Point *F* at 120° from point *B* represents the condition of stress for $\phi = 60°$. The normal stress is represented by the distance *OG*, and the shearing stress by distance *GF*. Their values are

$$s_n = 4{,}970 \text{ psi} \qquad s_s = 4{,}600 \text{ psi} \qquad Ans.$$

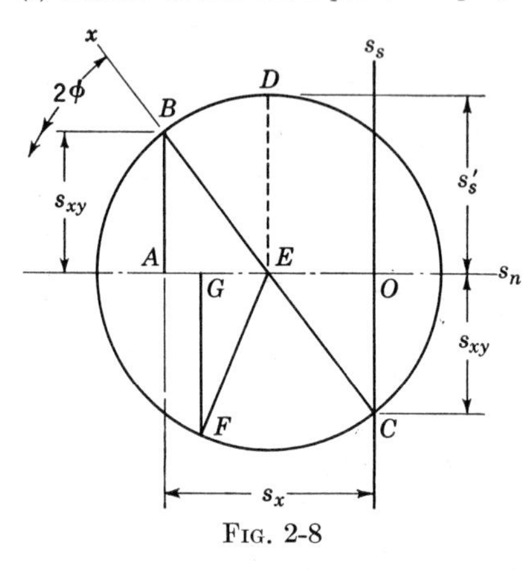

FIG. 2-8

2-4. Torsional Stresses. When a solid round bar is subjected to the action of a torque *T*, shearing stresses of magnitudes varying linearly from zero at the center to a maximum at the surface (Fig. 2-9) will be induced in the bar. The stress at the surface is

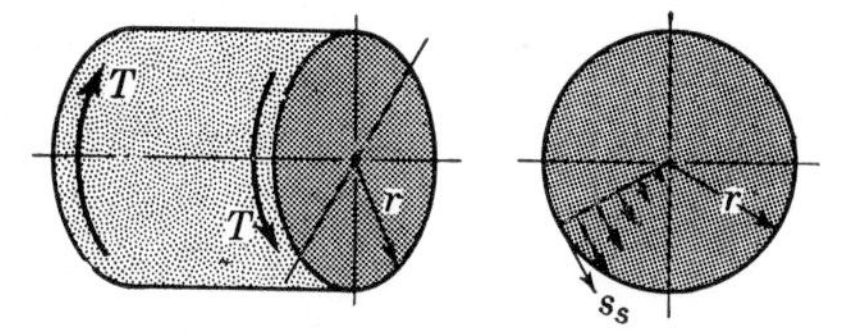

FIG. 2-9. A solid round bar under torsion

$$s_s = \frac{Tr}{J} \tag{2-18}$$

where s_s = shearing stress, psi
T = torque, lb-in.
r = radius, in.
J = polar moment of inertia, in.^4

For a solid round bar $J = \pi d^4/32$, and Eq. (2-18) becomes

$$s_s = \frac{16T}{\pi d^3} \tag{2-19}$$

where d is the diameter of the bar. For a hollow circular shaft

$$J = \frac{\pi(d_o^4 - d_i^4)}{32}$$

and Eq. (2-18) is

$$s_s = \frac{16Td_o}{\pi(d_o^4 - d_i^4)} \tag{2-20}$$

where d_o and d_i are the outside and inside diameters, respectively, in inches.

Assumptions. The following assumptions are used in deriving Eq. (2-18):

1. The bar is subjected to the action of a pure torque. By this we mean that there are no components of the twisting forces which might cause bending, tension, or compression to exist in the bar.

2. The shearing stress on a right cross section is directly proportional to the distance from the center of the bar. This assumption implies not only that the sections be circular but that they remain circular after twisting. It also requires that the material obey Hooke's law since the unit elongation must also be proportional to the radius.

3. The bar has no residual or built-in stresses.

4. The sections under consideration are remote from a change in diameter and from the point of application of the load.

It should be noted that Eqs. (2-18) to (2-20) give the stress in the outer fibers of the shaft. This is the maximum shearing stress and is ordinarily used in design. The equations may be used for circular bars only. They will not give the true shearing stress for bars of other shapes.[1]

In order to solve the equations for torsional shearing stress it is usually necessary to obtain the torque T from a consideration of the horsepower and speed of a rotating shaft. The relation is elementary and is repeated here for convenience:

$$T = \frac{63{,}000 \text{ hp}}{n} \tag{2-21}$$

Equation (2-21) gives the torque T in pound-inches when the horsepower and the speed n in rpm are used.

2-5. Bending Stresses. It is difficult to conceive of a machine or structure in which there do not exist at least a few elements subjected to bending forces.

Bending Forces. Shown in Fig. 2-10 is a beam supported by reactions R_1 and R_2 and subjected to loads F_1, F_2, and F_3. The beam might represent a rotating shaft with bearings at R_1 and R_2 and subjected to loads F_1, F_2, and F_3, which could be caused by gears, pulleys, or the like. If the beam is imagined to be cut at some point, say at $x = x_1$, and the left-hand portion removed as a free body, in order to maintain equilibrium it will be necessary to replace the action of the right-hand portion (Fig. 2-11). This action is replaced by a vertical force V, called the *shearing force*, and a couple M, called the *bending moment*.

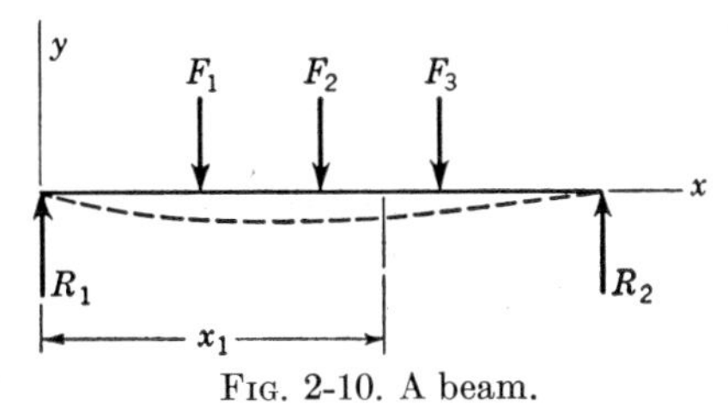

FIG. 2-10. A beam.

[1] For the shearing stresses on rectangular, elliptical, or other-shaped bars, reference should be made to an advanced text on strength of materials. See the bibliography at the end of this chapter.

The shearing force is obtained by summing the forces to the left of the section under consideration. The bending moment is found as a summation of all the forces to the left of the section multiplied by their respective distances to the section, with due respect paid to the signs of the quantities. The relation between shearing force and bending moment is

$$V = \frac{dM}{dx} \tag{2-22}$$

Normal Stresses. A portion of a beam of rectangular cross section under the action of bending forces is shown in Fig. 2-12. The fibers in the top plane are assumed to be shortened, those in the bottom plane to be lengthened, and those on plane A-A to remain at their original length.

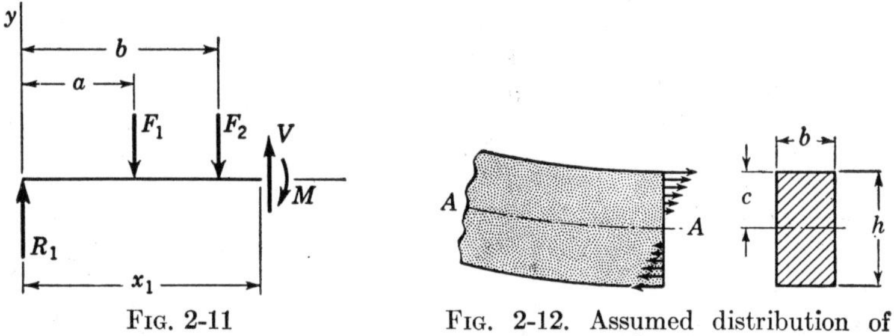

FIG. 2-11

FIG. 2-12. Assumed distribution of normal stresses in a beam.

The plane A-A is called the *neutral plane* and represents the point of zero stress. The stress in the outer fibers at distance c from the neutral plane is given by

$$s = \frac{Mc}{I} = \frac{M}{I/c} \tag{2-23}$$

where M is the bending moment at the section under consideration (usually expressed in pound-inches) and I is the moment of inertia in inches to the fourth power. The second form of the equation, in which the section modulus I/c appears in the denominator, is usually the preferred form. Formulas for I and I/c are tabulated in Table A-7 (in the Appendix).

Assumptions. The following assumptions apply to Eq. (2-23):

1. Cross sections at which the stress is to be determined are remote from the point of application of a load or reaction and also from a change in cross section. Loads on beams are very often assumed to be concentrated. A concentrated load is actually something which is impossible to achieve in practice because the contact stress would become infinite. Yielding would occur before this condition is obtained and would result in a redistribution of the stresses. Also, since a load is usually delivered

by another machine part which has size and dimensions, it is doubtful if the fact of a concentrated load is ever encountered.

However, the concept of a concentrated load is a very useful one because it so simplifies the calculations. It is almost always used when the load is distributed over a small area, as, for example, the shaft reaction of a ball bearing. The point is, since loads or forces are not really concentrated, that the stresses can probably be calculated on sections much closer to the point of application of the force than the theory would indicate. If the distribution is fairly good, then a slight correction factor may be used to account for the differences.[1]

2. The material is homogeneous and obeys Hooke's law. Cast iron, for example, is neither homogeneous nor does it obey Hooke's law. Figure 2-13 shows the stress-strain curve for cast iron, and it is clearly seen that only a small portion of the curve near zero can be considered to be a straight line. Gray cast iron contains an amount of free carbon or graphite; hence the material cannot be homogeneous. Timber is another material which is not homogeneous. Equation (2-23) is, however, used with these materials, and the designer must make an appropriate reduction in the working stress, based upon his judgment and experience, in order to account for the uncertainties involved.

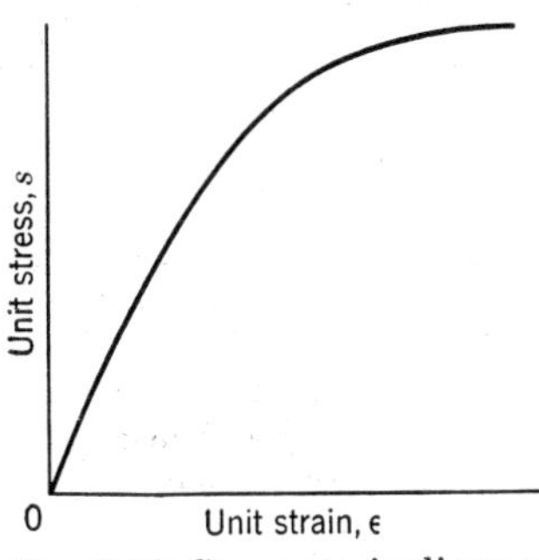

FIG. 2-13. Stress-strain diagram for cast iron.

3. Cross sections taken through the beam before bending remain plane after bending. It can be shown that, except for the cases in which the shearing stresses are zero, this is not the case.[2] However, when constant shearing stresses exist, the warping of the cross sections is also constant, and Eq. (2-23) can be relied upon.

4. The modulus of elasticity is the same in tension and compression. This assumption is not true for cast iron. Beams made of this material are usually constructed with a greater area of cross section on the side which is in tension, cast iron being weaker in tension, and with the working stress appropriately reduced.

5. The stress is proportional to the distance from the neutral plane. This assumption implies that initially all fibers were of the same length, that is, that the beam is straight. For this reason Eq. (2-23) applies only to straight beams.

[1] Such as a stress-concentration factor (see Sec. 2-8).

[2] S. Timoshenko, "Strength of Materials," vol. 1, p. 115, D. Van Nostrand Company, Inc., New York, 1940.

6. The proportions of the beam are such that it tends to fail by bending and not by buckling sidewise or by a local failure such as wrinkling.

7. The bending forces are perpendicular to the centroidal axis of the beam and are in a plane containing the centroidal axis. In addition, the plane of the bending forces is perpendicular to the neutral surface. This assumption requires that the cross section have two axes of symmetry and that the plane of the bending forces coincide with one of these axes. This is not true, for example, for a channel section unless the load passes through the shear center (Fig. 2-14).[1]

FIG. 2-14. The bending load F must pass through the shear center of unsymmetrical sections in order to avoid twisting.

EXAMPLE 2-2. For a design stress of 10,000 psi, determine the diameter of the solid round steel shaft, 18 in. long, shown in Fig. 2-15. The shaft is supported by self-aligning bearings at the ends. Mounted upon the shaft are a V-belt sheave which contributes a radial load of 400 lb to the shaft, and a gear which contributes a radial load of 150 lb. Both loads are in the same plane and have the same direction.

Assumptions. 1. Since the bearings are self-aligning, the shaft is assumed to be simply supported, with concentrated reactions at the bearings.

2. The pulley and gear loads are assumed to be concentrated.

3. The normal bending stress is assumed to govern the design.

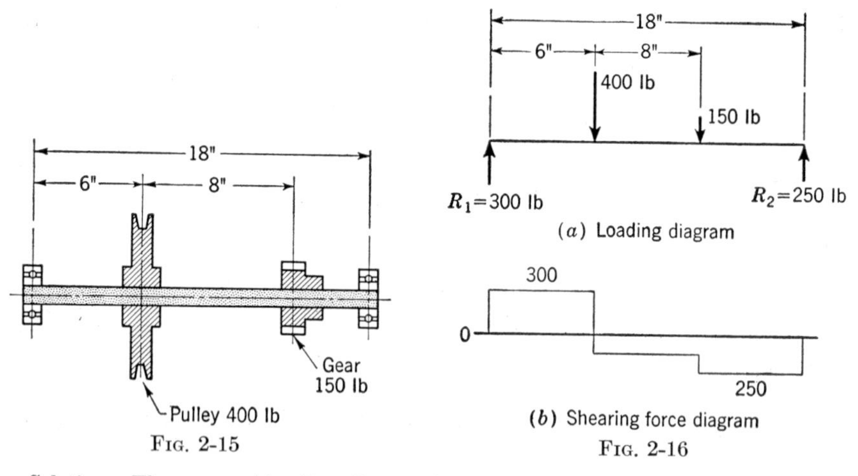

FIG. 2-15

FIG. 2-16

Solution. The assumed loading diagram is shown in Fig. 2-16*a*. Taking moments about R_2,

$$\Sigma M_{R_2} = 0 \qquad 18R_1 - (12)(400) - (4)(150) = 0$$

$$R_1 = \frac{(12)(400) + (4)(150)}{18} = 300 \text{ lb}$$

$$R_2 = 400 + 150 - 300 = 250 \text{ lb}$$

[1] Fred B. Seely, "Resistance of Materials," 3d ed., pp. 346–354, John Wiley & Sons, Inc., New York, 1947.

The shearing-force diagram (Fig. 2-16*b*) can now be drawn. The maximum moment occurs at the point of zero shearing force. Its value is

$$M_{\max} = (300)(6) = 1{,}800 \text{ lb-in.}$$

Equation (2-23) applies, and, solving for the section modulus, we find

$$\frac{I}{c} = \frac{M}{s} = \frac{1{,}800}{10{,}000} = 0.180 \text{ in.}^3$$

The section modulus for a circular section is $\pi d^3/32$ (Table A-7). This gives for the diameter

$$d = \sqrt[3]{\frac{32I/c}{\pi}} = \sqrt[3]{\frac{(32)(0.180)}{\pi}} = 1.22 \text{ in.}$$

Therefore, we shall use

$$d = 1\tfrac{1}{4} \text{ in.} \qquad \textit{Ans.}$$

EXAMPLE 2-3. Horizontal and vertical components of the shaft radial loads caused by gears are shown in Fig. 2-17. Find the location and value of the maximum bending moment.

Solution. Figure 2-18*a* is the loading diagram for the vertical components; the reactions R_{1y} and R_{2y} have been found, and the shearing-force diagram (Fig. 2-18*b*) drawn. Similarly, Fig. 2-18*c* and *d* are the loading and shearing-force diagrams for the horizontal components. The maximum bending moment will occur at either point *A* or point *B*. For point *A*, we have

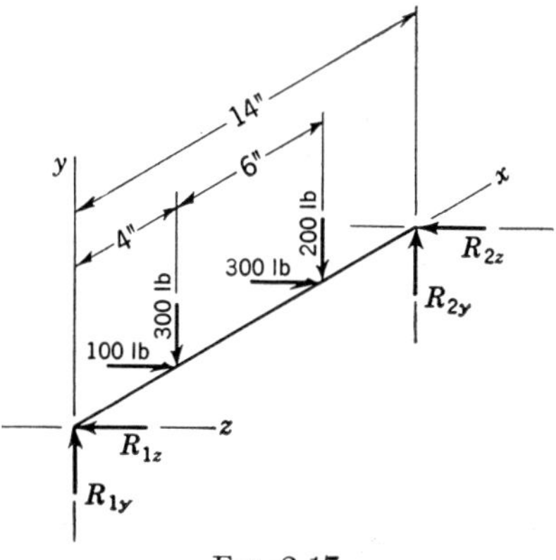

FIG. 2-17

$$M_y = (272)(4) = 1{,}090 \text{ lb-in.}$$
$$M_z = (157)(4) = 628 \text{ lb-in.}$$
$$M_A = \sqrt{M_y^2 + M_z^2} = \sqrt{(1{,}090)^2 + (628)^2} = 1{,}260 \text{ lb-in.}$$

For point *B*,

$$M_y = (272)(10) - (300)(6) = 920 \text{ lb-in.}$$
$$M_z = (157)(10) - (100)(6) = 970 \text{ lb-in.}$$
$$M_B = \sqrt{M_y^2 + M_z^2} = \sqrt{(920)^2 + (970)^2} = 1{,}340 \text{ lb-in. max} \qquad \textit{Ans.}$$

Shearing Stresses. When the bending moment varies along the length of a beam there exists in the beam a shearing stress whose value is a function of the rate of variation of the moment. From strength of materials this stress is given as

$$s_s = \frac{V}{Ib}\int_{y_0}^{c} y\,dA \tag{2-24}$$

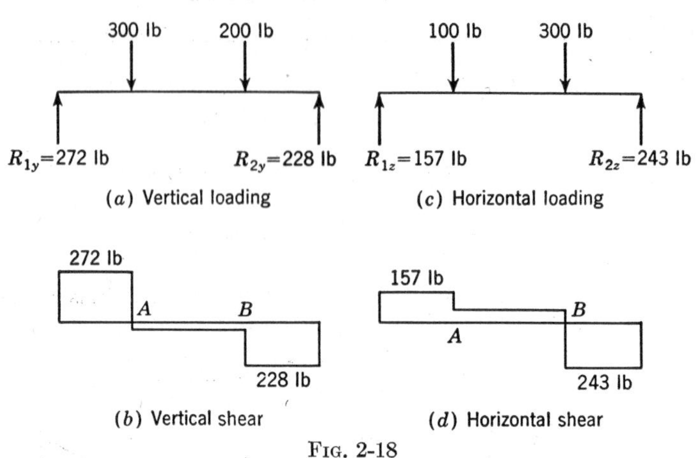

FIG. 2-18

The notation for a rectangular beam is shown in Fig. 2-19. In this equation the shearing stress is zero when $y_0 = h/2 = c$. As y_0 decreases in value, the shearing stress increases and reaches a maximum when $y_0 = 0$. Substitution of the value of I for a rectangular section into Eq. (2-24) gives the maximum shearing stress as

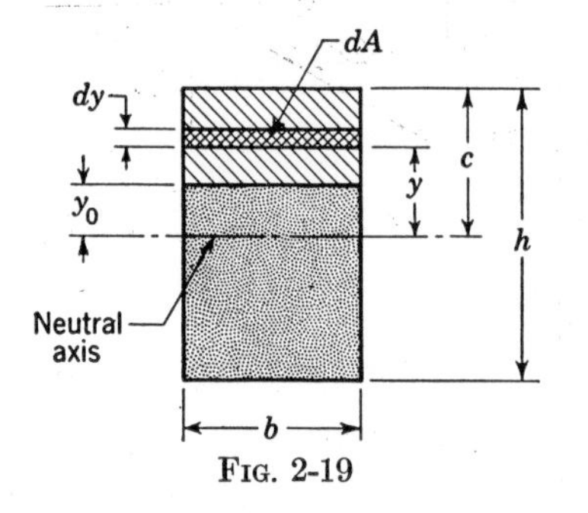

FIG. 2-19

$$s_{s,\max} = \frac{3}{2}\frac{V}{A} \tag{2-25}$$

Equation (2-24) may be used to determine the maximum shearing stress in beams of other shapes. Thus for a solid circular beam the stress is given by

$$s_{s,\max} = \frac{4}{3}\frac{V}{A} \tag{2-26}$$

For a hollow circular section the maximum stress also occurs at the neutral axis and is

$$s_{s,\max} = 2\frac{V}{A} \tag{2-27}$$

A good approximation for WF and **I** shapes is given by

$$s_{s,\max} = \frac{V}{A_w} \tag{2-28}$$

where A_w is the area of the web only.

The assumptions used in deriving Eq. (2-24) are:

1. The shearing stress throughout the cross section has the same direction as the shearing force.

2. The shearing stresses are uniformly distributed across the width of the beam.

Investigations which are beyond the scope of this book have shown that, except for the bending of plates (where b is large compared with h), the assumptions give accurate results.

EXAMPLE 2-4. A beam 12 in. long is to be designed to support a load of 488 lb which acts 3 in. from one end. The designer has assumed the load and reactions to be concentrated; he has selected a design bending stress of 1,000 psi for a 75S-O aluminum

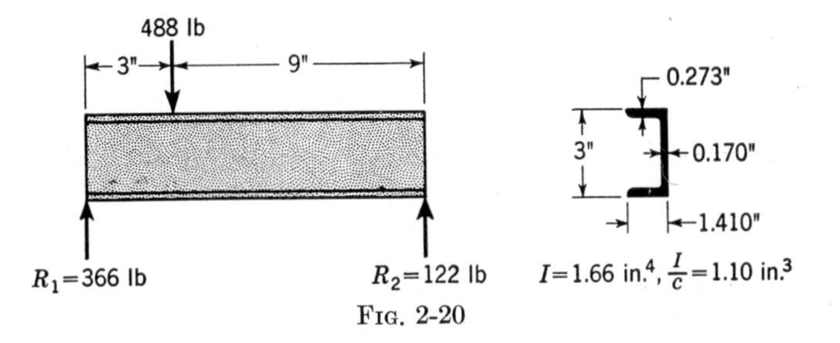

FIG. 2-20

[section. With these assumptions, he has tentatively selected a 3-in. [whose dimensions are shown in Fig. 2-20. However, at a point on the web adjacent to the flange there is the possibility that the combined normal stress will exceed the allowable normal stress. In order to determine if the tentatively selected section is safe, it is desired to calculate the combined normal stress.

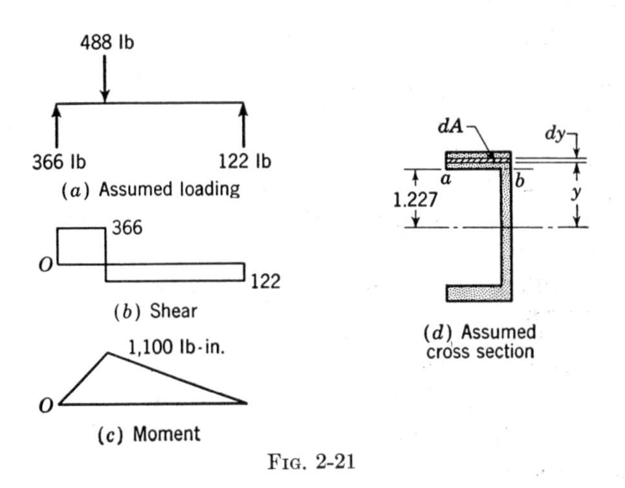

FIG. 2-21

Assumptions. 1. The aluminum channel is assumed to have the shape shown in Fig. 2-21*d*.

2. The load is assumed to pass through the center of shear.

Solution. The shearing-force and bending-moment diagrams are shown in Fig. 2-21*b* and *c*. The maximum shearing stress will occur to the left of the 488-lb load. The normal stress and shearing stress must first be determined along the plane *ab*

(Fig. 2-21*d*). The normal stress at *ab* is

$$s = \frac{My}{I} = \frac{(1{,}100)(1.227)}{1.66} = 814 \text{ psi}$$

The equation for the shearing stress is $s_s = (V/Ib) \int_{y_0}^{c} y\, dA$. Here, $dA = 1.410\, dy$, $y_0 = 1.227$ in., and $c = 1.500$ in. We then have

$$\int_{y_0}^{c} y\, dA = \int_{1.227}^{1.500} y(1.410)\, dy = \frac{1.410y^2}{2}\Bigg]_{1.227}^{1.500} = 0.521 \text{ in.}^2$$

Then

$$s_s = \frac{V}{Ib}\, 0.521 = \frac{(366)(0.521)}{(1.66)(0.170)} = 675 \text{ psi}$$

Using the normal stress of 814 psi and the calculated shearing stress of 675 psi, the circle diagram is constructed as shown in Fig. 2-22. From this diagram the maximum combined normal stress is read as 1,200 psi. Since this is only a slight increase over the allowable stress, the beam is safe.

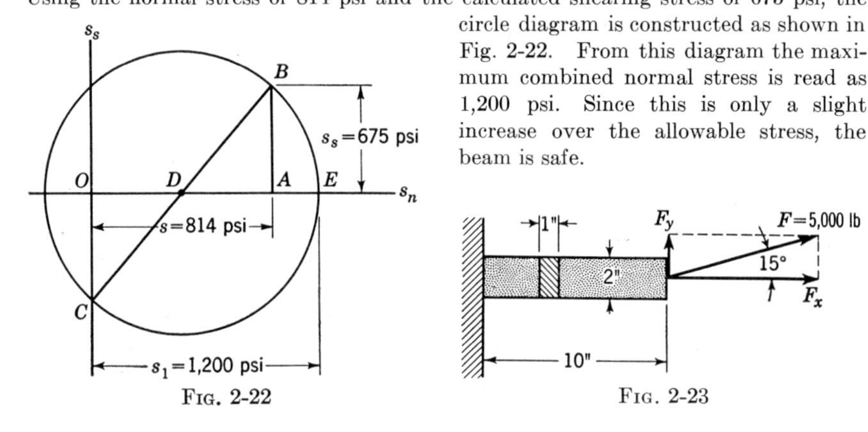

FIG. 2-22

FIG. 2-23

2-6. Superposition. When a body is acted upon by forces which have the effect of producing two kinds of stresses, but with the same directions, it is frequently possible to calculate the stresses independently and then to add them together, paying due respect to sign. This is called the *method of superposition* and is illustrated in Example 2-5.

EXAMPLE 2-5. The problem shown in Fig. 2-23 is a short cantilever beam with a load of 5,000 lb acting on the end at an angle of 15° from the horizontal. Determine the maximum stress in the beam.

Solution. The horizontal component F_x causes tension. The vertical component F_y causes bending, with the tensile side on the bottom. The components are

$$F_x = F \cos 15° = (5{,}000)(0.967) = 4{,}830 \text{ lb}$$
$$F_y = F \sin 15° = (5{,}000)(0.259) = 1{,}300 \text{ lb}$$

The section modulus is

$$\frac{I}{c} = \frac{bh^2}{6} = \frac{(1)(2)^2}{6} = 0.667 \text{ in.}^3$$

From Eq. (2-23) the bending stress is

$$s = \frac{M}{I/c} = \frac{F_y l}{I/c} = \frac{(1{,}300)(10)}{0.667} = 19{,}500 \text{ psi}$$

The tensile stress due to F_x is

$$s = \frac{F}{A} = \frac{F_x}{bh} = \frac{4{,}830}{(1)(2)} = 2{,}415 \text{ psi}$$

The maximum stress is the tension on the bottom. Using the method of superposition, this stress is found to be

$$s = 19{,}500 + 2{,}415 = 21{,}915 \text{ psi tension} \qquad \textit{Ans.}$$

We may use the same method to obtain the resultant stress in the top fiber. It is

$$s = 19{,}500 - 2{,}415 = 17{,}085 \text{ psi compression} \qquad \textit{Ans.}$$

The method of superposition may be used whenever the loads and the stresses produced by them are proportional. The method could not be used on a column subjected to both bending and compression, for example, because the loads and stresses (or deflections) are not proportional to each other.

2-7. Hertz Contact Stresses.[1] When two bodies having curved surfaces are pressed against one another they are deformed so that an area of contact is developed, accompanied by compressive stresses. This problem occurs frequently in machine design, as, for example, in the contact of a wheel and rail, cam and follower, antifriction-bearing race and ball, or mating gear teeth. The problem may be solved using the equations of the theory of elasticity. We shall give only the final results of the development.

Spherical Surfaces. When two solid spheres of diameters d_1 and d_2 are pressed together with a force F, a circular area of contact of radius a is obtained. This area is dependent on the diameters of the spheres, the force pressing them together, and the elastic constants. The radius of this circular area is

$$a = \sqrt[3]{\frac{3F}{8} \frac{(1 - \mu^2)(1/E_1 + 1/E_2)}{1/d_1 + 1/d_2}} \qquad (2\text{-}29)$$

where F = applied force, lb
μ = Poisson's ratio (Table A-1)
E = modulus of elasticity, psi

The pressure within each sphere has a hemispherical distribution, as shown in Fig. 2-24. The maximum pressure occurs at the center of the contact area and is

$$p_{\max} = \frac{3F}{2\pi a^2} \qquad (2\text{-}30)$$

[1] The solution to this problem is due to H. Hertz. See S. P. Timoshenko and J. N. Goodier, "Theory of Elasticity," 2d ed., pp. 372–382, McGraw-Hill Book Company, Inc., New York, 1951.

where p is the pressure in pounds per square inch, with p_{max} corresponding to the maximum compressive stress and having the same direction as the forces.

Equations (2-29) and (2-30) are perfectly general and also apply to the contact of a sphere and a plane surface or to the case of a sphere and an internal spherical surface. For a plane surface use $d = \infty$. For an internal spherical surface the diameter is expressed as a negative quantity.

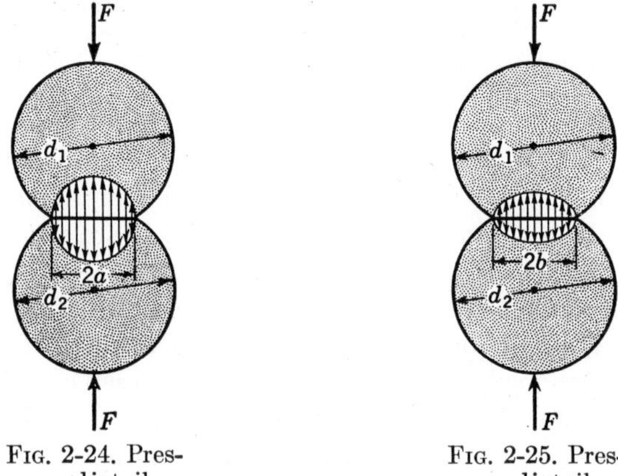

FIG. 2-24. Pressure distribution between two spheres.

FIG. 2-25. Pressure distribution between two cylinders.

Cylindrical Surfaces. When the contacting surfaces are cylinders, the area of contact is a narrow rectangle of half width b (Fig. 2-25). Denoting the length of the contacting surfaces by l, the half width is

$$b = \sqrt{\frac{2F}{\pi l} \frac{(1 - \mu^2)(1/E_1 + 1/E_2)}{1/d_1 + 1/d_2}} \tag{2-31}$$

where the meaning of the quantities is the same as before. The pressure has an elliptical distribution across the width $2b$ of the rectangle. The maximum pressure is

$$p_{max} = \frac{2F}{\pi b l} \tag{2-32}$$

This also corresponds to the maximum compressive stress in the material, and it has the same direction as the forces. Equations (2-31) and (2-32) also apply to a cylinder and a plane surface and to a cylinder and an internal cylindrical surface. As before, $d = \infty$ for a plane surface and is negative for an internal cylindrical surface.

2-8. Concentration of Stress. In the development of the basic stress equations for tension, compression, bending, and torsion, it was assumed that no irregularities occurred in the member under consideration. In the case of tension and compression the stresses were assumed to be uniformly distributed over the cross-sectional area. For bending of a beam the stresses varied linearly as their distances from the neutral axis, and for torsion the stresses increased in proportion to the distance from the center of a circular bar. These assumptions were mathematically necessary in order to obtain simple solutions applicable to many practical design problems.

Frequently, however, in machine design abrupt changes in sections are necessary. Shoulders are required on rotating shafts for the seating of bearings. Keyways are needed for fastening pulleys and gears. Screw threads represent an abrupt change in section. Other parts require holes and oil grooves. These variations in the cross section also change the stress distribution within the machine part so that within the vicinity of the variation the elementary equations no longer give satisfactory results because the actual distribution of stresses may be radically different from that assumed.

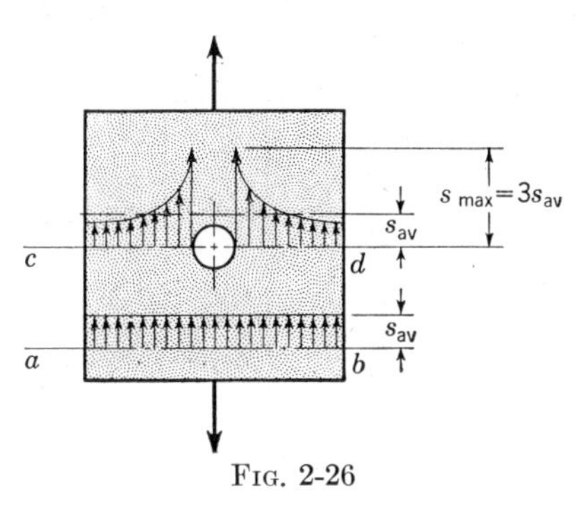

FIG. 2-26

In Fig. 2-26, for example, is shown a prismatical bar in tension. A cross section *ab* has an average tensile stress s_{av}. At section *cd* a small hole has been drilled in the bar. Experiments reveal that along the sides of the hole a stress exists which is approximately three times the average stress in the bar at points remote from the hole. These points of maximum stress are called *stress concentrations*. In the case of a ductile material with a static load this increase in stress in the region of the irregularity is not important, since yielding of the material will occur and the stress will be relieved. However, many machine parts are either made of brittle materials or subjected to repeated or alternating stresses, so that work hardening will eventually occur and rupture result.

Some problems in the determination of the values of concentrated stresses have been solved by the methods of elasticity, but they are too complex to be shown here. Others have been determined by experimental methods, although there is need for more exploration in this area.[1] The determination of the actual maximum stresses, based upon the results of either analytical or experimental methods, is quite simple. A stress-concentration factor k, defined as the ratio of the actual maximum stress to the nominal stress, is used. The nominal stress is the stress calculated

[1] M. Hetenyi, "Handbook of Experimental Stress Analysis," p. 447, John Wiley & Sons, Inc., New York, 1950.

using the usual elementary stress equations. In equation form it is expressed as follows:

$$s_{\max} = k\frac{F}{A} \qquad \text{for simple tension and compression} \tag{2-33}$$

$$s_{\max} = k\frac{Mc}{I} \qquad \text{normal bending stress} \tag{2-34}$$

$$s_{s,\max} = k\frac{Tr}{J} \qquad \text{torsional shearing stress} \tag{2-35}$$

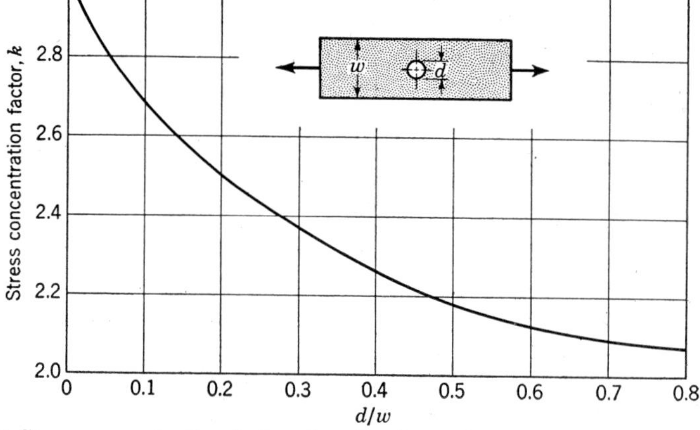

Fig. 2-27. Stress-concentration factors for a bar in tension or compression with a transverse hole. (*Courtesy of Machine Design, Penton Publishing Company, Cleveland.*)

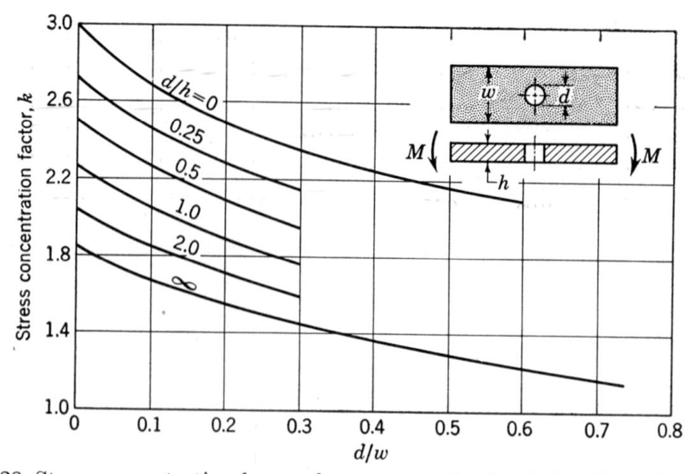

Fig. 2-28. Stress-concentration factors for a rectangular bar in bending with a transverse hole. (*Courtesy of Machine Design, Penton Publishing Company, Cleveland.*)

Figures 2-27 to 2-38 give the values of the stress-concentration factor for a variety of problems.[1] In each case the nominal stress calculation should be based upon the net cross section.

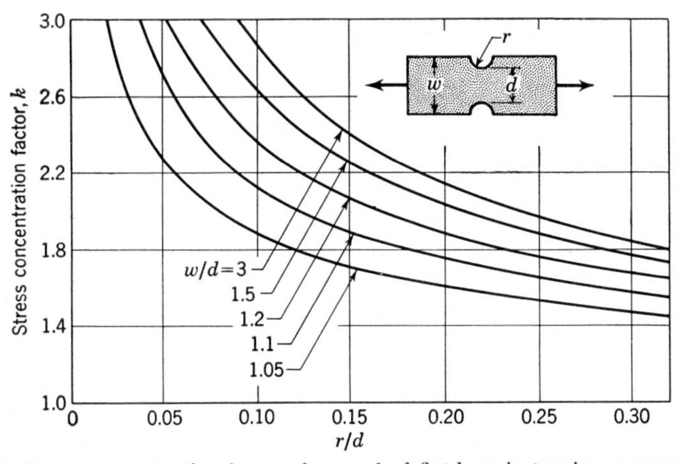

Fig. 2-29. Stress-concentration factors for notched flat bars in tension or compression. (*Courtesy of Machine Design, Penton Publishing Company, Cleveland.*)

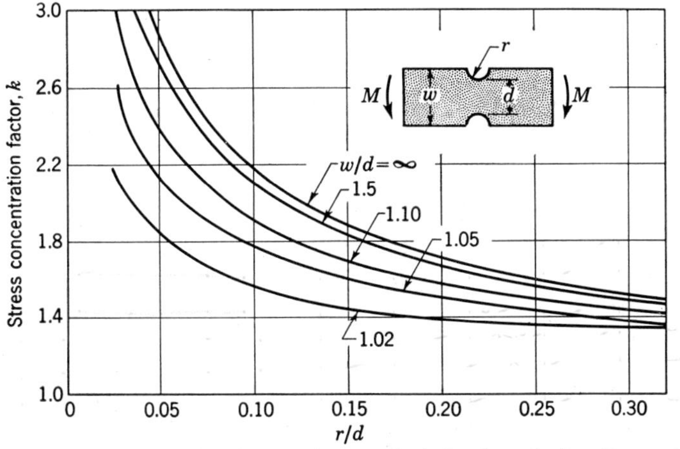

Fig. 2-30. Stress-concentration factors for notched flat bars in bending. (*Courtesy of Machine Design, Penton Publishing Company, Cleveland.*)

The stress-concentration effect of keyways needs more investigation; however, for keys of standard proportions a k of 1.7 may be used for torsion and a k of 1.5 for bending.

[1] These factors are from R. E. Peterson, Design Factors for Stress Concentration, *Machine Design*, vol. 23, no. 2, p. 169, February, 1951; no. 3, p. 161, March, 1951; no. 5, p. 159, May, 1951; no. 6, p. 173, June, 1951; no. 7, p. 155, July, 1951, and are reproduced with the permission of the author and publisher.

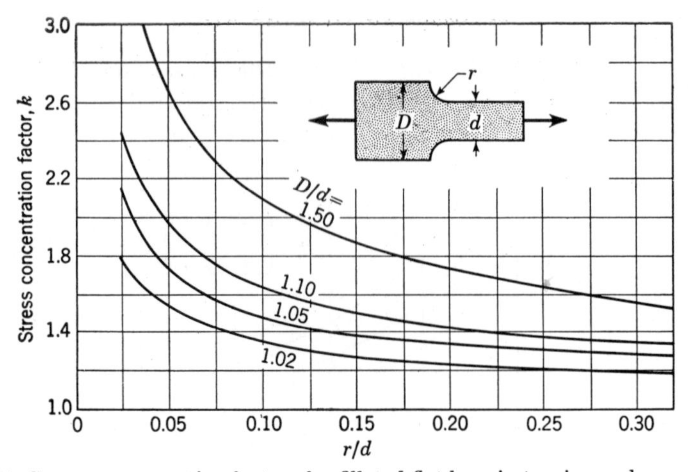

Fig. 2-31. Stress-concentration factors for filleted flat bars in tension and compression. (*Courtesy of Machine Design, Penton Publishing Company, Cleveland.*)

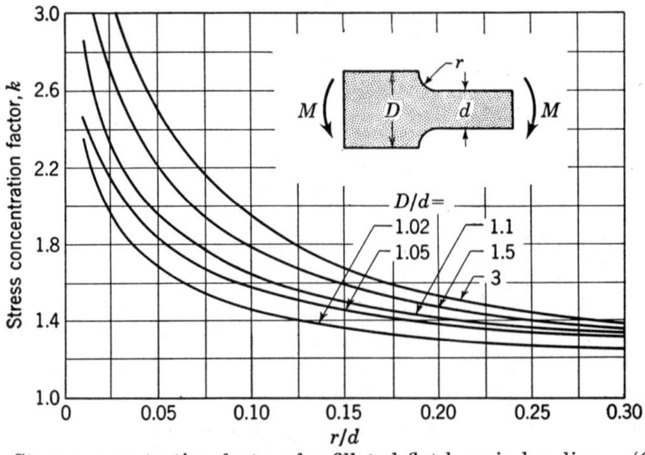

Fig. 2-32. Stress-concentration factors for filleted flat bars in bending. (*Courtesy of Machine Design, Penton Publishing Company, Cleveland.*)

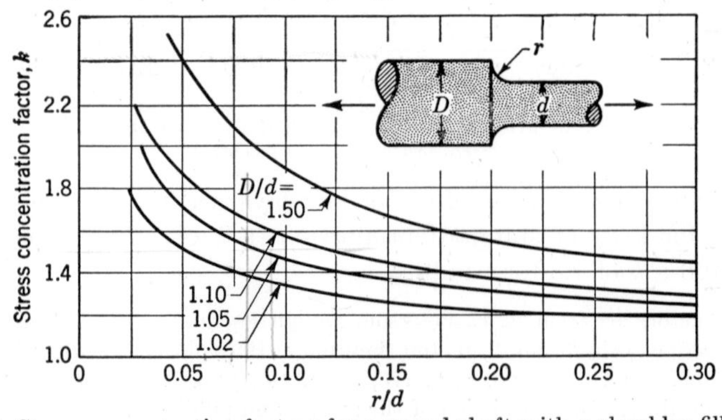

Fig. 2-33. Stress-concentration factors for a round shaft with a shoulder fillet in tension. (*Courtesy of Machine Design, Penton Publishing Company, Cleveland.*)

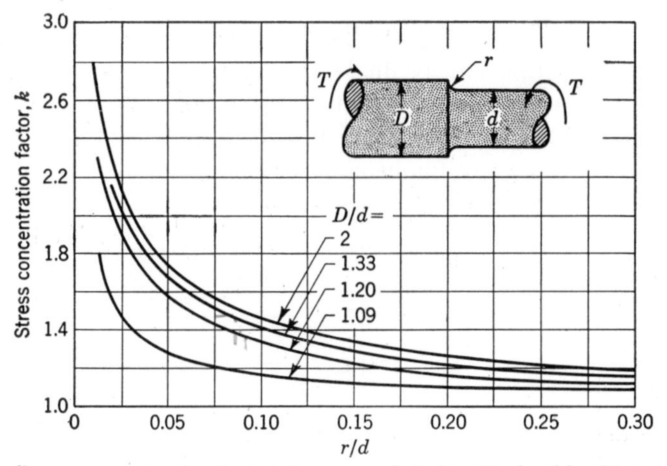

Fig. 2-34. Stress-concentration factors for a round shaft with shoulder fillets in torsion. (*Courtesy of Machine Design, Penton Publishing Company, Cleveland.*)

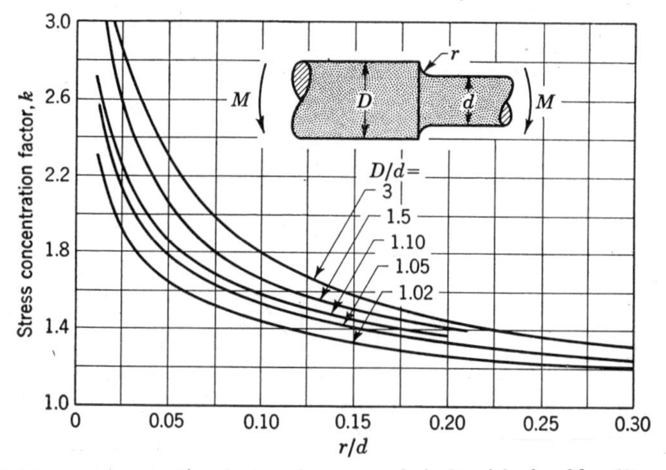

Fig. 2-35. Stress-concentration factors for a round shaft with shoulder fillets in bending. (*Courtesy of Machine Design, Penton Publishing Company, Cleveland.*)

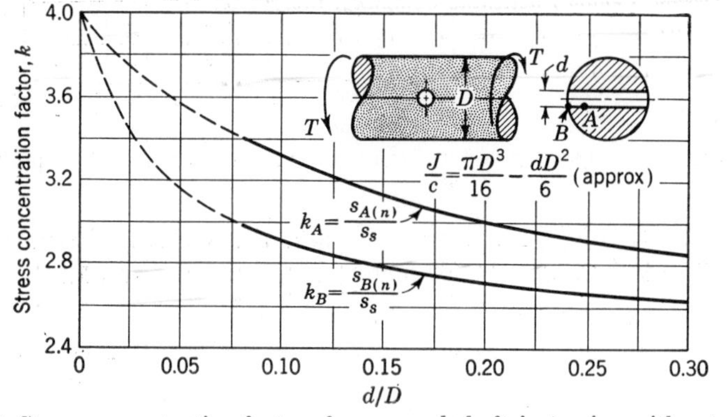

Fig. 2-36. Stress-concentration factors for a round shaft in torsion with a transverse hole. (*Courtesy of Machine Design, Penton Publishing Company, Cleveland.*)

Stress-concentration effects due to screw threads also require more investigation. Seely[1] gives values for k of 2.0 for square threads, 3.0 for sharp-V threads, 2.0 for Whitworth threads, and 2.5 for U.S. Standard threads; these factors are for bending or direct tension. Black[2] states

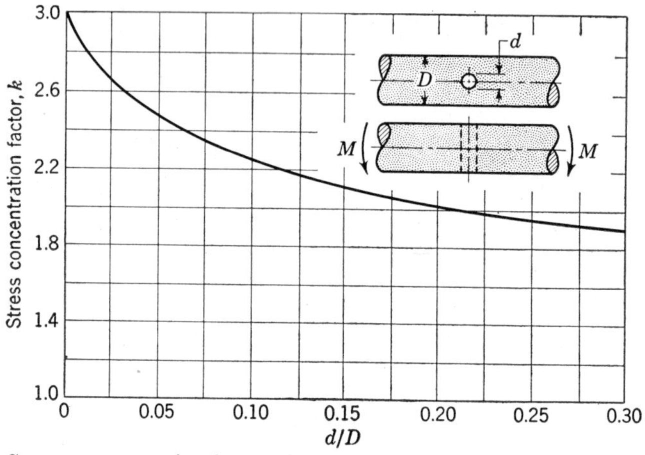

Fig. 2-37. Stress-concentration factors for a round shaft in bending with a transverse hole. (*Courtesy of Machine Design, Penton Publishing Company, Cleveland.*)

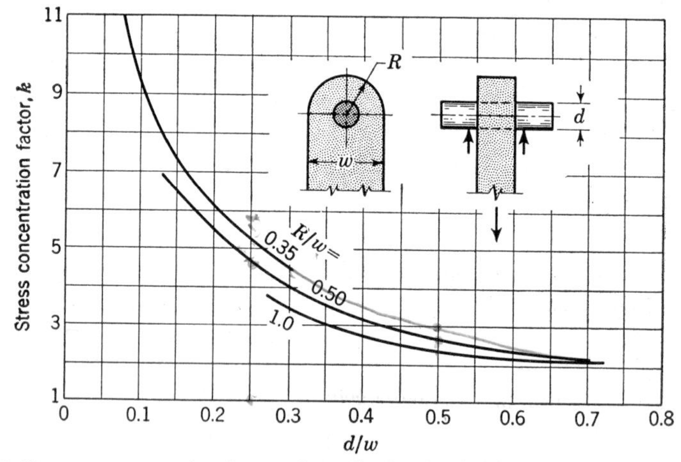

Fig. 2-38. Stress-concentration factors for a flat bar loaded in tension by a pin through a hole.

that tension tests on ⅜-in. National Coarse threads gave fatigue[3] stress-concentration factors of 2.84 for medium-carbon steel and 3.85 for heat-

[1] Seely, *op. cit.*, p. 285.

[2] Paul H. Black, "Machine Design," p. 55, McGraw-Hill Book Company, Inc., New York, 1948.

[3] See Chap. 4.

treated nickel steel. Peterson[1] gives an experimentally obtained value of 3.35 for Whitworth threads. These values are for screw threads subjected to the action of fatigue loads, that is, loads which are repeated or reversed. We shall see that under fatigue loading the degree of stress concentration is somewhat reduced. For this reason the geometric stress-concentration factors for screw threads will be somewhat more than the values indicated above. A k of 5 or 6 is suggested in the absence of additional information.

EXAMPLE 2-6. A rotating shaft has loads of 1,000 and 2,000 lb acting at distances of 4 and 10 in., respectively, from the left-hand bearing, as shown in Fig. 2-39. Point

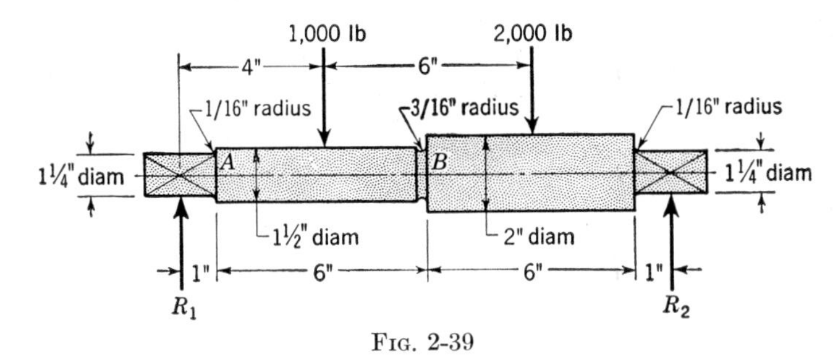

FIG. 2-39

A is a shaft shoulder which is required for positioning the left-hand bearing. Point B is a grinding-relief groove $\frac{3}{16}$ in. wide and $\frac{3}{32}$ in. deep. Using the dimensions shown, find the maximum stress at points A and B.

Solution. The reaction at R_1 is found to be 1,290 lb. The moment at point A is

$$M_A = (1{,}290)(1) = 1{,}290 \text{ lb-in.}$$

The section modulus for the $1\frac{1}{4}$-in. diameter is

$$\frac{I}{c} = \frac{\pi d^3}{32} = \frac{\pi(1.25)^3}{32} = 0.194 \text{ in.}^3$$

Referring to Fig. 2-35,

$$\frac{r}{d} = \frac{0.0625}{1.25} = 0.05 \qquad \frac{D}{d} = \frac{1.50}{1.25} = 1.20 \qquad k = 1.92$$

Then $$s_A = k\frac{M}{I/c} = \frac{(1.92)(1{,}290)}{0.194} = 12{,}800 \text{ psi} \qquad \textit{Ans.}$$

The moment at point B is

$$M_B = (1{,}290)(7) - (1{,}000)(3) = 6{,}030 \text{ lb-in.}$$

At point B the diameter at the bottom of the groove is 1.313 in., and the section modulus is

$$\frac{I}{c} = \frac{\pi d^3}{32} = \frac{\pi(1.313)^3}{32} = 0.222 \text{ in.}^3$$

[1] Peterson, *op. cit.*, p. 161, March, 1951.

Referring again to Fig. 2-35,

$$\frac{r}{d} = \frac{0.1875}{1.313} = 0.143 \qquad \frac{D}{d} = \frac{2.00}{1.313} = 1.522 \qquad k = 1.5$$

Then

$$s_B = k\frac{M}{I/c} = \frac{(1.5)(6{,}030)}{0.222} = 40{,}700 \text{ psi} \qquad Ans.$$

The reader should note that this stress may be dangerously high, but the decision as to what should be done about it depends upon the loading characteristics and the material of the shaft.

Reduction of Stress-concentration Effects. In the design of machine parts, every effort should be made to locate irregularities which are the cause of stress concentrations at points of low nominal stress. Shaft shoulders and holes can often be located at points where the bending moment is zero or at least very low. Consideration should be given also to the points at which torsion is applied and delivered, and, where possible, necessary irregularities should be located beyond these points. In the design of tension and compression members, abrupt changes in cross section can frequently be placed at points of zero stress.

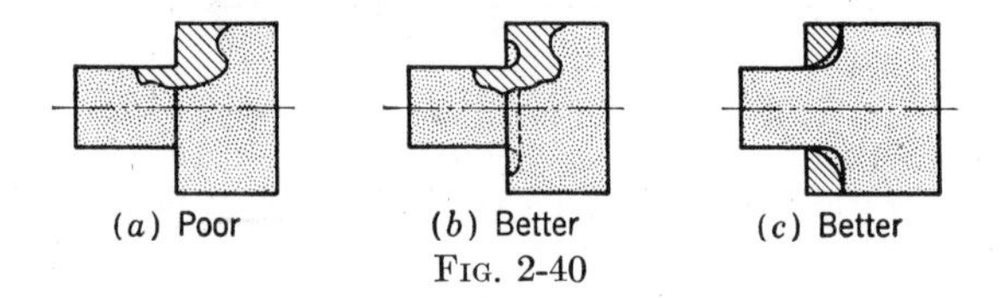

(*a*) Poor (*b*) Better (*c*) Better

Fig. 2-40

When irregularities are located at points of high nominal stress (point B in Example 2-6 illustrates this condition) it becomes necessary to resort to generous fillets, curves, and other devices, in order to decrease stress-concentration effects as much as possible. In Fig. 2-40*a* is shown a portion of a shaft having a square shoulder and consequently a high stress-concentration factor. If the square shoulder is necessary for proper seating of the mating machine part, then Fig. 2-40*b* shows a method of obtaining a generous fillet which makes use of an undercut groove. In Fig. 2-40*c* a chamfered ring is employed which permits a fillet with a large radius to be used on the shaft, thus reducing the stress-concentration factor.

Holes, grooves, and other devices can often be employed to reduce the abruptness of the irregularity and thus reduce the stress concentration. Figure 2-41, for example, illustrates members in tension which use various devices for relief of the concentrated stresses. No quantitative experimental data are available, however, to indicate the effect of these; it is suggested that, when they are employed, experimental evidence should be obtained to verify the design. Additional exploratory work is needed in this field.

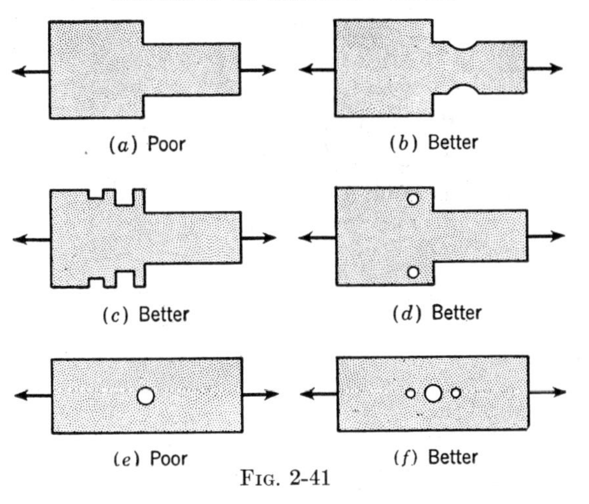

FIG. 2-41

BIBLIOGRAPHY

Hetenyi, M.: "Handbook of Experimental Stress Analysis," John Wiley & Sons, Inc., New York, 1950.

Lee, George H.: "Experimental Stress Analysis," John Wiley & Sons, Inc., New York, 1950.

Marin, Joseph: "Engineering Materials," Prentice-Hall, Inc., New York, 1952.

Roark, Raymond J.: "Formulas for Stress and Strain," 3d ed., McGraw-Hill Book Company, Inc., New York, 1954.

Seely, Fred B.: "Resistance of Materials," 3d ed., John Wiley & Sons, Inc., New York, 1947.

Timoshenko, S.: "Strength of Materials," 2d ed., vols. 1 and 2, D. Van Nostrand Company, Inc., New York, 1940, 1941.

PROBLEMS

Many of the problems in this book require that decisions be made before the problems can be solved. These decisions are many and varied, such as a selection of material, the value of the factor of safety, the simplifying assumptions to be made, or which pressure angle to use for gear teeth. Each type of problem generally will require a characteristic set of decisions. In the case of a true design, these decisions must be made by the designer. One of the principal purposes of this book is to teach the reader to make decisions for himself. Four types of problems will appear; they are:

1. Those in which the decisions are made for the reader. This is purely a practice type of problem and is *not* design. It is used to ground the reader in basic methods of analysis and problem solving.

2. Those in which the reader is required to make decisions and he is told what decisions he must make. This is a transitional type of problem and is almost design. Problems of this nature will usually be marked with an asterisk.

3. Those in which the reader is required to make decisions in order to solve the problem and he is not told what decisions to make. In general, with this type of problem, no two persons will obtain the same answer, because the answers depend

upon the decisions made. For example, different materials may be used with different factors of safety. The simplifying assumptions made may also be different, with each group leading to its distinct method of analysis. The evaluation of the results, too, will depend upon the previous chain of decisions. This is pure design, and these problems will always be marked with an asterisk.

4. A type of problem which cannot be classified as those above but which, in various ways, has a tendency to develop ingenuity or creative thinking. For example, a problem may give an absurd or unexpected result requiring evaluation by the student. These problems will also be marked with an asterisk.

2-1. A bar having a cross-sectional area of 4 in.^{2} is subjected to a tensile load of 20,000 lb. Determine the direction and magnitude of the maximum shearing stress.

Ans.: 2,500 lb at 45°.

2-2. A ¾-in.-diameter bar is acted upon by a tensile stress of 16,000 psi. Determine the value of the normal stress in the direction in which the shearing stress is a maximum.

2-3. Determine the normal and shearing stresses on the plane *mn* if s_x = 6,000 psi and ϕ = 30°.

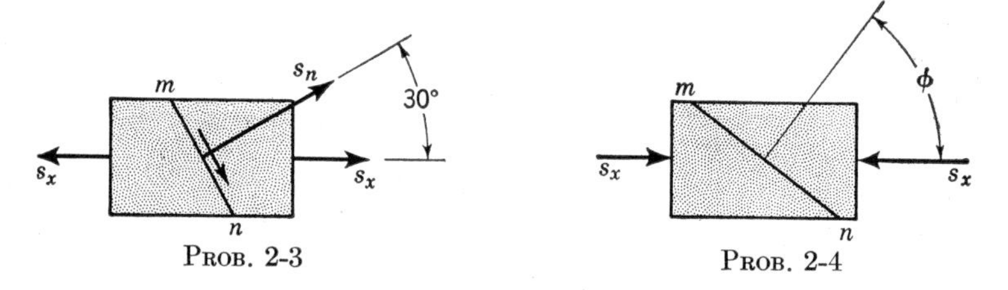

PROB. 2-3 PROB. 2-4

2-4. (*a*) If s_x is 10,000 psi, find s_n when ϕ is chosen so that $s_s = 0$. (*b*) Find s_n and s_s' when ϕ is such as to make s_s a maximum.

2-5. A 6-in.-diameter cylinder of concrete has a compressive load of 25,000 lb acting in the direction of its axis. On a sheet of coordinate paper, plot a polar diagram of the shearing stress and the normal stress, letting ϕ vary from 0 to 360°. Use 30° intervals. Use colored lines to differentiate between the stresses.

2-6. An element is subjected to a tensile stress of 10,000 psi in the x direction and a tensile stress of 4,000 psi in the y direction. (*a*) Find the maximum shearing stress. (*b*) Determine the shearing stress and the normal stress when ϕ = 30°.

Ans.: (*a*) 3,000 psi, (*b*) 8,500 psi, 2,600 psi.

2-7. A prismatical element is acted upon by a tensile stress of 9,000 psi in the x direction and a tensile stress of 1,000 psi in the y direction. (*a*) Find s_s and s_n when ϕ = 60°. (*b*) Find the maximum shearing stress.

2-8. If s_x = 3,000 psi and s_y = 15,000 psi, find s_s and s_n when ϕ = 30°.

Ans.: 5,200 psi, 6,000 psi.

2-9. If s_x = 1,000 psi and s_y = 3,000 psi, find s_s and s_n when ϕ = 45°.

2-10. If $s_x = s_y$ = 500 psi, find s_s and s_n when ϕ = 60°.

2-11. A bar is acted upon by a tensile stress of 4,000 psi in the x direction and a compressive stress of 2,000 psi in the y direction. (*a*) Find the maximum shearing stress. (*b*) Find the value of the normal stress when the shearing stress is a maximum. (*c*) Determine the value of the shearing stress when the normal stress is zero.

Ans.: (*a*) 3,000 psi, (*b*) 1,000 psi tension, (*c*) 2,830 psi.

2-12. A bar is acted upon by a compressive stress of 4,000 psi in the x direction and a compressive stress of 1,000 psi in the y direction. Find the values of the normal and shearing stresses when ϕ = 45°.

2-13. A bar is acted upon by a compressive stress of 7,000 psi in the x direction and a tensile stress of 1,000 psi in the y direction. (*a*) Find ϕ when $s_n = 0$. (*b*) What is s_n when s_s is a maximum? (*c*) Find s_s'.

2-14. A bar is acted upon by a tensile stress s_x and a compressive stress s_y. Find s_s' if $s_x = s_y$.

2-15. A bar is acted upon by the stresses $s_x = 16{,}000$ psi and $s_{xy} = 6{,}000$ psi. (*a*) Find s_1 and s_2 and their directions. (*b*) Find s_s'.

Ans.: (*a*) $-18°25'$, 18,000 psi, $-2{,}000$ psi, (*b*) 10,000 psi.

2-16. If $s_x = 2{,}000$ psi and $s_{xy} = 4{,}000$ psi, find s_1, s_2, and s_s'.

2-17. If $s_x = -4{,}000$ psi and $s_{xy} = 4{,}000$ psi, find the direction and magnitude of the principal stresses.

2-18. A bar is acted upon by a tensile stress $s_x = 8{,}000$ psi and a shearing stress $s_{xy} = 3{,}000$ psi. On a sheet of coordinate paper, plot a polar diagram of the normal and shearing stresses for values of ϕ from 0 to 360°. Use 30° intervals and a colored line to differentiate the stresses.

2-19. Find the magnitude and direction of the principal stresses if $s_x = 300$ psi, $s_y = -100$ psi, and $s_{xy} = 400$ psi. *Ans.:* 548 psi, -348 psi, $-31°45'$.

2-20. Let $s_x = 7{,}000$ psi, $s_y = 1{,}000$ psi, and $s_{xy} = 4{,}000$ psi. Find s_1, s_2, and s_s'.

2-21. If $s_x = -10{,}000$ psi, $s_y = -2{,}000$ psi, and $s_{xy} = 4{,}000$ psi, find the magnitude and direction of the principal stresses.

2-22. Find the diameter of a solid circular shaft which is to transmit 50 hp at 900 rpm if the shearing stress induced in the shaft is not to exceed 10,000 psi.

Ans.: Use $1\frac{1}{4}$-in. diameter.

2-23. Determine the diameter of a solid circular shaft which is to transmit $\frac{1}{10}$ hp at 1 rpm if a shearing stress of 6,000 psi is permitted.

2-24. What horsepower will a $1\frac{1}{4}$-in.-diameter solid circular shaft running at 1,725 rpm transmit if an induced shearing stress of 12,000 psi is allowed?

2-25. (*a*) Find the ratio of the torques that may be safely transmitted by a 4-in.-diameter solid circular shaft, as compared with a hollow shaft whose outside diameter is 4 in. and whose wall thickness is $\frac{3}{8}$ in. (*b*) Compare the strength-weight ratios of the two shafts.

***2-26.** A 1-in. OD hollow shaft is to transmit $\frac{1}{3}$ hp at 25 rpm. (*a*) If an induced stress of 16,000 psi is permitted, what should be the wall thickness? (*b*) Evaluate the result. a) t = 0.0375 in. Page 22 + 23

***2-27.** A $7\frac{1}{2}$-hp electric motor is capable of delivering 200 per cent of full-load torque. The motor has a full-load speed of 3,450 rpm. It is to be connected to a woodworking machine by means of a heat-treated alloy-steel shaft whose length is 20 in. (*a*) Determine the diameter of the shaft on the basis of strength if an induced shearing stress of 36,000 psi is permitted. (*b*) Evaluate the result.

2-28. A shaft 12 in. in length is loaded as shown in the figure. If a bending stress of 22,000 psi is permitted, what diameter shaft should be used? *Decisions:* Deflection is not important, and torsional stresses are negligible. *Ans.:* Use $1\frac{3}{16}$-in. diameter.

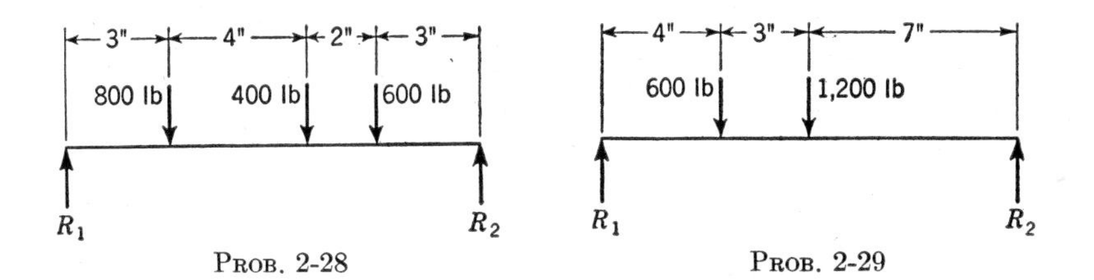

PROB. 2-28 PROB. 2-29

2-29. A shaft 14 in. long supports loads as shown in the figure. Using an allowable bending stress of 30,000 psi, determine the diameter of shaft to be used. *Decisions:* Deflection and torsional loads are neglected.

2-30. A shaft 26 in. in length is to support a load which is approximately 125 lb per in. of shaft. Determine the outside diameter of a hollow shaft such that the wall thickness is one-tenth of the outside diameter. Use an allowable bending stress of 16,000 psi. *Decisions:* The load is uniformly distributed, torsional stresses are negligible, and deflection is not important.

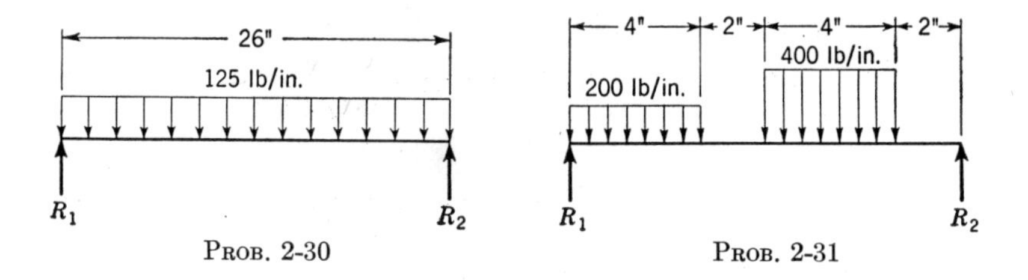

Prob. 2-30

Prob. 2-31

2-31. A round hollow shaft 12 in. long supports two distributed loads as shown in the figure. A bending stress of 24,000 psi is permitted. Determine the diameter of the shaft if the inside diameter is to be three-fourths of the outside diameter. *Decisions:* Each load is uniformly distributed, and deflection and torsion are neglected.

2-32. The distributed loads in Prob. 2-31 could represent the effect of hubs on pulleys or gears. If these loads were to be replaced by equivalent concentrated loads, how much would the calculated diameter be affected? Restate the decisions and calculate the new diameter.

2-33. Determine the diameter of the shaft shown in the figure if a bending stress of 16,000 psi and a shearing stress of 12,000 psi are permitted. *Decisions:* Stress concentration and deflection are neglected.

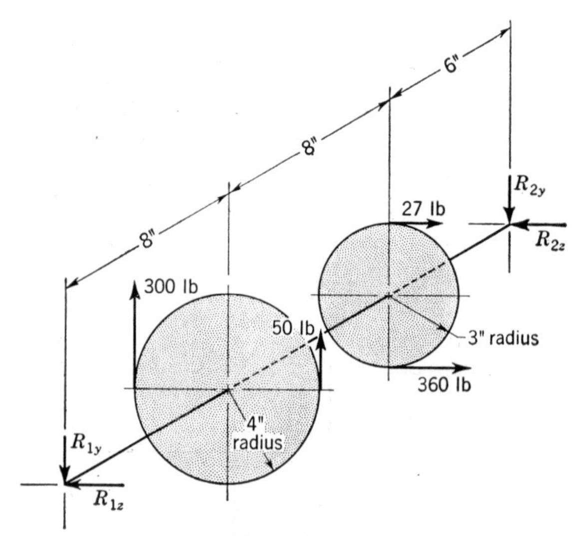

Prob. 2-33

2-34. If a shearing stress of 12,000 psi and a bending stress of 24,000 psi are permitted, find the diameter of the shaft shown in the figure. *Decisions:* Deflection and stress concentration are neglected.

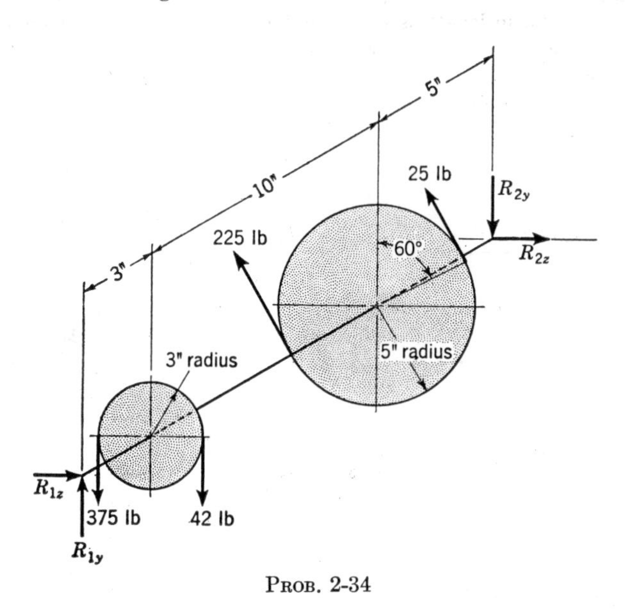

PROB. 2-34

***2-35.** In the figure is shown a shaft 34 in. in length, acted upon by bending forces caused by gears mounted upon the shaft at points A and B. The shaft is to transmit a maximum of 10 hp at a speed of 1,200 rpm. (*a*) If a shearing stress of 24,000 psi and a bending stress of 30,000 psi are permitted, find the shaft diameter. (*b*) Evaluate the results obtained.

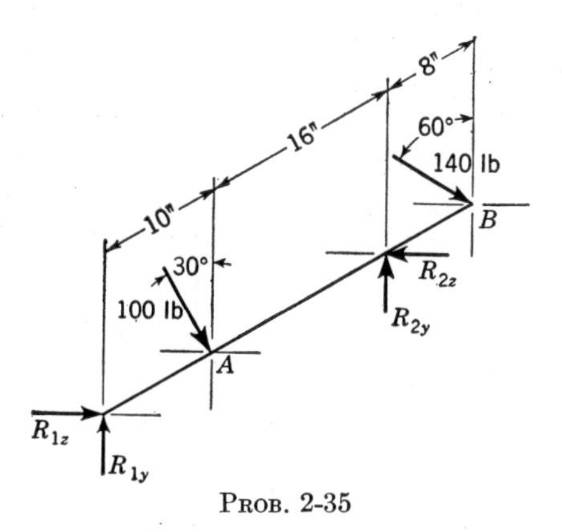

PROB. 2-35

2-36. A cast-iron beam 11 in. long has a T section as shown in the figure. If a normal tensile stress s_t = 8,000 psi, a normal compressive stress s_c = 14,000 psi, and a transverse shearing stress of $s_s = 5{,}000$ psi are permitted, will the beam safely support the load as shown in the figure? Show calculations for each induced stress.

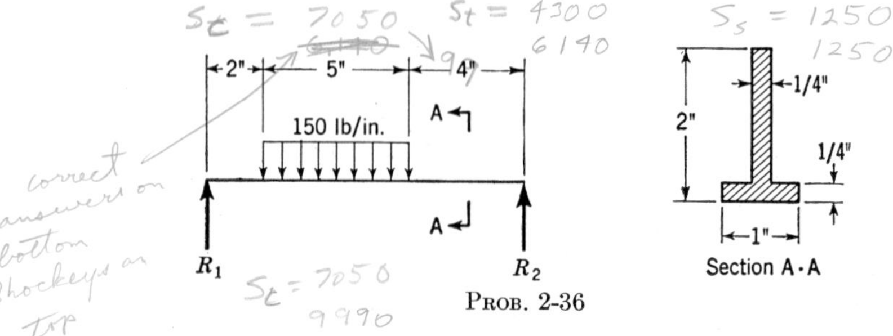

PROB. 2-36

2-37. In the figure, *ab* represents the neutral plane of bending. Using a sheet of coordinate paper, plot the transverse-shearing-stress distribution for the section shown in terms of the shearing force V.

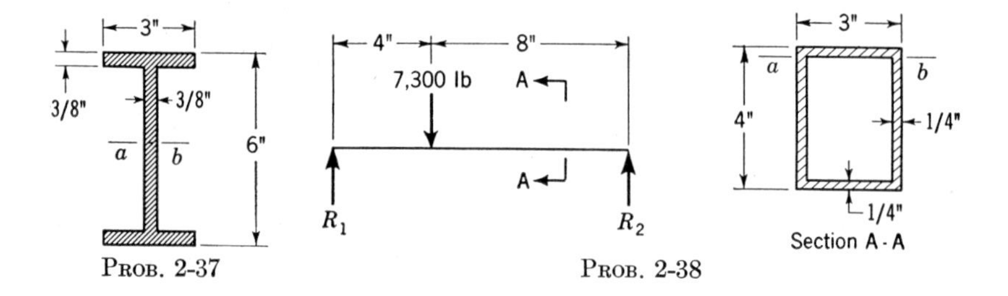

PROB. 2-37 PROB. 2-38

2-38. A beam 12 in. long is to support a load of 7,300 lb 4 in. from the left end, as shown in the figure. Based upon an allowable normal bending stress of 6,000 psi, a piece of extruded rectangular 75S aluminum tubing has been tentatively chosen. The dimensions are shown. At a section *ab* there exist a shearing stress and a normal stress. Using Mohr's circle, find the combined normal stress at section *ab* and compare it with the allowable normal stress.

2-39. Find the maximum stress in the bar shown in the figure. *Ans.:* 4,320 psi.

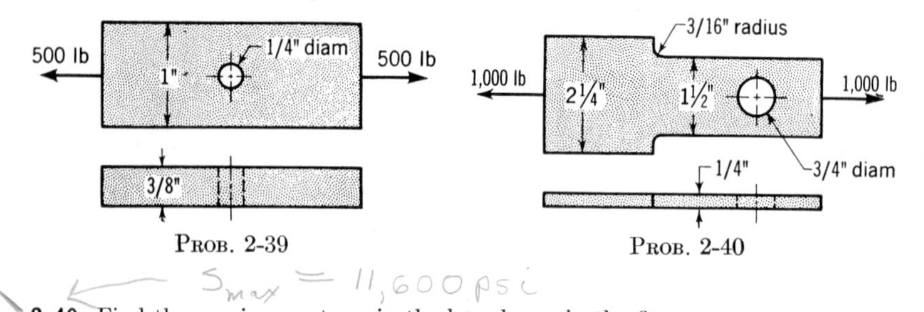

PROB. 2-39 PROB. 2-40

2-40. Find the maximum stress in the bar shown in the figure.

2-41. The bar shown in the figure is loaded in tension by a pin through a hole. Determine the safe load F that can be carried if a maximum stress of 10,000 psi is permitted.

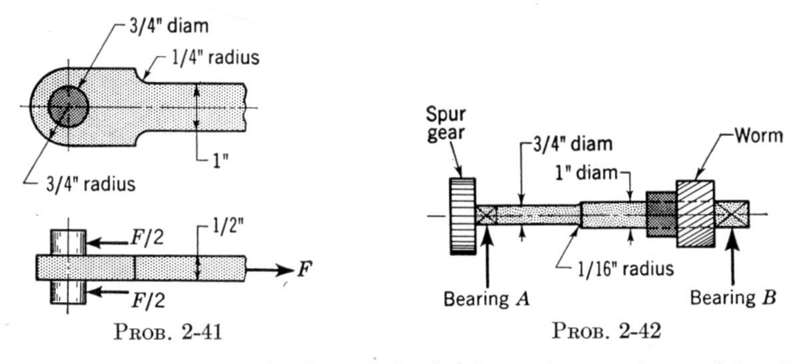

PROB. 2-41 PROB. 2-42

2-42. The shaft shown in the figure is loaded in torsion, tension, and bending, because of the action of the worm, spur gear, and bearings. A combined thrust and radial bearing A takes the axial tensile load of 120 lb caused by the worm. Bearing B is a pure radial bearing. The spur gear transmits a torque of 300 lb-in. to the shaft. Find the maximum stress in the shaft. *Decision:* Bending is neglected.

2-43. A rotating shaft is loaded in bending as shown. Find the maximum stress at each point of stress concentration. *Decision:* Torsion is neglected.

Ans.: 5,500 psi, 21,800 psi, 15,100 psi.

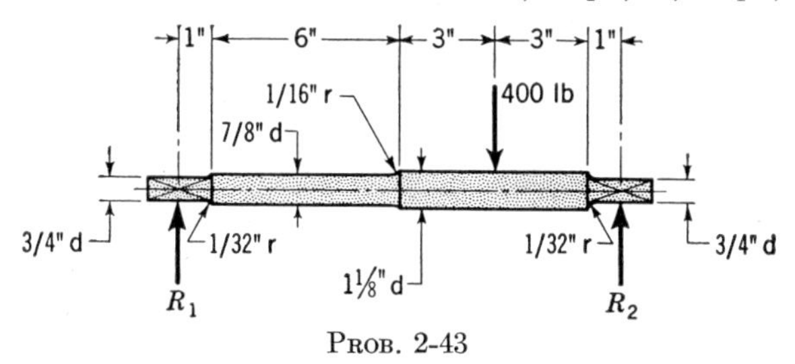

PROB. 2-43

***2-44.** Design a 12-ft ladder of wood. The wood used permits the following values of stresses: a compressive stress of 2,000 psi parallel to the grain; a compressive stress of 500 psi across the grain; a shearing stress of 200 psi parallel to the grain; and a normal bending stress of 2,000 psi. The material weighs 43 lb per ft³. The following decisions must be made:

1. The spacing of the rails
2. The pitch and location of the rungs
3. The magnitude of the maximum load
4. The shape of the rungs and rails
5. The end conditions for bending of the rungs
6. The stress-concentration effect of the rung holes
7. The maximum inclination of the ladder

CHAPTER 3

DEFLECTION OF MACHINE PARTS

3-1. Introduction. Chapter 2 was concerned with the stresses in machine parts and how these stresses influence the size, shape, and material of the part. Just as important as the strength of the part, however, is the deflection, or displacement, it may receive from loads acting upon it. A material which is absolutely rigid does not exist. When subjected to the action of any load, all materials experience a displacement. In the case of a rigid part or a lightly loaded part, this displacement is small, but it is a definite, measurable displacement. Since loads are always present in all machine structures, it follows that displacements are always present. It is the designer's responsibility to create a machine in which these elastic deformations are not only reasonable in magnitude but also, if possible, one in which they actually contribute to the proper functioning.

3-2. Elasticity. When a straight bar is subjected to a tensile load the bar becomes longer. The amount of this stretch, or elongation, is called *strain*. It is given by the expression

$$\epsilon = \frac{\delta}{l} \tag{3-1}$$

where the unit strain ϵ is measured in inches per inch and δ is the total elongation of the bar within the length l. The assumptions made are:

1. The cross section of the bar is and remains constant.
2. The material is homogeneous.
3. The strain is uniformly distributed.

If the bar is relatively short, so as to prevent bending or buckling, the same expression will apply for compression loading.

Shearing strain is defined by the equation

$$\gamma = \frac{r\theta}{l} \tag{3-2}$$

where θ = angular displacement of adjacent cross sections of uniform circular bar subjected to torsion

l = distance between cross sections, in.

r = radius of bar, in.
γ = shearing strain, radians

The assumptions used for tensile and compressive strain also apply, although it should be emphasized that a uniform distribution of shearing force is seldom obtained in practice.

Elasticity is that property of a material which enables it to regain its original shape and dimensions when the load is removed. Hooke's law states that, within certain limits, the stress in a material is proportional to the strain which produced it. An elastic material does not necessarily obey Hooke's law, since it is possible for some materials to regain their original shape without the limiting condition that stress be proportional to strain. On the other hand, a material which obeys Hooke's law is elastic. For the condition that stress is proportional to strain, we can write

$$s = E\epsilon \tag{3-3}$$

$$s_s = G\gamma \tag{3-4}$$

where E and G are the constants of proportionality.[1] Since the strains are dimensionless numbers, the units of E and G are the same as the units of stress, that is, in pounds per square inch. The constant E is called the *modulus of elasticity*. The constant G is called the *shearing modulus of elasticity*, or, sometimes, the *modulus of rigidity*. These two constants represent fundamental properties of a material.

By substituting $s = F/A$ and $\epsilon = \delta/l$ into Eq. (3-3) and rearranging, we obtain

$$\delta = \frac{Fl}{AE} \tag{3-5}$$

Also, if we substitute $s_s = Tr/J$ [Eq. (2-18)] and $\gamma = r\theta/l$, into Eq. (3-4), we obtain

$$\theta = \frac{Tl}{GJ} \tag{3-6}$$

where θ is the shearing deformation in radians. If we multiply Eq. (3-6) by $180/\pi$ and substitute the polar moment of inertia $J = \pi d^4/32$, we obtain the expression

$$\theta = \frac{585Tl}{Gd^4} \tag{3-7}$$

[1] The reader should note carefully that stress is an artificial concept which cannot be seen or measured directly. On the other hand, strain is visible to the eye and can be directly measured. Since strain can be made visible, it is often the only means for determining the stress distribution because, according to Hooke's law, stress is proportional to strain. There are many design problems in which the solution can be obtained only by first determining the strains, after which the stresses can be calculated.

where θ, in this equation, is in degrees. While restricted to a solid round shaft, it is more useful in this form.

Experiments demonstrate that when a material is placed in tension there exists not only an axial strain but also a lateral strain. Poisson demonstrated that these two strains were proportional to each other within the range of Hooke's law. This constant is expressed as follows:

$$\mu = \frac{\text{lateral strain}}{\text{axial strain}} \tag{3-8}$$

and is known as *Poisson's ratio.* These same relations apply for compression except that a lateral expansion occurs.

The three elastic constants are related to each other as follows:

$$E = 2G(1 + \mu) \tag{3-9}$$

3-3. Statically Indeterminate Problems. Problems frequently arise which cannot be solved by the use of statics alone. In these cases it is necessary to consider the deformations of the components. In solving such problems, the differences in the coefficients of expansion and the machining variations must be considered carefully, because these frequently cause the results to be quite inaccurate. The stresses must also be such that the material obeys Hooke's law.

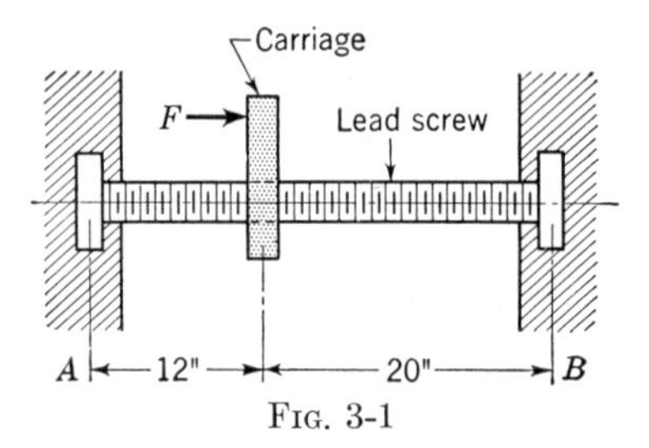

Fig. 3-1

Example 3-1. Figure 3-1 is a schematic diagram of a lead screw on a metalworking lathe. The screw is assumed to be mounted in two thrust bearings A and B. The force, $F = 400$ lb, represents the pressure of the cutting tool against the work. Find the axial force on each thrust bearing.

Solution. Designating F_A and F_B the respective axial forces on each bearing, we have

$$F_A + F_B = 400 \tag{a}$$

A second relation must be obtained because there are two unknowns. The left-hand portion of the screw is lengthened by an amount

$$\delta_A = \frac{F_A l_A}{AE}$$

The right-hand portion is compressed by an amount

$$\delta_B = \frac{F_B l_B}{AE}$$

These two deformations must be equal. Therefore

$$12F_A = 20F_B \tag{b}$$

Solving Eqs. (a) and (b) simultaneously, we have

$$F_A = 250 \text{ lb} \qquad F_B = 150 \text{ lb} \qquad \textit{Ans.}$$

3-4. Tensile or Compressive Strain in Two Directions. It has been demonstrated that, in the case of a bar in tension, an elongation occurs in the direction of the load and that a contraction occurs in a direction which is perpendicular to the direction of the load. Consider now a case in which a prismatical element is acted upon by a tensile stress s_x and also by a tensile stress s_y whose direction is at right angles to the direction of s_x (Fig. 3-2).

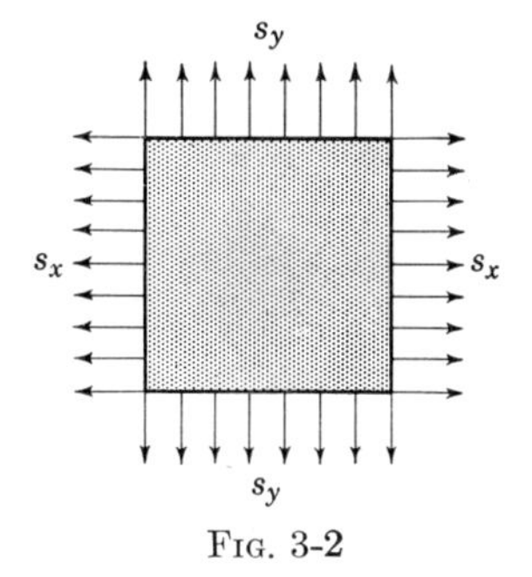

FIG. 3-2

Considering the forces in the x direction, a unit elongation (strain) whose value is s_x/E will occur as a result of s_x. But a unit contraction due to s_y will also occur. Its value is $-\mu s_y/E$. The resulting strain in the x direction will then be

$$\epsilon_x = \frac{s_x}{E} - \mu \frac{s_y}{E} \tag{3-10}$$

Following the same line of reasoning, the strain in the y direction will be

$$\epsilon_y = \frac{s_y}{E} - \mu \frac{s_x}{E} \tag{3-11}$$

Equations (3-10) and (3-11) can be solved simultaneously to obtain the stresses in terms of the strains. They are

$$s_x = \frac{(\epsilon_x + \mu\epsilon_y)E}{1 - \mu^2} \qquad s_y = \frac{(\epsilon_y + \mu\epsilon_x)E}{1 - \mu^2} \tag{3-12}$$

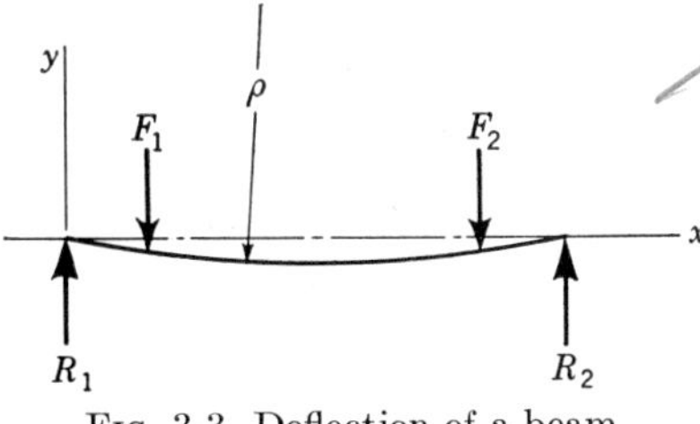

FIG. 3-3. Deflection of a beam.

3-5. Deflection of Beams. In strength of materials it is shown that

$$\frac{1}{\rho} = \frac{M}{EI} = \frac{d^2y}{dx^2} \tag{3-13}$$

where ρ is the radius of curvature of a beam deflected by a bending moment M (Fig. 3-3) which may be either variable or constant. Equation (3-13) expresses a fundamental relationship between the bending moment M and the resulting deflection y. Differentiating Eq. (3-13) gives

$$\frac{1}{EI}\frac{dM}{dx} = \frac{d^3y}{dx^3}$$

If we substitute the expression for shearing force $V = dM/dx$ [Eq. (2-22)], we obtain

$$\frac{V}{EI} = \frac{d^3y}{dx^3} \tag{3-14}$$

These and other relations from strength of materials are grouped below for convenience:

$$\frac{d^4y}{dx^4} = \frac{w}{EI} \qquad \text{loading} \tag{3-15}$$

$$\frac{d^3y}{dx^3} = \frac{V}{EI} \qquad \text{shear} \tag{3-14}$$

$$\frac{d^2y}{dx^2} = \frac{M}{EI} \qquad \text{moment} \tag{3-13}$$

$$\frac{dy}{dx} = \theta \qquad \text{slope} \tag{3-16}$$

$$y = \text{deflection}$$

These relations are used in various manners to obtain the deflection of a beam. Since the loading conditions are almost always given, the solution of a particular problem is usually obtained by integration.

The Double-integration Method. In this method statics is employed to obtain the equation of the moment diagram which is integrated twice to obtain the equation of the deflection curve. Equation (3-13) applies.

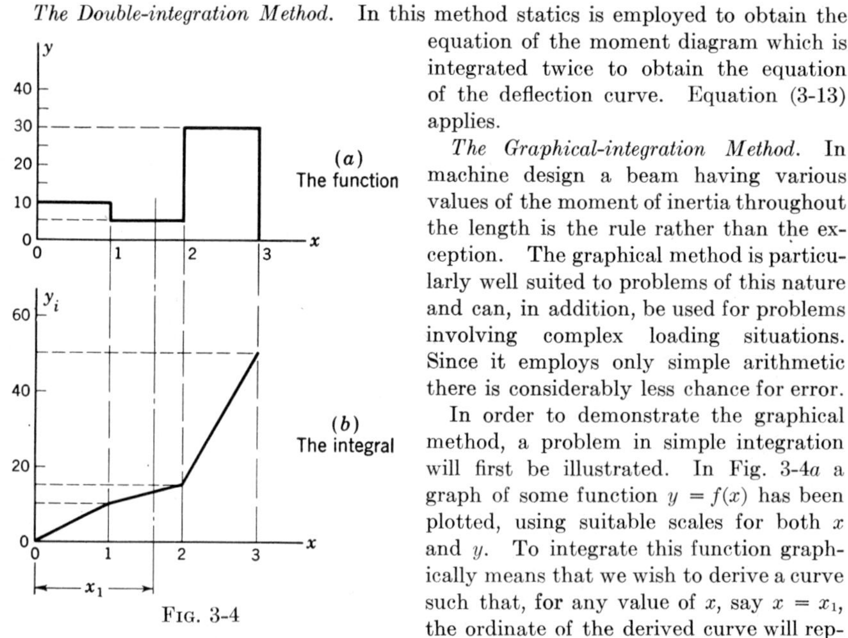

FIG. 3-4

The Graphical-integration Method. In machine design a beam having various values of the moment of inertia throughout the length is the rule rather than the exception. The graphical method is particularly well suited to problems of this nature and can, in addition, be used for problems involving complex loading situations. Since it employs only simple arithmetic there is considerably less chance for error.

In order to demonstrate the graphical method, a problem in simple integration will first be illustrated. In Fig. 3-4*a* a graph of some function $y = f(x)$ has been plotted, using suitable scales for both x and y. To integrate this function graphically means that we wish to derive a curve such that, for any value of x, say $x = x_1$, the ordinate of the derived curve will represent the area under the original curve between $x = 0$ and $x = x_1$. Between $x = 0$ and $x = 1$ there is a rectangular area of 10 square units. In Fig. 3-4*b* this point is plotted at the coordinates $x = 1$ and $y_i = 10$. Between $x = 0$ and $x = 1$ the area is directly proportional to x, so that a straight line can be drawn between the origin and the first point. Now between $x = 1$ and $x = 2$ the area is 5 square units, and so the total area up to $x = 2$ is 15 square units. This value is plotted on the line $x = 2$, and a second straight line is drawn. In the same way an area of 30 square units is found between $x = 2$ and $x = 3$, making a total of 45 square units under the curve. This value is now plotted on the line $x = 3$ and the points connected. This completes the integration. It is noted that the inclination of the lines in the derived curve is proportional to the height of the rectangles in the original curve. For example, between $x = 1$ and $x = 2$ the rectangle has a small height and the derived curve a small inclination; on the other hand, between $x = 2$ and $x = 3$ the rectangle has a large height and the inclination of the derived curve is large.

In Fig. 3-5a the problem is reproduced. Along the x axis the function is drawn so that 1 in. on the x axis represents 2 units. In other words, $S_x = 2$ units per inch,

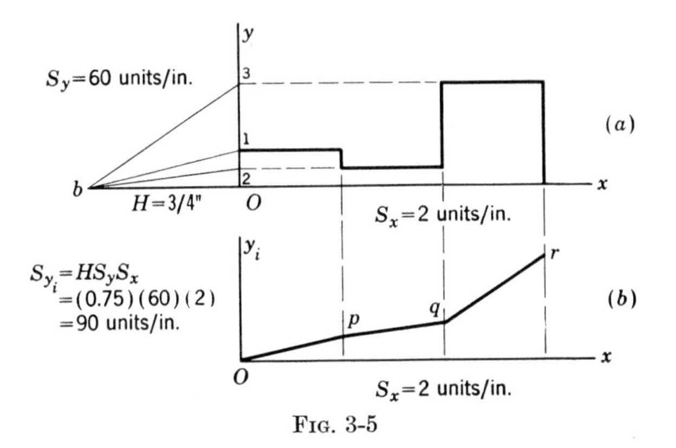

FIG. 3-5

which is called the *scale of x*. The y function is plotted at a scale $S_y = 60$ units per inch. To integrate this function graphically, we require a mechanism which will enable us to draw lines whose inclinations are proportional to the heights of the rectangles. Line Ob is such a mechanism. In this problem, Ob is made ¾ in. long, although any convenient length may be used. The length of this line is called the *pole distance*, and it is designated by H. The heights of the various rectangles are now projected to the y axis, and lines are drawn connecting these intersections with point b. Each of these lines, b-1, b-2, and b-3, has an inclination which is proportional to the height of the corresponding rectangle. The derived curve (integral) is obtained by drawing lines Op parallel to b-1, pq parallel to b-2, and qr parallel to b-3. The scale of the integral is obtained as follows:

$$S_{y_i} = HS_xS_y \tag{3-17}$$

where S_{y_i} is the scale of the integral in square units per inch.

EXAMPLE 3-2. This method of solution is now applied to the problem of obtaining the deflection of a beam (Fig. 3-6). In this figure (1) is a stepped shaft originally drawn one-fourth size which is further reduced for reproduction reasons. Loading diagram (2) shows a load of 50 lb per in. extending over a distance of 10 in. of the shaft length. The reactions at the bearings have been calculated and are indicated as R_1 and R_2. The shearing-force diagram (3) has been obtained from the loading diagram, using the conditions of statical equilibrium. The moment diagram

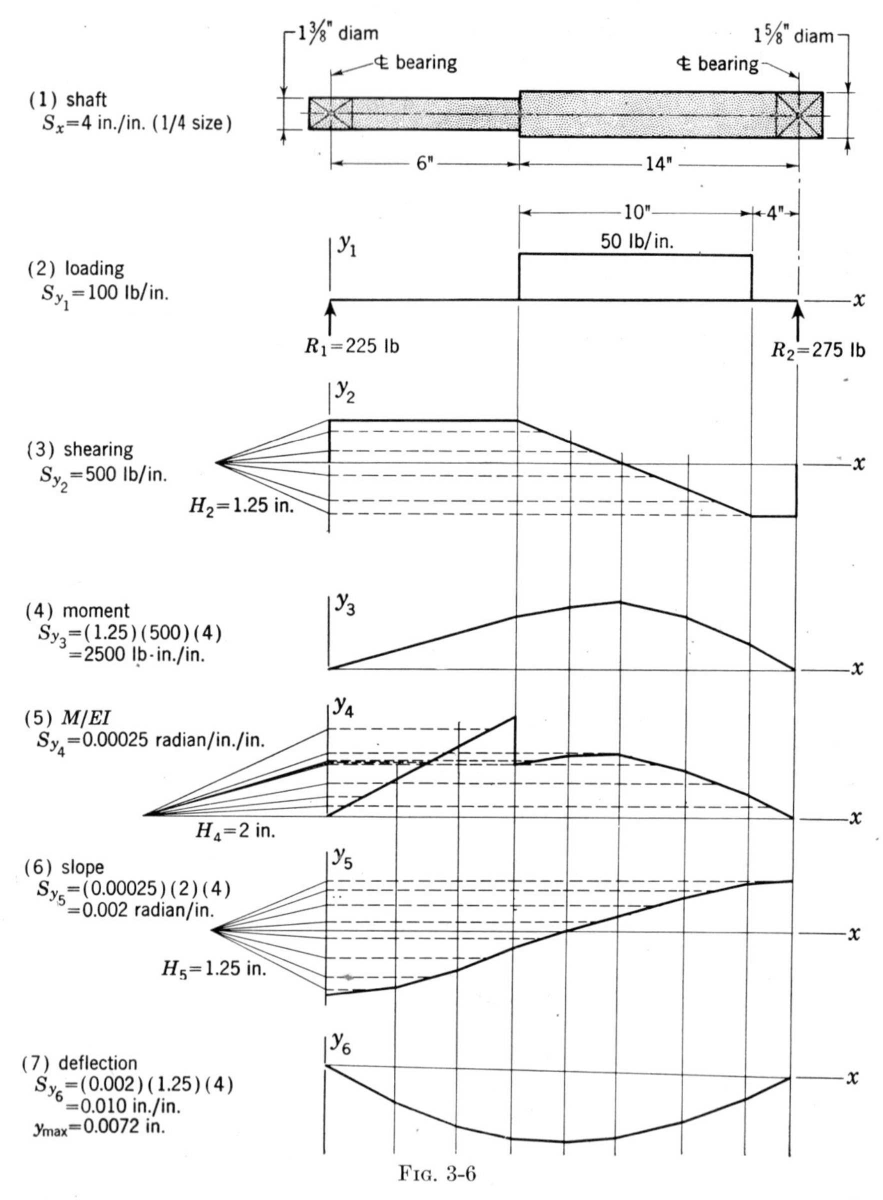

FIG. 3-6

(4) was obtained by graphically integrating the shearing-force diagram. The construction is shown and also the calculation for the scale of the moment diagram.

The next step is to obtain the numerical values of the moment at selected points along the shaft. This is done by scaling the diagram. The values of the moment of inertia are then calculated for each diameter. The moments are next divided by the products of the modulus of elasticity (E = 30,000,000 psi) and the moments of inertia, and these values are plotted in (5) to obtain the M/EI diagram. (If the moment of inertia is constant, this operation may be performed after the deflection curve is obtained. In case this is done, note that the deflection curve then becomes the yEI curve.) The M/EI diagram is now integrated twice to obtain the deflection curve (7). In integrating the slope diagram (6) it is necessary to guess at the location of zero slope, that is, the position at which to place the x axis. Should this guess be wrong, and it usually is, the deflection curve will not close with a horizontal line. The line should be drawn so as to close the deflection curve, and measurements of deflection made in the vertical direction. (Do not measure perpendicular to the closing line unless it is horizontal.) The correct location of zero slope is found as follows: Draw a line parallel to the closing line and tangent to the deflection curve. The point of tangency is the point of zero slope, and this is also the location of the maximum deflection.

The Area-moment Method. Reference to Eqs. (3-13) and (3-15) indicates that the moment diagram can be obtained from the loading diagram by a process of double

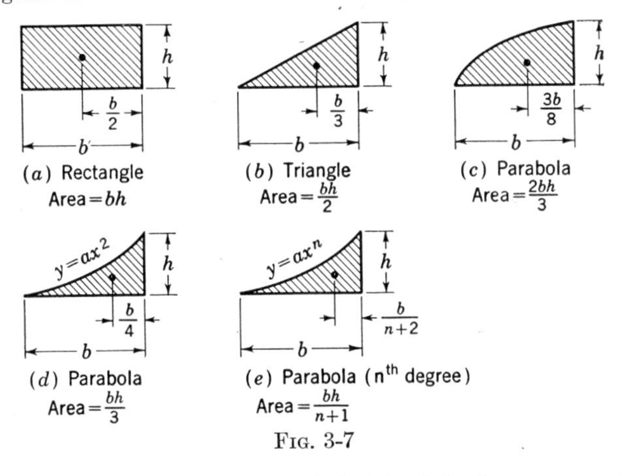

FIG. 3-7

integration. It has also been demonstrated that the deflection curve may be obtained by integrating the moment diagram twice. It is usually (though not necessarily) the procedure to apply statics to the loading diagram in order to obtain the moment diagram, since this process is generally quite simple. In the same way, simplification often occurs if the deflection curve is obtained by an application of the same rules of statics applied to the moment diagram. This method is called the *area-moment method*. It can be stated as follows: *The vertical distance between any point A on a deflection curve and a tangent through point B on the curve is the moment with respect to A of the area of the moment diagram between A and B divided by the stiffness EI.* This statement is used by first finding the area of the parts of the moment diagram or of the M/EI diagram. The moments are then found by multiplying the areas by their centroidal distances from the axis of moments. Figure 3-7 shows the centroidal distances and the areas for typical portions of moment diagrams.

Superposition. This method of finding the deflection of beams is useful with both the double-integration and area-moment procedures. In the case of a simply supported beam subjected to both uniformly distributed and concentrated loads, it is especially useful. By the method of superposition, the deflection at any point in a beam is equal to the sum of the deflections caused by each load acting separately. It is immaterial at which positions the loads act, but the deflections must be summed up for the same point on the beam.

3-6. Indeterminate Beams. Problems frequently arise in machine design in which there is not sufficient information to determine all the unknown reactions in a beam from a consideration of statics alone. This happens when there are a greater number of unknowns than there are equations of equilibrium. It was shown in Chap. 2 how the maximum bending stress was obtained from the maximum moment. In the case of indeterminate beams, the maximum moment cannot be determined from the conditions of statical equilibrium, so that it is necessary to find the deflection first in order that the moment may be found. The following example will illustrate one method in general use.

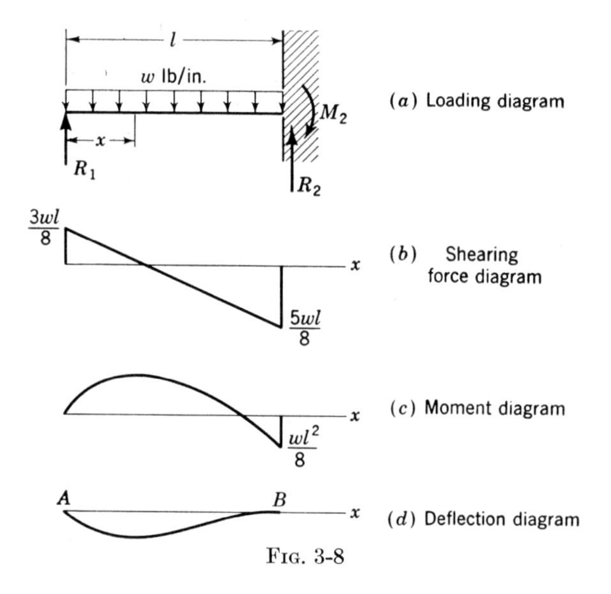

FIG. 3-8

EXAMPLE 3-3. Figure 3-8 shows a beam with a uniformly distributed load; the beam is fixed at one end and supported at the other by the reaction R_1. The built-in end has the reactions R_2 and M_2. For equilibrium, a summation of the vertical forces and a summation of the moments about any axis must equal zero. This will result in two equations of equilibrium, but since there are three unknowns these conditions are not sufficient.

Referring to the deflection curve (Fig. 3-8*d*), we must use the conditions that the deflection is zero at points A and B and that the slope of the curve is zero at point B. We first write the equation for the value of the moment in terms of any distance x measured from the left-hand support:

$$M_x = R_1 x - \frac{wx^2}{2}$$

Substituting this value of M in Eq. (3-13) gives

$$EI\frac{d^2y}{dx^2} = R_1 x - \frac{wx^2}{2} \tag{a}$$

Integrating Eq. (*a*) gives the slope:

$$EI\frac{dy}{dx} = \frac{R_1x^2}{2} - \frac{wx^3}{6} + C_1 \tag{b}$$

Since the slope must be zero at point B, we have the conditions that, when $x = l$, $dy/dx = 0$. When these conditions are substituted in (*b*) we have

$$C_1 = \frac{wl^3}{6} - \frac{R_1l^2}{2}$$

This value of C_1 is then placed in Eq. (*b*):

$$EI\frac{dy}{dx} = \frac{R_1x^2}{2} - \frac{wx^3}{6} + \frac{wl^3}{6} - \frac{R_1l^2}{2} \tag{c}$$

Integrating gives the deflection as

$$EIy = \frac{R_1x^3}{6} - \frac{wx^4}{24} + \frac{wl^3x}{6} - \frac{R_1l^2x}{2} + C_2 \tag{d}$$

The deflection must be zero at point A, so that the conditions are that, when $x = 0$, $y = 0$. Substituting these conditions in Eq. (*d*) gives $C_2 = 0$. Equation (*d*) becomes

$$EIy = \frac{R_1x^3}{6} - \frac{wx^4}{24} + \frac{wl^3x}{6} - \frac{R_1l^2x}{2} \tag{e}$$

The remaining condition is that the deflection is zero at point B or, when $x = l$, $y = 0$. Making this substitution in Eq. (*e*), we obtain

$$\frac{R_1l^3}{6} - \frac{wl^4}{24} + \frac{wl^4}{6} - \frac{R_1l^3}{2} = 0$$

$$R_1 = \frac{3wl}{8} \tag{f}$$

Having now obtained one of the reactions, the other two may be obtained from the conditions of equilibrium. Summing up the forces in the vertical direction, we find

$$R_2 = \frac{5wl}{8}$$

The bending moment at the fixed end is

$$M_2 = \frac{3wl^2}{8} - \frac{wl^2}{2} = -\frac{wl^2}{8}$$

Sufficient information is now available for calculation of the maximum moment which, at this point, can be determined in the usual manner. The shearing-force and bending-moment diagrams are shown in the figure. Substitution of R_1 from Eq. (*f*) into Eq. (*e*) gives the deflection:

$$y = \frac{w}{48EI}(3lx^3 - 2x^4 - l^3x)$$

The maximum deflection occurs when the slope is zero. To find the location of this point, Eq. (*c*) must be equated to zero. By substitution of the value of R_1 we have

$$\frac{3wlx^2}{16} - \frac{wx^3}{6} - \frac{wl^3}{48} = 0$$

$$x = 0.421l$$

Substitution of this value of x in the equation for the deflection curve yields the maximum deflection:

$$y_{\max} = 0.0054 \frac{wl^4}{EI}$$

3-7. Strain Energy in Tension and Compression. Machines having moving parts must resist loads which are applied by moving bodies. Since a body in motion possesses kinetic energy, any change in the motion of the body means a change in the kinetic-energy content. Both the stationary and moving parts of a machine are constantly acted upon by vibrating forces as well as by shock and impact forces. The dynamic forces of the moving parts, such as gears, cams, and flywheels, are transferred to the framework as the reactions at bearings and springs and other points of connection. Since absolute rigidity does not exist, these dynamic loads result in deformations of the various parts which represent an energy absorption. The parts must therefore be designed safely to withstand the energy loads.

The development of methods of determining deformations and stresses in machine parts and structures which are subjected to energy loads has not yet reached a state satisfactory to the machine designer. There are two reasons for this condition: (1) Generally there exists considerable uncertainty as to the actual value of either an impact or energy load and (2) energy loads are not usually absorbed by a single machine part but are transferred to the entire machine structure in varying amounts. For this reason it has become quite customary in design to multiply the static load by a shock or impact factor and then to design the part to resist this fictitious static load. The difficulty in this method comes from the fact that the dimensions and the properties of a part designed to withstand energy loads are altogether different from those for a part designed to withstand static loads. Methods are available for the determination of stresses during both elastic and plastic impact, but these are complex and difficult to apply even to relatively simple machine parts.[1] When statical methods of design are used, an understanding of the simpler theories of energy absorption will still be of considerable assistance.[2]

In Fig. 3-9*a* is shown a bar of area A and length l, loaded by a gradually applied force F. Since the bar is deformed by the force, the work done is transformed into potential energy of strain. The bar is considered to be perfectly elastic, so that the deformation is proportional to the force, as shown in Fig. 3-9*b*. The work done is equal to the potential strain energy stored in the bar. This is equal to the area of the triangle

[1] S. Timoshenko and J. N. Goodier, "Theory of Elasticity," 2d ed., chap. 15, pp. 438–456, McGraw-Hill Book Company, Inc., New York, 1951.

[2] For an excellent discussion of impact and energy loads see Fred B. Seely, "Resistance of Materials," 3d ed., chap. 11, John Wiley & Sons, Inc., New York, 1947.

ABO, or

$$U = \frac{F\delta}{2}$$

Since $\delta = Fl/AE$ and $s = F/A$, the strain energy is

$$U = \frac{s^2 lA}{2E} \tag{3-18}$$

When compared with the equation for static stress [Eq. (2-3)], this equation has startling implications. The static stress in a body depends only upon the area, but here we see that the capacity for absorbing energy depends both on the volume (lA) of the material and the modulus of elasticity. To absorb large amounts of energy, a machine part should therefore be long and have a low modulus of elasticity.

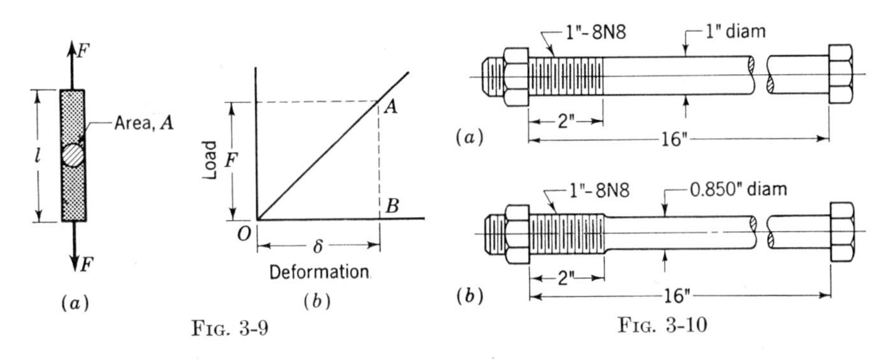

FIG. 3-9

FIG. 3-10

Equation (3-18) also shows that most of the energy absorption will occur in the part at points which are highly stressed. A part having localized stresses will absorb a great deal of energy at these points, resulting in a rapid failure or overdesigning of the part. For this reason, parts which are subjected to energy loads should be designed with a uniform stress distribution throughout their length in order to absorb a maximum amount of energy at low stress values. This is demonstrated by the following example.

EXAMPLE 3-4. Shown in Fig. 3-10 are two designs for a bolt subjected to tensile energy loads. The minor diameter of the threaded portion is 0.850 in. The bolts are to be made of steel which permits a stress up to 40,000 psi. Find the energy which each bolt can safely absorb.

Decisions. 1. Assume no stress-concentration effects.

2. Neglect the effect of the threads.

Solution. The area A_1 at the root of the threads and the area of the shank of the bolt in Fig. 3-10*b* is 0.565 in.^{2} The area A_2 of the shank of the bolt in Fig. 3-10*a* is 0.785 in.^{2} The stress at the root of the threads of the bolt in Fig. 3-10*a* is 40,000 psi, since this is the weakest section, and hence the stress in the shank is

$$s_2 = \frac{A_1}{A_2} s_1 = \frac{0.565}{0.785} 40{,}000 = 28{,}800 \text{ psi}$$

The energy that can be absorbed by this bolt is

$$\begin{aligned} U_a &= \frac{s_1^2 A_1 l_1}{2E} + \frac{s_2^2 A_2 l_2}{2E} \\ &= \frac{(40{,}000)^2(0.565)(2)}{(2)(30{,}000{,}000)} + \frac{(28{,}800)^2(0.785)(14)}{(2)(30{,}000{,}000)} \\ &= 30.2 + 152 = 182.2 \text{ lb-in.} \qquad \textit{Ans.} \end{aligned}$$

The other bolt will absorb

$$U_b = \frac{s_1^2 A_1 l}{2E} = \frac{(40{,}000)^2(0.565)(16)}{(2)(30{,}000{,}000)} = 241 \text{ lb-in.} \qquad \textit{Ans.}$$

The ratio $U_b/U_a = 241/182.2 = 1.32$ means that the reduction in the diameter of the shank permits a 32 per cent increase in the energy load without an increase in stress for the second bolt.

Impact Loads. Figure 3-11 illustrates an energy load which is caused by the weight W falling through the distance h. Since the bar will elongate a distance δ, the work done is

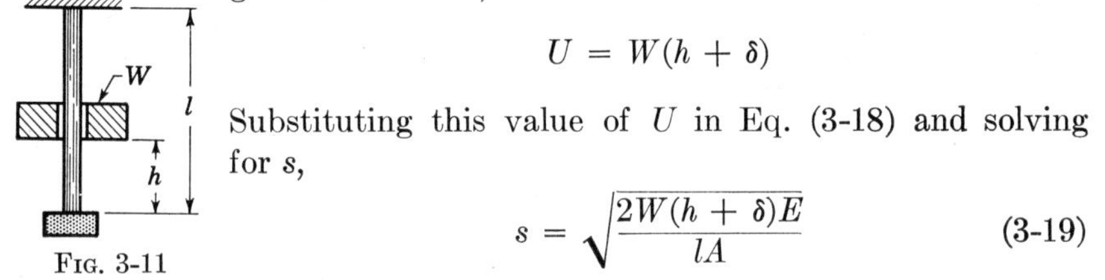

FIG. 3-11

$$U = W(h + \delta)$$

Substituting this value of U in Eq. (3-18) and solving for s,

$$s = \sqrt{\frac{2W(h + \delta)E}{lA}} \tag{3-19}$$

Equation (3-19) is difficult to handle in this form because the deformation δ is a function of the stress. Using the relation $\delta = sl/E$, the equation can be solved for the stress to yield

$$s = \frac{W}{A} + \frac{W}{A}\sqrt{1 + \frac{2hEA}{Wl}} \tag{3-20}$$

The first term in the expression is the stress which would exist if the load were gradually applied. It is interesting to see that, if the term h is allowed to become zero, the expression reduces to

$$s = \frac{2W}{A} \tag{3-21}$$

This relation, therefore, represents the stress in the bar when the load is applied suddenly but without initial velocity. Referring to Fig. 3-11, this is the stress that would be produced in the bar if the weight W were held in contact with the stop, but without exerting any force upon it, and then suddenly released. The stress is twice as large as that caused by a gradually applied load.

EXAMPLE 3-5. A steel bar 24 in. in length is to withstand a tensile impact load caused by a weight of 100 lb having a velocity on impact of 140 fpm. (*a*) Find the stress in the bar if the diameter is 1½ in. (*b*) What diameter should be used if a stress of 32,000 psi is permitted? Assume a rigid support.

Solution. The height corresponding to a velocity of 140 fpm is

$$h = \frac{v^2}{2g} = \frac{(140)^2(12)}{(60)^2(2)(32.2)} = 1.02 \text{ in.}$$

The area corresponding to 1½-in. diameter is 1.77 in.² Equation (3-20) is most convenient for (*a*):

$$s = \frac{W}{A} + \frac{W}{A}\sqrt{1 + \frac{2hEA}{Wl}} = \frac{100}{1.77} + \frac{100}{1.77}\sqrt{1 + \frac{(2)(1.02)(30{,}000{,}000)(1.77)}{(100)(24)}}$$
$$= 12{,}200 \text{ psi} \qquad \textit{Ans.}$$

Equation (3-19) is most convenient for (*b*). The deformation is

$$\delta = \frac{sl}{E} = \frac{(32{,}000)(24)}{30{,}000{,}000} = 0.0256 \text{ in.}$$

Solving Eq. (3-19) for A, we obtain

$$A = \frac{2W(h + \delta)E}{ls^2} = \frac{(2)(100)(1.02 + 0.0256)(30{,}000{,}000)}{(24)(32{,}000)^2} = 0.283 \text{ in.}^2$$

The diameter corresponding to this area is

$$d = 0.600 \text{ in.} \qquad \textit{Ans.}$$

The reader should note that if the load is applied under static conditions the stress would be 56.5 psi.

3-8. Strain Energy in Torsion. If a torque is gradually applied to a body, the work done is $T\theta/2$, where T is the torque and θ is the angular displacement in radians. The angular displacement is Tl/GJ, from Eq. (3-6). Assuming that the work done on the body is transformed into strain energy and that the body is cylindrical, the strain energy is

$$U = \frac{T\theta}{2} = \frac{T^2l}{2GJ} \tag{3-22}$$

By substituting the value of T from the equation $s_s = Tr/J$, we obtain

$$U = \frac{s_s^2Jl}{2Gr^2}$$

Since a solid round section is most generally encountered, the value of the polar moment of inertia, $J = \pi r^4/2$, and the area, $A = \pi r^2$, may be substituted to yield

$$U = \frac{s_s^2Al}{4G} \tag{3-23}$$

Here again we see that the strain energy is proportional to the square of the stress and to the volume (Al) of material. The same conclusions hold as were stated in Sec. 3-7 for strain energy in tension and compression. For this reason, machine elements which are to resist torsional energy loads must be designed with a uniform stress distribution so that a maximum amount of energy can be absorbed at low stress values.

3-9. Strain Energy in Bending. In Fig. 3-12a is shown a beam with a uniform load and simply supported at the ends, producing an elastic deflection curve which is concave upwards. Figure 3-12b shows a portion

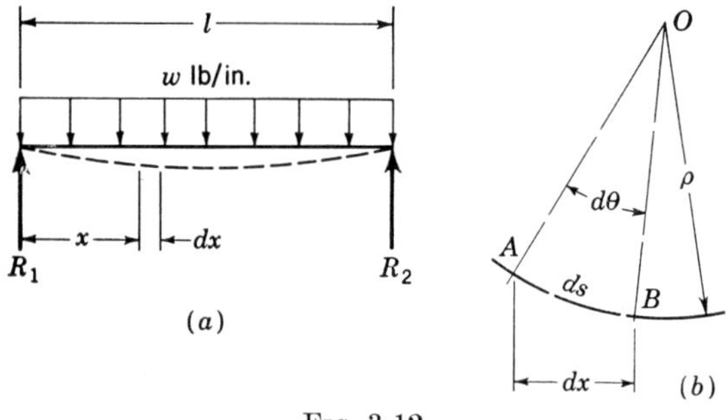

FIG. 3-12

of the elastic curve of length ds having a radius of ρ. The strain energy in this elementary section is

$$dU = M\frac{d\theta}{2} \tag{a}$$

Since $d\theta = ds/\rho$, this becomes

$$dU = \frac{M\,ds}{2\rho} \tag{b}$$

In Sec. 3-5 it was found that

$$\frac{1}{\rho} = \frac{M}{EI} \tag{3-13}$$

and hence the strain energy in the elementary section is

$$dU = \frac{M^2\,ds}{2EI} \tag{c}$$

The strain energy in the entire beam can now be obtained by adding the energies in the different elemental sections. Also, since ds is very nearly equal to dx for small deflections, we find

$$U = \int \frac{M^2\,dx}{2EI} \tag{3-24}$$

EXAMPLE 3-6. A cantilever beam has a concentrated load F at the end, as shown in Fig. 3-13. Find the strain energy in the beam.

Solution. At any point x along the beam the moment is

$$M = -Fx$$

Substituting the value of M into Eq. (3-24), we find

$$U = \int_0^l \frac{F^2x^2\,dx}{2EI} = \frac{F^2l^3}{6EI} \qquad \textit{Ans.}$$

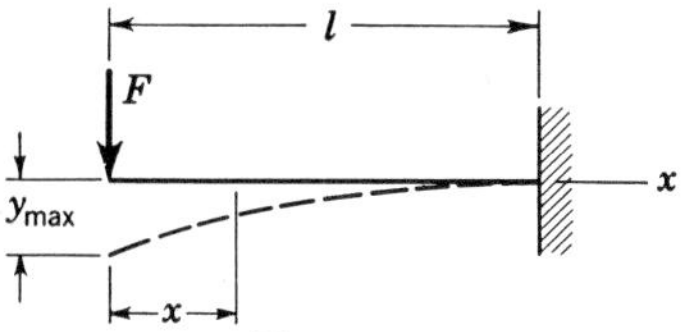

FIG. 3-13

The strain energy may also be obtained in another manner. At the end of the beam, at the point $x = 0$, the force F produces a deflection y_{max}. The strain energy is

$$U = \frac{Fy_{max}}{2}$$

But, from Table A-2, the maximum deflection of a cantilever beam is

$$y_{max} = \frac{Fl^3}{3EI}$$

so that

$$U = \frac{F}{2}\frac{Fl^3}{3EI} = \frac{F^2l^3}{6EI} \qquad \textit{Ans.}$$

This optional method of obtaining the strain energy can be employed when the beam has concentrated loads. When this method is used, y is the deflection of the point of application of the load.

3-10. The Theorem of Castigliano. A powerful tool for the determination of deflections of complex structures is provided by Castigliano's theorem. The problem of determining the deflections of fabricated machine parts and built-up machine frames occurs frequently in machine design. Energy methods often provide the only means of solving problems of this nature.

By substitution of $s = F/A$ in Eq. (3-18) for strain energy in tension and compression, it is found that

$$U = \frac{F^2l}{2AE}$$

Let us now take the derivative of this expression with respect to F:

$$\frac{dU}{dF} = \frac{Fl}{AE} = \delta$$

The reader will recognize the derivative as identically equal to the elongation [Eq. (3-5)]. In Sec. 3-8 the expression for torsional strain energy [Eq. (3-22)] was found to be

$$U = \frac{T^2l}{2GJ} \tag{3-22}$$

The derivative of this expression with respect to T is

$$\frac{dU}{dT} = \frac{Tl}{GJ} = \theta$$

which the reader will identify as the angular twist of a shaft under the action of a torsional load T [Eq. (3-6)]. In Example 3-6 the strain energy for a cantilever beam with a concentrated load at the end was

$$U = \frac{F^2l^3}{6EI}$$

and the derivative with respect to F is

$$\frac{dU}{dF} = \frac{Fl^3}{3EI} = y_{\max}$$

which is the deflection of the beam. The *theorem of Castigliano* is merely a statement of these facts. It states that *when forces operate on elastic systems the displacement corresponding to any force may be found by obtaining the partial derivative of the strain energy with respect to that force.* The terms "force" and "displacement" are to be broadly interpreted since they apply equally to moments and angular displacements. Mathematically, the theorem of Castigliano is stated as

$$\delta_n = \frac{\partial U}{\partial F_n} \tag{3-25}$$

where δ_n is the displacement in the direction of the force F_n and the displacement of the point of application of F_n. If no applied force exists at this point, then an imaginary force Q may be applied. After the expression for δ_n is obtained, the force Q is set equal to zero; the remaining expression is the displacement at the point of application of the imaginary force Q and in the direction in which Q was imagined to be acting.

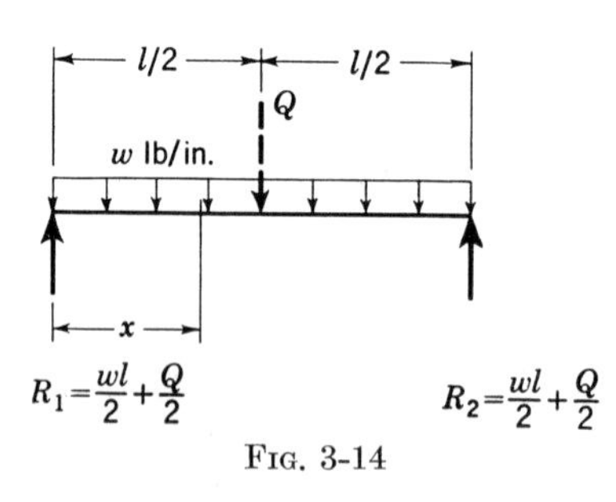

FIG. 3-14

EXAMPLE 3-7. Find the maximum deflection of a simply supported beam with a uniformly distributed load.

Solution. The problem is illustrated in Fig. 3-14. An imaginary load Q is placed in the center of the beam, which is the point of maximum deflection. Considering only the left portion, the moment is

$$M = \left(\frac{wl}{2} + \frac{Q}{2}\right)x - \frac{wx^2}{2}$$

The strain energy for the whole beam is twice as much as for one-half. Then, for the left half,

$$U = 2 \int_0^{l/2} \frac{M^2\,dx}{2EI}$$

Therefore the deflection at the center is

$$y_{\max} = \frac{\partial U}{\partial Q} = 2 \int_0^{l/2} \frac{2M}{2EI} \frac{\partial M}{\partial Q}\,dx$$
$$= \frac{2}{EI} \int_0^{l/2} \left(\frac{wlx}{2} + \frac{Qx}{2} - \frac{wx^2}{2} \right) \frac{x}{2}\,dx$$

Since Q is imaginary, we can now set it equal to zero. Integration yields

$$y_{\max} = \frac{2}{EI} \left[\frac{wlx^3}{12} - \frac{wx^4}{16} \right]_0^{l/2} = \frac{5wl^4}{384EI} \qquad \textit{Ans.}$$

EXAMPLE 3-8. In Fig. 3-15 a framework has a pin connection at point A and is permitted to move horizontally at point B. Find the horizontal deflection of point B due to the loads shown.

Solution. An imaginary force Q is located at point B. This force must be horizontal, because the deflection in the horizontal direction is to be found. Point A is taken as the origin of the coordinate system. At any point on the legs the moment is

$$M = Qy$$

For the horizontal member the moment at any point in the left half of the member is

$$M = \frac{Fx}{2} + Qh$$

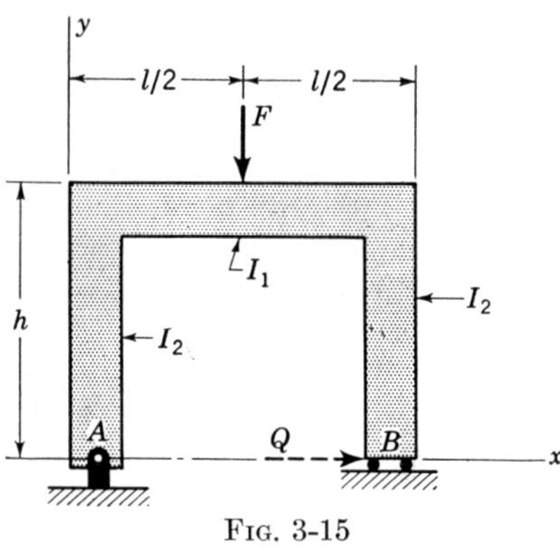

FIG. 3-15

The strain energy is the sum of the energy in each of the three members. Since the energy in each of the two legs is the same, this gives

$$U = 2 \int_0^h \frac{M^2\,dy}{2EI_2} + 2 \int_0^{l/2} \frac{M^2\,dx}{2EI_1}$$

The deflection of point B is equal to the partial derivative of this energy with respect to the imaginary force Q:

$$\delta_x = \frac{\partial U}{\partial Q} = 2 \int_0^h \frac{M}{EI_2} \frac{\partial M}{\partial Q}\,dy + 2 \int_0^{l/2} \frac{M}{EI_1} \frac{\partial M}{\partial Q}\,dx$$
$$= \frac{2}{EI_2} \int_0^h (Qy)(y)\,dy + \frac{2}{EI_1} \int_0^{l/2} \left(\frac{Fx}{2} + Qh \right) (h)\,dx$$

The imaginary force Q is now equated to zero. Then

$$\delta_x = \frac{2}{EI_1} \left[\frac{Fx^2h}{4} \right]_0^{l/2} = \frac{Fl^2h}{8EI_1} \qquad \textit{Ans.}$$

The theorem of Castigliano can also be used for the solution of statically indeterminate problems. Any structure acted upon by a system of forces is supported by the reactive forces. The deflection, or displacement, at the points of support is zero in the direction of the forces of reaction. Equation (3-25) can therefore be used to determine the unknown reactions by finding the partial derivative of the total strain energy with respect to the reaction whose value is desired, and equating it to zero.

If there exist more than one statically indeterminate reaction, then the reactive forces R_1, R_2, R_3, . . . , R_n are substituted for F_n in Eq. (3-25):

$$\frac{\partial U}{\partial R_1} = 0 \qquad \frac{\partial U}{\partial R_2} = 0 \qquad \frac{\partial U}{\partial R_3} = 0 \qquad \cdots \qquad \frac{\partial U}{\partial R_n} = 0 \qquad (3\text{-}26)$$

There will be as many equations as there are statically indeterminate reactions. These equations can then be solved simultaneously for the unknown forces.

The energy method of determining displacements is, of course, valid only for conditions in which the displacement is proportional to the load. Conditions exist, such as columns, for example, in which the displacements are not proportional to the loads, even though the material may obey Hooke's law, and the theorem of Castigliano does not hold.

3-11. Columns. A ball resting on a concave surface (Fig. 3-16*a*) is said to be in *stable equilibrium*. If the ball is given a slight displacement in either direction it will tend to return to its original position. The same ball resting on a convex surface (Fig. 3-16*b*) is said to be in *unstable equilibrium*, because a slight displacement of the ball in either direction will create forces which will tend to cause even larger displacements.

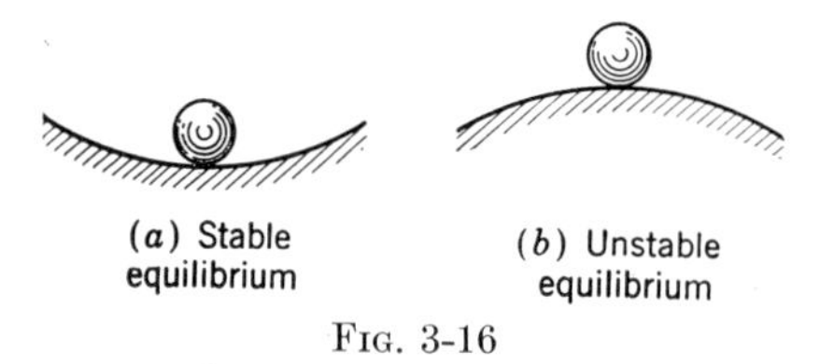

FIG. 3-16

A *column* is a compression member which tends to fail because of unstable equilibrium. A compression member which fails by crushing or bulging is not a column, since within the range of Hooke's law removal of the axial forces will permit the material to assume its original position of equilibrium. Except in the case of thin-walled compression members, the distinguishing characteristic of a column is that it is slender. The relative slenderness of a compression member is the ratio of the length to the radius of gyration (l/r), which is called the *slenderness ratio*. The radius of gyration must be with respect to the centroidal axis about which the column tends to bend. It is usually, although not necessarily, the least radius of gyration. Although the slenderness ratio is used to evaluate columns, it is a relative term. A column cannot be positively distinguished from a simple compression member since there is no particular value of l/r above which a member can be said to be a column.

Cox[1] states that, in addition to compressive failure by crushing of the material, there are four modes of column failure. These are: (1) elastic buckling over the length of the column; (2) inelastic buckling over the length of the column; (3) a local buckling, which may be elastic or inelastic, over a small portion of the column length; (4) a twisting or torsional failure in which cross sections rotate with respect to each other about the longitudinal axis.

Modes 3 and 4 are associated with columns having thin sections and will not be discussed in this book.[2]

Elastic Instability. Figure 3-17 shows a column of length l, with ends which are free to rotate, loaded by an axial load P. It is called a pin-ended or rounded-end column, and the pins are assumed to have no friction. The column is assumed to be straight before the load P is applied. As the load is increased from zero, the column shortens in accordance with Hooke's law and remains in stable equilibrium. If, however, some initial crookedness or eccentricity is present, then bending begins immediately. As the load P is increased still more, the column remains straight until P exceeds a certain value called the *critical load* and designated by P_{cr}. When the value of the critical load has been exceeded, the column is in a condition of unstable equilibrium. Under these conditions, a slight vibration of one support, a slight wind, or the existence of initial eccentricity or crookedness will cause the column to buckle and assume the shape shown in the figure.

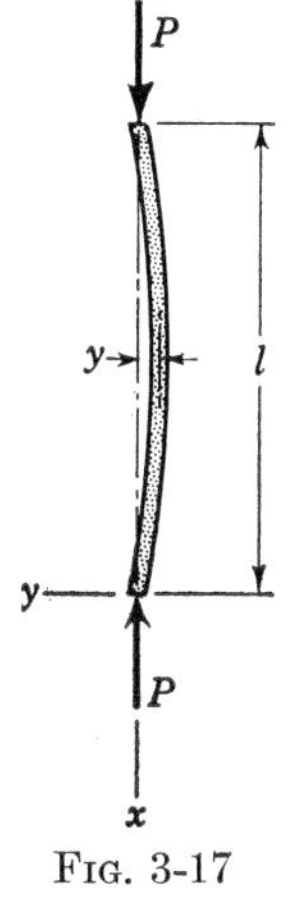

FIG. 3-17

It has been shown[3] that an increase of 6 per cent in the load P over P_{cr} will cause a sidewise deflection whose magnitude is 42 per cent of the column length! The problem is greatly aggravated by the fact that no warning of this dangerous condition is to be had. In the case of a beam acted upon by bending loads, an increase in the load causes a corresponding increase in the beam deflection so that excessive deflection is a visible indication of dangerous loading conditions. This is not true of columns

[1] Glen N. Cox, Frank J. Germano, and John H. Bateman, "Strength of Materials," p. 291, Pitman Publishing Corporation, New York, 1951.

[2] Herbert Wagner, Torsion and Buckling of Open Sections, *NACA TM* 807, 1936.

Robert Kappus, Twisting Failure of Centrally Loaded Open-section Columns in the Elastic Range, *NACA TM* 851, 1938.

J. N. Goodier, Flexural-torsion Buckling of Bars of Open Section under Bending, Eccentric Thrust, or Torsional Loads, *Cornell Univ. Eng. Expt. Sta. Bull.* 28, 1942.

[3] S. Timoshenko, "Theory of Elastic Stability," p. 72, McGraw-Hill Book Company, Inc., New York, 1936.

since they are assumed to remain straight until the critical load is reached. For this reason, column failures are nearly always unexpected, which makes them very dangerous. Since the actual stresses in columns are often quite low, a comparison of the actual load with the critical load becomes the most important criterion of column safety.

The value of the critical load for the column of Fig. 3-17 is

$$P_{cr} = \frac{\pi^2 EI}{l^2} \tag{3-27}$$

where P_{cr} is the maximum load that a slender column can resist without failure by sudden buckling. The other quantities are E, the modulus of elasticity in pounds per square inch; the moment of inertia I in inches to the fourth power; and the column length l in inches. Equation (3-27) is called the *Euler formula for rounded-end columns.*

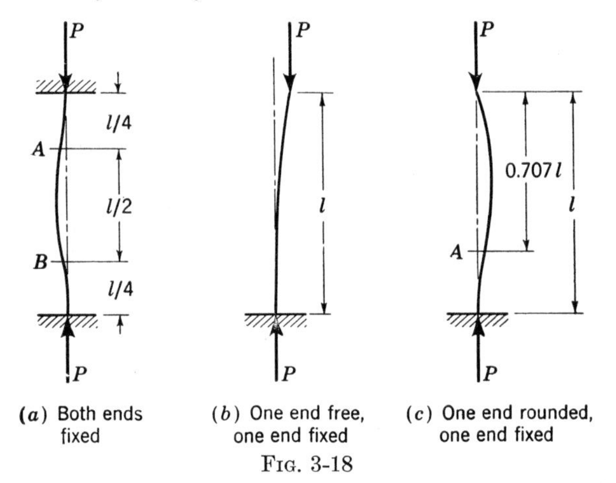

(*a*) Both ends fixed (*b*) One end free, one end fixed (*c*) One end rounded, one end fixed

FIG. 3-18

From the relation $I = Ar^2$, Eq. (3-27) may be rearranged to give

$$\frac{P_{cr}}{A} = \frac{\pi^2 E}{(l/r)^2} \tag{3-28}$$

where A is the area of the column and l/r is the previously defined slenderness ratio. It should be pointed out that the solution to Eq. (3-28) is *not* a stress! It is seen that the critical load is not a function of the strength of the material. It depends only on the stiffness of the material E (modulus of elasticity) and the slenderness ratio. Therefore a slender column made of high-strength alloy steel is no better than one made of low-carbon steel.

End Conditions. The critical loads for columns with different end conditions can be obtained by comparison. Figure 3-18 shows columns with different end conditions. In Fig. 3-18*a* both ends are fixed. The inflection points are at A and B at a distance of $l/4$ from each end. The portion of the column AB is the same curve as a rounded-end column. Substituting the length $l/2$ for l in Eq. (3-27), we obtain

$$P_{cr} = \frac{\pi^2 EI}{(l/2)^2} = \frac{4\pi^2 EI}{l^2} \tag{3-29}$$

In Fig. 3-18*b* is shown a column with one end free and one end fixed. This curve is equivalent to half the curve for columns with rounded ends, so that if a length of $2l$ is substituted into Eq. (3-27) the critical load becomes

$$P_{cr} = \frac{\pi^2 EI}{(2l)^2} = \frac{\pi^2 EI}{4l^2} \tag{3-30}$$

A column with one end fixed and one end rounded occurs frequently in machine design. This is illustrated in Fig. 3-18*c*. The inflection point occurs at A, which is 0.707 times the length. This length corresponds to the length of the rounded-end column; therefore,

$$P_{cr} = \frac{\pi^2 EI}{(0.707l)^2} = \frac{2\pi^2 EI}{l^2} \tag{3-31}$$

Defections of the Euler Formula. The development of the Euler equation is a beautiful example of classical mathematics at work.[1] The solution obtained involves only the square of pi and is typical of those which are said to be based upon "pure theory." The equation is simple and direct and apparently shows all the relations at a glance. There is, however, a difficulty. And this difficulty is a perfect example of the imperfections of mathematics which were discussed in Chap. 1.

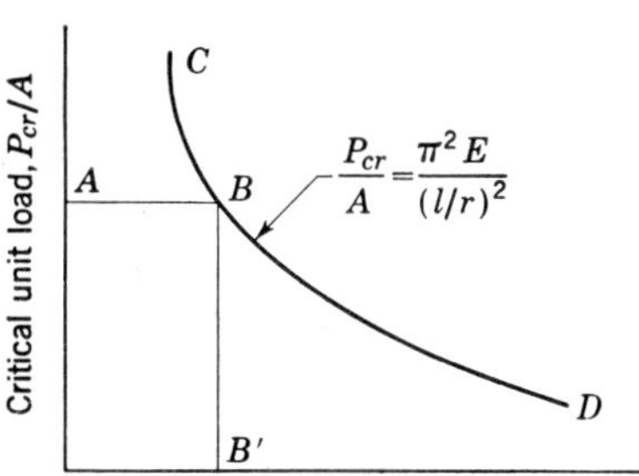

FIG. 3-19. Relation of the critical unit load to the slenderness ratio.

Suppose that we use Eq. (3-28) to plot a curve showing the relation between the unit load P_{cr}/A and the slenderness ratio l/r. This has been plotted in Fig. 3-19, with the curve CBD representing the relation expressed by the Euler formula. In common with so many other equations of mechanics, Euler's was developed on the assumption that the material obeys Hooke's law; and so in Fig. 3-19 the line AB has been constructed to represent the limit of proportionality of the material. In other words, for unit loads greater than that represented by point A, stress is not proportional to strain and Hooke's law no longer applies.

[1] *Ibid.*

The portion BC of the curve therefore has no meaning, and a column with a slenderness ratio less than B' would fail by crushing before the load represented by a point on BC could be applied. For this reason, the graph ABD represents the maximum load which can be applied to ideal columns of various slenderness ratios.

The results of a large number of experiments indicate that, within a broad region around point B (Fig. 3-19), column failure begins before the applied load reaches a point represented by the graph ABD. These experiments show that the test values of P are scattered. Within the region of point B it is also found that the columns fail by plastic yielding. This means that elastic buckling does not occur until the values of the slenderness ratios become somewhat larger than the theoretical values represented by the point B'.

The scattering of these experimental results can be explained by the fact that it is practically impossible to construct an ideal column. Only a very slight imperfection in the construction of a column can have an enormous effect upon the value of the critical load. Conditions such as initial stresses or initial crookedness in the member can greatly reduce the load-carrying capacity. It is also difficult to apply the loads without introducing eccentricities. The natural variations in physical properties introduce still more uncertainties. These conditions make it impossible to calculate the value of the bending moment in a column with any degree of precision. When a column buckles, the stress distribution on a cross section is made up of the axial compressive stress and the bending stress. But, since the bending stress is principally due to unpredictable factors introduced by the material and construction, it cannot be calculated.

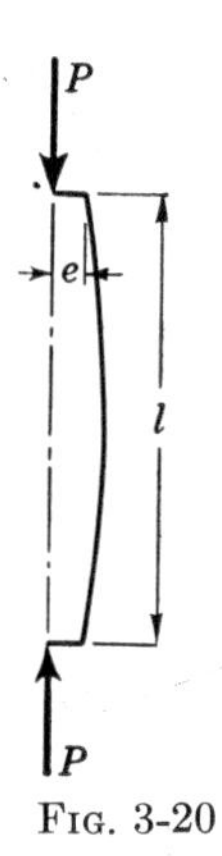

Fig. 3-20

The Secant Formula. Since eccentricities, crookedness, and initial stresses are to be expected in the construction or fabrication of columns, we might just as well introduce these variations quantitatively into the column equation. This is done in the secant formula by including a known amount of eccentricity which is assumed to be initially present in the column. In Fig. 3-20 a column of length l is shown having a load P applied with an initial eccentricity represented by e. The unit load is given by the equation

$$\frac{P}{A} = \frac{s_{yp}}{1 + \frac{ec}{r^2} \sec \frac{l}{r} \sqrt{\frac{P}{4AE}}} \tag{3-32}$$

This is known as the *secant formula.* In Eq. (3-32) c is the distance from the neutral plane of bending to the outermost fiber and s_{yp} is the yield strength of the material. The other quantities have the same meaning as before.

The secant formula is plotted in Fig. 3-21 for various values of the eccentricity ratio ec/r^2, using a steel with a yield-point strength of 40,000 psi and a modulus of elasticity of 30,000,000 psi. Euler's curve is included for comparison purposes.

Problems exist in machine design in which there is deliberate eccentricity. However, the range of problems in which there is no planned amount of eccentricity introduces the question of what value to use for the eccentricity ratio. This question can be answered only by judgment, a considerable amount of experience, and possibly experimentation.

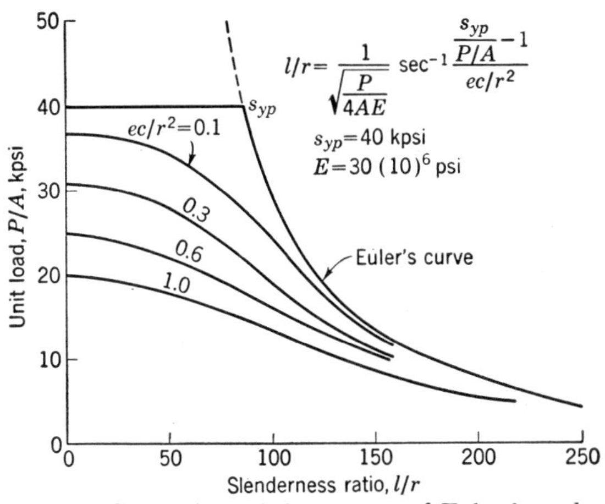

FIG. 3-21. Comparison of the secant and Euler formulas.

Knowledge of machining and assembly errors, together with information concerning the maximum variation from straightness of the members used, must all be considered. The secant formula has the advantage that it applies to all column lengths, but it is admittedly difficult to solve.

The J. B. Johnson Formula. Of the many column formulas available, one of the most widely used is called the *parabolic*, or *J. B. Johnson*, formula. It may be expressed as follows:

$$\frac{P_{cr}}{A} = s_{yp} - K\left(\frac{l}{r}\right)^2 \tag{3-33}$$

where

$$K = \left(\frac{s_{yp}}{2\pi}\right)^2 \frac{1}{nE} \tag{3-34}$$

The quantity n in Eq. (3-34) is an end-condition constant and has the following values:

End conditions	*Constant, n*
One end fixed, one end free	0.25
Both ends rounded	1.00
One end fixed, one end rounded	2.00
Both ends fixed	4.00

Equation (3-33) is the equation of a parabola which intersects the vertical axis at $P_{cr}/A = s_{yp}$ and is tangent to the Euler curve at $s_{yp}/2$ (Fig. 3-22). Obviously, the parabolic formula cannot be used for values of l/r greater than that at the point of tangency.

3-12. Curved Beams. Curved portions of machine frames and other members are frequently subjected to bending or axial loads or to a combination of the two. As the radius of the curved portion decreases, the stresses due to curvature become greater, and the results of the equations for straight beams, when used, become less satisfactory. For relatively small radii of curvature, the actual stresses may be several times greater than the figure obtained for straight members. Photoelastic experiments have demonstrated that, in the case of a curved beam, the neutral surface does not coincide with the centroidal axis but, instead, moves inward toward the center of curvature. It has also been shown that the stresses on the fibers of a curved beam are not proportional to the distances of the fibers from the neutral surface, as is assumed for a straight beam.

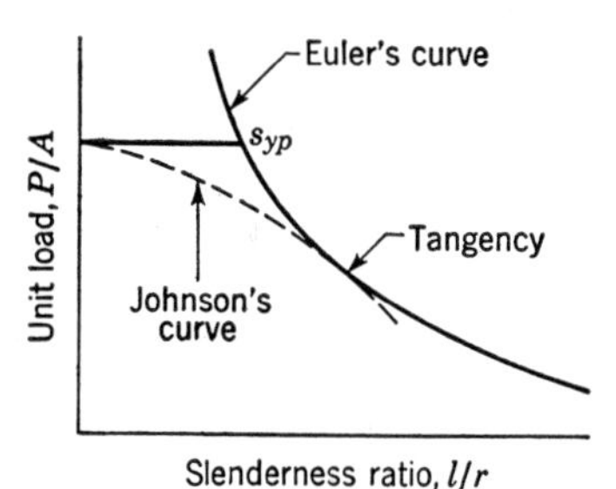

FIG. 3-22. Comparison of the J. B. Johnson and Euler formulas.

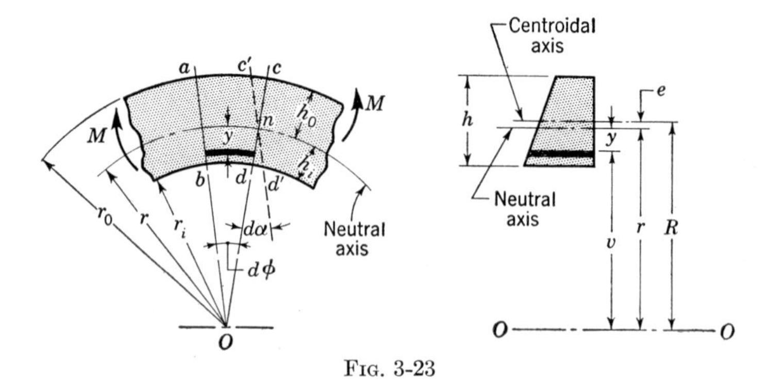

FIG. 3-23

Let it be required to determine the stress at any point on the fibers of a curved beam (Fig. 3-23). Here, R is the radius of the centroidal axis, r the radius of the neutral surface, and h the depth of the section. Lines ab and cd represent two adjacent cross sections separated from each other by the small angle $d\phi$. Because of the action of the bending moment M, section cd rotates through a small angle $d\alpha$. The unit deformation of any fiber at distance y from the neutral surface is

$$\epsilon = \frac{\delta}{l} = \frac{y\,d\alpha}{(r - y)\,d\phi} \tag{a}$$

The unit stress on this fiber is

$$s = \epsilon E = \frac{Ey\,d\alpha}{(r - y)\,d\phi} \tag{b}$$

For equilibrium, the summation of the forces acting over the cross-sectional area must be zero:

$$\int s\,dA = E\frac{d\alpha}{d\phi}\int \frac{y\,dA}{r - y} = 0 \tag{c}$$

Also, since the external applied moment is resisted by the internal moment, we have from (b)

$$\int y(s\,dA) = E\frac{d\alpha}{d\phi}\int \frac{y^2\,dA}{r - y} = M \tag{d}$$

Rearranging Eq. (d), we obtain

$$M = E\frac{d\alpha}{d\phi}\left[\int (-y)\,dA + r\int \frac{y\,dA}{r - y}\right] \tag{e}$$

The first integral is the moment of the cross-sectional area with respect to the neutral surface. The second term, from Eq. (c), is zero. We then have

$$M = \left(E\frac{d\alpha}{d\phi}\right) Ae \tag{f}$$

where e represents the distance between the neutral axis and the centroidal axis. Rearranging Eq. (f), we find

$$\frac{d\alpha}{d\phi} = \frac{M}{AeE} \tag{g}$$

which, when substituted in Eq. (b), gives

$$s = \frac{My}{Ae(r - y)} \tag{3-35}$$

This equation cannot be solved until the value of e is known. Returning now to Eq. (c) and substituting $v = r - y$ and $y = r - v$, we have

$$\int \frac{y\,dA}{r-y} = \int \frac{(r-v)\,dA}{v} = r\int \frac{dA}{v} - \int dA = 0$$

so that

$$r = \frac{A}{\int \frac{dA}{v}} \tag{3-36}$$

Since $e = R - r$, Eq. (3-36) can be used to determine the value of e. This is then substituted into Eq. (3-35) to determine the stress. The maximum stresses occur at the inner and outer fibers and are

$$s_i = \frac{Mh_i}{Aer_i} \qquad s_o = \frac{Mh_o}{Aer_o} \tag{3-37}$$

where h_i and h_o are the distances from the neutral axis to the inner and outer fibers, respectively, having radii of magnitude r_i and r_o. Equation

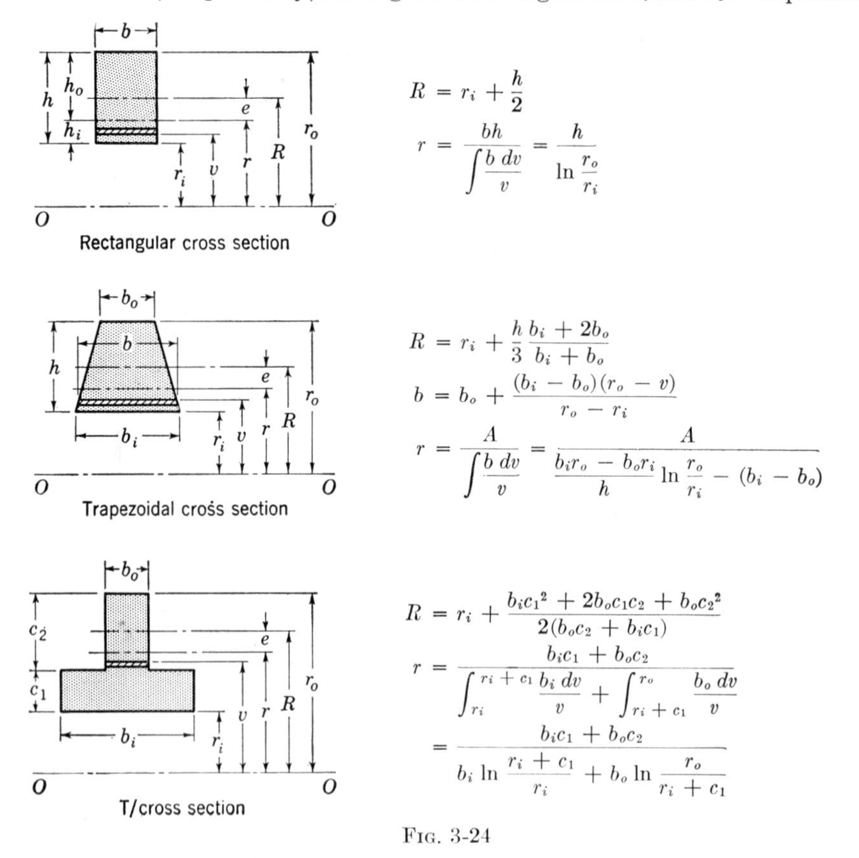

Fig. 3-24

(3-36) has been solved for sections which are encountered most often, and the results are given in Fig. 3-24.

Many of the problems met in the analysis of curved beams are such that an axial stress exists on the section, in addition to the bending stress. The method of superposition should then be used in order to determine the resultant stresses.

Deflection of Curved Beams. The deflection of a curved beam is obtained by the use of Castigliano's theorem. Figure 3-25 depicts a curved beam fixed at one end and loaded by a force F at the other end. By the theorem of Castigliano [Eq. (3-25)] we can write

$$\delta_x = \frac{\partial U}{\partial F} = \int_0^l \frac{M}{EI} \frac{\partial M}{\partial F} \, dl \qquad (a)$$

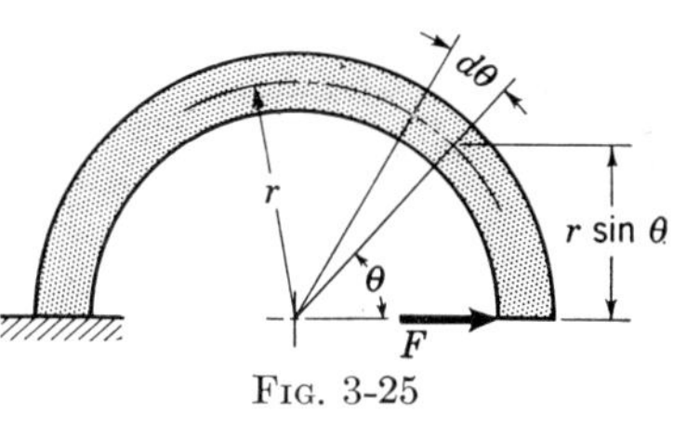

FIG. 3-25

If r is the radius of the neutral surface and the angle θ describes the location of any point on this axis, then $dl = r\,d\theta$. At the angle θ the bending moment is

$$M = Fr \sin \theta \qquad (b)$$

When these values are substituted in Eq. (a), we obtain

$$\delta_x = \int_0^\pi \frac{Fr \sin \theta}{EI} (r \sin \theta)(r\,d\theta) = \frac{Fr^3}{EI} \int_0^\pi \sin^2 \theta \, d\theta$$

$$= \frac{\pi F r^3}{2EI} \qquad (3\text{-}38)$$

This is the deflection of the free end of the beam in the direction of the force F. In using this equation, the dimensions of the cross section must be small relative to the radius of curvature. If the dimensions are large, then Eq. (a) must include the effect of shear as well.[1]

3-13. Vibration. Since machine members are elastic and frequently subjected to the action of vibratory forces, a knowledge of the mechanics of vibration will assist the designer in reducing to a low value the deflections which these forces are likely to produce. The various parts of a machine tend to vibrate at a frequency which is a function of the stiffness and the mass of the member. If the machine forces occur at a frequency which is near the natural vibrational frequency of the member, then forces will be set up which may cause serious difficulties in the operation of the machine and which will ultimately destroy it. Therefore, when vibratory forces are present, the designer should strive to design the members of the machine so that their natural frequencies are far removed from the frequencies of the forces.

[1] S. Timoshenko, "Strength of Materials," pt. II, p. 83, D. Van Nostrand Company, Inc., New York, 1941.

A great many problems in vibration can be reduced to a spring and a weight (Fig. 3-26) by employing simplifying assumptions. In analyzing this problem, the weight is assumed to slide over a frictionless surface. The weight is customarily assumed to be absolutely rigid and the spring to be massless. The spring constant k is defined as the amount of force required to deflect the spring 1 in. and has the units of pounds per inch.

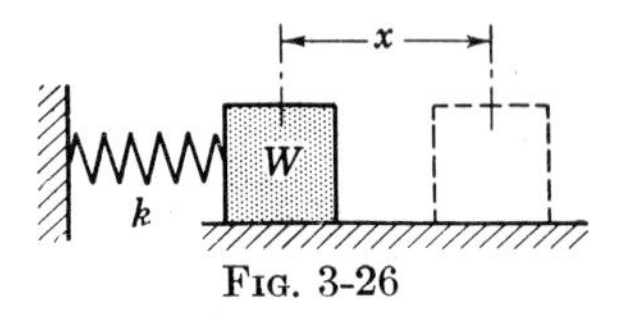

FIG. 3-26

Taking the origin of the coordinate system at the equilibrium position and picturing the weight at the position x, at some instant in time the spring force acting on the weight is

$$F = -kx \tag{a}$$

The force is negative because it is opposed to the direction of displacement. Writing Newton's law, we have

$$\frac{W}{g}\frac{d^2x}{dt^2} = -kx \tag{b}$$

Upon rearranging this equation,

$$\frac{d^2x}{dt^2} + \frac{kg}{W}x = 0 \tag{c}$$

The solution of this differential equation is well known. It is

$$x = C_1 \cos \sqrt{\frac{kg}{W}}\, t + C_2 \sin \sqrt{\frac{kg}{W}}\, t \tag{d}$$

where C_1 and C_2 are the two constants of integration. These two constants may be evaluated by stating the boundary conditions. We will choose

$$\text{when} \begin{cases} x = x_0 \\ t = 0 \end{cases} \qquad \text{and} \qquad \text{when} \begin{cases} \dfrac{dx}{dt} = 0 \\ t = 0 \end{cases} \tag{e}$$

Substitution of each condition in Eq. (d) yields

$$x = x_0 = C_1 \cos 0 + C_2 \sin 0 \qquad C_1 = x_0$$

$$\frac{dx}{dt} = 0 = -C_1\sqrt{\frac{kg}{W}} \sin 0 + C_2\sqrt{\frac{kg}{W}} \cos 0 \qquad C_2 = 0$$

The solution then becomes

$$x = x_0 \cos \sqrt{\frac{kg}{W}}\, t \tag{3-39}$$

This is a sine-wave motion having an amplitude of x_0 and a frequency of

$$f = \frac{1}{2\pi}\sqrt{\frac{kg}{W}} \tag{3-40}$$

where g is in inches per second per second and f is the frequency of vibration in cycles per second. If a weight W is suspended from a spring whose constant is k, a deflection δ_{st} will be produced whose value is

$$\delta_{st} = \frac{W}{k} \tag{f}$$

Substituting δ_{st} for W/k in Eq. (3-40), we find

$$f = \frac{1}{2\pi}\sqrt{\frac{g}{\delta_{st}}} \tag{3-41}$$

This is a most useful equation because, by substituting the static deflection caused by the weight of a member, its natural frequency may be found.

EXAMPLE 3-9. Figure 3-27 shows a cantilever beam of length l having a weight W mounted on the free end. Find the natural frequency of vibration.

Solution. From Table A-2, the static deflection is

$$\delta_{st} = \frac{Wl^3}{3EI}$$

Substitution in Eq. (3-41) yields

$$f = \frac{1}{2\pi}\sqrt{\frac{3EIg}{Wl^3}} \qquad \textit{Ans.}$$

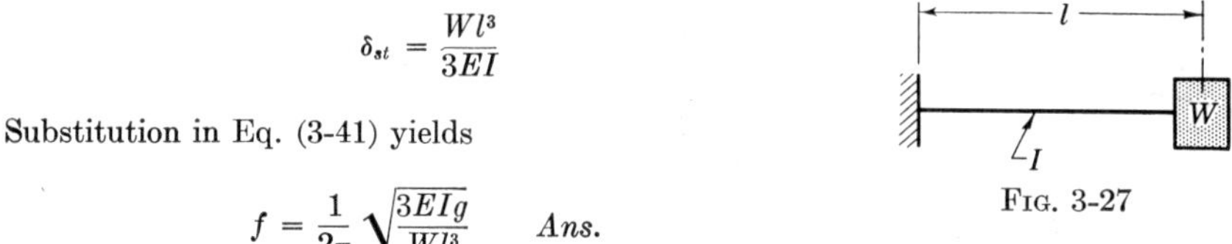

FIG. 3-27

The reader should note that Eq. (3-39) does not reflect the effect of the vibratory force. If a vibrating force is applied, then the amplitude will be different from that described by the equation. For the case in which the natural frequency is near the frequency of the force, the amplitude may become dangerously large.

It should also be noted that the demonstration given in this section does not include the effect of friction or damping. In many cases the amount of damping present has so little effect on the frequency that it can safely be neglected. However, where vibrational amplitudes or stresses are to be determined, the effect of damping should be carefully considered.

3-14. Thermal Stresses and Strains. When the temperature of an unrestrained bar is uniformly increased, the bar expands. The unit expansion (elongation) is

$$\epsilon = \alpha T \tag{3-42}$$

where ϵ = unit elongation, in. per in.

α = coefficient thermal expansion, in. per in. per deg change in temperature

T = temperature change, deg

Suppose that a straight bar is restrained at the ends so as to prevent lengthwise expansion and then is subjected to a uniform temperature change. If the temperature is increased, the bar will tend to expand, and a compressive stress will develop whose magnitude is

$$s = \epsilon E = \alpha T E \tag{3-43}$$

where E is the modulus of elasticity.

Similarly, if a uniform flat plate is restrained at the edges and subjected to a temperature rise, a compressive stress will result whose magnitude is

$$s = \frac{\alpha T E}{1 - \mu} \tag{3-44}$$

where μ is Poisson's ratio.

The stresses represented by Eqs. (3-43) and (3-44), though due to temperature, are not thermal stresses, inasmuch as they result from the fact that the edges were clamped. Properly defined, a *thermal stress* is one arising from a temperature gradient.

In the general case of heat flow, temperature is not a straight-line function of the dimensions of a body. Since each element of a body is constrained by the other elements, it is not free to expand, and consequently, if the temperature gradient is not linear, internal stress will develop. If the temperature distribution within a body of a particular shape is known, and also the constants E, α, and μ, then the stress may be determined using the theory of elasticity.[1]

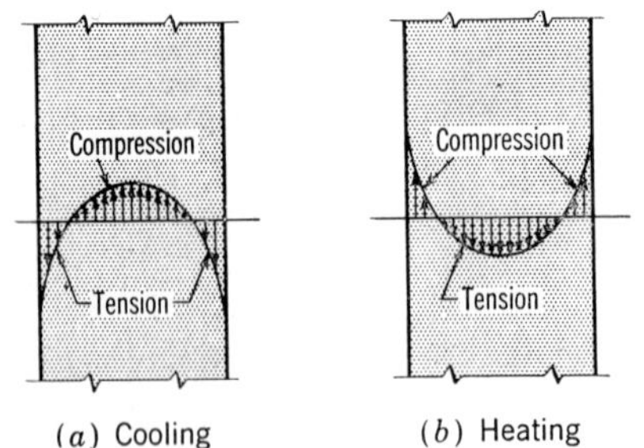

FIG. 3-28. Thermal stresses in an infinite slab during heating and cooling.

Figure 3-28 shows the internal stresses within a slab of infinite dimensions during heating and cooling. During cooling the maximum stress is tension and exists on the surface. For equilibrium a compressive stress must exist in the center of the slab. During heating the external surfaces are hot and tend to expand but are restrained by the cooler center. This causes the surface to be in compression and the center to be in tension. In this case the surface compressive stresses are maximum.

[1] Timoshenko and Goodier, *op. cit.*, pp. 399–437.

Approximate values of the coefficient α for various materials are listed in Table 3-1.

TABLE 3-1. COEFFICIENTS OF THERMAL EXPANSION (LINEAR)

Material	*Coefficient* α, *in. per in. per °F*
Aluminum	13.3×10^{-6}
Brass, cast	10.4×10^{-6}
Carbon steel	6.0×10^{-6}
Cast iron	5.9×10^{-6}
Nickel steel	7.3×10^{-6}
Magnesium	14.0×10^{-6}
Tungsten	2.4×10^{-6}

BIBLIOGRAPHY

"ASME Handbook, Metals Engineering—Design," McGraw-Hill Book Company, Inc., New York, 1953.

Marin, Joseph: "Strength of Materials," The Macmillan Company, New York, 1948.

Seely, Fred B.: "Advanced Mechanics of Materials," John Wiley & Sons, Inc., New York, 1932.

———: "Resistance of Materials," 3d ed., John Wiley & Sons, Inc., New York, 1947.

Timoshenko, S.: "Strength of Materials," pt. II, 2d ed., D. Van Nostrand Company, Inc., New York, 1941.

Wang, Chi-Teh: "Applied Elasticity," McGraw-Hill Book Company, Inc., New York, 1953.

PROBLEMS

3-1. A 2-in.-diameter cylinder, 3 in. in length, is acted upon by a compressive load of 40,000 lb. If the material is steel, having a modulus of elasticity of 30,000,000 psi, find (*a*) the compressive stress, (*b*) the strain, and (*c*) the deformation. (*d*) If Poisson's ratio is 0.30, find the increase in diameter.

Ans.: (*a*) 12,700 psi, (*b*) 0.000425 in., (*c*) 0.001275 in., (*d*) 0.000255 in.

3-2. A steel rod, ½ in. in diameter and 40 in. in length, carries a tensile load of 3,000 lb. (*a*) Find the stress and elongation of the rod. (*b*) If this is to be replaced by an aluminum rod, which is to have the same elongation, what should be its diameter? (*c*) Calculate the stress in the aluminum rod.

3-3. A press is to be so designed that the elongation of the two steel tension members *A*, as shown, does not exceed 1/64 in. (*a*) If the press is rated at 10,000 lb, determine their diameters. (*b*) If a maximum stress of 20,000 psi is permitted, are they safe? *Decisions:* neglect stress concentration.

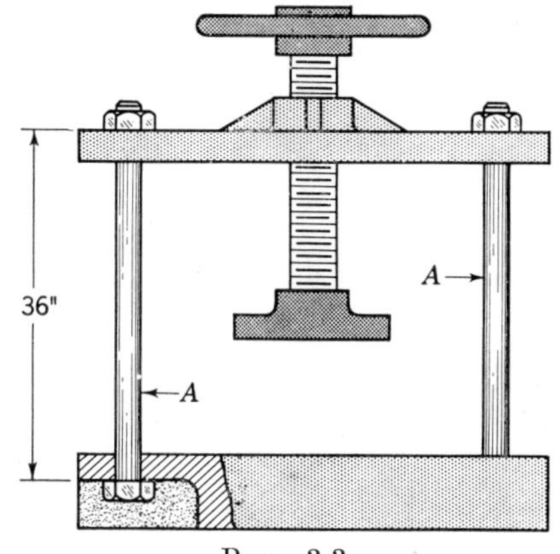

PROB. 3-3

a) d = 0.715 in.

b) s = 13,000 psi

3-4. A rectangular bar has a section 3/8 in. thick × 2¼ in. wide. It is 18 in. long and is acted upon by a tensile load of 14,000 lb. (*a*) Determine Poisson's ratio if $E = 28{,}000{,}000$ psi and $G = 10{,}000{,}000$ psi. (*b*) Calculate the strain. (*c*) Find the lateral deformation in each direction. *Ans.:* (*c*) 0.0000887 in., 0.000533 in.

3-5. An irregular-shaped bar was placed in tension, and measurements of the strain were recorded at ½-in. intervals over a 4-in. distance on the bar. The results have been plotted as a curve. The modulus of elasticity of the material is 29,000,000 psi. Find the maximum and average stresses in the bar.

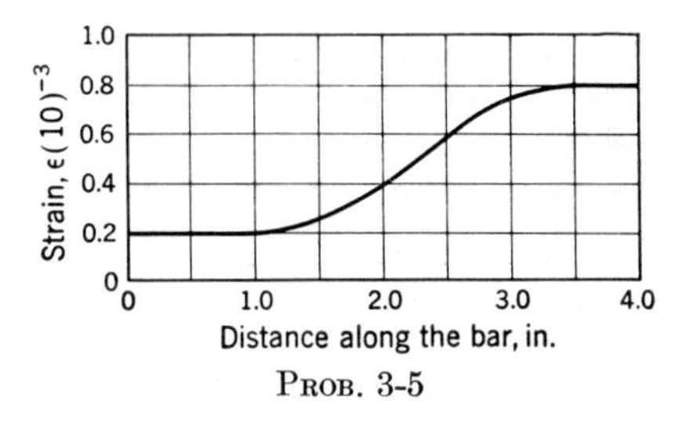

PROB. 3-5

3-6. A 1½-in.-diameter shaft transmits 50 hp at 900 rpm. Find the angular twist of the shaft in a length of 12 in. if $G = 11{,}500{,}000$ psi. *Ans.:* 25.2 min.

3-7. (*a*) Find the diameter of a solid round steel shaft which is to transmit 1/20 hp at 1 rpm if the angular deflection is not to exceed 1° in a length of 30 diameters. (*b*) Find the torsional stress in the shaft selected. *Ans.:* (*a*) 1¾-in. diameter.

***3-8.** (*a*) Find the diameter of a solid round steel shaft which is to transmit 20 hp at 3,600 rpm if the angular deflection is not to exceed 1° in a length of 30 diameters. (*b*) Find the torsional stress in the shaft selected. (*c*) Criticize the result.

3-9. The steel shaft shown in the figure is being twisted by a torque between points A and B. If the torque is 2,500 lb-in., find the angular displacement of the shaft. *Ans.:* 19.2 min.

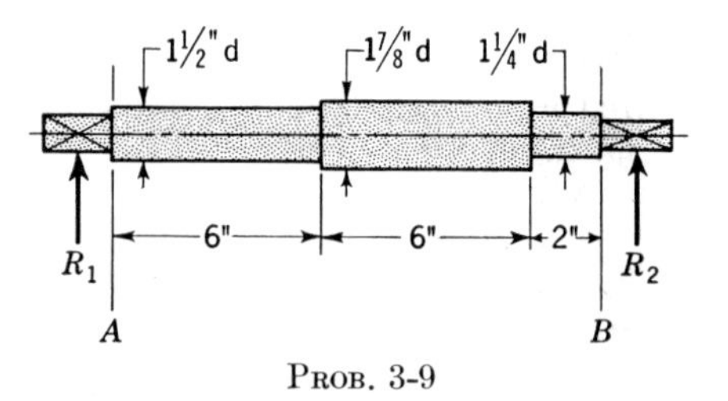

PROB. 3-9

3-10. Find the diameter of a solid round shaft which is to transmit 25 hp at 1,150 rpm. The shearing stress is not to exceed 6,000 psi, and the torsional stiffness is to be such that the angular deflection should not exceed 1° in 18 diameters. The material is 18-8 stainless steel having a modulus of rigidity of 10,000,000 psi.

3-11. A built-up connecting rod consists of three steel bars, each ¼ in. thick × 1¼ in. wide, as shown in the figure. During assembly it was found that one of the bars measured only 31.997 in. between pin centers, the other two bars measuring 32.000 in. (*a*) Determine the stress in each bar after assembly but before an external load is applied. (*b*) Determine the stress in each bar if an external load of 5,000 lb is applied in tension to the connecting rod. *Decisions:* (1) The stress-concentration effects are to be neglected. (2) A uniform cross section is assumed between the pin centers.

Ans.: (*a*) 1,880 psi, 940 psi; (*b*) 7,180 psi, 4,400 psi.

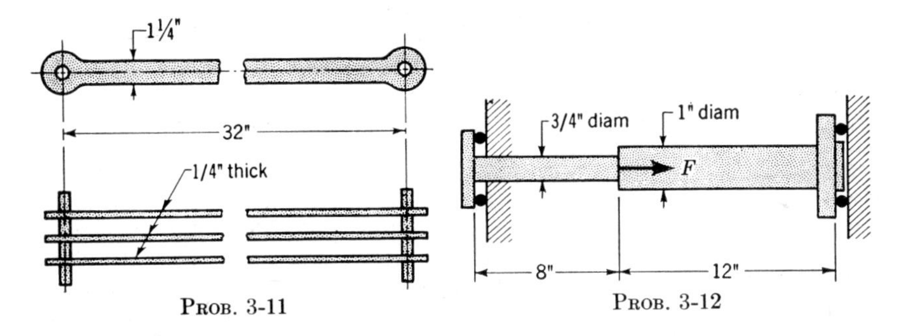

PROB. 3-11

PROB. 3-12

3-12. A shouldered shaft is supported at each end by thrust bearings as shown schematically in the figure. Determine the proportion of the axial load F to be taken by each bearing.

3-13. A ¾-in.-diameter aluminum rod, 48 in. long, and a ½-in.-diameter steel rod, 32 in. long, are spaced 60 in. apart and are fastened to a horizontal beam which carries a 2,000-lb load, as shown in the figure. The beam is to remain horizontal after the load is applied. (*a*) Find the location x of the load. (*b*) Find the stress in each rod. *Decisions:* (1) The beam is assumed to be absolutely rigid. (2) The weight of the beam is neglected.

Ans.: $x = 40$ in.

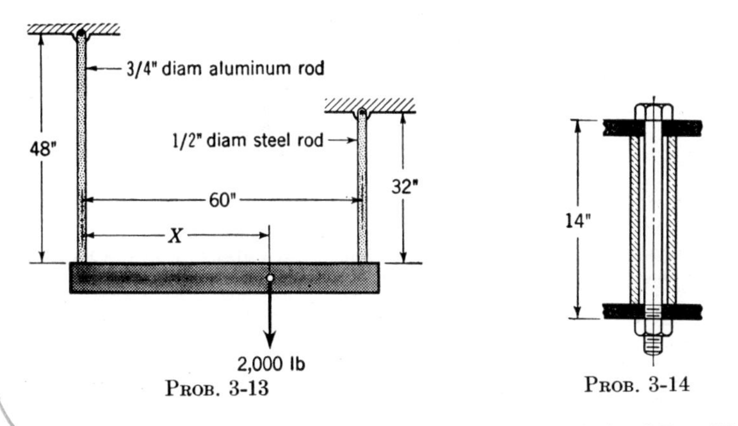

PROB. 3-13

PROB. 3-14

3-14. A ¾″-16 NF steel bolt and an aluminum tube, 1½ in. OD × ⅞ in. ID, act as a spacer for two plates, as shown in the figure. If the nut is pulled up snug and then given a one-third additional turn, find the stress in the bolt and in the tube. *Decisions:* Neglect the deformation of the plates.

3-15. Develop expressions for the strain in the x and y directions when the tensile stresses s_x and s_y are equal.

3-16. (*a*) Determine the diameter of a round shaft to support the bending load shown in the figure such that the deflection does not exceed 0.003 in. The material is steel. (*b*) Calculate the bending stress for the calculated diameter.

Ans.: (*a*) 1¼ in., (*b*) 3,820 psi.

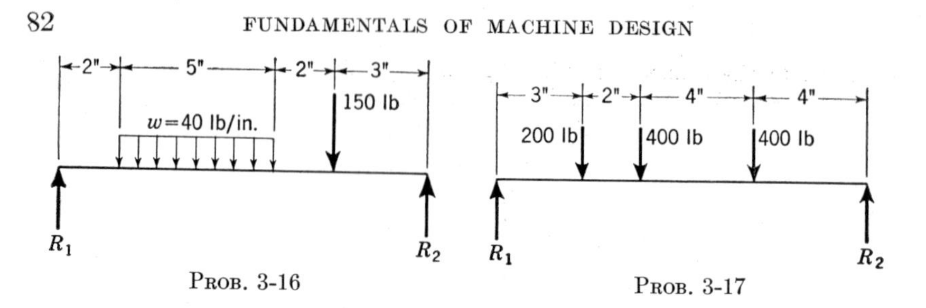

PROB. 3-16 PROB. 3-17

***3-17.** (*a*) Find the diameter of a solid round steel shaft to support the bending loads shown in the figure such that the maximum deflection does not exceed 0.001 in. (*b*) Suppose that the shaft is to be made of steel tubing of ¼-in. wall thickness; what outside diameter should be used? (*c*) Compare the ratio of the moment of inertia to the weight of each shaft.

3-18. In the figure are shown the shaft drawing and loading diagram. Bearings *A* and *B* are self-aligning. Find the maximum deflection.

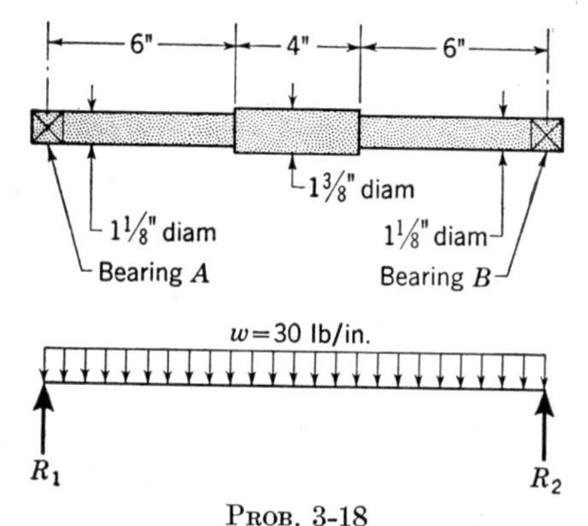

PROB. 3-18

***3-19.** Design a stainless-steel straightedge 60 in. long. It is to have no external loads. The straightedge is to have a guarantee that the deflection in the y direction will not exceed 0.0005 in. A reasonable deflection in the z direction would be 0.5 in. Use E = 28,500,000 psi and a density of 0.28 lb per in.³

3-20. Determine the maximum deflection of the shaft shown in the figure. The material is steel.

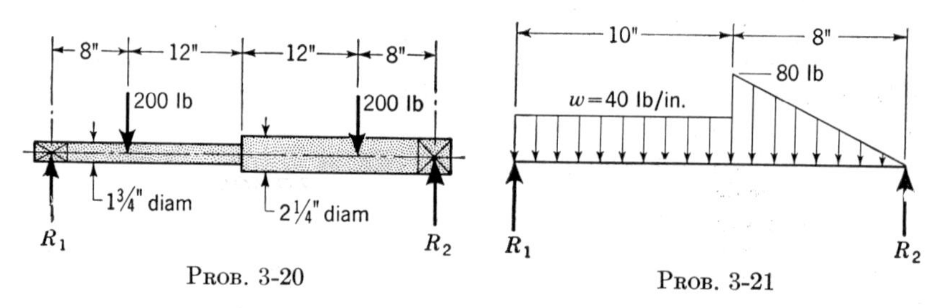

PROB. 3-20 PROB. 3-21

3-21. A rectangular steel bar is to support the loading which is distributed as shown in the figure. The height of the bar, which is in the plane of loading, is to be three times the thickness. For a maximum deflection of $\frac{1}{64}$ in., find the dimensions of the bar.

3-22. The figure shows a shaft drawing and the loading diagram. The shaft is steel. Find the maximum deflection if A and B are self-aligning bearings.

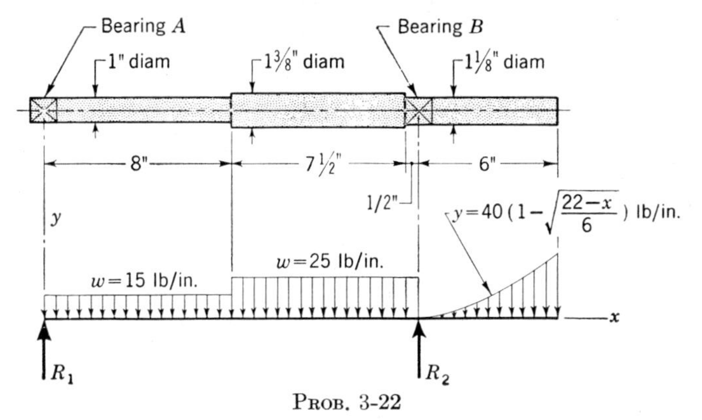

PROB. 3-22

3-23. The beam shown in the figure represents an aluminum tube welded to a framework at the right end and freely supported at the left end. The tubing has an outside diameter of 2 in., a wall thickness of $\frac{3}{16}$ in., and a moment of inertia of 0.443 in.^{4} The modulus of elasticity of aluminum is 10,000,000 psi. If the deflection is not to exceed $\frac{1}{8}$ in., what is the maximum load F that can be applied?

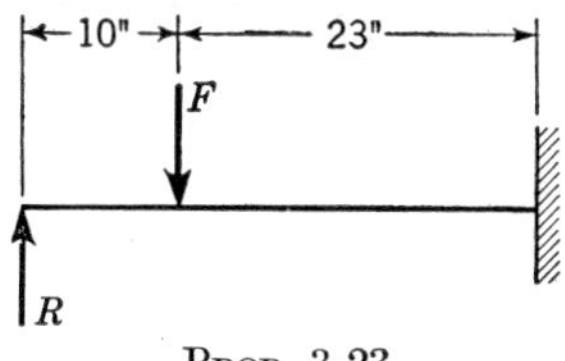

PROB. 3-23

3-24. The beam shown in the figure is a $1\frac{1}{2} \times 1\frac{1}{2} \times \frac{1}{8}$ steel angle having a moment of inertia of 0.08 in.^{4} in the bending plane. Find the deflection at the point of application of the 180-lb load. *Ans.:* 0.156 in.

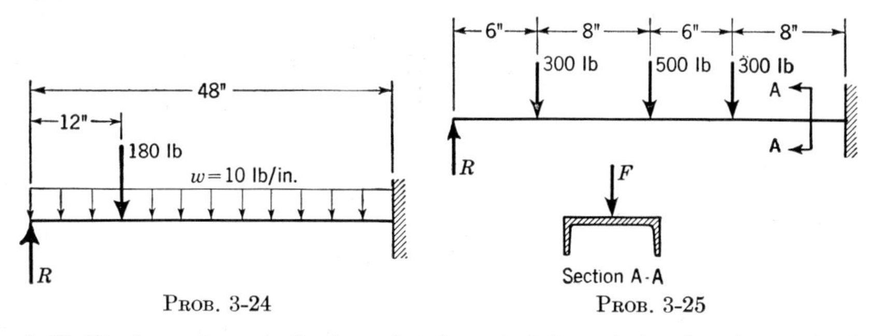

PROB. 3-24 PROB. 3-25

3-25. The beam shown in the figure is to be a steel channel placed so that the loads act upon the channel web as shown in section A-A. Select a suitable channel such that the deflection under each load will not exceed $\frac{1}{16}$ in.

3-26. A 2 × 2 × ⅜ steel angle supports the load shown in the figure. Find the maximum deflection.

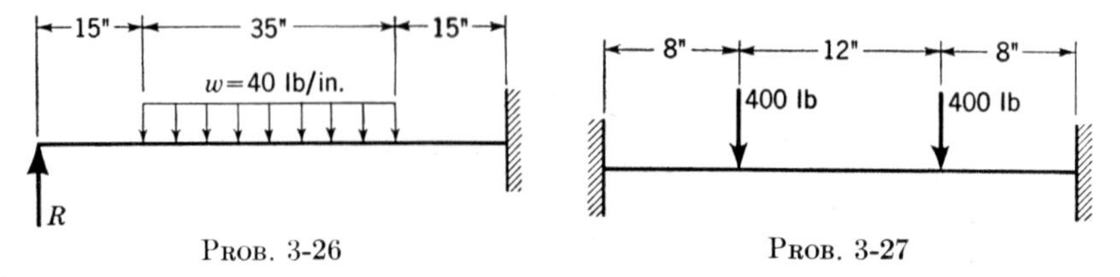

PROB. 3-26 PROB. 3-27

3-27. A round steel shaft 1⅛ in. in diameter supports the loads shown in the figure. The shaft rotates and is supported by the preloaded antifriction bearings; this introduces a degree of constraint at the ends. Find the deflection for each of the following assumptions: (*a*) The shaft is fixed at the ends as shown in the figure; (*b*) the shaft is simply supported at the ends.

***3-28.** Select a standard steel angle with equal legs to support the load in the figure such that the deflection will not exceed 1/16 in.

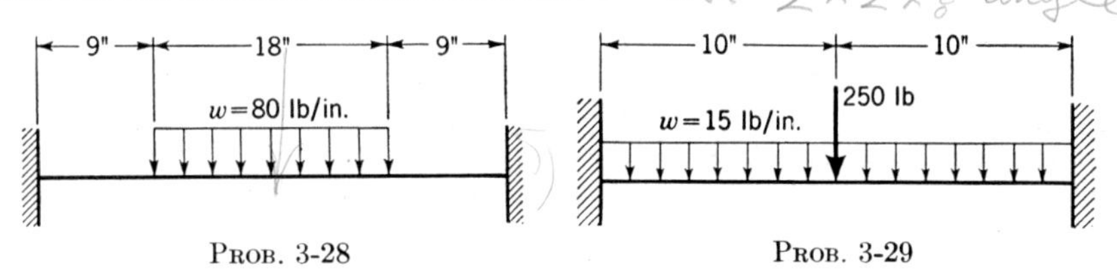

PROB. 3-28 PROB. 3-29

***3-29.** Select a round steel bar to support the load shown in the figure such that the maximum deflection will not exceed 0.015 in.

3-30. A solid round steel shaft is 14 in. long and is cantilevered. It supports a uniform bending load of 75 lb per in. of length. Determine the diameter if the stress and deflection are not to exceed 5,000 psi and 0.0004 in., respectively.

3-31. The figure shows a rectangular steel spring. The dimensions of the spring are to be adjusted so that the scale is 140 lb per in. This means that a force of 140 lb should produce a deflection of 1 in. (*a*) Find the required dimensions of the spring. (*b*) What is the factor of safety if the strength of the material is 100,000 psi? The operating range of the spring is ¼ in.

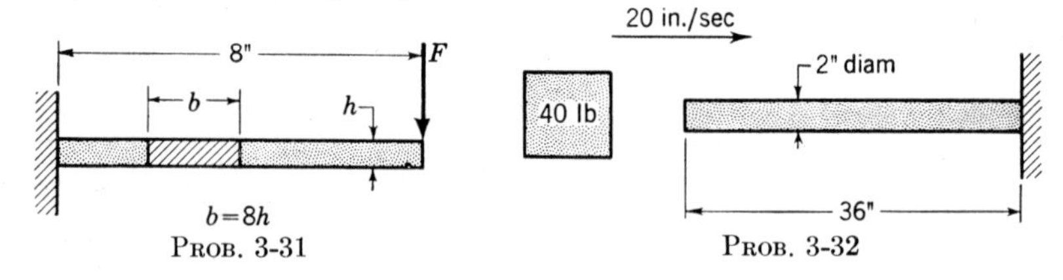

PROB. 3-31 PROB. 3-32

3-32. A steel bar 2 in. in diameter and 36 in. long is subjected to a longitudinal compressive impact load caused by a weight of 40 lb acting at a velocity of 20 in. per sec, as shown in the figure. Find the maximum stress in the bar. *Decisions:* Neglect column action.

3-33. Find the maximum stress in the bar of Prob. 3-32 if the length is decreased to 12 in.

3-34. A weight of 1,000 lb is being lowered on a 1-in.-diameter wire rope from a sheave when the brakes are suddenly applied. The area of the steel wires composing the rope is 0.400 in.², and the net modulus of elasticity is 12,000,000 psi. Find the maximum force in the rope. *Decisions:* Assume the brakes are applied instantaneously.

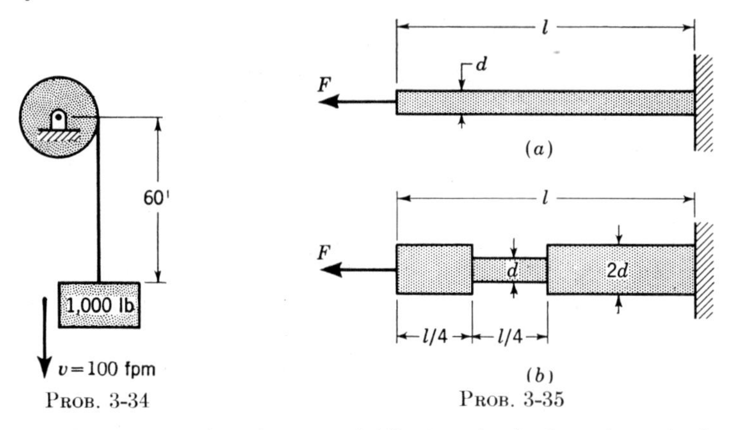

PROB. 3-34

PROB. 3-35

3-35. Compare the amounts of strain energy in the two circular bars shown in the figure. *Ans.:* $U_a = 2.28U_b$.

3-36. In the figure a steel bar A is brazed to an aluminum bar B. Find the strain energy that can be stored in the system if the stress in the aluminum is not to exceed 8,000 psi.

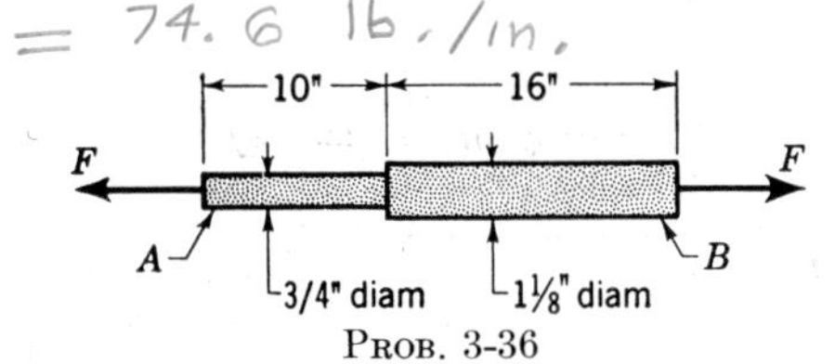

PROB. 3-36

3-37. A steel rod 42 in. long and 1⅞ in. in diameter is acted upon by a tensile energy load of 50 lb-in. (*a*) Find the maximum tensile stress in the rod. (*b*) Find the maximum stress in the rod if it is turned down to a diameter of ⅞ in. for a distance of one-half its length.

3-38. Using the theorem of Castigliano, find the maximum deflection of the cantilever beam shown in the figure. *Ans.:* $3Fl^3/16EI$.

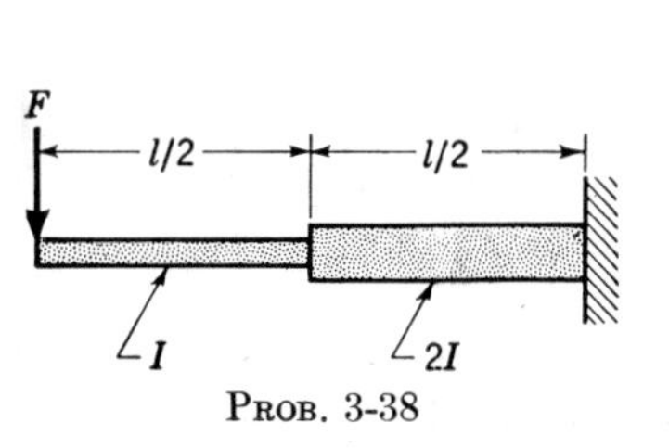

PROB. 3-38

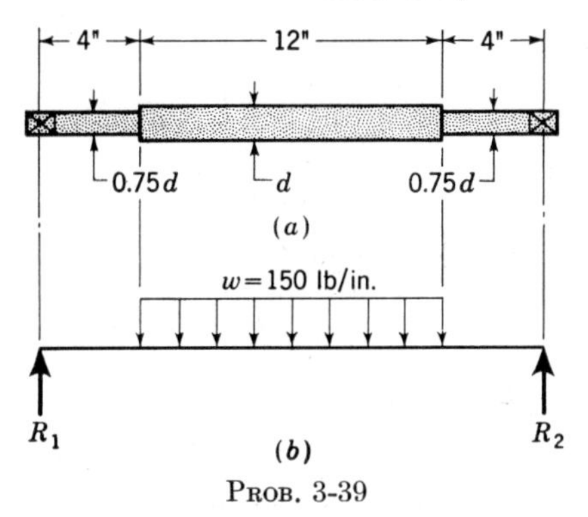

PROB. 3-39

3-39. In the figure, a is a drawing of a shaft and b is the loading diagram. Determine the diameter d so that the maximum deflection does not exceed 0.010 in. The material is alloy steel with a modulus of elasticity of 29,500,000 psi. Use energy methods.

3-40. Find the deflection at the point of application of the force F to the cantilever beam in the figure and the deflection at the free end. Use energy methods.

Ans.: $(17wl^4 + 16Fl^3)/384EI$, $(6wl^4 + 5Fl^3)/48EI$.

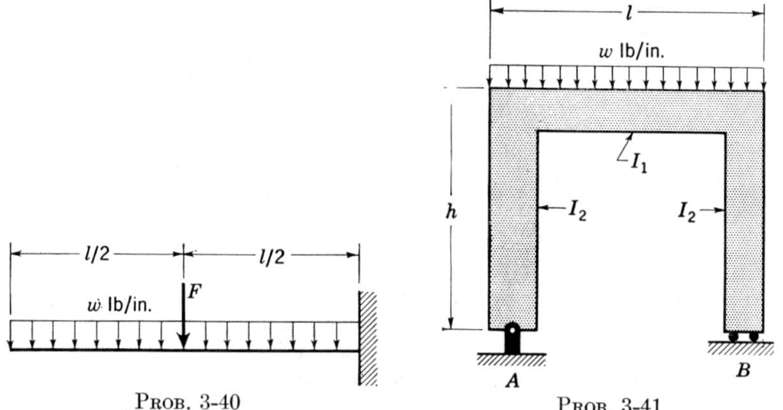

Prob. 3-40 Prob. 3-41

3-41. The framework which is illustrated is pin-connected at A and free to move horizontally at B. Using energy methods, find the horizontal deflection of point B.

Ans.: $wl^3h/12EI_1$.

3-42. Work Prob. 3-18 using an energy method.

3-43. Work Prob. 3-24 using an energy method.

3-44. Work Prob. 3-28 using an energy method.

***3-45.** The frame shown in the figure is composed of three structural aluminum angles welded at points B and C and bolted to a supporting structure at points A and D. Determine the magnitude of the load F such that the maximum deflection of BC is not greater than $\frac{1}{16}$ in.

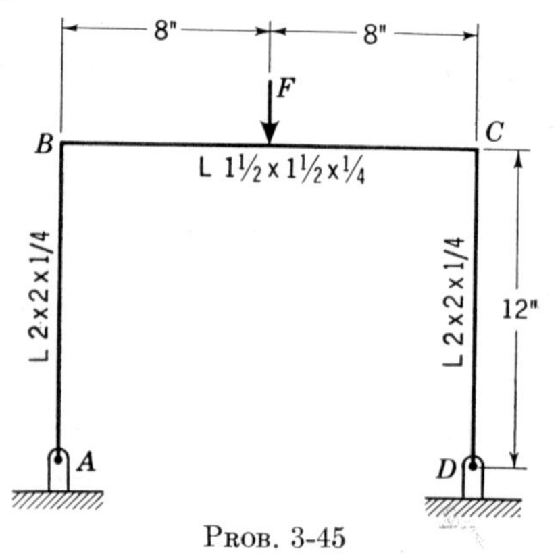

Prob. 3-45

3-46. Find the maximum compression load that can be supported by an aluminum tube $1\frac{3}{4}$ in. OD $\times$ 1 in. ID if the length is 54 in. The tube is fixed at one end and free at one end.

Ans.: 346 lb.

*__3-47.__ A steel bar has a ½ × 1¼-in. cross section and is 48 in. long. The bar is fixed at both ends and is loaded in axial compression. (*a*) Determine the critical load. (*b*) What is the critical load if the bar is braced at the center so as to prevent buckling in the weakest direction?

3-48. Determine the diameter for the piston rod of the hydraulic cylinder shown in the figure. The rod is to be a round steel forging. The cylinder is 3 in. in diameter, and the maximum hydraulic pressure is 3,500 psi. *Decisions:* (1) Assume the rod will not fail by any method other than column action. (2) Assume the piston end of the rod to be fixed in all planes. (3) The connecting-rod end is assumed to be fixed in one plane and pin-ended in the plane at right angles to the plane of the figure. (4) To account for eccentricities and load variations, the rod is to be designed for a maximum load of three times the actual hydraulic load.

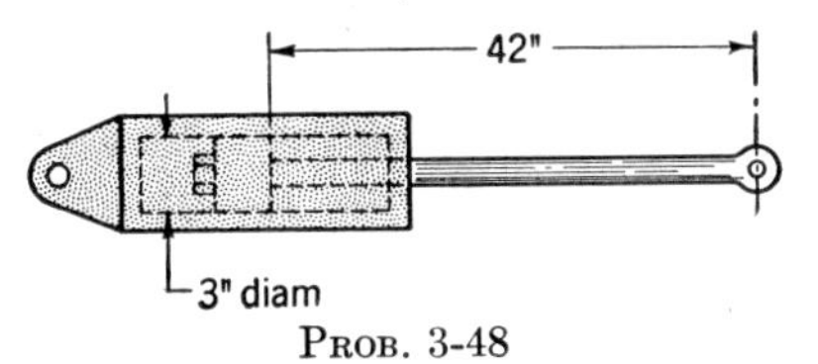

PROB. 3-48

3-49. Find the maximum axial compressive load that can be supported by a steel tube 30 in. long, 2 in. in diameter, and with a wall thickness of ¼ in. The material has a yield-point strength of 62,000 psi and a modulus of elasticity of 30,000,000 psi. The eccentricity is not to exceed ⅛ in. *Ans.:* P_{max} = 56,000 lb.

3-50. A round aluminum tube has a diameter of 3 in., a wall thickness of ½ in., and is 16 in. long. It is to support an axial compressive load which is applied 1½ in. from the center of the tube. The yield-point strength is 48,000 psi. What is the maximum load this member can support?

3-51. A steel tube 1½ in. in diameter is to support a compressive load of 4,000 lb. The yield-point strength of the material is 30,000 psi. If the tube is 8 in. long, find the minimum wall thickness for an eccentricity ratio of 0.25. *Decisions:* Use a factor of safety of 2.25.

3-52. Find the stresses in the inner and outer fibers at section *A-A* of the hook shown in the figure. The load *F* is 5,000 lb. *Ans.:* 15,540 psi, −4,980 psi.

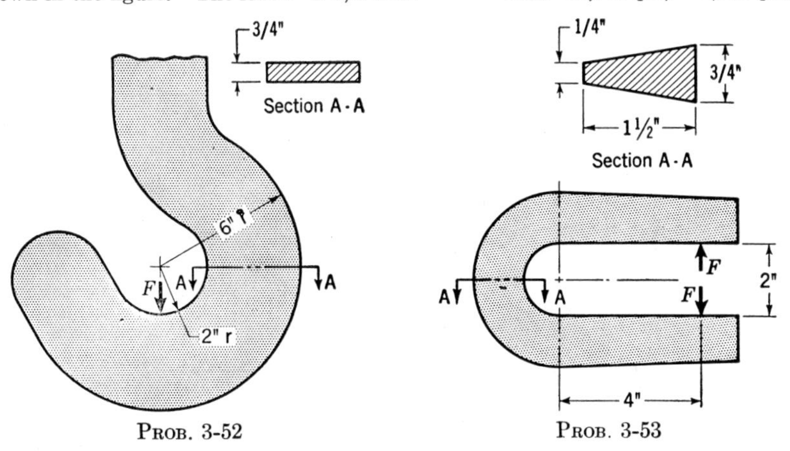

PROB. 3-52 PROB. 3-53

3-53. Find the stress at the inner and outer fibers at section *A-A* of the frame shown in the figure if *F* is 500 lb.

***3-54.** A clamp is to be designed according to the dimensions shown in the figure. The material to be used is cast iron having a tensile strength of 20,000 psi and a compressive strength of 60,000 psi. The clamp is to be designed for a limiting normal load of 1,200 lb. Referring to section *A-A* in the figure, the dimension *t* cannot be less than $\frac{3}{16}$ in. because of the limitations of the casting process; the final size of *t* should be an integral number of sixteenths. Determine a satisfactory set of dimensions for the cross section.

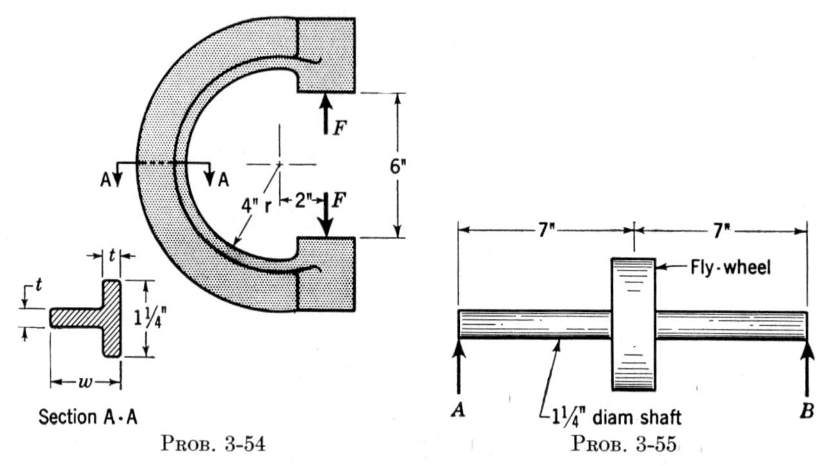

PROB. 3-54 PROB. 3-55

3-55. A 1¼-in.-diameter steel shaft is supported in self-aligning bearings at *A* and *B*. A flywheel mounted in the center of the shaft weighs 40 lb. Find the natural frequency of vibration. This corresponds to the critical speed and should be expressed in rpm.

***3-56.** One of the members of a machine frame is a rectangular steel bar with a ½ × 2-in. cross section. If the bar is 6 ft long, uniform in cross section, and fastened with a single bolt at each end, find the two natural frequencies of vibration.

CHAPTER 4

MATERIALS AND THEIR PROPERTIES

In Chaps. 2 and 3 methods of determining the stresses and deflections of machine members were discussed. In some of the cases it was found that the elastic properties of the material were used. The stress existing in a machine member has no meaning unless the strength of the material is known; this strength is a property of the particular material in use.

The selection of a material for a machine member is one of the decisions the designer is called upon to make. This decision is usually made before the dimensions of the part are determined. After choosing the material and process (the two cannot be divorced), the designer can then proportion the member so that the internal stresses and strains have reasonable and satisfactory values compared with the properties associated with failure of the material.

As important as the stress and deflection of machine parts are, the selection of a material is not always based upon these factors. There are many machine parts which have no loads on them whatever. These parts may be designed merely to fill up space. Members must frequently be designed to resist corrosion. Sometimes temperature effects are more important in design than stress and strain. Oftentimes the members must be designed to withstand wear. So many other factors besides stress and strain may govern the design of parts that a versatile background in materials and processes is necessary.

4-1. Static Strength. The strength of a member is defined as the maximum unit stress which can exist within the member without destroying its usefulness or ability to perform its required function in the machine. This stress may or may not correspond to a unique strength which is characteristic of the particular material in use. It will be shown that, for a specific material, there exist several stress magnitudes, any one of which may be regarded as the strength of the material. It is frequently possible for the designer to consider one of these stress magnitudes as the strength of the member as well as the strength of the material. But it must also be realized that sometimes the strength of a member corresponds to a stress which is in between the several unique stress magnitudes characteristic of any given material.

Tension Tests. A great deal of information concerning the characteristics of materials may be obtained from a standard tension test. This test uses a specimen which has been machined to stated dimensions. The original area and the length of the gauge used to measure strains are recorded prior to beginning the test. The specimen is then slowly loaded in tension, and observations of the load and the total strain within the length of the gauge are taken. At the conclusion of the test the data are plotted as a stress-strain diagram (Fig. 4-1). In this diagram the stress is plotted as the load divided by the original area of the bar. The strain is plotted as the total strain divided by the gauge length.

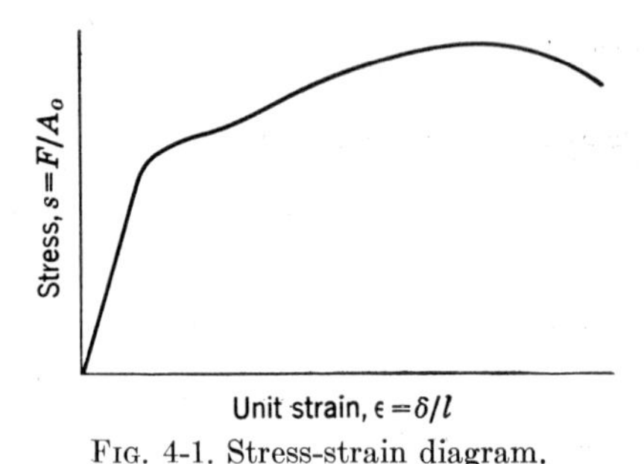

FIG. 4-1. Stress-strain diagram.

It is noted that points on the diagram do not represent the true stress, because the original area rather than the actual area under stress is used in the determination. For a ductile steel, such as in Fig. 4-1, the specimen develops a clearly visible neck in which failure occurs. Since most of the elongation occurs within the neck, the strain as plotted in the diagram is not the maximum strain but is the average, because it was recorded over the gauge length. However, the nominal stress and strain as used here are perfectly satisfactory for most purposes.

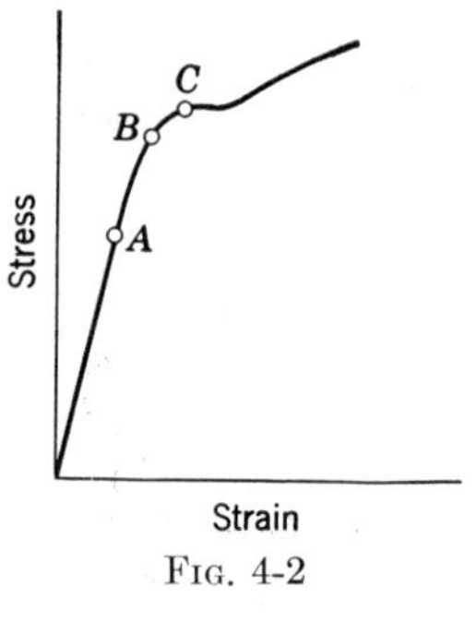

FIG. 4-2

Proportional Limit. The stress-strain diagram can be used to define a number of important stress magnitudes. In Fig. 4-2, which is an enlargement of a portion of the diagram, point A is called the *proportional limit.* This is the point at which the curve begins to deviate from a straight line. Beyond this point the material no longer obeys Hooke's law. The proportional limit is therefore defined as the greatest stress magnitude for which stress is still proportional to strain.

Elastic Limit. With many materials it is possible to increase the load until the stress is higher than the proportional limit, and yet when the load is decreased to zero no permanent set is observable. Since the material returns to its original length, it is still elastic. Point B is such a point, and it is called the *elastic limit.* The elastic limit is defined as the maximum stress which can be applied to a material without obtaining a permanent set. In actual tests this point is somewhat difficult to obtain. It is necessary to load and unload the specimen until a stress magnitude is found for which there exists a small permanent set. Because of this difficulty, *Johnson's apparent elastic limit* is sometimes used. This is an arbitrary value whose magnitude may be obtained from the stress-strain diagram. It corresponds to the stress intensity for which the rate of change of strain is 50 per cent greater than at the origin.

Yield Point. For many materials a point is obtained at which the strain begins to increase very rapidly without a corresponding increase in the stress. This is called the *yield point* and is indicated by point C on the diagram. The material has now passed from an elastic condition into a plastic state, and at this point yielding is said to begin. For ductile materials this is easily observable because of the sudden drop in the load. In many cases the load drops off so sharply that the curve actually slopes in the negative direction for a time. Hence these materials are said to have both an upper and a lower yield point. Because of

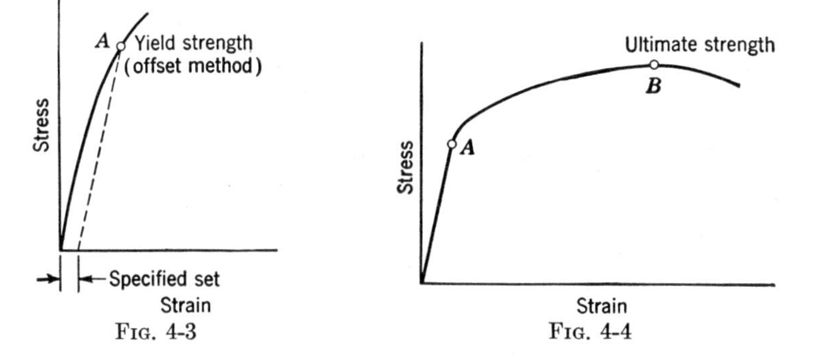

FIG. 4-3 FIG. 4-4

the fact that the yield-point strength is so easily observable, it has become an important figure in the evaluation of materials.

Yield Strength. Materials exist, however, in which there is no sudden change of slope in the stress-strain diagram. Since the stress corresponding to the yield point has had such wide usage in design, there is considerable demand for a comparable strength figure which can be used for materials not having a sharply defined yield point. To satisfy this demand an arbitrary stress intensity, called the *yield strength*, was devised. The yield strength is the stress magnitude which corresponds to a definite amount of permanent set, usually 0.10 or 0.20 per cent of the original gauge length. When the yield strength is given, the amount of permanent set should be specified (Fig. 4-3).

Ultimate Strength. The *ultimate strength*, or *tensile strength*, is the maximum stress reached on the stress-strain diagram (point B, Fig. 4-4). Some materials, such as soft steel, exhibit a downward trend after the maximum stress is reached. Others, such as cast iron, fracture when the stress corresponding to the ultimate strength is reached.

Compression. Many, but not all, materials used in the design of machines have substantially the same properties in compression as in tension. The specimens used for compression testing differ, however, from those used in tension tests. These differences are due to the fact that bending or instability is likely to occur and also to the difficulty of obtaining uniformly distributed stresses. The bending action may occur when the specimen is long, whereas if the specimen is short, friction at the ends complicates the stress distribution. There is also difficulty in obtaining a true axial-loading condition. In the case of ductile materials, the ultimate strength in compression cannot be found because, in the plastic region, the increase in area decreases the true stress. Also, for ductile materials, as the load is increased the material bulges and is eventually squeezed into a flat disk, so that there exists no definite point at which failure can be said to occur.

The results of compression tests are plotted on a stress-strain diagram in the same manner as for tension tests, and the strength definitions apply equally well. When the strength of a material in compression differs materially from its strength in tension, then these two sets of figures should be separately stated; otherwise it will be assumed that the two strengths are equal.

Direct Shear. Rivets, bolts, welded parts, and other machine elements are often required to resist direct shearing loads. The stress distribution in these elements is not uniform, and there usually are bending forces present so that the stress is not pure shear. A schematic diagram (Fig. 4-5) illustrates a direct shear test. The specimen C is placed between two hardened plates, A and B. In applying the load, no means of recording the strains is available. For this reason, measurements of the yield strength or the elastic limit cannot be made. The load at failure divided by the cross-sectional area is called the ultimate shearing strength for direct shear. This is only an approximation of the true strength, since the value of the load seems to depend upon the sharpness of the two hardened plates. Also, in testing rivets and bolts for single and double shear, experiments indicate that the shearing strength for single shear is sometimes as much as 20 per cent greater than that for double shear.

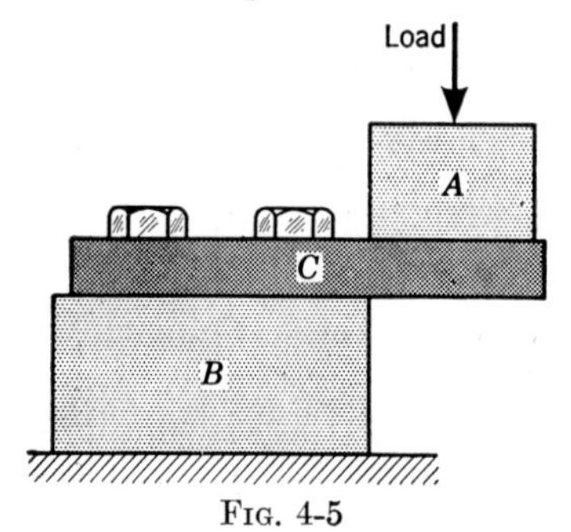

FIG. 4-5

In the absence of other information, the following can be used as a rough indication of the direct shearing strengths:[1]

[1] James F. Young (ed.), "Materials and Processes," p. 51, John Wiley & Sons, Inc., New York, 1944.

Material	$R = \dfrac{\text{ultimate shear strength}}{\text{ultimate tensile strength}}$
Aluminum	0.60
Steel	0.75
Copper	0.90
Malleable iron	0.90
Cast iron	1.30

Torsion. In determining the torsional strength of materials, solid round bars are tested by twisting them. Readings of the torque and the resultant angle of twist are plotted in much the same manner as the stress-strain diagram, producing a *torque-twist* diagram (Fig. 4-6). The elastic limit is usually obtained by finding the torque corresponding to Johnson's elastic limit (point A). If the value of this torque is designated as T_{el}, then the elastic limit is

$$s_{s(el)} = \frac{T_{el}r}{J} \tag{4-1}$$

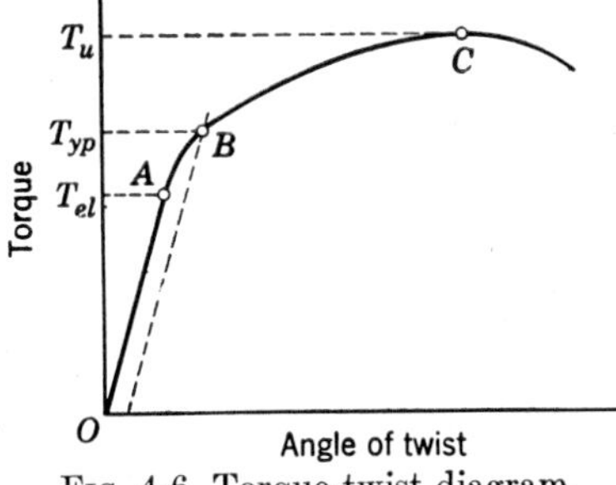

FIG. 4-6. Torque-twist diagram.

where J is the polar moment of inertia. The yield strength is ordinarily obtained as the strength corresponding to a specified permanent-twist angle. Point B in the diagram was obtained by drawing the dotted line parallel to OA but offset from point O by an amount equal to the specified permanent-twist angle. The yield strength is then determined by substituting the torque T_{yp}, corresponding to point B on the curve, in the equation

$$s_{s(yp)} = \frac{T_{yp}r}{J} \tag{4-2}$$

The *ultimate torsional strength* corresponds to the torque T_u represented by point C on the diagram. The torsional strength is

$$s_{s(u)} = \frac{T_u r}{J} \tag{4-3}$$

Equation (4-3) was originally developed on the basis that the material obeyed Hooke's law. Obviously, when used with a torque in the plastic range this is not true, and the stress figure obtained is not the true maximum stress. Figure 4-7 shows such a stress distribution and indicates that when the outer fibers are near failure the inner fibers remain in an elastic state. Since the strength obtained by Eq. (4-3) is not a true value of the stress, the value obtained is called the *modulus of rupture.*

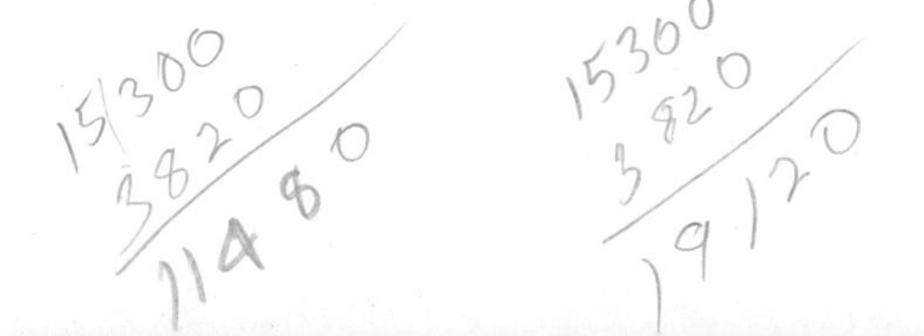

4-2. Ductility. It is possible for two metals to have exactly the same strength and hardness, yet one of these metals may have a superior ability to absorb overloads, because of the property called *ductility*. Two such materials having approximately the same strength and hardness are illustrated in Fig. 4-8. In *a*, a brittle material is shown, and it is seen that it is one which has a small plastic deformation. On the other hand, a ductile material as in *b* will be capable of a relatively large plastic deformation before fracture. Ductility is measured by the *percentage elongation* which occurs in the material at fracture. The usual dividing line between ductility and brittleness is 5 per cent elongation. A material having less than 5 per cent elongation at fracture is said to be *brittle*, while one having more is said to be *ductile*.

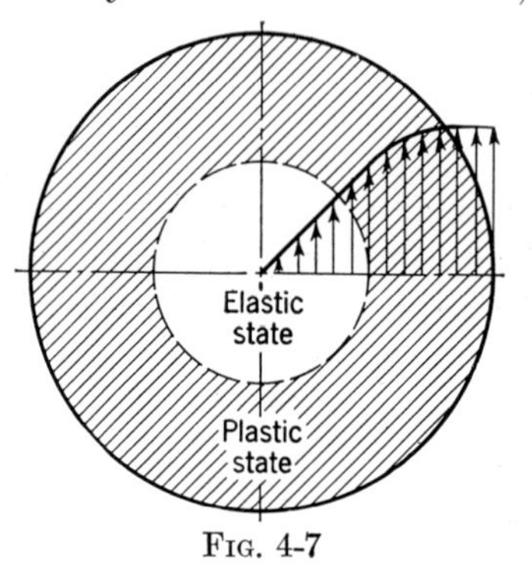

Fig. 4-7

The elongation of a material is usually measured over a 2-in. gauge length. Since this is not a measure of the actual strain, another method of determining ductility is sometimes used. After the specimen has been fractured, measurements are made of the area of the cross section at the fracture. Ductility can then be expressed as the *percentage reduction in cross-sectional area*.

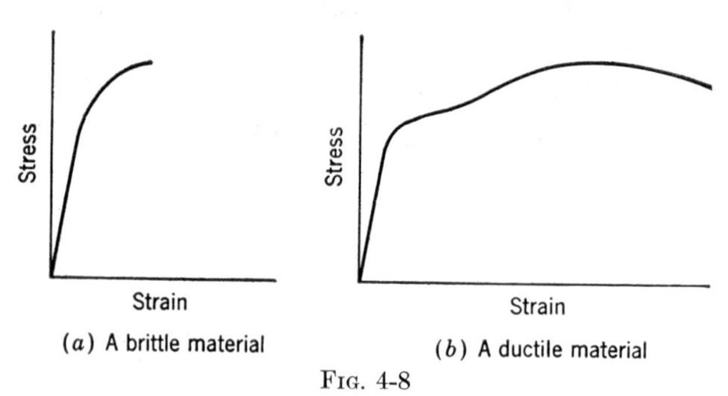

Fig. 4-8

The characteristic of a ductile material which permits it to absorb large overloads is an additional safety factor in design. Ductility is also important because it is a measure of that property of a material which permits it to be cold-worked. Such operations as bending, drawing, heading, and stretch forming are metal-processing operations which require ductile materials.

Malleability. Malleability is a term which is frequently used interchangeably with ductility. If a distinction is desired, malleability can be considered as a compressive quality. A malleable material, then, is one which is capable of being flattened or squeezed. When employed in this way, ductility is used in the tensile sense.

4-3. Resilience. The *resilience* of a material is its capacity to absorb energy within the elastic range. It is measured by the *modulus of resilience*. From Eq. (3-18) the total strain energy is

$$U = \frac{s^2lA}{2E} \tag{a}$$

The modulus of resilience is the strain energy that can be absorbed by a unit volume of material when the stress is at the proportional limit. Substituting $s = s_p$ for the stress at the proportional limit, and $lA = 1 \text{ in.}^3$ for unit volume, Eq. (a) becomes

$$U_p = \frac{s_p{}^2}{2E} \tag{4-4}$$

which defines the modulus of resilience. The meaning of the modulus is shown graphically on the stress-strain diagram (Fig. 4-9). Point A represents the stress intensity at the proportional limit. The line AB is drawn vertical. The shaded area then represents the amount of energy which can be stored in a unit volume of material without exceeding the proportional limit. It can be seen from the diagram that if a material is to be capable of absorbing large amounts of energy, that is, if it is to have a high modulus, the area OAB must be large. This area is large if (1) the proportional limit is high and (2) the modulus of elasticity is low.

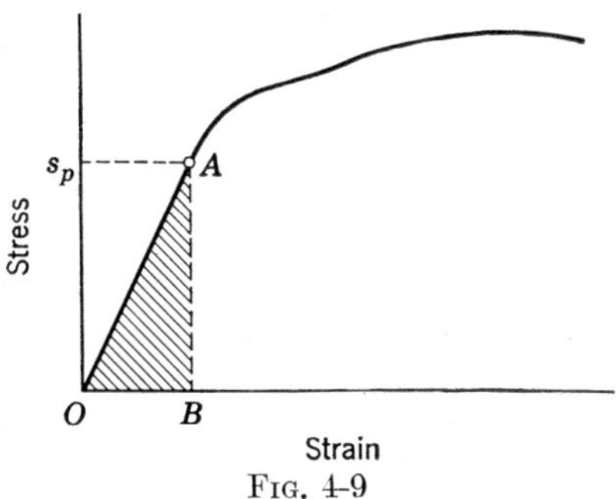

FIG. 4-9

4-4. Toughness. The ability of a material to absorb energy in the plastic range is called *toughness*. Most authorities are agreed upon this definition, but there exists considerable disagreement concerning how toughness can be measured. Some say that the impact strength of a material is the best measure; others prefer to use the stress-strain diagram in various ways. The diagram is, however, an evaluation of static properties, while toughness is a property which is desirable in parts subjected to shock and impact loads.

The *modulus of toughness* is obtained by integrating the stress-strain diagram (Fig. 4-10) up to fracture. Mathematically, it is expressed as follows:

$$T = \int_0^{\epsilon_t} s \, d\epsilon \tag{4-5}$$

where ϵ_t is the strain at fracture. The integration may conveniently be performed graphically, as demonstrated elsewhere in this book.

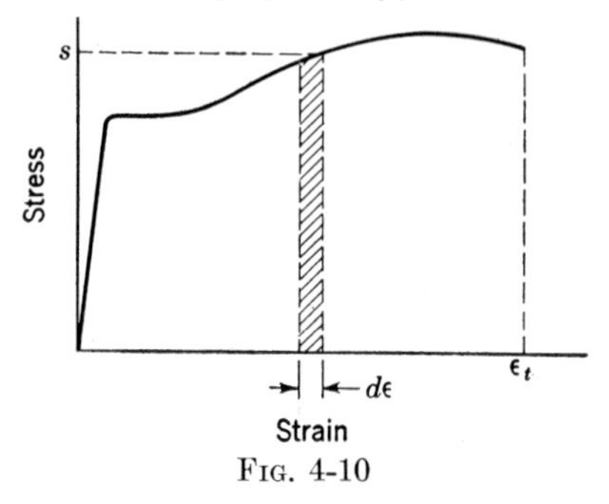

FIG. 4-10

A relatively simple method of evaluating toughness is to calculate the *toughness index number*. This is obtained by multiplying the ultimate strength of the material by the strain at fracture:

$$T = s_u \epsilon_t \tag{4-6}$$

Since these two values are widely available for many materials, the toughness index number can be determined quite rapidly.

Another method is to multiply the strain at fracture by the average of the ultimate strength and the yield-point strength. Mathematically, this is

$$T = \frac{s_{yp} + s_u}{2} \epsilon_t \tag{4-7}$$

For brittle materials, sometimes the strain at fracture is multiplied by two-thirds of the ultimate strength. Regardless of the method used, the toughness is expressed as the amount of energy absorbed per unit volume of material and is usually in pound-inches per cubic inch.

4-5. Hardness. When a material is to be selected to resist wear, erosion, or plastic deformation, hardness is generally the most important property. Several methods of hardness testing are available, depending upon which particular property is most desired. The four hardness numbers which are in greatest use are the Brinell, Rockwell, Vickers, and Scleroscope.

Most hardness-testing systems employ a standard load which is applied to a ball or pyramid in contact with the material to be tested. The hardness is then expressed as a function of the size of the resulting indentation.

It is not possible to convert hardness numbers from one system of measurement to another with mathematical exactness, because of variation of the material. However, some method of comparison between the numbers is desirable, and Table 4-1 gives the relative values for nickel steel. These are approximately true. The values for other materials vary somewhat.

Since hardness is an easy property to measure, it has come into rather wide use as a means of comparing materials. The relation between hardness and tensile strength for carbon and alloy steels shown in Fig.

TABLE 4-1. RELATION BETWEEN HARDNESS VALUES FOR NICKEL STEEL*

Vickers hardness numbers, Vhn 1, 5, 10, 30 kg	Brinell hardness numbers, Bhn 3,000 kg	Rockwell hardness numbers		Scleroscope hardness numbers
		B 100 kg	C 150 kg	
513	479	...	50	63
481	450	...	48	61
452	425	...	46	58
427	403	...	44	56
404	382	...	42	54
382	363	...	40	52
362	346	...	38	49.5
344	329	...	36	47
326	313	...	34	45
309	298	106	32	42
285	275	104	28.5	38
266	258	102	25.5	35
248	241	100	22.5	33
220	215	96	17	30
198	194	92	12	28
179	176	88	6.5	27
164	161	84	2.0	
145	144	78		
130	129	72		
115	114	64		
100	100	54		

* These hardness numbers are slightly different for other materials.

4-11 will remain substantially the same, regardless of the steel or its method of processing.[1]

4-6. Fatigue. In obtaining the properties of materials relating to the stress-strain diagram, the load is applied gradually, giving sufficient time for the strain to develop. With the usual conditions, the specimen is tested to destruction so that the stresses are applied only once. These conditions are known as static conditions and are closely approximated in many structural and machine members.

The condition frequently arises, however, in which the stresses vary or fluctuate between values. For example, a particular fiber on the sur-

[1] C. Lipson, G. C. Noll, and L. S. Clock, Significant Strength of Steels in the Design of Machine Parts, pt. I, *Product Eng.*, vol. 20, no. 4, pp. 145–146, 1949.

face of a rotating shaft, subjected to the action of bending loads, undergoes both tension and compression for each revolution of the shaft. If the shaft is a part of an electric motor rotating at 1,725 rpm, then the fiber is stressed in tension and in compression 1,725 times each minute. If, in addition, the shaft is also axially loaded (caused, for example, by a helical or worm gear), then an axial component of stress is superimposed upon the bending component. This results in a stress, in any one fiber, which is still fluctuating but which is fluctuating between different values. These and other kinds of loads occurring in machine members produce stresses which are called repeated, alternating, or fluctuating stresses.

Machine members are often found to have failed under the action of repeated or fluctuating stresses, and yet the most careful analysis reveals that the actual maximum stresses were below the ultimate strength of

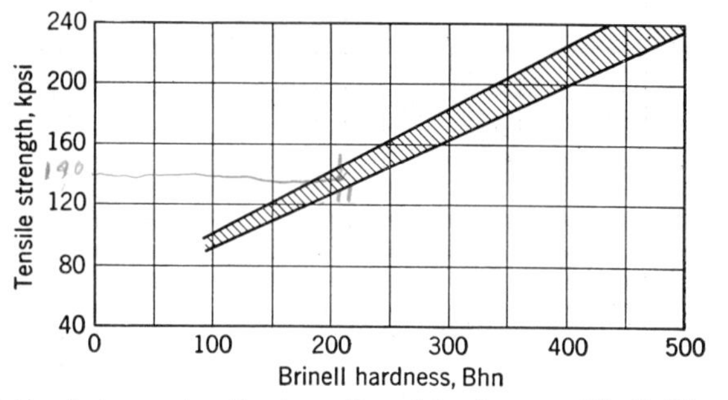

FIG. 4-11. Relation between tensile strength and hardness. *(By C. Lipson, G. C. Noll, and L. S. Clock.)*

the material and quite frequently even below the yield strength. The most distinguishing characteristic of these failures has been that the stresses have been repeated a very large number of times. Hence, the failure is called a *fatigue* failure.

A fatigue failure begins with a small crack. The initial crack is so minute that it cannot be detected by the naked eye and is even quite difficult to locate in a Magnaflux or X-ray inspection. The crack will develop at a point of discontinuity in the material, such as a change in cross section, a keyway, or a hole. Less obvious points at which fatigue failures are likely to begin are inspection or stamp marks, internal cracks, or even irregularities caused by machining. Once a crack has developed, the stress-concentration effect becomes greater and the crack progresses more rapidly. As the stressed area decreases in size, the stress increases in magnitude until, finally, the remaining area fails suddenly. A fatigue failure, therefore, is characterized by two distinct areas of failure (Fig. 4-12). The first of these is that due to the progressive development of the crack, while the second is due to the sudden fracture. The zone of the sudden fracture is very similar in appearance to the fracture of a brittle material, such as cast iron, which has failed in tension.

Fatigue Strength. In order to determine the strength of materials under the action of fatigue loads, specimens are subjected to repeated or

Fig. 4-12. A fatigue failure of a 7½-in.-diameter forging at a press fit. The specimen is 1045 steel, normalized and tempered, and has been subjected to rotating bending. (*Courtesy of The Timken Roller Bearing Company.*)

varying forces of specified magnitudes while the cycles or stress reversals are counted to destruction. One such test uses a specimen which acts as a rotating beam.[1] A constant bending load is applied, and the number of revolutions of the beam required for failure are recorded. A number of these tests are necessary in order to establish the fatigue strength of the material. The first test is made at a stress which is somewhat under the ultimate strength of the material. The second test is made with a stress which is less than that used in the first. This process is continued and the results plotted as an *s-n* diagram (Fig. 4-13) to show the relation between the value of the fluctuating stress and the number of cycles required to produce failure. The ordinate of this curve defines the *fatigue*, or endurance, strength of the material corresponding to the number of stress cycles required for failure. In the case of ferrous metals and alloys, the curve becomes horizontal after the material has been stressed for a certain number of cycles; failure will not occur if the stress

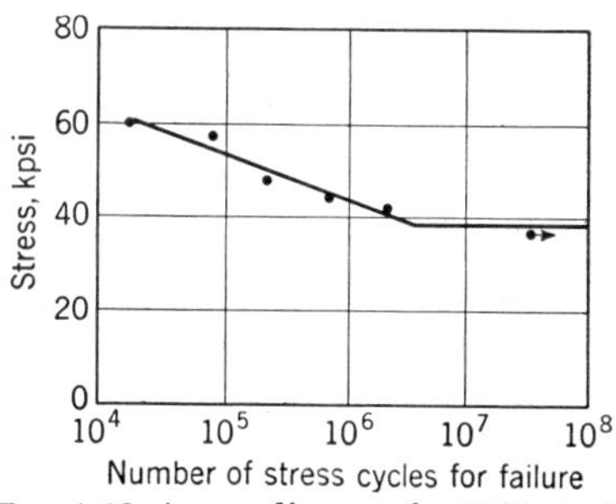

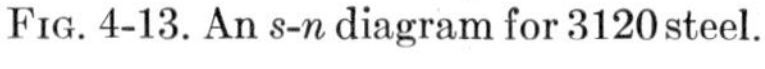

Fig. 4-13. An *s-n* diagram for 3120 steel.

[1] Joseph Marin, "Engineering Materials," p. 184, Prentice-Hall, Inc., New York, 1952.

is below this value, no matter how many stress cycles are applied. When this is the case, the stress intensity represented by the horizontal line is called the *endurance limit.* In the case of nonferrous metals and alloys, the line never becomes horizontal, and hence these metals do not have an endurance limit. Results of tests should always be plotted on log paper in order to emphasize the break in the curve.

4-7. Results of Fatigue Tests. The most convenient method of fatigue testing is that which uses completely reversed stresses. This condition occurs a great deal in practice, and it is also a simple method of testing because it employs a rotating beam. However, conditions arise in machine design in which the stresses are not completely reversed or only fluctuate in value without passing through a zero-stress condition. For this reason it is desirable to obtain the fatigue strength corresponding to stress situations other than complete reversals. The stress-time relationship is indicated graphically in Fig. 4-14, where in *a* is illustrated a stress which fluctuates between the values of s_{max} and s_{min}. The average stress is the mean of these values and is

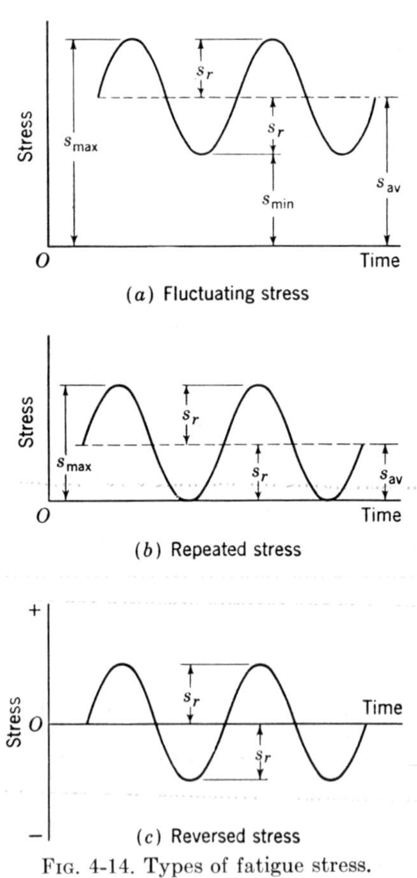

FIG. 4-14. Types of fatigue stress.

$$s_{av} = \frac{s_{max} + s_{min}}{2} \qquad (a)$$

Any stress situation may be described by an average component s_{av} and a fluctuating component s_r which varies between positive and negative maximum values:

$$s_r = \frac{s_{max} - s_{min}}{2} \qquad (b)$$

The average stress may have any positive or negative value. For example, in *b*, s_{min} is zero and $s_{av} = s_{max}/2$. This is known as a repeating, or pulsating, stress. In *c*, s_{av} is zero, which gives a completely reversed stress. Although a sine curve has been used in this example to illustrate the fluctuating component, the actual stress-time relationship may be quite different. Since only the maximum, minimum, and average values are used, the exact form of the stress-time relation is not important to this discussion.

Having defined these stress values, we can now proceed to a study of some experimental results. It must be noted, however, that results of fatigue tests are far more sensitive to slight variations in the specimen and in apparently similar materials than the results of tests for static properties. Large variations in results can be expected because of size and machining effects. There is always the possibility that the material may have been prestressed in some manner and the stress history of the specimen forgotten. Final results should always be interpreted statistically.

In order to determine the fatigue strength for various values of the s_r/s_{av} ratio the graph of Fig. 4-15 has been prepared. Corresponding to

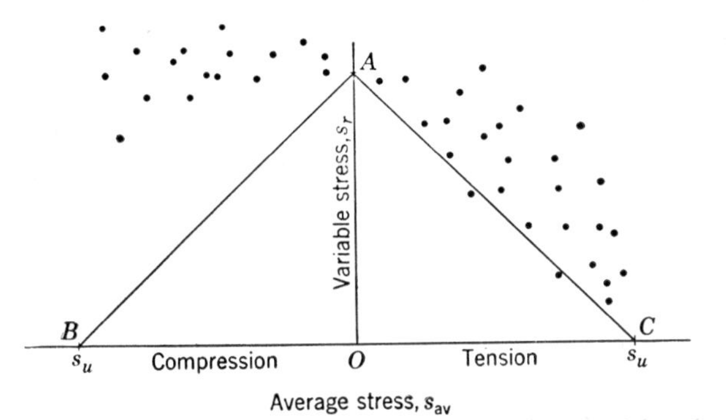

FIG. 4-15. Stress range for repeated axial stresses for ductile materials.

a specified number of cycles, the fatigue strengths for various s_r/s_{av} ratios are taken from the s-n diagrams and plotted upon this graph. The variable stresses s_r are plotted as the ordinates, and the average stresses are plotted as the abscissas, with tension being plotted to the right and compression plotted to the left. Point A is the fatigue strength for completely reversed bending. Point B is the ultimate static compressive strength, and point C is the ultimate static tensile strength. Considering only the right-hand portion of the graph, the test points are seen to be arranged from left to right in a decreasing order. Any curve drawn through the points would necessarily require a rather wide paint brush because considerable scatter is to be expected. However, if a straight line is drawn from A to C it is seen that only a few of these points occur below this line. The empirical relation identified by the line AC is known as the *modified Goodman law*.

The left side of the figure (Fig. 4-15) gives the relations when the average stress is compression. As the average compressive stress increases there is some evidence to indicate that the stress range (s_r)

decreases, but this decrease is apparently not as much as it is on the tensile side. The evidence compiled to date is inconclusive as regards compression, but it does seem on the side of safety to assume a line AB, to the ultimate strength in compression, as identifying the limiting variable stress when the average stress is compression.[1]

4-8. Designing for Fatigue Conditions. The problem arises as to how to determine the limiting stress conditions when variable and steady stresses are present. When the endurance limit and the yield strength of a member are known, the results of Sec. 4-7 furnish a method, first suggested by Soderberg,[2] for defining the limiting stress condition.

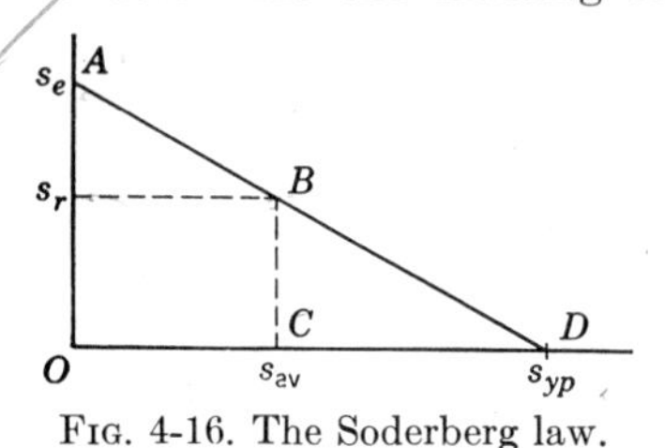

FIG. 4-16. The Soderberg law.

The ordinate of Fig. 4-16 represents the variable stress s_r, with point A the magnitude of the endurance limit s_e. The steady- or average-stress component is the abscissa, with point D as the yield strength. From similar triangles BCD and AOD we can write

$$\frac{s_r}{s_{yp} - s_{av}} = \frac{s_e}{s_{yp}}$$

from which

$$s_r = s_e\left(1 - \frac{s_{av}}{s_{yp}}\right) \tag{4-8}$$

Equation (4-8) may be called the *Soderberg law*, and it gives the limiting value of the variable stress s_r for various values of the endurance limit, the average stress, and the yield strength. In developing this equation, the yield strength has been used because in machine design it is seldom intended that the yield strength be exceeded. It must be pointed out, however, that some designers prefer to use the tensile strength; this can be done by substituting s_u for s_{yp} in Eq. (4-8).

Figure 4-17 shows how the factor of safety is applied when fatigue loading exists. Here, both the endurance limit and the yield strength are divided by a factor of safety, which is usually the same. This gives a line, representing the safe value of the stress, which is parallel to the line representing fatigue failure. Any stress situation which comes within the triangle Oab is considered to be safe. Introducing the factor of safety into Eq. (4-8), we obtain

$$s'_r = \frac{s_e}{\text{f.s.}}\left(1 - \frac{s'_{av}}{s_{yp}/\text{f.s.}}\right) \tag{4-9}$$

[1] John M. Lessells, "Strength and Resistance of Metals," pp. 161–186, John Wiley & Sons, Inc., New York, 1954.

[2] C. R. Soderberg, Working Stresses, *Trans. ASME*, p. A106, 1935.

where s_r' and s_{av}' are, respectively, the safe values of the varying and average stresses.

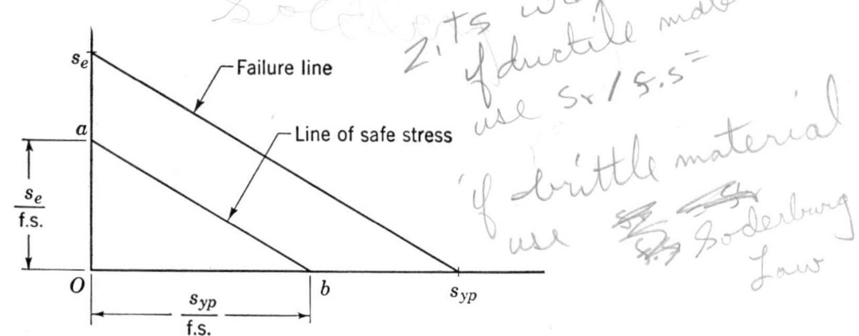

FIG. 4-17. Factor of safety applied to both the endurance limit and the yield strength.

EXAMPLE 4-1. The tensile load on a bar varies from 24,000 lb maximum to 8,000 lb minimum. The material has a yield strength of 80,000 psi and an endurance limit of 50,000 psi in reversed bending. If the factor of safety is 2, find the safe area of the bar.

Solution. The average load is

$$F_{av} = \frac{24,000 + 8,000}{2} = 16,000 \text{ lb}$$

The varying load is

$$F_r = \frac{24,000 - 8,000}{2} = 8,000 \text{ lb}$$

The safe average stress is

$$s_{av}' = \frac{16,000}{A}$$

The safe varying stress is

$$s_r' = \frac{8,000}{A}$$

Dividing both the endurance limit and the yield strength by the factor of safety, we obtain

$$\frac{s_e}{\text{f.s.}} = \frac{50,000}{2} = 25,000 \text{ psi} \qquad \frac{s_{yp}}{\text{f.s.}} = \frac{80,000}{2} = 40,000 \text{ psi}$$

Substitution of these values in Eq. (4-9) yields

$$s_r' = \frac{s_e}{\text{f.s.}}\left(1 - \frac{s_{av}'}{s_{yp}/\text{f.s.}}\right) \qquad \frac{8,000}{A} = 25,000\left(1 - \frac{16,000/A}{40,000}\right)$$

and solving for A,

$$A = 0.72 \text{ in.}^2 \qquad \textit{Ans.}$$

Another method of solution is to apply the factor of safety to the equation

$$s_{max} = s_{av} + s_r$$

This is illustrated by the following example:

EXAMPLE 4-2. Solve Example 4-1 using an alternate method.

Solution. It is necessary to find the ratio s_r/s_{av}. This is

$$\frac{s_r}{s_{av}} = \frac{F_r}{F_{av}} = \frac{8,000}{16,000} = 0.500$$

It is now easy to find the maximum stress s_{max}, using a graphical solution. Referring to Fig. 4-18, the line representing the Soderberg law is constructed from an endurance

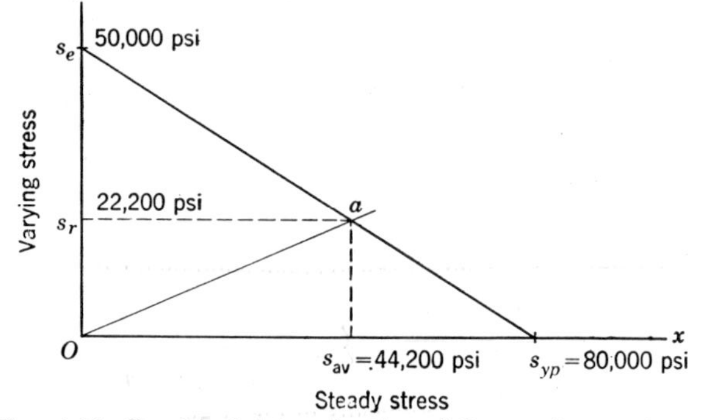

FIG. 4-18. Graphical determination of the maximum stress.

limit of 50,000 psi on the y axis to a yield strength of 80,000 psi on the x axis. A straight line Oa, with a slope of $s_r/s_{av} = 0.500$, is now constructed through the origin. Line Oa intersects the failure line at point a. The stresses are read from the diagram as $s_r = 22,200$ psi and $s_{av} = 44,200$ psi. Therefore, the maximum stress is

$$s_{max} = s_{av} + s_r = 44,200 + 22,200 = 66,400 \text{ psi}$$

Applying the factor of safety,

$$\text{Safe stress} = s = \frac{s_{max}}{\text{f.s.}} = \frac{66,400}{2} = 33,200 \text{ psi}$$

Therefore, the required area is

$$A = \frac{F_{max}}{s} = \frac{24,000}{33,200} = 0.72 \text{ in.}^2 \qquad \textit{Ans.}$$

Stress Concentration. The effects of stress concentration must be considered in fatigue problems, no matter whether the stresses are completely reversed or fluctuating. When the stresses are fluctuating it is the frequent practice to apply the stress-concentration factor to the varying component only. Of course, if the material is brittle it must be applied to both components.

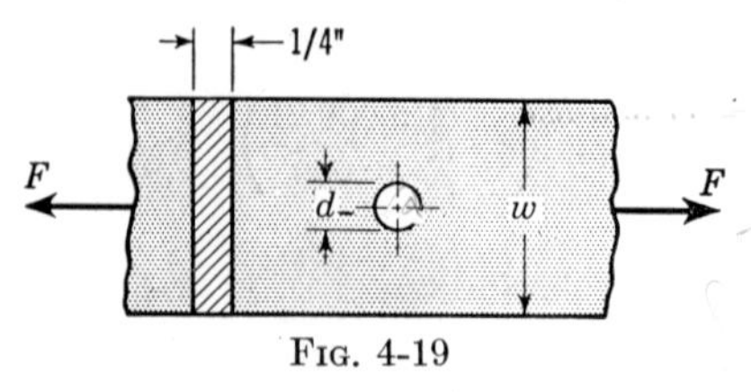

FIG. 4-19

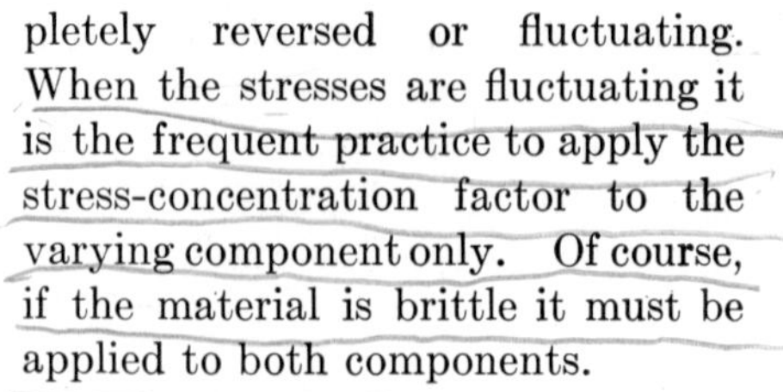

EXAMPLE 4-3. The bar shown in Fig. 4-19 is subjected to fluctuating tensile loads of $F_{max} = 30,000$ lb and $F_{min} = 7,500$ lb. The material has a yield strength of 60,000 psi and an endurance limit of 25,000 psi. Use a fatigue stress-concentration

factor of 1.8. (It will be shown in the next section that the stress concentration for fatigue loading is less than the geometric conditions would indicate.) If the ratio $d/w = 0.20$, and the factor of safety is 2.0, find the width of the bar.

Solution. The average load is

$$F_{av} = \frac{30{,}000 + 7{,}500}{2} = 18{,}750 \text{ lb}$$

The fluctuating load is

$$F_r = \frac{30{,}000 - 7{,}500}{2} = 11{,}250 \text{ lb}$$

The safe average stress is

$$s'_{av} = \frac{F_{av}}{A} = \frac{18{,}750}{A}$$

The safe fluctuating component of stress is

$$s'_r = k_f \frac{F_r}{A} = \frac{(1.8)(11{,}250)}{A}$$

The ratio of the varying component to the average component is

$$\frac{s'_r}{s'_{av}} = \frac{(1.8)(11{,}250)/A}{18{,}750/A} = 1.08$$

The maximum stress is determined graphically in Fig. 4-20. The failure line is plotted as in Example 4-2. The line Oa is constructed at a slope of 1.08. The intersection

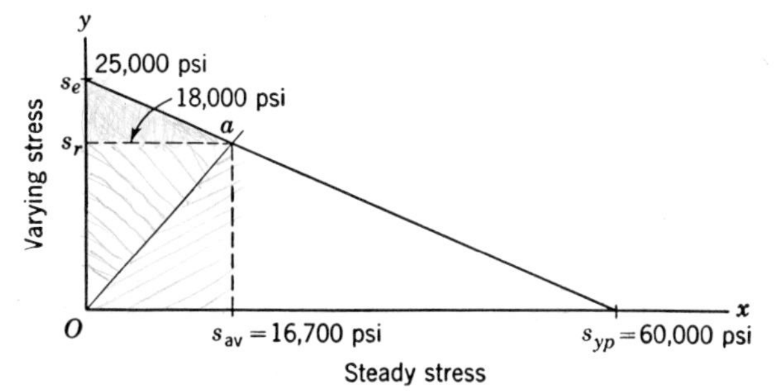

FIG. 4-20. Determination of the maximum stress.

at point a gives $s_r = 18{,}000$ psi and $s_{av} = 16{,}700$ psi. The maximum stress is

$$s_{max} = s_r + s_{av} = 18{,}000 + 16{,}700 = 34{,}700 \text{ psi}$$

The safe stress is

$$s = \frac{s_{max}}{\text{f.s.}} = \frac{34{,}700}{2} = 17{,}350 \text{ psi}$$

Therefore, the required area is

$$A = \frac{F_{max}}{s} = \frac{F_{av} + k_f F_r}{s} = \frac{18{,}750 + (1.8)(11{,}250)}{17{,}350} = 2.24 \text{ in.}^2$$

The area of the bar is $A = (w - d)/4$. Substituting $d = 0.20w$, the required width is

$$w = \frac{4A}{0.8} = \frac{(4)(2.24)}{0.8} = 11.16 \text{ in.} \qquad \textit{Ans.}$$

The relations indicated above are recommended for ductile materials, including steels and some nonferrous metals. Brittle materials such as cast iron may have a higher strength in compression, permitting an alternate equation to be used. The following equation is suggested:[1]

$$s_r = s_e \frac{1 - s_{av}/s_u}{1 + s_{av}/s_u} \qquad (4\text{-}10)$$

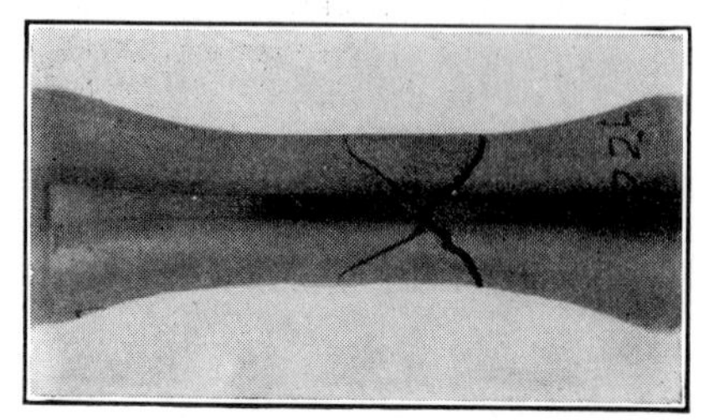

FIG. 4-21. A torsional fatigue fracture in a ⅝-in. specimen machined from drill rod. (*Courtesy of The Timken Roller Bearing Company.*)

When torsion or combined stresses are present, then a suitable strength theory should be used with Eqs. (4-9) and (4-10). For example, the effect of cyclic torsional stresses on a specimen machined from drill rod clearly shows a tensile failure (Fig. 4-21).

4-9. Factors Affecting Fatigue Strength. Efforts directed toward finding a correlation between the fatigue strength and other static properties of materials have met with little success. Most of the data available have been obtained from rotating-beam fatigue tests, although a

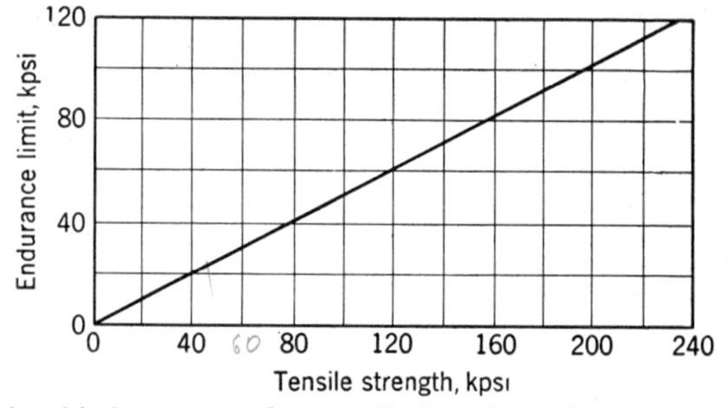

FIG. 4-22. Relationship between endurance limit and tensile strength of polished steel. (*Moore and Jasper.*)

small volume of data exists for reversed torsion and other tests. A rough correlation has been found between the endurance limit and the ultimate tensile strength. When specimens of polished steel without stress concentrations were tested, using completely reversed cycles of flexural stress, Moore and Jasper[2] found that the ratio of the endurance limit to the ultimate strength was about 0.50 (Fig. 4-22). This ratio was found

[1] Thomas J. Dolan, Stress Range, Sec. 6-2 in Oscar J. Horger (ed.), "ASME Handbook, Metals Engineering—Design," McGraw-Hill Book Company, Inc., New York, 1953.

[2] H. F. Moore and T. M. Jasper, An Investigation of the Fatigue of Metals, *Univ. Illinois Eng. Expt. Sta. Bull.* 136, 1923.

to vary from 0.40 to 0.60, and above 200,000 psi tensile strength it dropped below 0.50. The range of 0.40 to 0.60 also seems to hold for polished specimens of cast irons, malleable cast irons, cast steels, and wrought iron.[1]

Surface Condition. The effect of surface preparation upon the endurance limit for ferrous metals and alloys is shown in Fig. 4-23.[2] These curves represent the results of tests, are corrected for size, and are probably accurate within a 10 per cent range. They should not be used to establish minimum values.

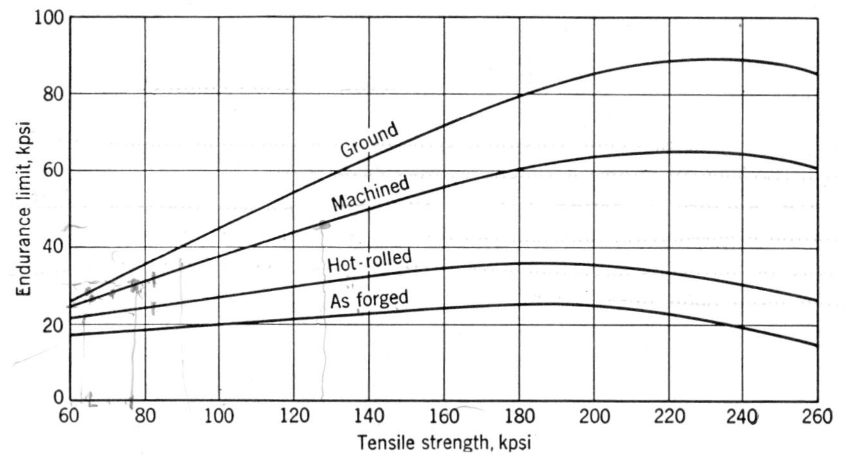

FIG. 4-23. Relationship between the endurance limit and the surface finish. (*By C. Lipson, G. C. Noll, and L. S. Clock.*)

Decarburization of the surface of metals by heating in an oxidizing atmosphere has a weakening effect upon the endurance limit. The lower carbon content of the surface metal results in a soft case which causes a lowered resistance to fatigue, especially when the material is subjected to bending loads. Surface irregularities such as pits, marks, or scale from rolling or forging operations also reduce the endurance limit.

Metallic coatings, such as chromium plating, nickel plating, or cadmium plating, reduce the endurance limit by as much as 35 per cent. In some cases the reduction by coatings has been so severe that it has been necessary to eliminate the plating process.

It is to be expected that parts which operate in a corrosive atmosphere will have a lowered fatigue resistance. This is, of course, true, and it is due to the roughening or pitting of the surface by the corrosive material. But the problem is not as simple as the one of finding the endurance

[1] Battelle Memorial Institute, "Prevention of Fatigue of Metals under Repeated Stresses," John Wiley & Sons, Inc., New York, 1946.

[2] Lipson, Noll, and Clock, *op. cit.*, p. 144.

limit of a specimen which has been corroded. The reason for this is that the corrosion and the stressing occur at the same time, so that the resultant weakening is much greater than that produced by the two factors acting one at a time. In fact, the result of the stresses is to increase the amount of corrosion. Further discussion of this subject is beyond the purposes of this book; the interested reader should consult the references at the end of this chapter.

Residual Stresses. The previous stress history of a specimen has an important influence upon the endurance limit. It has been shown[1] that any metalworking or metal-treating process which applies residual compressive stresses to the material is beneficial, provided it is not stressed to exhaustion. Some of this benefit, however, is due to the increase in strength from "work hardening." Cold-working operations which can be used to improve the endurance limit are shot peening, rolling, drawing, hammering, and stretching. These processes are especially useful at points of stress concentration, such as holes, keyways, or fillets, and provide an additional safety allowance.

A process which hardens the surface of the material for resistance to wear is also beneficial in increasing the endurance limit. Processes such as case carburizing, nitriding, or flame hardening are used for this purpose.

Endurance limits have been improved up to 25 per cent by applying many millions of cycles of completely reversed stresses, called *understressing*, to materials. The value of the stress to be applied is quite critical; a stress which is too high will cause *overstressing* and result in a deterioration of the endurance limit.

Stress Concentration. It has been shown in Chap. 2 that for ductile materials under static loads stress concentration is not a serious problem. This is because the local yielding of the material at the point of stress concentration redistributes the stresses. However, under conditions of fatigue loading, stress concentration is a very serious problem, even when the material is ductile, because the metal is stressed repeatedly. Repeated yielding will work the material to exhaustion, allowing a fatigue fracture to occur very early in the life of the part.

Stress-concentration factors k_f for fatigue loading are usually somewhat less than their geometric values.[2] The *fatigue stress-concentration factor*, sometimes more appropriately called the *fatigue-strength reduction factor*, is defined as

$$k_f = \frac{s_e}{s_e'} = \frac{\text{fatigue strength of notch-free specimens}}{\text{fatigue strength of notched specimens}} \tag{4-11}$$

[1] J. O. Almen, Fatigue Weakness of Surfaces, *Product Eng.*, vol. 21, no. 11, 1950.

[2] R. E. Peterson and A. M. Wahl, Two and Three-dimensional Cases of Stress Concentration and Comparison with Fatigue Tests, *Trans. ASME*, vol. 58, p. A15, 1936.

Peterson first suggested the use of a *notch-sensitivity index* q, which he defined as

$$q = \frac{k_f - 1}{k - 1} \tag{4-12}$$

where the value of q varies from 0 to 1. This equation shows the sensitivity index to be dependent upon two characteristics of the member. The stress-concentration factor k is dependent only on the geometry of the part, while the fatigue stress-concentration factor k_f depends upon the material and processing of the part as well as upon the geometry.

The values of the notch sensitivity have not yet been obtained for many materials. However, a considerable number of tests which have been made on various steels indicate that they may be classified into two groups. The first group includes all the fine-grained, quenched and

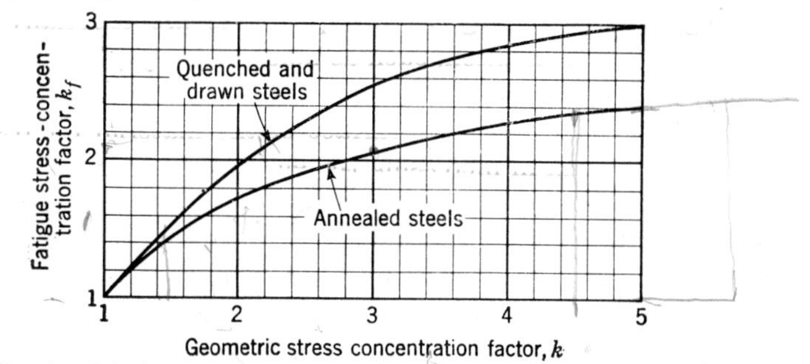

FIG. 4-24. Graph of fatigue versus geometric stress-concentration factors for two classes of steels. *(By C. Lipson, G. C. Noll, and L. S. Clock.)*

drawn steels having a hardness greater than 200 Bhn. The second group includes the coarse-grained steels, that is, the annealed steels having a hardness of less than 200 Bhn. For these two classes the values of k_f, from Eq. (4-12), have been plotted for various values of k in Fig. 4-24.

4-10. Failure Theories. The mechanical properties of materials which have thus far been defined are properties related to simple stresses, such as tension, compression, and shear. Problems arising in machine design are often not as simple as the tests used to obtain these properties. Bending is often accompanied by torsion. Tension or compression sometimes occurs with bending. Biaxial and triaxial stresses occur in machine members. When they are subjected to such combinations of stresses, what stress values will cause failure? Many theories have been proposed to explain test results of members under various combinations of stresses. No single theory is perfect, and hence several are necessary in order to describe the failure of different groups of materials.

Maximum-stress Theory. This theory states that failure of the material depends solely upon the intensity of the maximum principal normal stress. The stress condition of an element of a stressed body may be described by the two principal normal stresses, s_1 and s_2. Tension is considered as positive and compression as negative, and the two stresses are assumed to have the following relation:

$$s_1 > s_2 \tag{a}$$

Since s_1 is the larger, the maximum-stress theory states that s_2 is disregarded and that s_1 is the only stress to be considered.

For this theory the criterion of failure is

$$s_1 = s_{yp} \tag{4-13}$$

or

$$s_1 = s_u \tag{4-14}$$

Equation (4-13) defines the failure of a member if the material has a yield strength and if yielding of the member will destroy its usefulness in the machine. Equation (4-14) is used to define failure whenever the yield strength of the material is not defined (this is frequently the case with brittle materials) and when the designer chooses to base his design on the ultimate strength of the material.

Equations (4-13) and (4-14) will hold for either tension or compression by substitution of the appropriate strength value. When the principal stresses have opposite signs the results of this theory do not agree with test results.

EXAMPLE 4-4. Determine the diameter of a solid round section of a machine part twisted by a static torsional load of 2,400 lb-in. and acted upon by a static bending load of 1,800 lb-in. The member is to be manufactured of class 25 cast iron. Use a factor of safety of 4.

Solution. Cast iron has no yield point. The ultimate tensile strength is therefore the criterion of failure. Class 25 cast iron has a tensile strength of 25,000 psi. Therefore, the maximum combined stress must not exceed

$$s_1 = \frac{s_u}{\text{f.s.}} = \frac{25{,}000}{4} = 6{,}250 \text{ psi}$$

From Eq. (2-19) the torsional stress is

$$s_s = \frac{16T}{\pi d^3} = \frac{(16)(2{,}400)}{\pi d^3} = \frac{12{,}200}{d^3}$$

The bending stress is obtained from Eq. (2-23):

$$s = \frac{M}{I/c} = \frac{32M}{\pi d^3} = \frac{(32)(1{,}800)}{\pi d^3} = \frac{18{,}400}{d^3}$$

This problem is solved graphically in Fig. 4-25 by means of Mohr's circle. The bending stress is first plotted as distance $OA = 18{,}400/d^3$. From point A the distance $AB = 12{,}200/d^3$ is laid off as the shearing stress. A circle with its center at E is constructed through point B. Point C is then the maximum combined stress; its value may be obtained by scaling the diagram and is found to be $24{,}500/d^3$. Since this stress must not exceed 6,250 psi, the diameter must be

$$d = \sqrt[3]{\frac{24{,}500}{6{,}250}} = 1.58 \text{ in.} \qquad \textit{Ans.}$$

Maximum-shear Theory. This theory states that failure of the material depends only upon the value of the maximum shearing stress. For a specimen stressed in simple tension the maximum shearing stress occurs

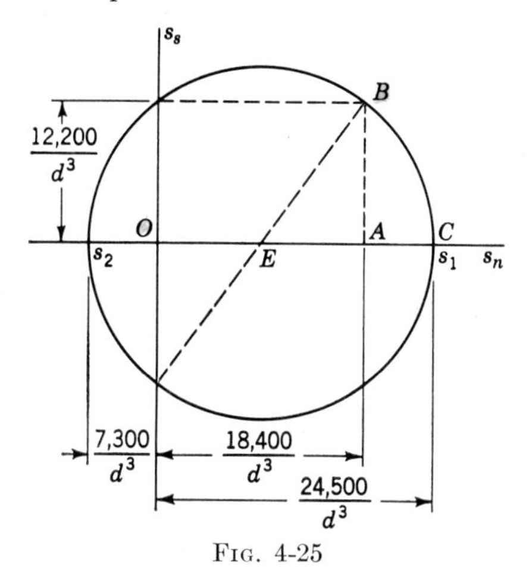

FIG. 4-25

when the material begins to yield, if the yield strength is the criterion of failure, and from Sec. 2-3 is

$$s_s' = \frac{s_{yp}}{2} \tag{b}$$

The maximum combined shearing stress for biaxial stresses is either

$$s_s' = (\tfrac{1}{2})(s_1 - s_2) \qquad \text{or} \qquad s_s' = s_1/2 \tag{c}$$

whichever is largest, where s_1 and s_2 are, as before, the principal normal stresses. Substitution of Eq. (*b*) in (*c*) gives:

$$s_{yp} = s_1 - s_2 \qquad \text{or} \qquad s_{yp} = s_1 \tag{4-15}$$

The right-hand equation governs when the biaxial stresses have like signs. If failure is defined by the ultimate strength, then use s_u instead of s_{yp} in Eq. (4-15).

The maximum-shear theory is on the safe side of test results both when the biaxial stresses have like signs and when they have unlike signs. It is simple to use and has been adopted in several codes.

EXAMPLE 4-5. Repeat Example 4-4 for the maximum-shear theory.

Solution. Referring to Fig. 4-25, the principal normal stresses are

$$s_1 = \frac{24{,}500}{d^3} \qquad s_2 = -\frac{7{,}300}{d^3}$$

Equation (4-15) applies, with s_u substituted for s_{yp}. Applying the factor of safety, we obtain

$$\frac{s_u}{\text{f.s.}} = s_1 - s_2$$

$$\frac{25{,}000}{4} = \frac{24{,}500}{d^3} + \frac{7{,}300}{d^3}$$

$$d = \sqrt[3]{\frac{(31{,}800)(4)}{25{,}000}} = 1.72 \text{ in.} \qquad \textit{Ans.}$$

Distortion-energy Theory. This theory is an extension of the now abandoned maximum-energy theory and is sometimes called the *von Mises-Hencky theory.* It assumes that failure of the material is caused only by the energy which causes shearing deformations. Mathematically, it is stated as follows:[1]

$$s_{yp}^2 = s_1^2 - s_1 s_2 + s_2^2 \tag{4-16}$$

for two-dimensional stress, where s_{yp} is the yield strength in simple tension. Except for brittle materials, this theory agrees closely with test results.

Of the three theories presented here the maximum-stress theory is in poorest agreement with test results but is most often used for brittle materials and for conditions of fatigue loading. The maximum-stress theory is also useful when a difference exists between the values of the tensile and compressive strengths. For ductile materials having the same strength in tension as in compression either the maximum-shear theory or the distortion-energy theory should be used. The distortion-energy theory gives the most accurate results, but the maximum-shear theory is easiest to apply. A great many design problems have been solved without regard to these theories. Their inclusion in the analysis of many problems is, however, justified and would result in a more rational design.

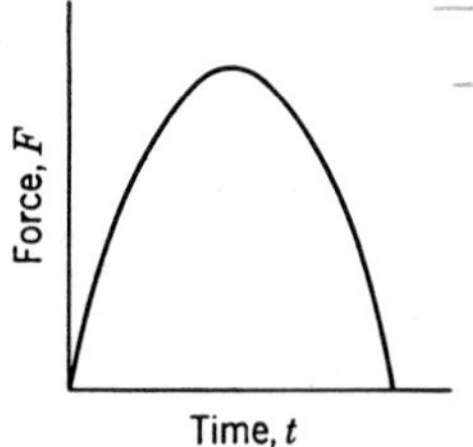

FIG. 4-26. An impact load.

4-11. Impact Properties. Figure 4-26 shows the load-time curve for a typical impact load. While the curve shown is a sine wave, an impact load is not restricted to a particular shape of curve. The area under the curve $\int F\,dt$ defines the value of the impulse and is more important than the maximum value of the force. The differentiating characteristic of an impact load is the time required for the force to rise from zero to a maximum. If this time is small compared with the lowest natural period of vibration of the structure, then the load is said to be an impact load. In general, if the time

[1] The development of this relation is beyond the purposes of this text. The reader should refer to Marin, *op. cit.*, pp. 134–137.

of application of the load is less than one-half the natural period of the structure, the load is clearly an impact load. If, on the other hand, the time of application is greater than three times the natural period, then the load may be considered as static.

Notched-bar Tests. The *Charpy* and *Izod* notched-bar tests, while of great value in the determination of low-temperature brittleness and in

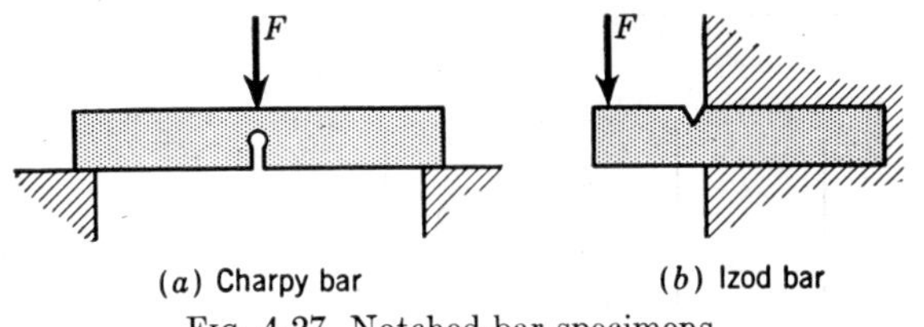

FIG. 4-27. Notched-bar specimens.

metallurgical control, are of little use in design. Results of these tests may, in fact, convey misleading information to the designer.

The Charpy impact test uses a notched bar, as shown in Fig. 4-27. The specimen is mounted in the machine and is struck by a pendulum which is released from a fixed height. The amount of energy given up by the pendulum is calculated from the height of swing after fracture. This is called the *impact value.* The Izod test is similar except that the specimen is mounted as a cantilever beam. For both tests the amount of energy required to fracture the specimen is measured in foot-pounds. Also, the specimens are mounted so that the impact load places the bottom of the notch in tension. This is done in order to provide enough stress concentration so that ductile materials will always fracture.

The effect of temperature on impact values is shown in Fig. 4-28.[1] It is seen that as the temperature increases there occurs a region in which the impact values increase very rapidly. The appearance of the fractured surface on each side of this region is of greater importance than the actual impact values. The low-temperature fracture is a brittle, shattering type, whereas the fracture in the high-temperature region is a tough, tearing type. Examination of the curve also reveals that the range of temperatures in the transition region is quite short. In fact, frequently only one temperature is associated with this region. Further-

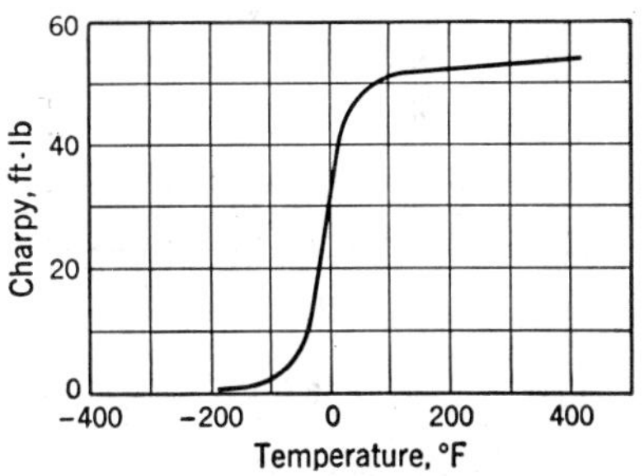

FIG. 4-28. The effect of temperature on impact values.

[1] H. W. Gillett and F. T. McGuire, Report on Behavior of Ferritic Steels at Low Temperatures, pts. I and II, ASTM Pamphlet, December, 1945.

more, the region often occurs very near room temperature. Two types of ship plate tested revealed transition temperatures of 70 and −10°F.* This temperature seems to be a function of the steel as well as of the characteristics of the notch. These tests indicated clearly that the notched-bar tests are not reliable.

Strain Rate. The average rate of strain in obtaining the usual stress-strain diagram is 0.001 in. per in. per sec. Recently an extended series of tests has been made on various materials in order to determine the

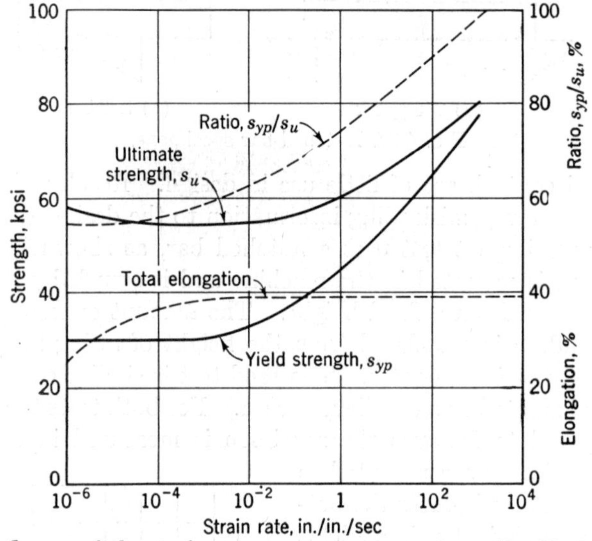

FIG. 4-29. Influence of the strain rate on tensile properties. (*By M. J. Manjoine.*)

effect of the rate of strain on their properties.[1] Figure 4-29 illustrates the effect of the strain rate on the tensile properties. These curves show little change in elongation, so that the ductility remains about the same. The ultimate strength shows an increase for very high strain rates. The most important effect obtained is the increase in yield strength. At very rapid strain rates the yield strength seems to approach the ultimate strength as a limit, indicating that, for high-speed loading, mild steel could be expected to behave elastically throughout practically its entire strength range.

Experiments on other materials also show that the ultimate strength increases when the loading speed is increased, and the conclusion is justified that an increase in yield strength can also be expected. These

* N. A. Kahn and E. A. Imbembo, Reproducibility of the Single-blow Charpy Notched-bar Test, *ASTM Bull.*, pp. 66–74, May, 1947.

[1] M. J. Manjoine, Influence of Strain and Temperature on Yield Stresses of Mild Steel, *Trans. ASME*, vol. 66, pp. A211–A218, 1944. Also *Proc. ASTM*, pt. I, vol. 40, pp. 822–837, 1940, and *Trans. ASME*, pts. II and III, vol. 63, pp. A77–A91, 1941.

investigations indicate clearly that, except for fatigue loading, the use of static properties for the design of members to resist impact is on the conservative side. For impact loading under fatigue conditions, the fatigue strength corresponding to the number of cycles defining the expected life of the member should be used.

4-12. Creep and Temperature Properties. Machine members are frequently required to operate at temperatures different from that at which the mechanical properties are ordinarily obtained. For example, the metal parts of aircraft and marine equipment are often required to operate at subzero temperatures. Gas- and steam-turbine parts must

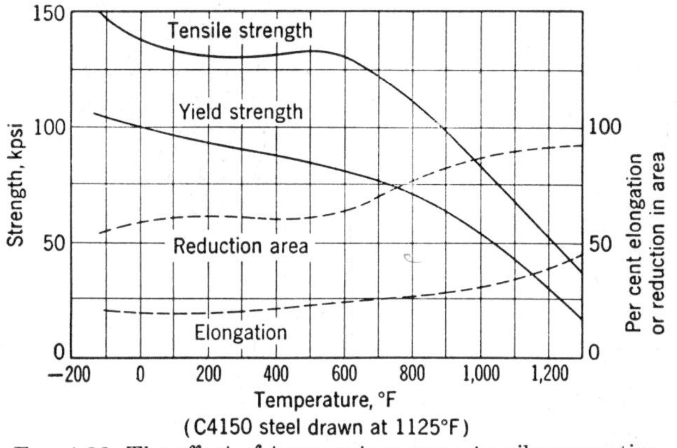

Fig. 4-30. The effect of temperature upon tensile properties.

operate at elevated temperatures. Important changes occur in the properties of materials at temperatures which differ from normal room temperature.

Temperature Properties. The effect of temperature upon the static properties of a particular steel is shown in Fig. 4-30. Although manufacturers' bulletins should be consulted for the exact properties in the operating temperature range for the material to be used, the curves shown are characteristic of many steels. As the temperature is increased from any value, it is characteristic of the yield strength to decrease. The tensile strength is usually high at low temperatures; as the temperature is increased above room temperature, it is characteristic of the tensile strength that a maximum value will be reached, after which the curve will fall off very rapidly.

Few data are available concerning the fatigue strength of steels at various temperatures. Although some improvement seems evident at low temperatures, until more information becomes available the fatigue strength should probably be evaluated as a function of the ultimate strength in any given temperature range.

Creep. Many tests have been made of ferrous metals subjected to constant loads for long periods of time at elevated temperatures. The specimens were found to be permanently deformed during the tests, even though at times the actual stresses were less than the yield strength of the material obtained from short-time tests made at the same temperature. This continuous deformation under load is called *creep.*

The usual problem in the design of members subjected to elevated temperatures is to select a material and stress such that, for the life of the part, a certain limiting value of the creep will not be exceeded. In the case of parts which have a very short life, it is not difficult to devise tests which will provide the necessary information. On the other hand, some steam-turbine parts are expected to have a life of 20 years or more. Since it is not practical to run such long tests, experimental results must be extrapolated in order to provide the necessary design information.

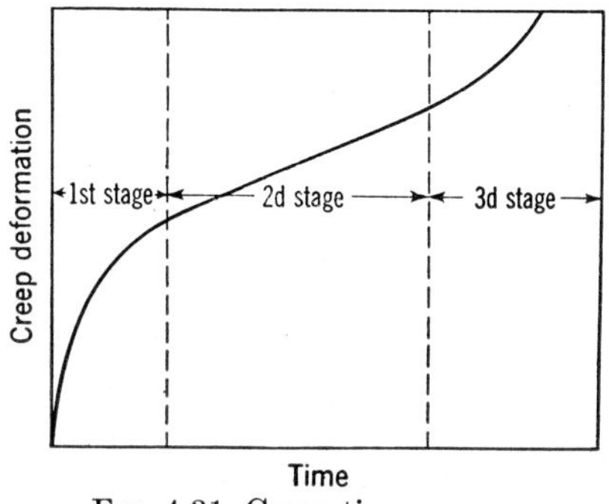

FIG. 4-31. Creep-time curve.

One of the most useful tests that has been devised is the long-time creep test under constant load. Figure 4-31 illustrates a curve which is typical of this type of test. The curve is obtained at a constant stated temperature, and a number of tests are usually run simultaneously at different stress intensities. The curve exhibits three distinct regions. In the first stage are included both the elastic and the plastic deformation. This stage shows a decreasing creep rate which is due to the strain hardening. The second stage shows a constant minimum creep rate caused by the annealing effect. In the third stage the specimen shows a considerable reduction in area, the unit stress is increased, and a higher creep rate eventually leads to fracture.

A stress which would cause fracture within the time usually available for testing would normally be too high, except for members with a very short life. For this reason creep-time tests are usually extended only long enough to establish the first stage, or the first and a portion of the second. Investigators must be cautious in ending the tests too soon. The shape of the curve is influenced by such factors as the crystal grain size, corrosion, and age hardening. Since some of these factors may not show up during the early portions of the test, the (American Society for Testing Materials) Standards state that "tests extending to 10 per cent of the expected life are preferable where feasible."

4-13. Numbering Systems. The Society of Automotive Engineers (SAE) first recognized the need for and adopted a system of numbering steels. Later the American Iron and Steel Institute (AISI) adopted a similar system. In this system there is a letter prefix which designates the process by which the steel is made. For instance, A designates a basic open-hearth alloy steel, B is an acid-bessemer carbon steel, C is a basic open-hearth carbon steel, D is an acid open-hearth carbon steel, and E is an electric-furnace steel. The first two numbers following the letter prefix indicate the composition, excluding the carbon content. The various compositions used are as follows:

10 plain carbon
11 free-cutting carbon steel with more sulfur or phosphorus
13 manganese
23 nickel
25 nickel
31 nickel-chromium
33 nickel-chromium
40 molybdenum
41 chromium-molybdenum
43 nickel-chromium-molybdenum
46 nickel-molybdenum
48 nickel-molybdenum
50 chromium
51 chromium
52 chromium
61 chromium-vanadium
86 chromium-nickel-molybdenum
87 chromium-nickel-molybdenum
92 manganese-silicon
94 nickel-chromium-molybdenum

The last two numbers (three for the high-carbon steels in the 51- and 52-chromium groups) refer to the approximate carbon content. Thus AISI C1040 is a basic open-hearth carbon steel with a carbon content of 0.37 to 0.44 per cent. Similarly, SAE 2330 is a nickel-alloy steel with 0.28 to 0.33 per cent carbon.

The wrought stainless steels have a similar system of numbering but not quite so systematic. Stainless steels whose first number begins with 3 are chromium-nickel. Those whose first number begins with 4 have only chromium as the principal alloying element. Sometimes stainless steels are indicated as, for example, 18-8, meaning 18 per cent chromium and 8 per cent nickel. Or a designation might be 16-13-3 Cr-Ni-Mo, indicating the approximate percentages of the principal alloying elements.

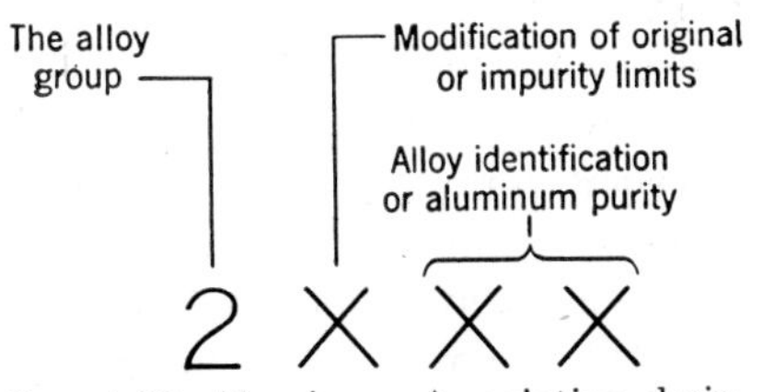

FIG. 4-32. Aluminum Association designation system for wrought aluminum and wrought-aluminum alloys.

Cast iron is not designated by composition but rather by the tensile-strength level. For example, a No. 30 cast iron is expected to have a tensile strength of not less than 30,000 psi.

Wrought aluminum and wrought-aluminum alloys are designated by a four-digit index system, as shown in Fig. 4-32. Table 4-2 gives the designation system for these materials.

TABLE 4-2. DESIGNATIONS FOR ALUMINUM-ALLOY GROUP

	AA number
Aluminum—99.00% minimum and greater	1xxx
Aluminum alloys:	
Copper	2xxx
Manganese	3xxx
Silicon	4xxx
Magnesium	5xxx
Magnesium and silicon	6xxx
Zinc	7xxx
Other element	8xxx
Unused series	9xxx

The temper designation is separated from the alloy designation by a hyphen. This designation is usually composed of a prefix letter and a number, although sometimes the number is not required. The designation of temper is as follows:

-F as fabricated
-O annealed
-H strain-hardened
-T treated

A commercially pure wrought aluminum would be designated 1100-O. A 4032-T6 is a wrought-silicon-aluminum alloy with a temper of -T6, which means the metal has been solution-treated and then artificially aged. Additional information may be obtained from Table A-3 and from the various aluminum handbooks.

4-14. Processing Methods—General. The selection of a material for a machine part and the selection of the method of processing the material in order to produce the part are two decisions which the designer must make early in the design process. These two decisions cannot always be divorced and considered separately, even though the designer would often like to do so. Although a given material may have the properties required for satisfactory service in the machine, it must also lend itself to the desired method of processing. The choice of the material and of the method of processing it determines the cost of the part and should represent the maximum value for the money expended.

4-15. Casting Processes. *Sand-casting.* The oldest, and probably the most versatile, method of forming metals is the sand-casting process. Sand-casting is a basic low-cost process, and it lends itself to economical production in large quantities with practically no limit to the size, shape, or complexity of the part produced.

In sand-casting, the casting is made by pouring molten metal into sand molds. A pattern, constructed of metal or wood, is used to form the cavity into which the molten metal is poured. Recesses or holes in the casting are produced by sand cores introduced into the mold. The designer should make an effort to visualize the pattern and casting in the mold. In this way he can study the problems of core setting, pattern removal, draft, and solidification. In order to design an easily produced, low-cost casting the designer should envisage how the metal will enter the mold and how solidification will proceed.

Steel castings are the most difficult of all to produce because steel has the highest melting temperature of all materials normally used for casting. This high melting temperature aggravates all the casting problems.

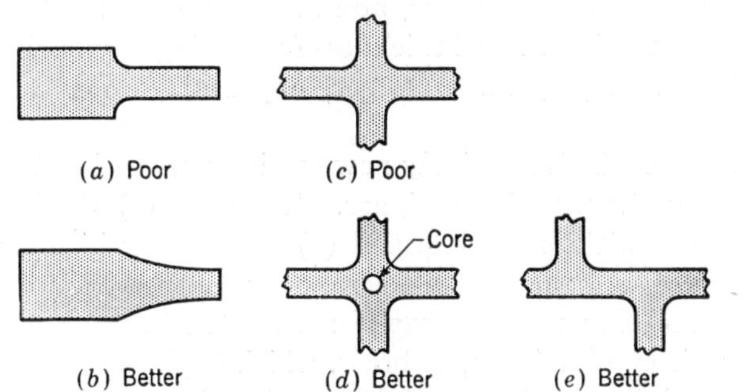

Fig. 4-33. Methods of obtaining uniform solidification in castings.

The U.S. Navy Research Laboratories' rules for producing steel castings can be used in the design of any sand casting. They are as follows:[1]

1. All sections should be designed with a uniform thickness.
2. The casting should be designed so as to produce a gradual change in a section where this is necessary.
3. Adjoining sections should be designed with generous fillets or radii.
4. A complicated part should be designed in two or more simple castings to be assembled by fasteners.

The section thickness should generally be the minimum which is necessary to obtain the required strength and stiffness. An ideal casting is produced when solidification begins at the bottom of the mold and proceeds uniformly to the top. The tensile strength of the cast metal is lowest just after solidification has set in. When uniform-section thicknesses are not maintained, the light section will freeze first and shrink, while the heavy section is just beginning to solidify. If the shrinkage is in the wrong direction, this could set up a condition which would cause the two sections to separate. The use of chills on the heavier section will cause it to solidify earlier, but this problem is usually left to the foundryman or metallurgist. Figure 4-33 illustrates various methods in

[1] Herbert Chase (ed.), "Handbook on Designing for Quantity Production," p. 106, McGraw-Hill Book Company, Inc., New York, 1944.

which more uniform solidification may be achieved in design. When these recommended designs cannot be obtained, large fillets should be used. Sharp corners must always be avoided especially, because of the stress-concentration effects and the possibility of fatigue failure.

The use of ribs as stiffeners, reinforcing members, and as means for reducing section thickness is especially desirable. Large flat areas have a tendency to warp during cooling; this can easily be corrected by the use of stiffeners or ribs. These are usually made slightly thinner than the sections they reinforce in order that they will cool first and act as bonds and heat conductors for the reinforced section.

Steel, gray iron, brass, bronze, and aluminum are most often used in castings. The minimum wall thickness for casting any of these materials is about $\frac{1}{8}$ in. to $\frac{3}{16}$ in. or larger, depending upon the size of the casting.

Shell Molding. This relatively new casting process has two important advantages for the machine designer. They are (1) the high degree of mechanization which is possible and (2) the savings in machining costs by virtue of the fact that closer-tolerance castings are obtained.

The shell-molding process employs a heated metal pattern, usually made of cast iron, aluminum, or brass, which is placed in a shell-molding machine containing a mixture of dry sand and powdered thermosetting resin. The hot pattern melts the plastic which, together with the sand, forms a shell about $\frac{3}{16}$ to $\frac{3}{8}$ in. thick around the pattern. The shell is then baked at from 500 to 1000°F for a short time while still on the pattern. It is then stripped from the pattern and placed in storage for use in casting.

In the next step the shells are assembled by clamping, bolting, or pasting; they are placed in a backup material, such as steel shot; and the molten metal is poured into the cavity. The thin shell permits the heat to be conducted away so that solidification proceeds rapidly. As solidification takes place, the plastic bond is burned and the mold collapses. The permeability of the backup material allows the gases to escape and the casting to air-cool. All this aids in obtaining a fine-grain stress-free casting.

Shell-mold castings feature a smooth surface, a draft which can be as small as $\frac{1}{4}°$, and tolerances as close as ± 0.002 to ± 0.005 in. Although this is a relatively new process with some possibilities remaining to be explored, it has been used successfully with aluminum, tin bronze, gray iron, ductile iron, and medium-carbon, stainless, and alloy steels. In general, the rules governing the design of sand castings also apply to the design of shell-mold castings.

Investment Casting. This process has been used only for parts weighing a few pounds; recently, however, castings weighing up to 35 lb have been successfully produced. It is particularly useful for complicated shapes of hard-to-machine materials which must resist high temperatures and high stresses. The tolerances may be held very close (± 0.003 to ± 0.005 in.), and the surface is smooth with very good detail.

Investment casting uses a pattern which may be made from wax, plastic, frozen mercury, or other material. After the mold is made, the pattern is melted out. Thus a mechanized method of casting a great many patterns is necessary. The mold material is dependent upon the melting point of the cast metal. For low-melting-point metals a plaster mold may be used, but if the melting point is high then a ceramic or refractory material must be employed. After melting out the pattern, the mold must be baked. When the mold is finished, the molten metal may be poured in and allowed to cool. If the casting metal is at a high temperature, it may be necessary to preheat the mold. Sometimes the hot mold is quickly transferred to a casting machine, clamped in position, and the molten metal conveyed to the mold under pressure.

Almost any metals that are castable may be used. These include the carbon, low-alloy, and stainless steels as well as the cobalt- and nickel-base, high-temperature alloys.

Metal-mold Casting. One of the difficulties of the sand-casting process is that the mold can be used only once; it must be destroyed in order to remove the casting. If a number of castings are to be made, metal molds can be used to save material and labor. These, however, are not suitable for large castings or for materials having a high melting point. These metal or permanent molds have the additional advantage that the surfaces are smooth, bright, and accurate, so that little, if any, machining is required. Metal-mold casting processes may be classified as permanent-mold casting, die casting, and centrifugal casting.

4-16. Powder-metallurgy Process. This is a quantity-production process which uses powders from a single metal, several metals, or a mixture of metals and nonmetals. It consists essentially of mechanically mixing the powders, compacting them in dies at high pressures, and heating the compacted part at a temperature which is less than the melting point of the major ingredient. The particles are united into a single strong part similar to what would be obtained by melting the same ingredients together. The advantages are (1) the elimination of scrap or waste material, (2) the elimination of machining operations, (3) the low unit cost when mass produced, and (4) the exact control of composition. Some of the disadvantages are (1) the high cost of dies, (2) the lower physical properties, (3) the higher cost of materials, (4) the limitations on the design, and (5) the limited range of materials which can be used. Parts commonly made by this process are oil-impregnated bearings, incandescent lamp filaments, cemented-carbide tips for tools, and permanent magnets. Figure 4-34 illustrates some other parts which have been produced by this process.

4-17. Hot-working Processes. By "hot working" is meant such processes as rolling, forging, hot extrusion, and hot pressing, in which the metal is heated sufficiently to make it plastic and easily worked.

Hot rolling is usually used to create a bar of material of a particular shape and dimensions. Figure 4-35 shows some of the various shapes

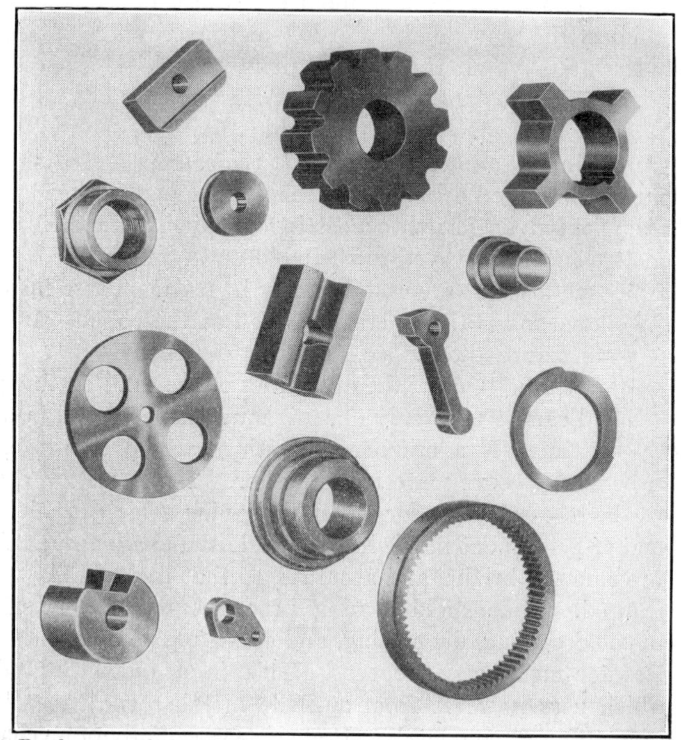

Fig. 4-34. Products made by the powder-metallurgy process. (*Courtesy of The United States Graphite Company.*)

which are commonly produced by the hot-rolling process. All of them are available in many different sizes as well as in different materials. The materials most available in the hot-rolled-bar sizes are steel, aluminum, magnesium, and copper alloys.

Tubing may be manufactured by hot-rolling strip or plate. The edges of the strip are rolled together, creating seams which are either butt-welded or lap-welded. Seamless tubing is manufactured by roll-piercing a solid heated rod with a piercing mandrel.

Extrusion is the process by which great pressure is applied to a heated metal billet or blank, causing it to flow through a restricted orifice. This

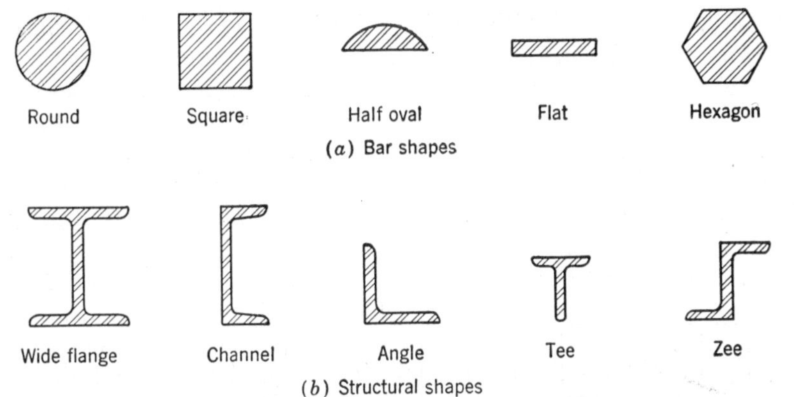

FIG. 4-35. Common shapes available by hot rolling.

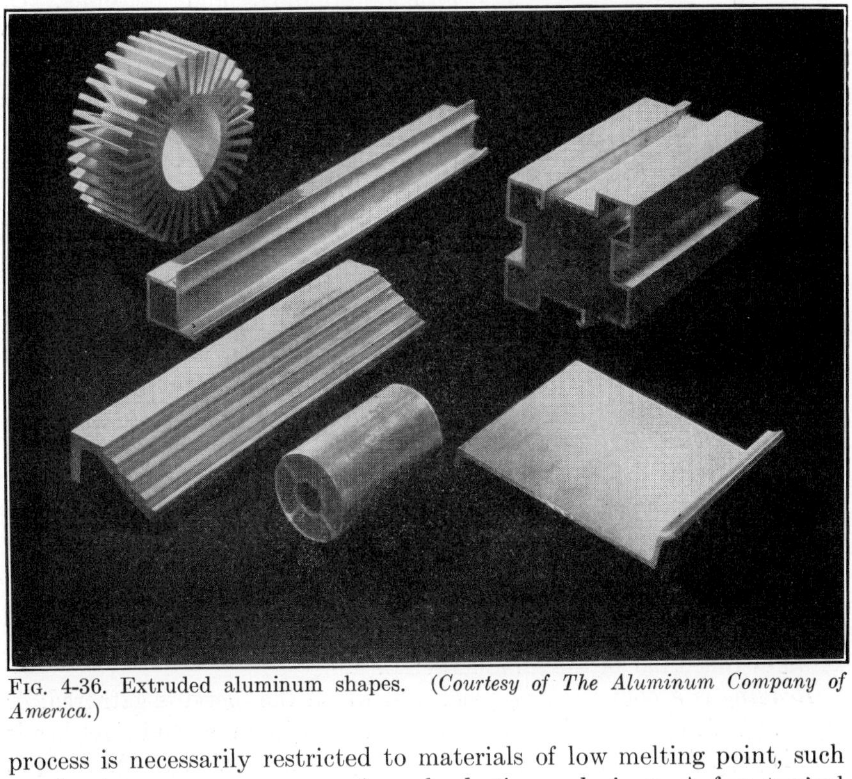

FIG. 4-36. Extruded aluminum shapes. (*Courtesy of The Aluminum Company of America.*)

process is necessarily restricted to materials of low melting point, such as aluminum, copper, magnesium, lead, tin, and zinc. A few typical shapes produced by the extrusion process are shown in Fig. 4-36.

Forging is the hot working of metal by hammers, presses, or forging machines. In common with other hot-working processes, forging produces a refined-grain structure which results in increased strength and ductility. Compared with castings, forgings have greater strength for the same weight. In addition, drop forgings can be made smoother and more accurate than sand castings, so that less machining is necessary. However, the initial cost of the forging dies is usually greater than the cost of patterns for castings, although the greater unit strength rather than the cost is usually the deciding factor between these two processes.

4-18. Cold-working Processes. By "cold working" is meant the forming of the metal while at a low temperature (usually room temperature). In contrast to parts produced by hot working, cold-worked parts have a bright new finish, are more accurate, and require less machining.

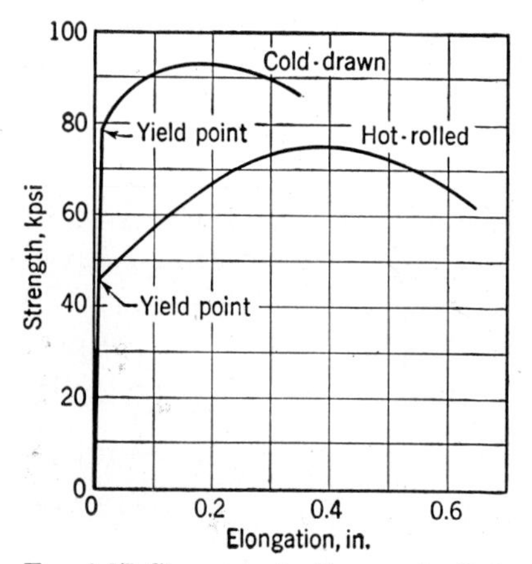

FIG. 4-37. Stress-strain diagram for hot-rolled and cold-drawn SAE 1035 steel.

Cold-finished bars and shafts are produced by rolling, drawing, turning, grinding, and polishing. Of these methods, by far the largest percentage of products are made by the cold-rolling and cold-drawing processes. Cold rolling is now used mostly for the production of wide flats and sheets. Practically all cold-finished bars are made by cold-drawing and are sometimes mistakenly called "cold-rolled bars." In the drawing process the hot-rolled bars are first cleaned of scale and then drawn by pulling them through a die which reduces the size about $\frac{1}{32}$ to $\frac{1}{16}$ in. This process does not remove material from the bar but reduces, or "draws" down, the size. Many different shapes of hot-rolled bars may be used for cold-drawing.

Cold rolling and cold-drawing have the same effect upon the mechanical properties. The cold-working process does not change the grain size but merely distorts it. There is a large increase in yield strength, an increase in ultimate strength and hardness, and a decrease in ductility. In Fig. 4-37 the properties of a cold-drawn bar are compared with those of a hot-rolled bar of the same material.

Heading is a cold-working process in which the metal is gathered, or upset. This operation is commonly used to make screw and rivet heads and is capable of producing a wide variety of shapes. *Roll threading* is the process of rolling threads by squeezing and rolling a blank between two serrated dies. *Spinning* is the operation of working sheet material around a rotating form into a circular shape. *Stamping* is the term used to describe punch-press operations such as *blanking, coining, forming,* and *shallow drawing*.

4-19. Equilibrium Diagrams. The properties of a material are dependent upon the chemical composition of the material and the method by which it is processed. Metals used for machine parts are made up of a large number of units called *grains*, or crystals, each of which has a large number of atoms arranged in a definite manner. The characteristics of this arrangement, which is called a *space lattice*, are dependent upon the chemical composition of the material. On the other hand, the size, shape, and directional arrangement of the crystals are determined by the physical processes which the material undergoes.

The chemical composition influences the properties in two ways. If a second material is added to a base material, resulting in a homogeneous assembly of crystals of uniform composition, then the strength of the material is increased. The strength can also be increased if the addition of a second material results in a mixture of crystals having two or more compositions. Steel, for example, consists of a mixture of iron and iron carbide crystals. Since iron carbide is brittle, the mixture is much stronger than the pure iron.

It is well known that fine grain size is accompanied by high strength. Since the grain size is a function of the physical method of processing the material, the mechanical properties are also influenced by the method of processing. The orientation of the crystals may be changed by such operations as rolling, drawing, or forging. The strength in one direction is improved by such operations.

An equilibrium diagram is a graph which shows, under conditions of equilibrium, the relationship existing between the amounts of solid and liquid portions of the various elements making up the composition over a range of temperatures. The data for these diagrams are taken from a series of cooling curves of alloys containing different percentages of the constituent elements. A cooling curve is obtained by measuring the temperature as a function of time as the metal or alloy is cooled from the molten state to the solid state. In Fig. 4-38 are shown two typical cooling curves. Curve a represents a pure metal. The curve falls smoothly until the solidification temperature at point B is reached. Between points B and C the latent heat is dissipated, and the curve then proceeds smoothly downward to point D. In the case of an alloy, the melting point of the various constituents is, in general, not the same, so that the curve between points B and C (curve b) is not horizontal.

Figure 4-39 is an equilibrium diagram for copper-nickel, the metals in which are mutually soluble in both the liquid and solid states. This diagram is made from a series of cooling curves of copper-nickel, each curve having been obtained for different percentages of the two. The upper line is called the *liquidus* and is the temperature at which the solution begins to freeze. The lower line is called the *solidus* and is the temperature at which the entire solution has become solid. The left boundary represents the condition in which the material is pure nickel, while the right boundary is the condition for pure copper. Suppose, now, that a liquid composed of 40 per cent copper and 60 per cent nickel is cooled from a molten condition. When the melt reaches the temperature indicated by point A crystals will begin to form. The composition of these first crystals will be indicated by point B, that is, it will be 17 per

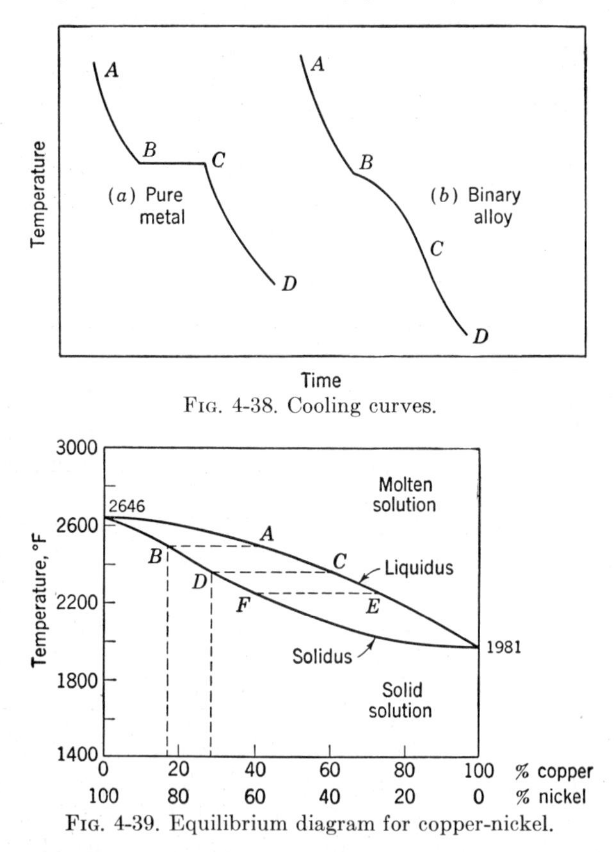

FIG. 4-38. Cooling curves.

FIG. 4-39. Equilibrium diagram for copper-nickel.

cent copper and 83 per cent nickel. Since the first crystals formed have 83 per cent nickel instead of 60 per cent nickel, there will be less nickel in the remaining molten solution. Suppose then, for example, that the remaining molten solution has been enriched with copper by this process so that point C represents the temperature, at any given time, at which crystals are being formed. These crystals will have a composition indicated by point D on the diagram, or about 28 per cent copper and 72 per cent nickel. The crystals formed at A will not be in equilibrium with those formed at C, and hence those formed at A will absorb more copper.

At point E on the liquidus line the crystals formed will have the same composition as the original melt. The crystals which were formed first will continue to absorb more copper even after all the liquid has solidified. The rate of temperature change, however, must be slow enough to allow this diffusion to occur. When sufficient time is given, the solid will be composed of crystals, all of which have the same composition as the original melt. If, on the other hand, the melt is cooled rapidly, sufficient time is not available for a state of equilibrium. Under these conditions the resulting solid will be a mixture of crystals having various compositions. In the example shown, the first crystal formed would theoretically

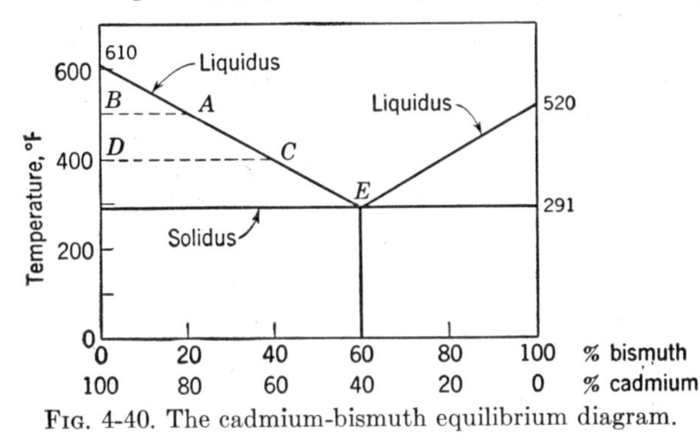

FIG. 4-40. The cadmium-bismuth equilibrium diagram.

have a composition of 17 per cent copper and 83 per cent nickel, while the last crystal formed would have a composition of 100 per cent copper.

Figure 4-40 is the bismuth-cadmium equilibrium diagram and is illustrative of alloys which are soluble in the liquid state but insoluble in the solid state. In this diagram pure cadmium is shown as having a melting point of 610°F, and pure bismuth a melting point of 520°F. When bismuth is added to cadmium the melting point becomes lower. The same is true when cadmium is added to bismuth. When the composition is 60 per cent bismuth and 40 per cent cadmium a minimum melting point of 291°F is obtained. Such an alloy is called the *eutectic alloy*, and the temperature at which this occurs is called the *eutectic temperature*. A eutectic alloy consists of an intimate mixture of very fine crystals of the two elements. When a eutectic alloy is cooled from the liquid state the temperature remains constant during solidification. A eutectic thus behaves like a pure metal. Suppose, now, that an alloy consisting of 20 per cent bismuth and 80 per cent cadmium is slowly cooled from the molten condition. Solidification will begin at point A on the diagram, corresponding to a temperature of approximately 500°F. The crystals formed will be pure cadmium, corresponding to point B. Because of the crystallization of the cadmium, the remaining melt becomes progressively richer in bismuth. Therefore, sometime later, the melt will have reached a condition, represented by point C, in which pure cadmium crystals are still being formed, but at a temperature of about 400°F. As this process continues, the percentage of bismuth in the melt will become richer until point E, representing the eutectic temperature, is reached. At this point the composition of the alloy corresponds to the eutectic alloy. Crystallization will now occur at constant temperature until solidification is complete. The resulting solid will be composed of pure cadmium crystals and the eutectic alloy. For a composition of, say, 80 per cent bismuth and 20 per cent cadmium, the process would be reversed. The right-hand liquidus line would come into use, and crystals of pure bismuth would be precipitated out. The resulting solid would be composed of pure bismuth and the eutectic alloy.

Figure 4-41 illustrates the cooling curve for pure iron. At room temperature pure iron is very soft, ductile, and magnetic. When it is heated above 1430°F the same atomic structure seems to be retained, but there is a loss in the magnetic properties. When it is heated to 1670°F the density increases, the atomic structure changes, and a considerable absorption of heat occurs. At 2552°F the atomic structure again undergoes a change, and magnetic properties are regained. At 2795°F the iron absorbs the heat of fusion and changes to the liquid state.

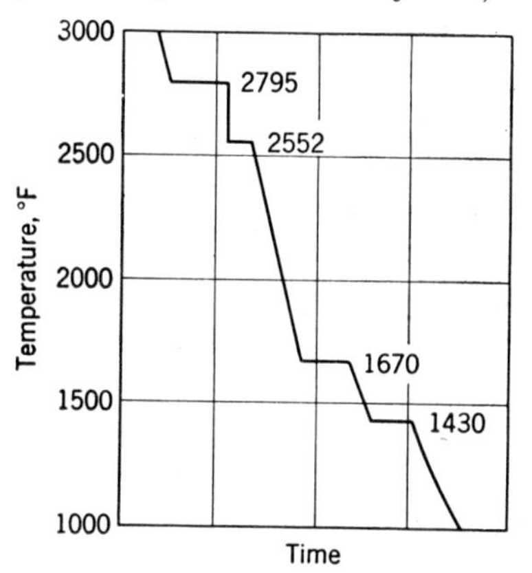

FIG. 4-41. Cooling curve for pure iron.

Several difficulties are involved in a study of iron and steel. The alloy of iron and carbon is really quite complex because it often also contains manganese, phosphorus, silicon, and sulfur. When these elements are present in small proportions their effect on the alloy is small in comparison with the effect of carbon, but larger proportions result in a substantial change in the properties of the alloy. The addition of other elements, such as nickel, chromium, molybdenum, or vanadium, complicates the equilibrium diagram so much that little is known at this time.

The carbon-iron equilibrium diagram (Fig. 4-42) represents the results of the work of many investigators. In this diagram wrought iron is a carbon-iron alloy with 0.1 per cent carbon or less and with small amounts of slag. The alloys containing from 0.1 to 2.0 per cent carbon are classed as carbon steels. The cast irons used generally contain from 2 to 5 per cent carbon.

Referring now to Fig. 4-42, the liquidus is the line $ADIF$ and the solidus is the line $ABCHIJ$. The eutectic I is called *ledeburite*. Ledeburite is an intimate mixture of iron carbide (Fe_3C), which is called *cementite*, and a solid solution of Fe_3C in iron, which is called *austenite*. The solid at the point M is called a *eutectoid*. It consists of a mixture of ferrite and cementite and is called *pearlite* because, when it is viewed under the microscope, it has a pearl-like iridescence. This eutectoid occurs at 0.83 per cent carbon. Steels containing less than 0.83 per cent carbon are called

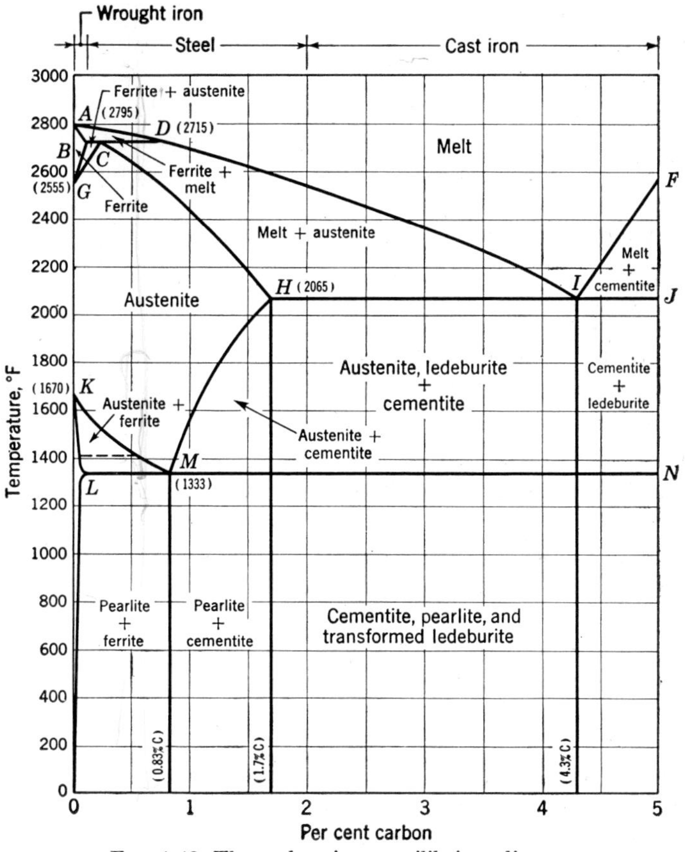

FIG. 4-42. The carbon-iron equilibrium diagram.

hypoeutectoid steels, while those containing more than 0.83 per cent are called *hypereutectoid* steels. The hypoeutectoid steel contains ferrite with small quantities of pearlite which makes it softer and more ductile than the eutectoid. On the other hand, the hypereutectoid steel, containing pearlite with cementite at the crystal boundaries, is harder and less ductile.

4-20. The Heat-treatment of Steel. Heat-treatment refers to processes which interrupt or vary the transformation process described by the equilibrium diagram. Other mechanical or chemical operations are sometimes grouped under the heading of heat-treatment. The common heat-treating operations are annealing, quenching, tempering, and casehardening.

Annealing. When a material is cold- or hot-worked residual stresses are built in, and, in addition, the material usually has a higher hardness due to these working operations. These operations change the structure of the material so that it is no longer represented by the equilibrium diagram. Annealing is a heating operation which permits the material to transform according to the equilibrium diagram. The material to be annealed is heated to a temperature which is approximately 100°F above the critical temperature. It is held at this temperature for a time which is sufficient for the carbon to become dissolved and diffused through the material. The object being treated is then allowed to cool slowly, usually in the furnace in which it was treated. If the transformation is complete, then it is said to have a full anneal. Annealing is used to soften a material and make it more ductile, to relieve residual stresses, and to refine the grain structure.

Annealing includes the process which is called *normalizing.* Parts to be normalized may be heated to a slightly higher temperature. This produces a coarser grain structure which is more easily machined if the material is a low-carbon steel. In the normalizing process the part is cooled in still air at room temperature. Since this cooling is more rapid, less time is available for equilibrium, and the material is harder than fully annealed steel. Normalizing is often used as the final treating operation for steel. The cooling in still air amounts to a slow quench.

Hardening. Eutectoid steel which is fully annealed consists entirely of pearlite which is obtained from austenite under conditions of equilibrium. A fully annealed hypoeutectoid steel would consist of pearlite plus ferrite, while hypereutectoid steel in the fully annealed condition would consist of pearlite plus cementite. The hardness of steel of a given carbon content depends upon the structure that replaces the pearlite when full annealing is not carried out.

The absence of full annealing indicates a more rapid rate of cooling. The rate of cooling is the factor which determines the hardness. A controlled cooling rate is called *quenching.* A mild quench is obtained by cooling in still air, which, as we have seen, is obtained by the normalizing process. The two most widely used mediums for quenching are water and oil. The oil quench is quite slow but prevents quenching cracks caused by rapid contraction of the object being treated. Quenching in water is used for carbon steels and for medium-carbon, low-alloy steels.

The effectiveness of quenching depends upon the fact that when austenite is cooled it does not transform into pearlite instantaneously but requires time to initiate and complete the process. Since the transformation ceases at about 800°F, it can be prevented by rapidly cooling the material to a lower temperature. When the material is cooled rapidly to 400°F or less, the austenite is transformed into a structure called *martensite*. Martensite is a supersaturated solid solution of carbon in ferrite and is the hardest and strongest form of steel.

If steel is rapidly cooled to a temperature between 400 and 800°F and held there for a sufficient length of time, the austenite is transformed into a material which is generally called *bainite*. Bainite is a structure which is intermediate between pearlite and martensite. Although there are several structures which can be identified between the temperatures given, depending upon the temperature used, they are collectively known as bainite. By the choice of this transformation temperature, almost any variation of structure may be obtained. These range all the way from coarse pearlite to fine martensite.

Tempering. When a steel specimen has been fully hardened it is very hard and brittle and has high residual stresses. The steel is unstable and tends to contract on aging. This tendency is increased when the specimen is subjected to externally applied loads, because the resultant stresses contribute still more to the instability. These internal stresses can be relieved by an additional heating process which softens the material and toughens it. This heating process is called *tempering*, or *drawing*. After the specimen has been fully hardened by being quenched from above the critical temperature, it is reheated to some temperature below the critical temperature for a certain period of time and then allowed to cool in still air. The temperature to which it is reheated depends upon the composition and the degree of hardness or toughness desired. This reheating operation releases the carbon held in the martensite, forming carbide crystals. The structure obtained is called *tempered martensite*.

The effect of heat-treating operations upon the various mechanical properties of steel is shown graphically in Fig. 4-43.

Casehardening. The purpose of casehardening is to produce a hard outer surface on a specimen of low-carbon steel while at the same time retaining the ductility and toughness in the core. This is done by increasing the carbon content at the surface. Either solid, liquid, or gaseous carburizing materials may be used. The process consists of introducing the part to be carburized into the carburizing material for a stated time and at a stated temperature, depending upon the depth of case desired and the composition of the part. The part may then be quenched directly from the carburization temperature and tempered, or in some cases it must undergo a double heat-treatment in order to assure that both the core and the case are in proper condition. Some of the more useful casehardening processes are pack carburizing, gas carburizing, nitriding, cyaniding, induction hardening, and flame hardening.

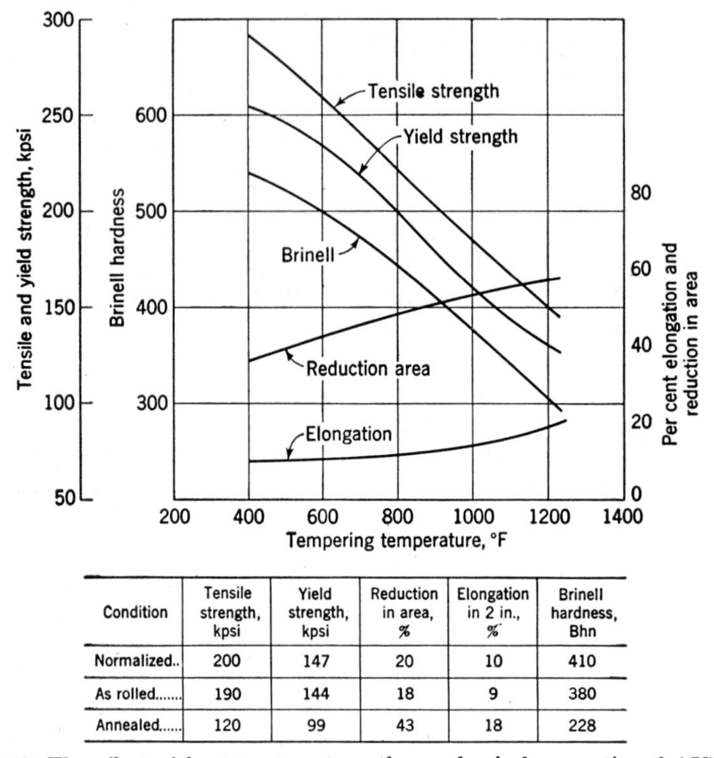

Condition	Tensile strength, kpsi	Yield strength, kpsi	Reduction in area, %	Elongation in 2 in., %	Brinell hardness, Bhn
Normalized..	200	147	20	10	410
As rolled......	190	144	18	9	380
Annealed.....	120	99	43	18	228

FIG. 4-43. The effect of heat-treatment on the mechanical properties of AISI 4340 steel. (*Prepared by The International Nickel Company.*)

4-21. Alloy Steels. While a plain carbon steel is an alloy of iron and carbon with small amounts of manganese, silicon, sulfur, and phosphorus, the term "alloy steel" is applied when one or more elements other than carbon is introduced in sufficient quantities to modify its properties substantially. The alloy steels not only possess more desirable physical properties but also permit a greater latitude in the heat-treating process.

Chromium. The addition of chromium results in the formation of various carbides of chromium which are very hard, yet the resulting steel is more ductile than a steel of the same hardness produced by a simple increase in carbon content. Chromium also refines the grain structure so that these two combined effects result in both increased toughness and increased hardness. The addition of chromium increases the critical range of temperatures and moves the eutectoid point to the left. Chromium is thus a very useful alloying element.

Nickel. The addition of nickel to steel also causes the eutectoid point to move to the left and increases the critical range of temperatures. Nickel is soluble in ferrite and does not form carbides or oxides. This increases the strength without decreasing the ductility. Casehardening of nickel steels results in a better core than can be obtained with plain carbon steels. Chromium is frequently used in combination with nickel to obtain the toughness and ductility provided by the nickel and the wear resistance and hardness contributed by the chromium.

Manganese. Manganese is added to all steels as a deoxidizing and desulfurizing agent, but if the sulfur content is low and the manganese content is over 1 per cent, then it is classified as a manganese alloy. Manganese dissolves in the ferrite and also forms carbides. It causes the eutectoid point to move to the left and lowers the critical range of temperatures. It increases the time required for transformation, so that oil quenching becomes practicable.

Silicon. Silicon is added to all steels as a deoxidizing agent. When added to very-low-carbon steels it produces a brittle material with a low hysteresis loss and a high magnetic permeability. The principal use of silicon is with other alloying elements, such as manganese, chromium, and vanadium, to stabilize the carbides.

Molybdenum. While molybdenum is used alone in a few steels, it finds its greatest use when combined with other alloying elements such as nickel, chromium, or both. Molybdenum forms carbides and also dissolves in ferrite to some extent, so that it adds both hardness and toughness. Molybdenum increases the critical range of temperatures and substantially lowers the transformation point. Because of this lowering of the transformation point, molybdenum is most effective in producing desirable oil-hardening and air-hardening properties. Except for carbon, it has the greatest hardening effect, and because it also contributes to a fine grain size this results in the retention of a great deal of toughness.

Vanadium. Vanadium has a very strong tendency to form carbides; hence it is used only in small amounts. It is a strong deoxidizing agent and promotes a fine grain size. Since some vanadium is dissolved in the ferrite, it also toughens the steel. Vanadium gives a wide hardening range to steel, and the alloy can be hardened from a higher temperature. It is very difficult to soften vanadium steel by tempering; hence it is widely used in tool steels.

Tungsten. Tungsten is widely used in tool steels because the tool will maintain its hardness even at red heat. Tungsten produces a fine dense structure and adds both toughness and hardness. Its effect is similar to molybdenum except that greater quantities must be added.

4-22. Cast Steels. Steel castings are used in design whenever the properties of steel are desired and when fabrication of wrought steels is impractical. Of course, the advantages gained by hot or cold working of steels cannot be obtained in castings; yet, on the other hand, a wider range of compositions is possible since the hot- or cold-working capabilities of the material are not a consideration. All the alloying elements used in wrought steels are in general use in steel castings, and they create substantially the same effects. Steel castings can also be made with the same range of carbon content. Heat-treatment processes are similar to those used for wrought steels.

Steel is difficult to cast because of its high melting point. This makes it necessary for the designer to collaborate closely with the foundryman

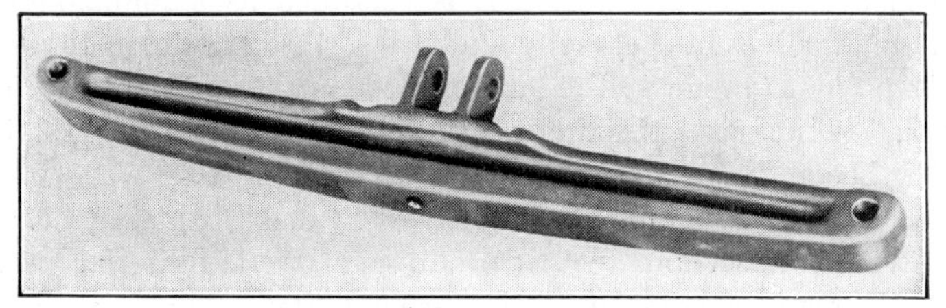

FIG. 4-44. A cast-steel truck-spring lock-out beam. (*Courtesy of the Superior Steel and Malleable Castings Company.*)

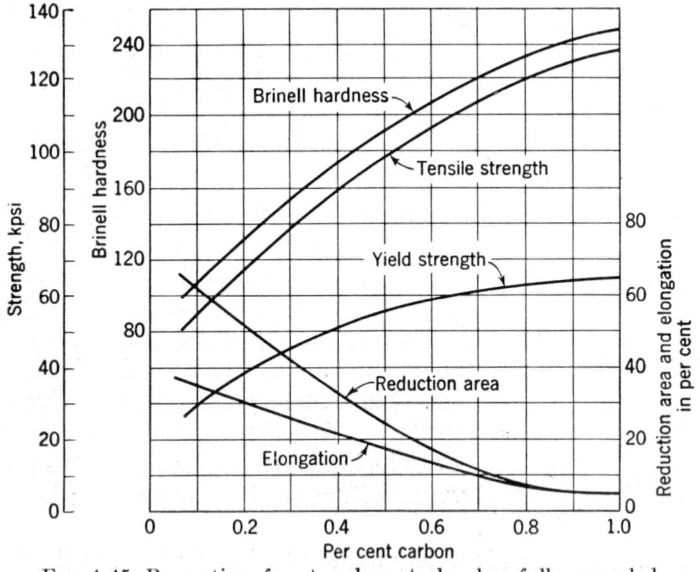

FIG. 4-45. Properties of cast carbon steels when fully annealed.

in order to obtain a sound casting. Since steel castings are easily welded, it is frequently possible to cast the part in two or more sections, after which they may be welded together. Defects can be repaired by welding also. Steel castings are used for a wide variety of parts and probably find their greatest application in the large- and heavy-machinery field.

Typical properties of cast carbon steels in the fully annealed condition are shown in Fig. 4-45. Naturally, the medium- and high-carbon steels should be heat-treated in order to obtain full advantage of the carbon content, but the information may be used for purposes of comparison.[1]

4-23. Stainless Steels. Iron-base alloys containing at least 12 per cent chromium are called *stainless steels*. The most important characteristic of these steels is their resistance to many, but not all, corrosive conditions. The two types available are the ferritic chromium steels and the austenitic chromium-nickel steels.

The ferritic chromium steels have a chromium content ranging from as little as 2 up to 27 per cent. Their corrosion resistance is a function of the chromium content, so that alloys containing less than 12 per cent still exhibit some corrosion resistance, although they are not rustless. The quench-hardenability of these steels is a function of both the chromium content and the carbon content. The very-high-carbon steels have good quench-hardenability up to about 18 per cent chromium, while in the lower carbon ranges it ceases at about 13 per cent. If a little nickel is added they retain some degree of hardenability up to 20 per cent chromium. If the chromium content exceeds 18 per cent they become difficult to weld, and at the very high chromium levels the hardness becomes so great that very careful attention must be paid to the service conditions. Since chromium is expensive, the designer will choose the lowest chromium content consistent with the corrosive conditions.

The chromium-nickel stainless steels retain the austenitic structure at room temperature; hence they are not amenable to heat-treatment. The strength of these steels can be greatly improved by cold working, and they are not magnetic unless cold-worked, but their work-hardenability properties also cause them to be difficult to machine. All the chromium-nickel steels may be welded. They have greater corrosion-resistant properties than the plain chromium steels. When more chromium is added for greater corrosion resistance, more nickel must also be added if the austenitic properties are to be retained.

4-24. Cast Iron. As we have seen from the equilibrium diagram (Fig. 4-42), cast iron is merely an iron-carbon alloy with a larger carbon content than steel.

Gray Cast Iron. Of all the cast materials, gray cast iron is the most widely used. This is because it has a very low cost, is easily cast in large quantities, and is easy to machine. The principal objections to the use of gray cast iron are that it is brittle and that it is weak in tension. In addition to a high carbon content (over 1.7 per cent and usually greater than 2 per cent), cast iron also has a high silicon content, with low percentages of sulfur, manganese, and phosphorus. The resultant alloy is

[1] For additional data on the properties of cast steels, see "Steel Castings Handbook," Steel Founders Society of America, Cleveland, 1941.

composed of pearlite, ferrite, and graphite, and under certain conditions the pearlite may decompose into graphite and ferrite. The resulting product then contains all ferrite and graphite. The graphite in the form of thin flakes distributed evenly throughout the structure darkens it, hence the name gray cast iron.

Gray cast iron is not readily welded because it may crack, but this tendency may be reduced if it is carefully preheated in advance. While the castings are generally used in the as-cast condition, a mild anneal reduces cooling stresses and improves the machinability. The tensile strength of gray cast iron varies from 15,000 to 60,000 psi, with the compressive strength being much higher. The ASTM has classified gray cast irons according to their tensile strengths, a No. 30, for example, having a minimum tensile strength of 30,000 psi. The modulus of elasticity varies widely, with values extending all the way from 11,000,000 to 22,000,000 psi.

White Cast Iron. If all the carbon in cast iron is in the form of cementite and pearlite, with no graphite present, then the resulting structure is white and is known as "white cast iron." This may be produced in two ways. The composition may be adjusted by keeping the carbon and silicon content low, or the gray-cast-iron composition may be cast against chills in order to promote rapid cooling. By either method a casting with large amounts of cementite is produced, and as a result the product is very brittle and hard to machine but also very resistant to wear. A chill is usually used in the production of gray-iron castings in order to provide a very hard surface within a particular area of the casting, while at the same time retaining the more desirable gray structure within the remaining portion. This produces a relatively tough casting with a wear-resistant area.

Malleable Cast Iron. If white cast iron within a certain composition range is annealed, a product called *malleable cast iron* is formed. The annealing process frees the carbon so that it is present as graphite, just as in gray cast iron but in a different form. In gray cast iron the graphite is present in a thin flake form, while in malleable cast iron it has a nodular form and is known as "temper carbon." A good grade of malleable cast iron may have a tensile strength of over 50,000 psi, with an elongation of as much as 18 per cent. The percentage elongation of a gray cast iron, on the other hand, is seldom over 1 per cent. Because of the time required for annealing (up to six days for large and heavy castings), malleable iron is necessarily somewhat more expensive than gray cast iron.

Ductile Cast Iron. Because of the lengthy heat-treatment required to produce malleable cast iron, a cast iron has long been desired which would combine the ductile properties of malleable iron with the ease of casting and machining of gray iron and at the same time possess these properties in the as-cast condition. A process for producing such a material, using magnesium,[1] has recently been patented and seems to fulfill these requirements. Since this is a new material, it should not be used in design purely on the basis of the results of mechanical tests, because it may have unexpected properties which are not as yet determined.

Ductile cast iron, or nodular cast iron, as it is sometimes called, is essentially the same as malleable cast iron, because both contain graphite in the form of spheroids. However, ductile cast iron in the as-cast condition exhibits properties very close to those of malleable iron, and, if a simple one-hour anneal is given and followed by a slow cool, it exhibits even more ductility than the malleable product. Ductile iron is made by adding magnesium to the melt; since magnesium boils at this temperature, it is necessary to alloy it with other elements before it is introduced.

Ductile iron has a high modulus of elasticity (25,000,000 psi) as compared with gray cast iron, and it is elastic in the sense that a portion of the stress-strain curve is a straight line. Gray cast iron, on the other hand, does not obey Hooke's law, because the modulus of elasticity steadily decreases with increase in stress. Like gray cast iron, however, nodular iron has a compressive strength which is higher than the tensile strength, although the difference is not as great. Since this is a new product, its full range of application has not as yet developed, but an obvious area of application is for those castings requiring shock and impact resistance.

Alloy Cast Irons. Nickel, chromium, and molybdenum are the most common alloying elements used in cast iron. Nickel is a general-purpose alloying element, usually added in amounts up to 5 per cent. Nickel increases the strength and density, improves the wearing qualities, and raises the machinability. If the nickel content is raised to 10 to 18 per cent an austenitic structure with valuable heat- and corrosion-resistant properties results. Chromium increases the hardness and wear resistance and, when used with a chill, increases the tendency to form white iron. When chromium and nickel are both added the hardness and strength are improved without a reduction in the machinability rating. Molybdenum added in quantities up to 1.25 per cent increases the stiffness, hardness, tensile strength, and impact resistance. It is a widely used alloying element.

4-25. Aluminum and Its Alloys. The outstanding characteristics of aluminum and its alloys are their strength-weight ratio, their resistance to corrosion, and their high thermal and electrical conductivity. The density of aluminum is about 0.10 lb per in.^{3}, compared with 0.28 for

[1] Patented by the International Nickel Co., Inc., U.S. Patents Nos. 2,485,760 and 2,485,761.

steel. Pure aluminum has a tensile strength of about 13,000 psi, but this can be improved considerably by cold working and also by alloying with other materials. The modulus of elasticity of aluminum, as well as of its alloys, is 10,300,000 psi, which means that it has about one-third the stiffness of steel.

Considering the cost and strength of aluminum and its alloys, they are among the most versatile materials from the standpoint of fabrication. Aluminum can be processed by sand-casting, die-casting, hot or cold working, or extruding. It can be machined, press-worked, soldered, brazed, or welded. Aluminum melts at 1215°F, which makes it very desirable for the production of either permanent or sand-mold castings. It is commercially available in the form of plate, bar, sheet, foil, rod, and tube, and in structural and extruded shapes. Certain precautions must be taken in joining aluminum by soldering, brazing, or welding, and these joining methods are not recommended for all the alloys.

The corrosion resistance of the aluminum alloys depends upon the formation of a thin oxide coating. This film forms spontaneously because aluminum is inherently very reactive. Constant erosion or abrasion removes this film and allows corrosion to take place. An extra-heavy oxide film may be produced by the process called *anodizing*. In this process the specimen is made to become the anode in an electrolyte which may be chromic acid, oxalic acid, or sulfuric acid. It is possible in this process to control the color of the resulting film very accurately.

The most useful alloying elements for aluminum are copper, silicon, manganese, magnesium, and iron. Aluminum alloys are classified as casting alloys or wrought alloys. The casting alloys have greater percentages of alloying elements to facilitate casting, but this makes cold-working difficult. Many of the casting alloys, and some of the wrought alloys, cannot be hardened by heat-treatment. The alloys which are heat-treatable use an alloying element which dissolves in the aluminum. The heat-treatment consists in heating the specimen to a temperature which permits the element to pass into solution, then quenching so rapidly that the alloying element is not precipitated. This produces a supersaturated solid solution, and upon standing or aging at room temperature the solute is precipitated. The aging process may be accelerated by heating slightly, which results in even greater hardness and strength. One of the better-known heat-treatable alloys is duraluminum, or 17S (4 per cent Cu, 0.5 per cent Mg, 0.5 per cent Mn). This alloy hardens in four days at room temperature. Because of this rapid aging, the alloy must be stored under refrigeration after quenching and before forming, or it must be formed immediately after quenching. Other alloys have been developed (such as 53S) which age-harden much more slowly, so that only mild refrigeration is necessary prior to forming. After forming they are artificially aged in a furnace and possess approximately the same strength and hardness as duraluminum. Those alloys of aluminum which cannot be heat-treated can be hardened only by cold working. Both work hardening and the hardening produced by heat-treatment may be removed by an annealing process.

Some of the high-strength wrought alloys are available in the form of sheet with a coating of pure aluminum or an alloy different from the core. The coating used is very resistant to corrosion by atmosphere or salt water. These are called *clad sheets.*

4-26. Magnesium. Magnesium has a density of about 0.065 lb per in.^{3}, which is two-thirds that of aluminum and one-fourth that of steel. Since it is the lightest of all commercial metals, its greatest use is in the aircraft industry, but as it becomes available uses are being found for it in other industries. Although the magnesium alloys do not have great strength, because of their light weight the strength-weight ratio compares

TABLE 4-3. TYPICAL PROPERTIES OF MAGNESIUM ALLOYS*

Magnesium alloy	Tensile strength, kpsi	Tensile yield strength, kpsi	Elongation in 2 in., %	Compressive yield strength, kpsi	Brinell hardness, Bhn	Shear strength, kpsi	Endurance limit, kpsi
Cast AM 265C	27	11	6	11	48	...	11
Cast AM 240-T4	35	12	9	12	52	20	11
Cast AM 260-T6	38	20	3	20	78	22	11.5
Die-cast AM 263	34	22	3	...	...	...	14
Wrought AM 3S	40	30	7	11	40–52	16.7	11
Wrought AM C52S	40	30	17	20	50–71	19	15
Wrought AM C57S	44	32	14	20	55–74	20.5	17
Wrought AM 59S	51	38	9	27	70	22	18

* Courtesy of American Magnesium Corporation.

favorably with the stronger aluminum and steel alloys. Magnesium alloys find their greatest use where strength is not an important consideration. For example, use of a magnesium alloy might be dictated by an application requiring a complicated but lightweight casting with thick walls. Its use might also be dictated for parts which create large inertia forces because of their weight and motion. Magnesium will not withstand elevated temperatures; the yield point is definitely reduced when the temperature is raised to that of boiling water.

Magnesium and its alloys have a modulus of elasticity of 6,500,000 psi in tension and compression, although they are not as strong in compression as in tension. The modulus of rigidity is 2,400,000 psi. If magnesium is cold-worked at stresses above the yield point, the modulus of elasticity is reduced to about 4,000,000 psi. Other properties of these alloys are shown in Table 4-3.

The corrosion resistance of the magnesium alloys is not good, although some improvement has been made in recent years. Magnesium work-hardens so rapidly that for all practical purposes it cannot be cold-worked. The temperature required for hot working varies from 400 to 700°F. At these temperatures it can be press-worked, hand-worked, or extruded. For best results the hot-working processes should be those which permit relatively slow working. All the alloys have excellent machining characteristics. Magnesium alloys are easy to cast since they have a low melting temperature. Sand-casting, permanent mold-casting, and die-casting are the methods usually employed. All the alloys are readily welded by either gas- or resistance-welding procedures.

Particular care must be taken in the joining of magnesium parts to avoid galvanic action and points of stress concentration. Magnesium has high notch sensitivity, and therefore points of stress concentration must be avoided in any design. Magnesium rivets or screws are not recommended for any condition. An aluminum 56S rivet is recommended for all conditions of stress or corrosive atmosphere. Certain other aluminum alloys may be used under certain conditions. If steel bolts or screws are used, they should be galvanized or cadmium-plated in order to avoid galvanic action. Washers used should be thick and large in diameter in order that tightening stresses may be better distributed.

4-27. Copper-base Alloys. When copper is alloyed with zinc it is usually called *brass.* If it is alloyed with another element it is often called *bronze.* Sometimes the other element is specified too, as, for example, tin bronze or phosphor bronze. Included in each category are hundreds of variations.

Brass with 5 *to* 15 *Per Cent Zinc.* These brasses are easy to cold-work, especially those with the higher zinc content. They are ductile but often hard to machine. The corrosion resistance is good. Alloys included in this group are *gilding brass* (5 per cent Zn), *commercial bronze* (10 per cent Zn), and *red brass* (15 per cent Zn). Gilding brass is used mostly for jewelry and articles to be gold-plated; it has the same ductility as copper but greater strength, accompanied by poor machining characteristics. Commercial bronze is used for jewelry and for forgings and stampings because of its ductility. Its machining properties are poor, but it has excellent cold-working properties. Red brass has good corrosion resistance as well as high-temperature strength. Because of this it is used a great deal in the form of tubing or piping to carry hot water in such applications as radiators or condensers.

Brass with 20 *to* 36 *Per Cent Zinc.* Included in this group are *low brass* (20 per cent Zn), *cartridge brass* (30 per cent Zn), and *yellow brass* (35 per cent Zn). Since zinc is cheaper than copper, these alloys cost less than those with less zinc. They also have better machinability and slightly greater strength; this is offset, however, by poor corrosion resistance and the possibility of season cracking at points of residual stresses. Low brass is very similar to red brass and is used for articles requiring deep-drawing operations. Of the copper-zinc alloys, cartridge brass has the best combination of ductility and strength. Cartridge cases were originally manufactured entirely by cold working; the process consisted of a series of deep draws, each draw being followed by an anneal to place the material in condition for the next draw; hence the name, cartridge brass. While the hot-working ability of yellow brass is poor, it can be used in practically any other fabricating process and is therefore employed in a large variety of products.

When small amounts of lead are added to the brasses their machinability is greatly improved and there is some improvement in their abilities to be hot-worked. The addition of lead impairs both the cold-working and welding properties. In this group are *low-leaded brass* (32½ per cent Zn, ½ per cent Pb), *high-leaded brass* (34 per cent Zn, 2 per cent Pb), and *free-cutting brass* (35½ per cent Zn, 3 per cent Pb). The low-leaded brass is not only easy to machine but has good cold-working properties. It is used for various screw-machine parts. High-leaded brass, sometimes called "engraver's brass," is used for instrument, lock, and watch parts. Free-cutting brass is also used for screw-machine parts and has good corrosion resistance with excellent mechanical properties.

Admiralty metal (28 per cent Zn) contains 1 per cent tin which imparts excellent corrosion resistance, especially to salt water. It has good strength and ductility but only fair machining and working characteristics. Because of its corrosion resistance it is used in power-plant and chemical equipment. *Aluminum brass* (22 per cent Zn), contains 2 per cent aluminum and is used for the same purposes as admiralty metal because it has nearly the same properties and characteristics. In the form of tubing or piping, it is favored over admiralty metal, because it has better resistance to erosion caused by high-velocity water.

Brass with 36 *to* 40 *Per Cent Zinc.* Brasses with more than 35 per cent zinc are brittle and cannot be cold-worked. They may be hot-worked, however, and many extruded shapes are available. *Muntz metal* (40 per cent Zn) is low in cost and mildly corrosion-resistant. *Naval brass* has the same composition as Muntz metal except for the addition of 0.75 per cent tin which contributes to the corrosion resistance.

Bronze. Silicon bronze, containing 3 per cent silicon and 1 per cent manganese in addition to the copper, has mechanical properties equal to those of mild steel, as well as good corrosion resistance. It can be hot- or cold-worked, machined, or welded. It is useful wherever corrosion resistance combined with strength is required.

Phosphor bronze, made with up to 11 per cent tin and containing small amounts of phosphorus, is especially resistant to fatigue and corrosion. It has a high tensile strength and a high modulus of resilience, and it is also resistant to wear. These properties make it very useful as a spring material.

Aluminum bronze is a heat-treatable alloy containing up to 12 per cent aluminum. This alloy has strength and corrosion-resistance properties which are better than brass, and, in addition, its properties may be varied over a wide range by cold working, heat-treating, or changing the composition. When iron is added in amounts up to 4 per cent, the alloy has a high endurance limit, a high shock resistance, and excellent wear resistance.

Beryllium bronze is another heat-treatable alloy, containing about 2 per cent beryllium. This alloy is very corrosion-resistant and has high strength, hardness, and resistance to wear. Although it is expensive, it is used for springs and other parts subjected to fatigue loading where corrosion resistance is required.

BIBLIOGRAPHY

Chase, Herbert (ed.): "Handbook on Designing for Quantity Production," McGraw-Hill Book Company, Inc., New York, 1944.

Gillett, H. W.: "The Behavior of Engineering Metals," John Wiley & Sons, Inc., New York, 1951.

Heyer, Robert H.: "Engineering Physical Metallurgy," D. Van Nostrand Company, Inc., New York, 1939.

Horger, Oscar J. (ed.): "ASME Handbook Metals Engineering—Design," McGraw-Hill Book Company, Inc., New York, 1953.

Hoyt, Samuel: "Metals and Alloys Data Book," Reinhold Publishing Corporation, New York, 1943.

Jefferson, T. B., and Gorham Woods: "Metals and How to Weld Them," The James F. Lincoln Arc Welding Foundation, Cleveland, 1954.

Keyser, Carl A.: "Basic Engineering Metallurgy," Prentice-Hall, Inc., New York, 1952.

Marin, Joseph: "Engineering Materials," Prentice-Hall, Inc., New York, 1952.

Williams, Robert S., and Victor O. Homerberg: "Principles of Metallography," McGraw-Hill Book Company, Inc., New York, 1939.

Young, James F. (ed.): "Materials and Processes," John Wiley & Sons, Inc., New York, 1944.

PROBLEMS

4-1. A 24S-O aluminum-alloy specimen 0.498 in. in diameter was tested in tension, using a 2-in. gauge length. The results in the following table were obtained. Plot the stress-strain diagram and determine the following: (*a*) proportional limit, (*b*) Johnson's apparent elastic limit, (*c*) yield strength (0.2 per cent offset), (*d*) ultimate strength, (*e*) modulus of elasticity, (*f*) percentage elongation, (*g*) modulus of resilience, (*h*) modulus of toughness, and (*i*) toughness index number.

Load, lb	Elongation, in.	Load, lb	Elongation, in.	Load, lb	Elongation, in.
1,680	0.00167	3,940	0.020	6,300	0.240
2,030	0.00202	4,200	0.030	6,600	0.320
2,630	0.004	4,320	0.040	6,840	0.400
3,200	0.008	4,730	0.060	7,090	0.480
3,560	0.012	5,090	0.080	7,320	0.548
3,840	0.016	5,610	0.120		

4-2. An annealed low-carbon steel was tested in tension. The initial gauge length was 2 in., the initial diameter 0.504 in., and the final diameter 0.327 in. The following data were obtained:

Load, lb	Elongation, in.	Load, lb	Elongation, in.	Load, lb	Elongation, in.
1,195	0.00040	7,520	0.00302	10,860	0.160
2,490	0.00084	7,520	0.00360	12,240	0.300
3,780	0.00128	7,520	0.00680	12,530	0.400
4,910	0.00166	7,520	0.0200	12,280	0.520
6,070	0.00206	7,860	0.0400	9,060	0.700
6,860	0.00234	8,760	0.0800		
7,420	0.00266	10,050	0.120		

Calculate the stress and strain for each point, plot the stress-strain diagram, and determine the following: (*a*) proportional limit, (*b*) yield point, (*c*) yield strength (0.2 per cent offset), (*d*) ultimate strength, (*e*) modulus of elasticity, (*f*) percentage elongation, (*g*) percentage reduction of area, (*h*) modulus of resilience, and (*i*) toughness index number.

4-3. A heat-treated high-carbon steel was tested in tension. The original diameter of the specimen was 0.501 in., and the final diameter was 0.456 in. Using a 2-in. gauge length, the following data were obtained:

Load, lb	Elongation, in.	Load, lb	Elongation, in.	Load, lb	Elongation, in.
5,820	0.0020	18,100	0.0120	25,500	0.0800
8,100	0.0028	19,100	0.0160	26,400	0.100
10,480	0.0036	19,900	0.0200	27,200	0.120
12,240	0.0042	21,000	0.0280	27,700	0.140
15,900	0.0060	22,200	0.0400		
16,800	0.0080	24,100	0.0600		

Find (*a*) the yield strength, (*b*) the ultimate strength, (*c*) the percentage elongation, and (*d*) the percentage reduction in area.

4-4. Compare the toughness of 1040, 1141, 4140, and 4340 steels when heat-treated and drawn at 1000°F. Use Table A-3. To calculate the toughness, multiply the strain at fracture by the average of the ultimate strength and yield strength.

4-5. Using the properties of materials given in the Appendix, find and tabulate the toughness index number for the following materials:

1. Low-carbon steel (cold-drawn)
2. Low-carbon steel (hot-rolled)
3. 2S-O aluminum (wrought)
4. 2S-H16 aluminum (wrought)
5. ASTM-B107-48T magnesium (extruded)
6. Low-carbon cast steel (annealed)
7. Commercial bronze (hard)
8. Commercial bronze (soft)
9. Phosphor bronze (hard)
10. Beryllium bronze (hard)

4-6. Using Table A-3 and Fig. 4-23, find the endurance limit of the following materials in 1-in. sizes: (*a*) C1018 hot-rolled; (*b*) C1018 cold-drawn; (*c*) 1035 drawn at 800°F and ground; (*d*) C1045 drawn at 800°F, forged; and (*e*) 4340 drawn at 600°F and ground.

4-7. A steel bar is subjected to a repeated stress which varies from zero to 16,000 psi. (*a*) Find the average stress and the fluctuating component. (*b*) If the material is cold-drawn C1019 steel, find s_{max}, assuming a 1-in. size and using Soderberg's law.

4-8. A steel bar is acted upon by a fluctuating axial tensile load which varies from 20,000 to 14,000 psi. (*a*) Find the average stress and the fluctuating component of stress. (*b*) Assuming a 1-in. size and 2317 cold-drawn steel, find s_{max}, using Soderberg's law. (*c*) What is the factor of safety?

4-9. A machine member is subjected to the action of axial stresses alternating between the values of 20,000 psi in tension and 10,000 psi in compression. (*a*) Find the average stress and the fluctuating component of stress. (*b*) If the material is a forged and ground 3240 steel, drawn at 600°F, what is the fatigue strength of the material in reversed bending? (*c*) Find s_{max}. (*d*) Calculate the factor of safety.

4-10. A round shaft, $2\frac{15}{16}$ in. in diameter, rotates at 1,150 rpm and is loaded as shown in the figure. (*a*) Find the maximum and minimum stresses in the shaft.

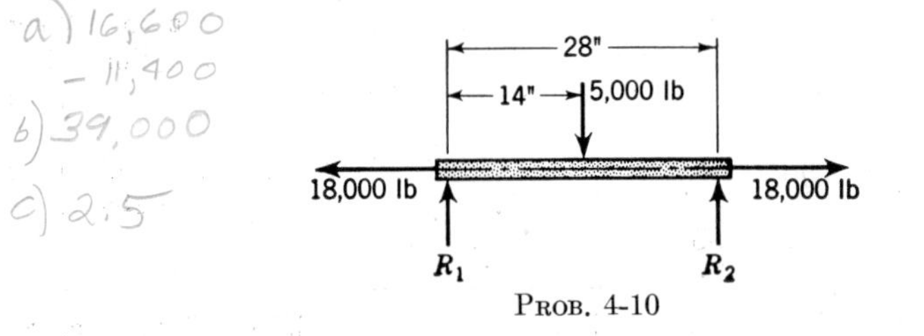

PROB. 4-10

(*b*) The shaft is to be made of C1045 steel drawn at 800°F, with a machined finish. Using Table A-3 and Fig. 4-23, find the fatigue strength for completely reversed bending. (Note that Table A-3 may be roughly interpolated.) (*c*) What is the factor of safety? *Ans.*: (*a*) +16,600 psi, −11,400 psi; (*b*) 39,000 psi; (*c*) 2.5.

4-11. A forged round bar is subjected to a fluctuating axial load which varies from 6,000 lb tension to 2,000 lb compression. If the diameter of the bar is 0.875 in., find (*a*) the maximum tensile stress, (*b*) the maximum compressive stress, (*c*) the average stress, and (*d*) the fluctuating component of stress.

4-12. If the material in Prob. 4-7 is AISI 2330 steel, heat-treated and drawn at 1000°F with a ground finish, find (*a*) the maximum permissible fluctuating component of stress, using the Soderberg law, and (*b*) the factor of safety.

4-13. The rotating shaft in the figure is $1\frac{1}{8}$ in. in diameter and is made of AISI C1020 cold-drawn steel. It is loaded as shown. What is the factor of safety?

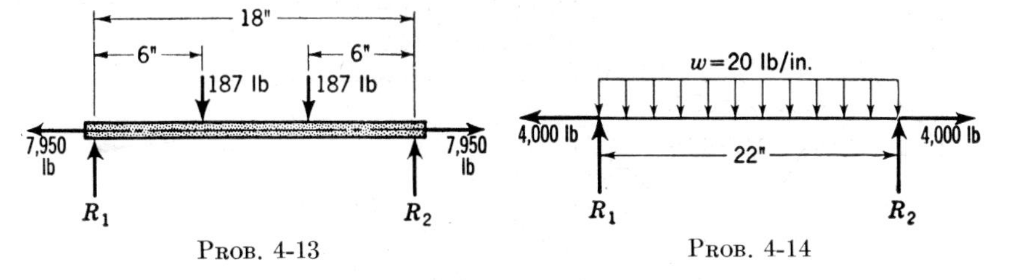

PROB. 4-13 PROB. 4-14

*4-14. The figure shows a beam which is to represent a rotating shaft carrying a uniformly distributed bending load of 20 lb per in. and an axial tensile load of 4,000 lb. Using C1020 cold-drawn steel and a factor of safety of 3, determine the diameter of a solid round shaft to support the load.

4-15. A portion of a machine member shown in the figure is loaded by completely reversed axial forces. If the material is a C1018 cold-drawn steel flat, determine (*a*) the fatigue stress-concentration factor and (*b*) the fatigue strength of the member.

Ans.: (*a*) 1.83, (*b*) 13,500 lb.

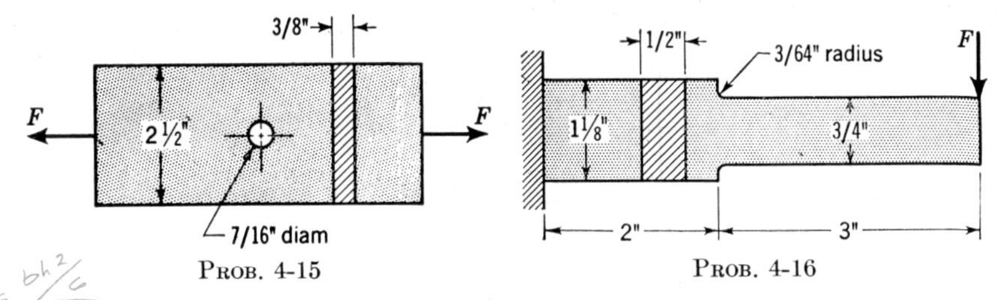

PROB. 4-15 PROB. 4-16

4-16. The figure is an idealized representation of a machine member subjected to the action of an alternating force F which places the member in completely reversed bending. The material is ground 9442 steel, heat-treated and drawn at 800°F. (*a*) Find the fatigue stress-concentration factor. (*b*) Find the fatigue strength of the member in terms of F_{max}.

4-17. A rotating shaft subjected to the action of bending forces has a dangerous section at A-A because of the small fillet. Find the maximum permissible stress at this section if the shaft is made of ground 3130 steel drawn at 1000°F.

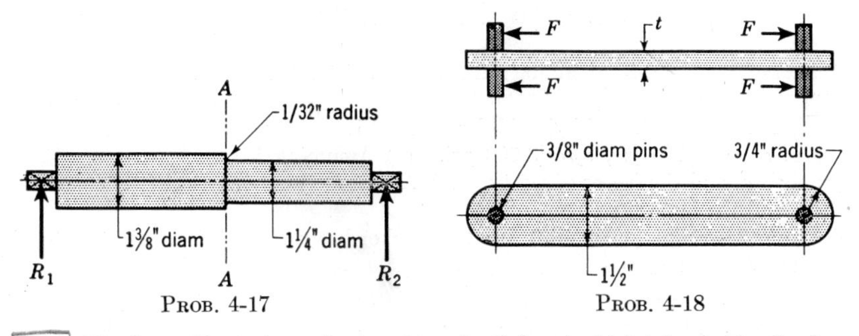

PROB. 4-17 PROB. 4-18

*4-18. The figure illustrates a short rectangular link rod which is loaded by the forces F acting upon the pins at each end. The forces F vary so as to produce axial tension ranging from 6,000 to 2,450 lb. Select a plain low-carbon steel, specify the finish, and determine the dimension t, using a factor of safety of 3.

*4-19. The short section of a machine member shown in the figure is axially loaded by forces which vary from 4,000 lb tension to 16,000 lb compression. Neglecting column action, specify a heat-treated and ground medium-alloy steel for the member, using a factor of safety of 4.

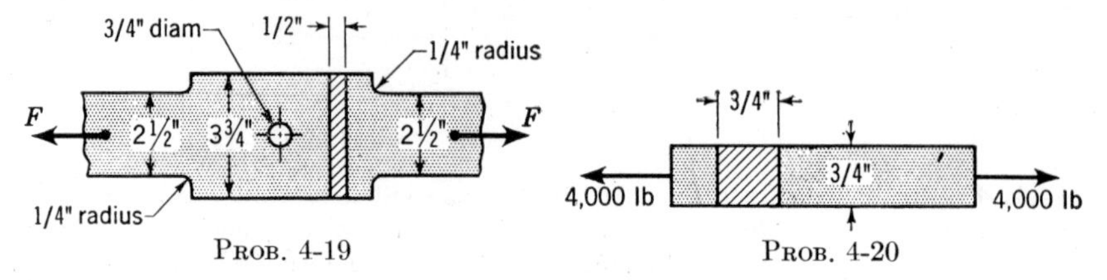

Prob. 4-19

Prob. 4-20

4-20. The cold-drawn C1035 steel bar shown in the figure is acted upon by the 4,000-lb load. Assume the bar tends to fail according to the maximum-shear theory and find the factor of safety. *Ans.:* 11.1.

4-21. An element from a machine part made of B1112 cold-drawn steel is acted upon by the loads shown in the figure. Assume that the bar may fail according to the maximum-shear theory and find the factor of safety. The load acts upon unit areas. *Ans.:* 7.1.

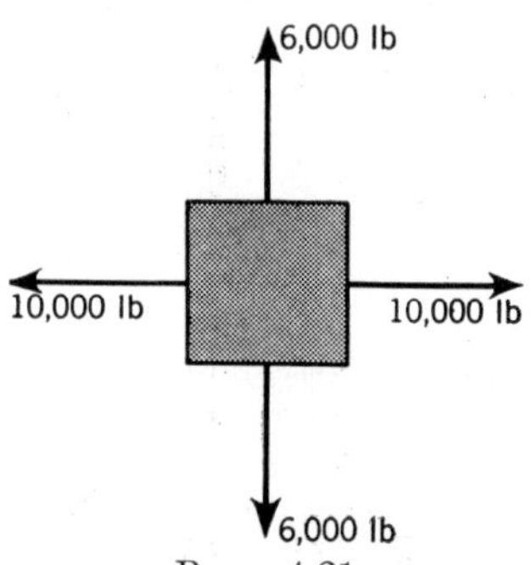

Prob. 4-21

4-22. Solve Prob. 4-21 if the 6,000-lb load is a compressive load instead of a tensile one. *Ans.:* 4.45.

4-23. Solve Prob. 4-21 assuming failure by the distortion-energy theory. *Ans.:* 8.12.

4-24. Solve Prob. 4-22 assuming failure by the distortion-energy theory. *Ans.:* 5.07.

4-25. A 14-gauge (0.0747-in.) cold-drawn C1015 sheet is acted upon by the following stresses: $s_x = 12{,}000$ psi, $s_y = 3{,}000$ psi. (*a*) Assuming failure by the maximum-shear theory, find the factor of safety. (*b*) Assuming failure by the distortion-energy theory, find the factor of safety.

4-26. A 24-gauge (0.0201-in.) hard phosphor-bronze sheet is subjected to the following stresses: $s_x = -8{,}000$ psi, $s_y = 3{,}000$ psi. (*a*) Assuming failure by the maximum-shear theory, find the factor of safety. (*b*) The same as (*a*) except that failure is by the distortion-energy theory.

4-27. An element of a machine member is acted upon by the tensile and shearing stresses shown in the figure. If the material is 24S-T4 aluminum-alloy sheet, find the factor of safety for (*a*) failure by the maximum-shear theory, (*b*) failure by the maximum-stress theory, and (*c*) failure by the distortion-energy theory.

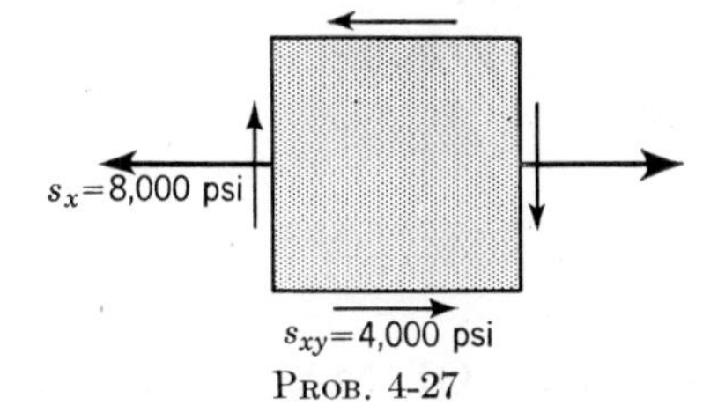

PROB. 4-27

***4-28.** Determine the diameter of a solid round section of a machine member acted upon by a static bending moment of 1,200 lb-in. and a static torsional load of 1,600 lb-in. The material is class 20 cast iron, and a factor of safety of at least 4 should be used.

4-29. A 14S-T4 aluminum-alloy tubing is to support a static load of 800 lb-in. in bending and a static torsional load of 1,400 lb-in. Let the wall thickness be one-eighth the outside diameter, and select a standard size of tubing such that the factor of safety is at least 3.6. Use the maximum-shear theory.

***4-30.** The shaft shown in the figure is to transmit 50 hp at 1,150 rpm. The torsional load is highly vibratory. Determine the diameter d for a maximum shearing stress of 9,000 psi.

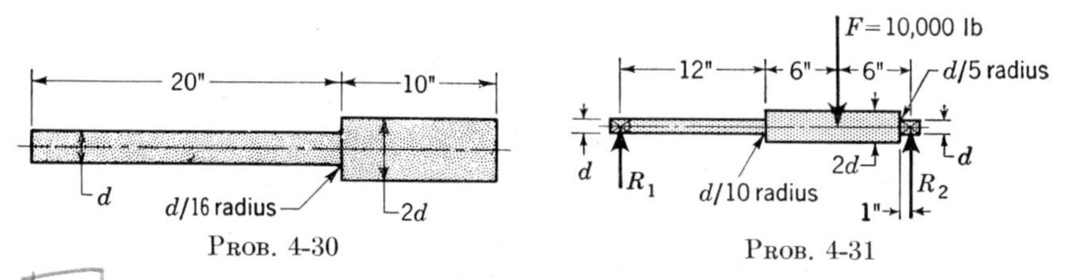

PROB. 4-30 PROB. 4-31

4-31. The figure shows a shaft rotating at 1,150 rpm and loaded by the force F = 10,000 lb. The shaft is ductile steel having the following properties:

$$s_u = 120{,}000 \text{ psi} \qquad s_{yp} = 90{,}000 \text{ psi} \qquad s_e = 48{,}000 \text{ psi}$$

Using a factor of safety of 2.4, determine the diameter d of the shaft.

4-32. The same as Prob. 4-31 except that the shaft is not rotating.

4-33. The round shaft shown in the figure is simply supported in bearings at R_1 and R_2 and is loaded by the static force F. The shaft rotates at 600 rpm. The material is SAE 1035 steel, heat-treated to 350 Bhn, with all surfaces ground. The ultimate strength is 164,000 psi, the yield strength is 146,000 psi, and the endurance limit is 72,000 psi. Using a factor of safety of 2, find the diameter d.

PROB. 4-33

4-34. The same as Prob. 4-33 except that the shaft does not rotate.

4-35. The same as Prob. 4-33 except that the shaft does not rotate, the factor of safety is 5, and the material is cast iron. The cast iron used has an ultimate strength of 25,000 psi in tension and 50,000 psi in compression. The endurance limit is 10,000 psi.

CHAPTER 5

PRINCIPLES OF MACHINE DESIGN

Having investigated what might be best described as a minimum of fundamentals, we are now nearly ready for a first excursion into design. Before proceeding with this step, however, it is necessary to pause and consider in some detail the problem of design.

It is the intention of machine design to create a plan for the construction of a machine or device to accomplish some useful function. Three types of design are evident:

1. The design of a machine or device which has never before existed
2. The redesign of an existing machine or device
3. The design of a single machine member

In the first type, design consists of conceiving of an arrangement of parts which will accomplish the purpose and then of designing each part. This is the most creative form of design and requires the utmost in ingenuity.

When an existing machine is to be redesigned the arrangement of the parts is more or less specified, or at least the designer may be limited in his choice of arrangements. For example, in the redesign of a typewriter he is required to place the keys in a stepped horizontal position with the alphabet arranged in a prescribed order. Even though he knows that a different order for the alphabet, or another position for the keys, would result in a substantial saving in typewriting time and economy, he cannot change this because of the habits of a nation of stenographers. The redesign of an existing machine, therefore, generally consists of, at most, minor rearrangement of parts, followed by the design of each part.

The design of a single machine member is usually accomplished by determining the loads acting on the member, selecting the material and manufacturing process, and proportioning the member to perform its function satisfactorily.

5-1. The Specifications. The specifications are all the information, both stated and implied, which defines the machine or product to be constructed. In their obvious sense, they express the input and output quantities of the machine, the characteristics and dimensions of the space it must occupy, and the limitations upon these quantities. Another very important function of the specifications is to define the amount of money which is to be expended upon the project. Also included are the restrictions due to the manufacturing processes available or to material shortages.

The form of the specifications will, in general, range all the way from a very precise written form (as would be the case, for example, in a governmental contract for design services) to a vaguely defined form existing only in the mind of one or two persons. The more usual form is intermediate between these extremes. In this case, the problem, technically, may be fairly well defined, with only a few of the limitations on the design to be sought out by the designer.

The items making up the specifications cannot be recorded in exact form because they are dependent upon the very nature of the machine or member to be designed. However, the following can be used for study:

Specifications for the Design of a Flexible Shaft

1. Quantity required ______; use ______
2. Torque ______ in.-lb, horsepower ______
3. Speed ______ rpm
4. Element to be driven turns clockwise ______ or counterclockwise ______
5. Maximum starting torque ______ in.-lb
6. Over-all length ______ in.
7. Minimum operating radius ______ in.
8. Service is continuous ______ or intermittent ______
9. Remote-controlled; the greatest torque is clockwise ______, counterclockwise ______, or nearly the same ______
10. Maximum permissible deflection ______
11. Temperature conditions ______
12. Corrosive conditions ______
13. Moisture conditions ______
14. Abrasive conditions ______
15. Other conditions ______

Specifications for the Design of a Pump

1. Description of the service required
   a. Suction head ______ psi
   b. Discharge head ______ psi
   c. Driver, whether motor, gas engine, or turbine, ______ hp at ______ rpm
   d. Type of connection, direct, belt, or gears
2. Quantity required ______
3. Maximum volume ______ gpm
4. Cycle of operation ______
5. Fluid
   a. Commercial name
   b. Highest temperature ______°F
   c. Lowest temperature ______°F
   d. Viscosity ______ SSU at ______°F

e. Specific gravity at ______°F
f. Baume gravity at ______°F
g. Percentage in solution of acids, alkalies, salts, or abrasives

6. Installation
   a. Sketch of mounting, pipe sizes, and fittings
   b. Horizontal pipe ______ ft
   c. Vertical pipe ______ ft
   d. Pipe size ______
   e. Total length of piping ______ ft
   f. Number of elbows ______45°, ______90°
   g. Valves ______ gate, ______ globe
   h. Other fittings ______
7. Power supply
   a. ______ volts, ______ a-c, ______ d-c
   b. Phase

The specifications shown above lack two very important items. These are the facilities, equipment, and manufacturing processes available and the competitive situation. Both of these items must be regarded as part of the specifications, although they are often implied rather than stated.

The manufacturing processes which are available, together with the facilities of a certain plant, constitute restrictions on the designer's freedom and hence should be considered as part of the specifications. Although the designer is not forced to rely on the facilities of his plant alone, since some of the items to be manufactured can be "farmed out," it is generally more economical to do so. Another limitation on his design is the one on the availability of materials and sizes. Although many sizes and many materials are listed in catalogues, these are not all easily available, and shortages frequently occur. For this reason the designer is often limited to the use of those materials and sizes which are either in stock or can quickly be obtained.

In design, the competitive situation is all-important. The machine or device to be designed must be capable of being manufactured to sell at a price the customer will pay! The total cost of the manufactured product is made up of four items:

1. The labor cost
2. The cost of materials and purchased parts
3. The engineering costs
4. The overhead costs

Labor Cost. The labor cost is the price paid for direct labor used to convert the materials and purchased parts into the completed machine or product. The labor cost affects the design of the machine in the following manner: If only a single machine is to be built, the labor cost will be high, because no advantage can be taken of labor-saving machinery. Jigs or fixtures and other devices that could be employed to speed up production cannot be used because of their additional cost. Ordinarily a greater degree of skill will be required, which costs more money. Hence the designer will be limited in his choice of materials and processes to those which require only the simplest tooling. However, as the number of parts to be produced increases, lower-cost, mass-production processes begin to come into the picture. For high-run production many processes are often available, and the question of which one to use will require very close study.

Raw Materials. The cost of raw materials is generally, but not always, a very minor item. It must be studied closely in connection with the other costs. It is frequently possible to purchase a more expensive material which will result in a great reduction in labor costs.

Purchased Parts. Sometimes subassemblies such as clutches, power units, bearings, or brakes may be purchased. Whether to purchase these units or to manufacture them is a decision which the designer must make. This decision is based upon the following:

1. The number of machines to be built
2. The degree to which the use of a purchased part or subassembly will limit or restrict the output, dimensions, or versatility of the completed machine
3. The variety of parts or subassemblies available for purchase
4. The shop facilities and engineering know-how which are available for the manufacture of a satisfactory part or assembly

Assuming a purchased part or subassembly can be used, the final decision is, of course, based upon the relative cost of purchasing or manufacturing. When a great many machines are to be built, these costs must often be analyzed in considerable detail in order to find the break-even point.

Engineering Costs. Engineering costs are an important item in the design and production of a given machine. They can be broken down into two items: the design or development costs and the engineering costs accompanying production and sales. Since the latter are usually included in overhead, we shall concern ourselves only with the engineering development expenses. For a typical design these might be divided as follows:

1. The preliminary design work consisting of an exploration of various avenues of approach. Usually one or two designs in sketch form result from this exploratory work.
2. The production of a layout drawing from one set of the design sketches. The layout drawing is carried to a point at which a model can be constructed or the tentative design can be thoroughly evaluated.
3. The construction of a working model from the layout drawing.

These costs include the skilled workmen required to produce the model, the overhead expenses of the model shop, and the necessary materials and parts.

4. The experimental investigation or direct research required thoroughly to evaluate the model. This includes the changes made necessary by defects in the model and all other experimental work needed to obtain a satisfactory design.

5. The reduction of the knowledge gained in all the previous steps to produce the final design sketches.

6. The detail and assembly drawings, including tooling drawings, necessary to produce the machine. These costs also include the engineering and drafting costs and any associated expenses.

It is possible in a given design that some of these items would be omitted or combined with others. On the other hand, in the case of a complex product or one manufactured in large quantities, each item would have many subdivisions.

Since the engineering costs are an important part of the total, they must be considered as a part of the specifications for a machine. The reason for this is that the allowable expenses for engineering necessarily limit the designer's freedom. If, for example, only one machine is to be constructed and money for engineering services is limited (which, unfortunately, is usually the case), then the engineer must short-cut the lengthy, and usually more accurate, methods of design.[1] Such a limitation on his time will have tremendous effects. These effects will include an increased product cost, an uncertainty as to the durability of the machine, an uncertainty as to the strength of some of the components, and the possibility of other defects which might have been found with a more painstaking analysis of the problem.

Overhead Costs. The overhead costs are generally assigned as a percentage of the other costs. For this reason they do not affect the specifications, and no further consideration will be given to them.

5-2. The Selection and Arrangement of the Parts. We are concerned here with the very earliest stage in the design process—in particular, with that stage which is best described as the scheming, or "pencil-thinking," stage. It is the "idea" phase, in which the preliminary synthesizing is performed but which precedes the proportioning of the parts according to the strength required or to other design factors. The thinking, or scheming, is aided by freehand sketches not drawn to any particular size or scale. Briefly, this stage of design consists of the study of the problem, the recording of a number of possible solutions, an evaluation of these solutions, and a synthesizing of the best one.

[1] Short-cut methods are to be deplored—they are not good engineering. When they are used, the designer must be ultraconservative in making all design decisions.

The mental approach used by the designer in attacking a problem is of supreme importance in obtaining a successful design. The mind must be completely free of preconceived notions and complex details associated with the solution. In order to achieve this mental condition prior to initiating a design, development laboratories have been known to employ engineers because of their ignorance of existing solutions to the problem. It is possible to go even further and cite cases in which nonengineers have been employed to solve certain problems on the premise that, if they did not know a certain thing could not be done, they might go ahead and do it anyway! Although these cases are admittedly extreme, they do illustrate a proper mental approach. The student, at first, will find this mental conditioning difficult to attain. But by following the suggestions to be given in this section, together with practice, he will find that it will become successively easier.[1]

Let us now examine the various steps used in this phase of the design:

Step 1. *State the objective in words, using the simplest possible form.* This is a very helpful step in achieving a proper mental conditioning. Unless the real objective is stated in so many words, it may remain obscured by the many details. In this step we are reducing the problem to its barest elements. If it cannot be stated as a single objective, then use two or more.

Step 2. *Separate the action of the machine into a group of operations, and record these operations in block-sketch form, relating them, one to the other.* It is interesting to know that it was this step which made possible Mergenthaler's Linotype, one of the world's greatest mechanical inventions. It was his division of the function of the machine into steps which made it possible for him to study each step separately and so arrive at a solution. This is, of course, often a very difficult thing to do, and there are many possible variations in these steps.

In recording each of these steps in block form, show the input and output items, and attach the blocks to each other to designate relationship or order. Record everything that is known about each step.

Step 3. *Itemize all the possible methods of solution in the most general form.* This step is taken to preclude the omission of one or more solutions which could be quite simple and yet which might otherwise be eliminated. An engineer usually thinks in terms of his own specialty; methods of solution which are outside this special field may not occur to him unless

[1] The beginner may often feel handicapped here because of an imagined lack of creative ability. This is simply not true! All persons are born with a greater or lesser amount of this ability. Somewhere in the educational process this ability is stifled, and it may remain in this condition for many years, or forever, unless positive steps are taken. The very fact that the reader has educated himself to the extent that he is studying this book is sufficient evidence that he has this ability. He must now develop it by practice.

his attention is deliberately focused upon them. But the design engineer must be a coordinator. He consults specialists in the fields of metallurgy, chemistry, electronics, power, stress analysis, fluid mechanics, and other technical fields and coordinates their activities with the entire design. There exist, for example, mechanical brakes, air brakes, hydraulic brakes, and magnetic brakes. In the areas of lifting, moving, and exerting forces, hydraulic and pneumatic means are replacing mechanical methods. A problem cannot be said to be solved until all the probable methods of solution have been exhausted. The designer should always consider as many of the following means as possible:

a. Mechanical
b. Electrical
c. Hydraulic
d. Magnetic
e. Pneumatic
f. Electronic
g. Chemical
h. A combination of the above

Step 4. *Study each of the methods in step* 3 *in detail and record all the solutions that can be found for each method.* In making this initial recording of possible methods of solution, keep the sketches simple; do not add excessive or complex detail. The aim is to obtain as many different solutions as possible, and so record all of them, no matter how absurd they may appear. It is wise not to examine the solutions to similar designs until the possibilities in this step have been nearly exhausted. The following suggestions may be of assistance:

1. *Try inversion.* This is a reversal of the order of things. Subtraction is the inverse of addition; division is the inverse of multiplication. The bench-type crosscut saw is made so that, to saw, it is necessary for the operator to push the wood into the teeth of the rotating blade; an inversion is produced if the wood is held stationary while the rotating blade is pushed through the wood. An inversion is produced with a clock or watch if the hands are made stationary and the face of the clock is made to rotate. An inversion of an electric motor is produced by making the rotor stationary and permitting the field windings to rotate.

2. *Change the normal position or character of things.* If it operates horizontally, try operating it vertically. If it is round, try making it square. The following are examples of common articles, but with the normal position changed:

a. A horizontal drill press
b. A washing machine with horizontal spindle

c. Doors hinged at top or bottom
d. Sliding automobile doors
e. Piano with vertical keyboard

3. *Itemize the disadvantages.* Make a complete list of all the disadvantages of each of the proposed methods of design. These disadvantages should be written in detail and explanations given. The intention here is that the designer shall place himself in opposition. It is quite usual to find an answer to the problem before these are complete.

4. *Talk it over.* If the designer has faithfully followed these suggestions thus far, he is now familiar with the problem in the most minute detail. He has found many solutions, but none of them is quite satisfying. Having worked to this point, his mind is in a receptive condition and will instantly recognize a solution. The problem is to bridge a gap between two groups of ideas—to make an association of ideas, as it were. It is generally conceded that this bridging occurs by pure chance.[1] For this reason, it is now necessary to create a series of opportunities which would be likely to permit this bridging by pure chance to happen. The event is most likely to occur when the problem is being discussed with another person or a group of persons. If talking it over fails to provide a satisfying solution or clue, then steps 1 to 4 have not been carried out thoroughly, and additional work is required.

Step 5. Make a detailed sketch of the apparently best solution of the problem. Sometimes this will help to solve some of the problems, and before the solution is completed there are usually a great number of changes. These changes are to be regarded as design—not drafting—and, no matter how disagreeable they may be, they should be made. An error in a sketch or drawing is not sufficient justification for changing the design to suit the drawing. This is a very difficult lesson for most beginners, but the process of drawing or sketching is a fundamental part of the design process, and these changes would not have been found without making the drawing in the first place.

The sketch may be either freehand or mechanical. Of course, it cannot be drawn to scale because only minor calculations will have been made. It must show all the major components, as in the previous sketches, and, in addition, will show other components not strictly necessary for the machine's operation but required to hold the parts in working position and perform other minor functions. These sketches will be suitable for use in making the preliminary design calculations. When the calculations have been completed, the design is ready for preliminary board work and detailed calculations.

[1] Jacques Hadamard, "The Psychology of Invention in the Mathematical Field," chap. 4, Princeton University Press, Princeton, N.J., 1945.

5-3. Design Factors. At this point it is assumed that a sketch or drawing showing all the various members making up the design is available and that the specifications have been clearly defined. The designer is therefore ready to begin the task of accurately defining the material, the process of manufacture, and the dimensions of each member making up the design. In performing this task he presumably takes one member at a time, makes the necessary calculations and decisions, and records these in the form of a detail drawing. Actually, the process is not quite so simple. Since the parts are interdependent, decisions made concerning the design of a given member affect those made concerning another. For this reason, the design process is often a trial-and-error one. A few decisions are tentatively made, and these are checked against the remaining members to determine their effects. The necessary corrections and changes are then made, and the design proceeds. This procedure is repeated again and again until eventually the design reaches completion.[1]

Being now ready to begin the design of a single member, we must ask the question, Upon what basis shall it be designed? Can one single factor be found upon which its dimensions depend? Or do they depend upon a group of factors? If so, is one of these more important than the others? The answers to these questions are essential. If the design is to be based upon only one controlling factor, then the trials, experiments, or calculations, on the basis of this limiting factor, may be carried out, and as a result of this work the material, manufacturing processes, and dimensions will be determined. In the usual case, however, the design depends upon a group of factors. One of these will usually turn out as the one which governs the design, but in the beginning the designer does not know which one it will be. He must therefore investigate all of them, one at a time, until it is found. Having found this factor, he may then use it as the basis of design, keeping the effects of the others continually in mind.

In subsequent portions of this book the factors affecting the design of various members will be treated in detail. In order that the reader may appreciate their importance, some of them are listed here. Their importance varies from one design to another, so that the order in which they are listed has no meaning. They are:

[1] Academically, such a procedure would be difficult to teach. It would be necessary to jump from one subject to another so often that the reader would soon become lost. It would also involve a great deal of repetition. Similar members occur in a great many different kinds of machines. The reader would therefore acquire a great deal of information about a relatively few members which occur quite often, at the expense of others, just as important, which occur less frequently. For this reason, in this book, the various members will be studied one at a time.

1. Strength
2. Stiffness
3. Thermal properties
4. Corrosion properties
5. Wear properties
6. Friction characteristics
7. Processing or manufacturing considerations
8. Utility
9. Cost
10. Safety
11. Noise
12. Appearance
13. Shape
14. Size
15. Flexibility
16. Control
17. Surface finish
18. Tolerances
19. Lubrication

In a great many cases the design factors are such that no calculations or experiments are necessary in order to define the part accurately. For example, an adding-machine frame must be designed to hold the parts in operating position and to present a good appearance. The loads are probably insignificant, and so no calculations are required. In commercial work for some industries this type of design occurs very frequently. The best preparation for it is simply experience. The design of members of this nature is usually pure drawing-board work, with appearance and manufacturing ease being primary considerations.

5-4. The Strength Design Factor.[1] Strength is the limiting design factor in so many machine members to be studied that a complete discussion of it at this point is essential. In developing this subject several definitions are necessary.

Strength. The strength of a machine member may be stated in two ways:

1. The *strength* of a machine member is measured by the maximum load in pounds which may be applied to the member without impairing its ability to perform the required function.

2. The *strength* of a machine member is the maximum value of the stress in pounds per square inch which may exist at a specific point in the member without impairing its ability to perform the required function.

The reader should note particularly that the strength of a *machine member* and the strength of a *material* are two different things. The two may, or may not, have the same values.

When the strength of the member is measured in pounds per square inch, the strength of the weakest section may be selected as follows:

1. For fatigue loading, the strength is selected equal to the fatigue strength corresponding to the required number of loading cycles expected during the anticipated life of the part.

[1] The greater portion of this section was written by Dr. Joseph P. Vidosic, Professor of Mechanical Engineering, Georgia Institute of Technology, Atlanta, Ga.; it originally appeared in the *Journal of Engineering Education*, May, 1948, under the title "Design Stress Factors," and is reproduced with the permission of Dr. Vidosic.

2. For brittle materials or materials having no yield point, the strength is selected equal to the ultimate strength of the material. Members subjected to dead static loads are often designed on this basis too, even though the material may have a yield point.

3. For all other materials and conditions of loading, under ordinary circumstances the strength is selected equal to the yield strength of the material.

Design Stress. To allow for inaccuracies in knowledge, the stress which is used to design the member is always less than the strength of the member. This stress is called the *design stress.*

Working Stress. When the member is designed, manufactured, and assembled into the machine and the machine is placed in operation, it is possible to determine the actual maximum values of the stresses at various points in the member. In the general case, these stresses are different for different points on the member. The stress at any single point, when determined in this manner, is called the *working stress* at that point.

Factor of Safety. Two types of factors of safety will be defined. The *design factor of safety* is the number which is used to obtain the *design stress* or the *design load* from the strength of the member. It is used as follows:

$$s_d = \frac{s}{\text{f.s.}} \qquad \text{or} \qquad F_d = \frac{F}{\text{f.s.}} \tag{5-1}$$

where s is the strength and s_d is the design stress and both are in pounds per square inch. In the second form of the equation, F is the strength of the member and F_d is the design load, and both values are in pounds.[1]

The *true factor of safety* is a number which designates the actual margin of safety involved. The designer cannot use this number to produce his designs, but, after the machine has been constructed and experiments made, he may use it to check the accuracy of his work, or he may obtain an approximate value for it by other experimental means. The true factor of safety may be defined by the equation

$$\text{f.s.} = \frac{s}{s_w} \qquad \text{or} \qquad \text{f.s.} = \frac{F}{F_w} \tag{5-2}$$

where, in this case, s and F are the actual strengths of the member and s_w and F_w are, respectively, the working stress and the working load.

[1] The words "stress" and "strength" are used here in the broadest sense. The "stress" may be a simple stress, such as a tensile or bending stress, or it may be a stress value obtained from any biaxial or even triaxial stress situation. In the same way, the "strength" may be a simple yield or ultimate strength, or it may be a value obtained from a consideration of one of the failure theories. It will be seen that the designer uses Eq. (5-1) very liberally, choosing the factor of safety after making his decision on which "stress" and which "strength" to use.

In this book the term "factor of safety" will usually be used to mean "design factor of safety." Whenever the true factor of safety is intended, it will always be so stated.

Selection of the Factor of Safety. The factor of safety must account for the unknowns and uncertainties involved in the design. These are as follows:

1. The degree of uncertainty of the magnitude and kind of applied load
2. The degree of reliability of the material
3. The extent to which assumptions must be made in the analysis for nominal stress
4. The extent to which localized stress may be developed
5. The kind of environment to which the machine may be subjected
6. The extent to which human life may be endangered or failure may be embarrassing or costly
7. The uncertainty as to the exact cause of failure
8. The extent to which properties of the material may be altered during service
9. The extent to which initial stresses may be set up during processing, fabrication, or assembly
10. The uncertainty as to the appropriateness of using the material properties measured on a test specimen of one size in designing a part of another size

Each of the above must be carefully considered and evaluated when deciding upon the factor of safety to use. Whenever exact facts concerning any of the uncertainties can be established, the effects can be separately accounted for. Much work has been done, for instance, to learn of the effect of size of part as compared with size of test specimen used to determine the material properties. Size coefficients can thus often be used to take care safely of this variable. Localized stresses resulting from contour discontinuities cause stress concentrations which can be provided for in many instances by the use of stress-concentration factors (form stress factor corrected for the index of sensitivity). Furthermore, minute surface roughness and environmental influences such as corrosion can be accounted for through surface coefficients. When existing conditions do not exactly correspond to investigated or otherwise known cases, the possibility of undue stress must be guarded against by the use of large factors of safety.

The evaluation of the effect of many of the uncertainties remains, however, almost entirely a matter for the experienced designer to handle. Experience with the material under consideration as well as with the design, operation, and maintenance of a particular type of equipment cannot be replaced. The beginner must therefore supplement the lack of personal experience by reviewing practices that have been accepted because of the knowledge of those who have proposed and used them.

Factors of safety commonly used in basic design, based upon the elastic limit, fall within the range of 1.25 to 4. When commercially available elements are incorporated into the design, larger factors are used for these in cases where their manufacture cannot be or is not critically controlled. Such cases are becoming the exception rather than the rule. In normal design, factors of safety are usually taken according to the schedule that follows:

1. f.s. = 1.25 to 1.5 for exceptionally reliable materials used under controllable conditions and subjected to loads and stresses that can be determined with certainty. Used almost invariably where low weight is a particularly important consideration.

2. f.s. = 1.5 to 2 for well-known materials under reasonably constant environmental conditions, subjected to loads and stresses that can be determined readily.

3. f.s. = 2 to 2.5 for average materials operated in ordinary environments and subjected to loads and stresses that can be determined.

4. f.s. = 2.5 to 3 for less tried as well as for brittle materials under average conditions of environment, load, and stress.

5. f.s. = 3 to 4 for untried materials used under average conditions of environment, load, and stress.

6. f.s. = 3 to 4 should also be employed with better-known materials that are to be used in uncertain environments or subjected to uncertain stresses.

7. f.s. = 2 for impact of very ductile materials where the small index of sensitivity results in low stress-concentration factors; f.s. = 1.5 for less ductile materials where a higher sensitivity will provide a larger factor of stress concentration.

8. f.s. = 1.5 for design at higher temperatures, based on the creep strength of the material that will result in a permissible plastic deformation over a preestablished life period.

9. Repeated loads—the factors of safety established in items 1 to 6 are acceptable but must be applied to the endurance limit rather than the yield strength of the material.

10. Castings, forgings, stampings, and welded components—factors of safety here used do not usually vary appreciably from those presented above.

11. Special elements—factors of safety to be used with standard design elements, commercially available, should be those recommended for them by reliable manufacturers and/or by established codes for design of machines.

12. Where higher factors of safety might seem desirable, a more thorough analysis should be undertaken before deciding upon their use.

The large number of uncertainties presented, as well as the generalities that had to be used in discussing the information contained herein, provide sufficient proof of the fact that basic knowledge is limited. Therefore the subject is, of necessity, very fluid. As discoveries and experiment supply more data and practice provides more experience, concepts, theories, and factors will change accordingly.

5-5. The Material and Process. Before the actual calculations are made to determine the dimensions of the member, it is necessary for the

TABLE 5-1. USES FOR STEEL BY CARBON CONTENT*

Carbon class	Carbon range, %	Use
Low.........	0.05–0.15	Chain, nails, pipe rivets, screws, sheets for pressing and stamping, wire
Medium.....	0.15–0.30	Bars, plates, structural shapes
	0.30–0.45	Axles, connecting rods, shafting
High........	0.45–0.60	Crankshafts, scraper blades
	0.60–0.75	Automobile springs, anvils, band saws, drop-hammer dies
Very high....	0.75–0.90	Chisels, punches, sand tools
	0.90–1.00	Knives, shear blades, springs
	1.00–1.10	Milling cutters, dies, taps
	1.10–1.20	Lathe tools, woodworking tools
	1.20–1.30	Files, reamers
	1.30–1.40	Dies for wire drawing
	1.40–1.50	Metal-cutting saws

* T. B. Jefferson and Gorham Woods, "Metals and How to Weld Them," The James F. Lincoln Arc Welding Foundation, Cleveland, 1954.

designer to decide upon the material to be used and the method by which it is to be processed. This is a difficult decision to make because in nearly every case there will be a number of materials and processes which appear to be equally satisfactory. Usually in a designer's experience there exist materials with which he has worked; the parts produced from them have been successful; he is familiar with their processing peculiarities; and consequently he is inclined to choose one of them. The designer must also consider the particular facilities available at his plant for processing the material which he selects. If the plant has a reputation for producing good sound castings at a low cost, he will naturally lean toward their use. If the plant has a wide variety of cold-heading facilities, this process may be specified instead of the automatic-screw-machine process.

Another plant may be excellently equipped for forging and heat-treating processes, in which case these will be favored.

Although the designer is inclined to favor those materials and processes which his plant is best equipped to handle, when the choice of another material or process is clearly indicated, then that one should be selected. After the primary design considerations have been satisfied, cost is the factor which determines both the material and the process.

When the part is to be made of steel, Table 5-1 will assist the designer in choosing a steel of proper carbon content. After the approximate carbon content of the steel to be used has been determined, the designer must decide whether to use a plain carbon steel or an alloy steel.

5-6. Methods of Solution. Three general methods of solving specific problems in design are in use. They are:

1. The statement of a theory to explain the behavior of the machine member under the action of the applied forces; a mathematical statement of this theory in equation form; and a solution of this equation to obtain the dimensions.

2. The use of available experimental data to obtain the dimensions, or a series of experiments made to determine them.

3. The use of experimental data to alter the results obtained from theoretical equations in order to correct those equations for observed inaccuracies or variations.

The equation $s = Mc/I$, for bending stress, is an example of the first method, with the addition that it must be shown that the machine member under consideration is really acted upon by a bending load, that there are no other combinations of loading, and that strength is the principal design factor. An example of the second method is the selection of V belts. These are selected from tables in manufacturers' catalogues which are based on experimental data. The equation $s = kF/A$ is an example of the third method. Here, k is the stress-concentration factor which is determined experimentally. The stress-concentration factor is used to correct the deficiencies of the theoretical equation $s = F/A$.

The choice of the method of solution depends, of course, on the problem to be solved. A more important factor influencing the choice of method, however, is the amount of time available to the designer. Or, to put it bluntly, how much time, in terms of dollars per hour, can he spend in obtaining a solution? The answer depends upon the particular application. If a part is produced in large quantities, or if it is an expensive part, then a complete investigation is justified. On the other hand, if it is a relatively inexpensive part, not of major importance in the machine, or perhaps not made in large quantities, then an elaborate investigation may not be justified. The designer must be acutely aware of the economic situation and temper his design in accordance with it.

5-7. Assumptions. We have seen how the designer's decision on the value of the factor of safety to be used depends upon the uncertainties involved. It should be pointed out that a large factor of safety (which implies that the uncertainties are large) increases the direct cost of the machine out of all proportion to the increase in the factor of safety. For example, the size of many machines depends upon the size of shaft used. Suppose that a shaft 30 per cent larger than normal is used because of a larger factor of safety. The rotating components mounted upon the shaft must also be larger. The bearings and bearing housings must be larger. As a result of this, the supporting framework is increased in size. Because of these larger components, the machine tools used to make them will be larger. Large machine tools have slower production rates, and so the labor cost will be greater. In fact, the only saving to be credited to a larger factor of safety is the saving in engineering services.

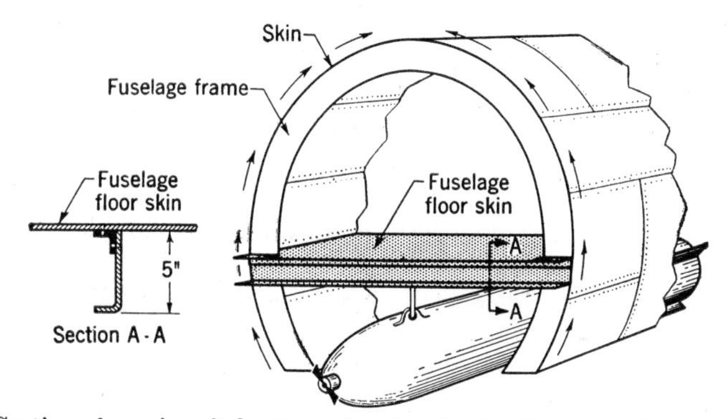

Fig. 5-1. Section of an aircraft fuselage, showing the bomb-support beam. (*Courtesy of The Glenn L. Martin Company.*)

In the example just cited, the reason that a larger factor of safety resulted in a saving of engineering services is that, by the simplifying assumptions which were used in the solution of the problem, the designer was able to short-cut some of the more lengthy methods of analysis. Since the longer and more accurate methods were not used, it was necessary to increase the value of the factor of safety in order to compensate for the greater degree of uncertainty. Therefore the assumptions which are made have a direct effect upon the cost of the machine and upon the engineering time required to design it.

The type of assumption mentioned above is not the kind which is used in developing the fundamental laws of mechanics but, on the contrary, is a second type which might be called a design assumption and which is necessary to simplify an actual physical machine part to the point where it can be handled by the laws of mechanics. The following example should illustrate this point:

EXAMPLE 5-1. Figure 5-1 illustrates a fuselage frame supporting a horizontal bomb beam which is subjected to a bomb load. In order to determine the deflection and stress in the beam, an assumption must be made concerning the reactions at the ends of the beam. This assumption is a design one and is in contrast to those which are necessary to develop the basic equations of mechanics. In this case, the bomb beam is assumed to be simply supported at the ends, as shown in Fig. 5-2*a*. A second possible assumption is illustrated in Fig. 5-2*b*. It will be left as an exercise for the reader to determine which of these two is the more practical.

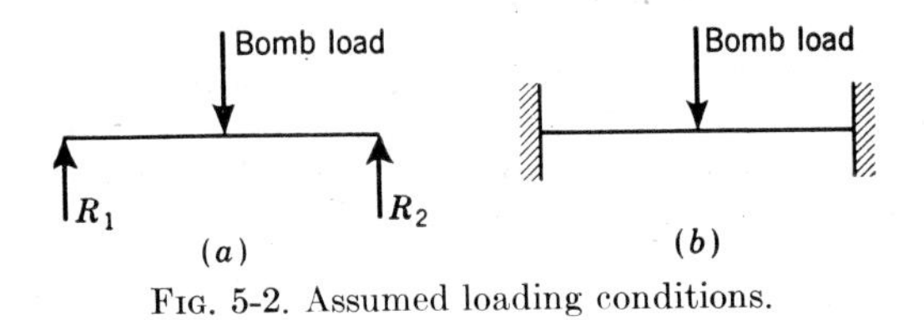

FIG. 5-2. Assumed loading conditions.

5-8. Recording the Design. The importance of accurately and clearly recording everything which is done in connection with the design cannot be overemphasized. The reasons for this are as follows:

1. Accurate dated records of invention are the strongest kind of evidence in a patent lawsuit. When invention is a possibility, the records should be witnessed, preferably by two persons who have read and understood them. Naturally, all the recorded matter should be dated and signed by the designer.
2. It is the practice in most design or engineering offices for the calculations to be checked by someone.
3. Design records are usually filed for future reference for the reason given above, and also in case the machine fails, or the capacity is changed, or the shape changed for one reason or another. In any of these cases, the designer must be able to read his own work even as much as five years later.
4. In a great deal of design work the first calculations are made by the engineer, who then turns over the remaining calculating work to a subordinate who follows the same procedure although he may not be familiar with the equations.
5. The design is often discussed by the engineer's superiors, and they must be able to read and understand it.
6. In the long run, less time will be spent and fewer mistakes will be made if the calculations, decisions, and sketches are made clear and easy to understand.

In addition to the sketches and drawings, the completed design is composed of written material in the form of assumptions, calculations, decisions, and justification for all these. This material must be arranged clearly and in orderly fashion and must be written so that it can be easily understood. There are many excellent forms in which it may be recorded, and the method to be given here is suggested in the absence of other methods.

Form for Solution of Design Problems[1]

1. *Paper.* Use only 8½- × 11-in. paper. Many design offices use ¼-in. cross-section paper because it is convenient for sketches and calculations, as well as for written material. The designer should have pencils of several different colors, as these are convenient for checking, drawing contrasting curves, and underlining important items.

2. *Heading.* Use both main headings and subheadings. These should be numbered and underlined and should state precisely the information which is sought.

3. *Sketch.* A sketch of the particular problem to be investigated is usually necessary. If there is any doubt, make it anyway. The sketch should show all the known or given data and information, using appropriate symbols and units, together with those quantities which it is desired to find. Sometimes the problem may seem too simple to require a sketch, but the reader will often find that its construction will add to his store of information or contribute items which he might otherwise overlook.

4. *Explanation.* Sometimes an explanation of the problem is necessary. This might be an explanation of certain features of the sketch, where the given data came from, how the problem originated, or justification for making this particular search.

5. *Procedure.* In this paragraph the designer should state the means or method of attack to be used to find the information for which he is searching. He should also present arguments for choosing this method in preference to other methods, to justify its use.

6. *Assumptions.* The design assumptions to be used in solving the problem should be listed here. Unless the reasons for using these assumptions were stated in the previous paragraph, they should also be given. The assumptions should be underlined, preferably with a colored pencil, because the success or failure of the entire design hinges upon them.

7. *Preliminary decisions.* These are usually the tentative material and manufacturing process to be used and the factor of safety. In specifying the material, remember to give enough information so that all its properties are completely identified. For example, a 1020 steel may be cold-drawn, hot-rolled, or carburized; a 6150 steel may have a variety of heat-treatments, all of which result in different properties. Sometimes the factor of safety is specified by a design code; more often, at least in machine design, the designer is required to choose its value. In selecting the factor of safety, the reasons for its choice must be given.

In addition to these decisions, there are also others to be made which are usually peculiar to the particular member to be designed. These may involve such things as a tentative relation between a group of dimensions all of which are unknown, the tooth system to be employed when gears are to be designed, the surface finish to be used where fatigue is a factor, the operating temperature, the degree of noise suppression, or the method of lubrication.

8. *The calculations.* This is the least important step in design because the problem has now been completely set up and awaits only the solution to this purely mechanical step in order that the final conclusions and decisions may be made. This is, however,

[1] This form is an adaptation of a form suggested by Prof. Arthur H. Burr, Head of the Department of Machine Design, Cornell University, Ithaca, N.Y., and was published in the *Machine Design Clearinghouse Bulletin* for September, 1945; it is included with Professor Burr's permission.

the step in which the beginner is most likely to make errors. Therefore the formation of habits of writing in an orderly manner and of checking each step will pay large dividends in results. The following form is recommended:

a. Since the calculations will usually be composed of more than one step, use a subheading for each step. This is the quantity or relation to be found.

b. Now put down the equation or the relationship which is to be used. Unless this is a well-known equation, it should be identified. This is done by means of a sketch or, if it is from a book, catalogue, or engineering periodical, by equation number with complete identification of its source. The symbols may be identified, where necessary, on a sketch or by a statement of the meaning of each one.

c. Convert all the quantities to the same system of units. Students often fail to do this or else attempt to make the conversion in the equation itself. Failure to make this conversion is probably one of the greatest sources of error to be found in the work of beginners.

d. Substitute the known values for the symbols in the equation. These should appear in the same place in which they are located in the original equation. If the value of any symbol is unity or zero, place these values in the equation just as any other value. There should be as many items in the substitution as there are symbols in the equation.

e. Mathematically simplify or rearrange the equation to solve for the unknown. For the simpler equations, most designers find it unnecessary to write this down since it can be done mentally while using the slide rule. If this step is not required, it should be omitted because it detracts from readability. Cancellation and factoring of the numerical terms after substitution should not be done by crossing out the values just substituted. The crossing out of terms and the writing in of the factored remainder make the original substitution unreadable. Use a scratch pad if necessary to factor before using the slide rule.

f. Put down the slide-rule results, with the units, and underline them.

g. Check the calculation for accuracy and for error. Is the result reasonable? This step is generally ignored by beginners, but experienced designers stop at this point and often spend a considerable amount of time to assure themselves that the result is both reasonable and accurate. Quite frequently alternate equations can be used to give a rough result, which acts as a check.

9. *Final decisions*. It must be pointed out here that while the results of the calculations made in step 8 are the numerical answers to an algebraic problem, *they are not* the answers to the design problem. The numerical answers must be interpreted according to the standard sizes of parts and materials available. Sometimes the answer is merely the verification of a conjecture; sometimes it is too small to be used, and the designer will double it or even triple it, because of the process used or some other factor, in order to obtain a reasonable design. This step will consist, then, in a verification or an alteration of the preliminary decisions which were made and, usually, one or more direct decisions. Before going to the next major heading, the designer should itemize all the decisions made under the present major heading. This may be done either by a sketch or a statement. In either event, they should be contrasted from the body of the work by being enclosed by colored lines.

The example below is intended to illustrate the form of the written material. Naturally each design will be somewhat different, and the various items may or may not all be used. In the example to follow the items in the form are indicated by numbers to the right of the text.

EXAMPLE **5-2.** Figure 5-3 is a drawing of a proposed tail-pulley assembly for a flat-belt conveyor. The problem is to design the shaft. The specifications are:

1. Maximum belt pull = 3,600 lb.
2. Belt width = 30 in.
3. Belt speed = 100 fpm.
4. Pulley diameter = 16 in.
5. The proposed shaft will not be made in large quantities, but the drawings will be filed and the shafts will be manufactured on order.
6. The shaft should be conservatively designed for a long trouble-free life.

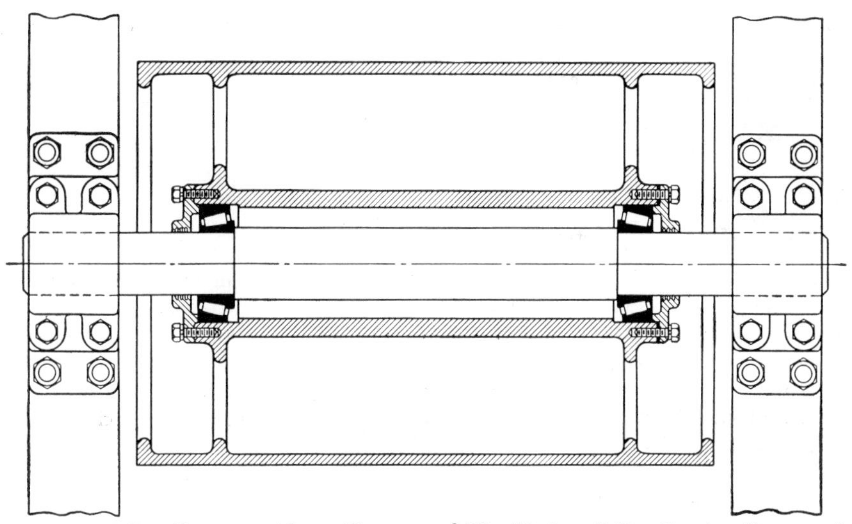

FIG. 5-3. Tail-pulley assembly. (*Courtesy of The Timken Roller Bearing Company.*)

Solution

1. Design of the tail-pulley shaft

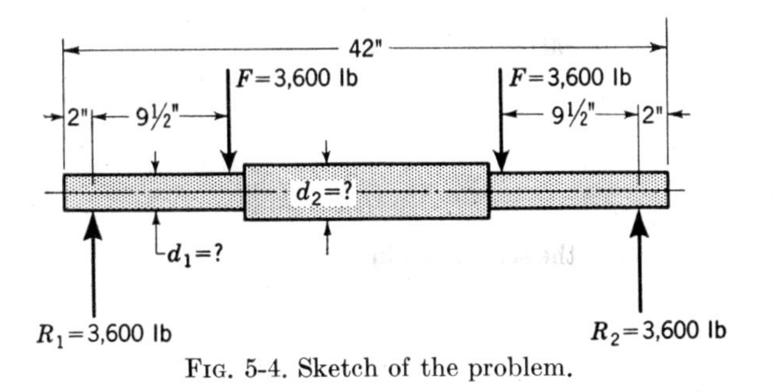

FIG. 5-4. Sketch of the problem.

In order to allow for variations in the belt width, the pulley will be made 32 in. long. A clearance of 1 in. between the ends of the pulley and the structural supporting members will be allowed. It is expected that the structural supporting members will be 4-in. angles. This makes the over-all length of the shaft equal to 42 in. By locating the bearings at the quarter points, the dimensions shown in the figure are obtained.

Since there are no limitations on the diameter of the shaft, a plain carbon steel of relatively low strength can be used. The additional diameter obtained in this manner will add to the stiffness, so that stiffness need not be a design factor. The actual shaft diameter and shoulder diameter will depend upon the bearings selected, and so the values obtained will necessarily be tentative. The equation for simple bending stress will be used. Since the shaft does not rotate, fatigue loading is not present and will not be considered even though the actual load may fluctuate slightly. 5

The assumptions are: 6

a. The shaft is in pure bending.

b. Fatigue loading is neglected.

c. The reactions and bearing loads are assumed to be concentrated.

d. The stress concentration at the shoulders is neglected because the material is ductile and the loads are static.

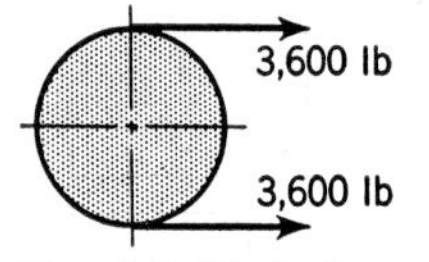

FIG. 5-5. End view of tail pulley.

The justification for these assumptions is shown in Fig. 5-5. The end view of the pulley shows a maximum belt pull of 3,600 lb; since the shaft does not rotate, this represents a unidirectional load. Although some fluctuation can be expected, the load can still be regarded as static. Stress concentration is not a problem with ductile materials and static loads; therefore this assumption is also justified.

Preliminary decisions 7

a. No. 1020 hot-rolled steel will be used without heat-treatment.

b. A factor of safety of 4.5 will be used. Although this may seem somewhat high, it is justified because of the conservative design requested, the neglect of fatigue loading and stress concentration, and the size effect of the material.

Solution 8

a. The design stress

From Table A-3, the yield-point strength of hot-rolled 1020 steel is 43,000 psi. The design stress is, therefore,

$$s_d = \frac{s_{yp}}{\text{f.s.}} = \frac{43{,}000}{4.5} = 9{,}570 \text{ psi}$$

b. The maximum bending moment

The maximum moment occurs between the loads, where it is constant. Its value is

$$M_{\max} = (3{,}600)(9.50) = 34{,}200 \text{ lb-in.}$$

c. The section modulus

Using the equation $s = Mc/I$, we obtain

$$9{,}570 = \frac{(34{,}200)c}{I}$$

so that

$$\frac{I}{c} = \frac{34{,}200}{9{,}570} = 3.57 \text{ in.}^3$$

d. The minimum shaft diameter

For a round solid shaft the section modulus is $I/c = \pi d^3/32$. Therefore,

$$d = \sqrt[3]{\frac{(32)(3.57)}{\pi}} = \underline{1.54 \text{ in.} \qquad \text{Ans.}}$$

Final decisions

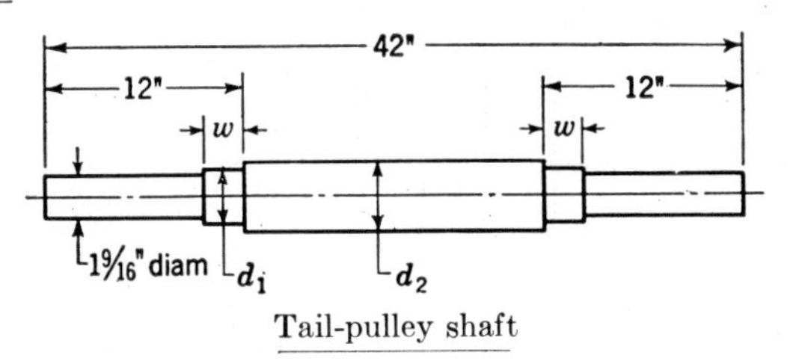

Tail-pulley shaft

Material: No. 1020 HR steel

Pulley length = 32 in.

Center-to-center distance between structural supports = 38 in.

Width of structural supports = 4 in.

FIG. 5-6. Final decisions.

The decisions which have been made as a result of these calculations are shown in Fig. 5-6. The ends of the shaft have been made 1⁹⁄₁₆ in. in diameter. A diameter d_1 for a bearing seat has been created; the width and diameter of this seat will depend upon the bearing which is selected. The diameter d_2 depends upon the recommended shaft-shoulder diameter for the bearing.

5-9. Cost Reduction.[1] The importance of the cost factor in design has been previously emphasized. Let us now study some of the relationships of cost to design. In such a study, it must be remembered that all the items making up the total cost of a machine are constantly changing. The introduction of a new process for producing a material or a part may drastically change the cost of a particular item. The prices of materials, labor, and processes are constantly shifting up and down and changing their relationships with each other. These costs even vary from one plant to another because of the freight differential, the overhead costs, and the variation in the details of a process. For this reason the reader must bear in mind that anything stated here can be interpreted only in a very liberal sense.

Processes. In many instances, any one or several of a group of processes may be satisfactory for production of a part without affecting the functional characteristics desired. For instance, the stainless-steel elbow shown in Fig. 5-7 was designed for machining from bar stock. Specification change to permit cast rather than wrought material permitted a saving of $2.18 per piece.

[1] The greater portion of this section is a condensation of the article by Roger W. Bolz entitled "Processes and Costs" which appeared in *Machine Design*, July, 1953. It is reproduced with the permission of *Machine Design* and Mr. Bolz, who is Contributing Editor.

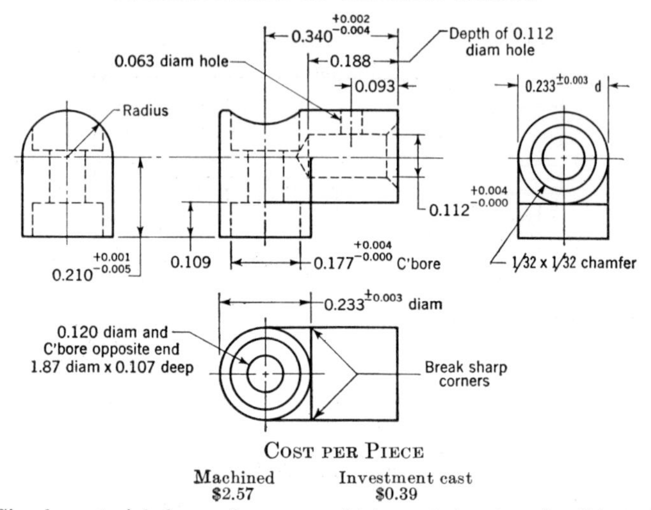

FIG. 5-7. Simple material change from wrought to cast structure for this part effected a cost reduction of 85 per cent.

The part illustrated in Fig. 5-8 was originally designed to be machined from plate. However, a specification change to permit use of an extruded shape brought about a cost reduction of $3.37 per piece.

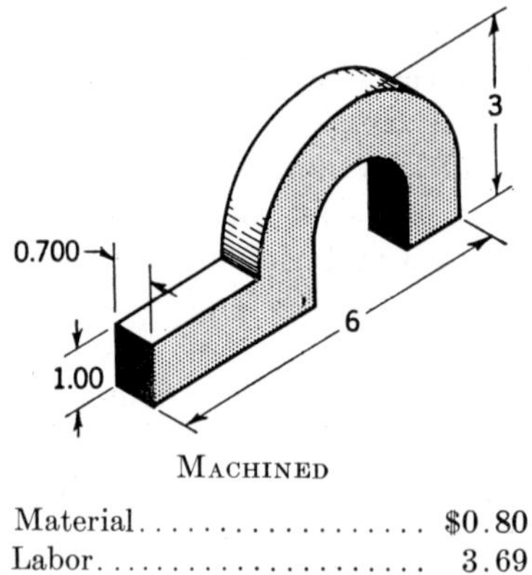

MACHINED

Material	$0.80
Labor	3.69
Tooling	0.05
	$4.54

EXTRUDED

Material	$0.85
Labor	0.32
	$1.17

FIG. 5-8. A change from plate to extruded material for this part produced a 74 per cent saving in quantities of 2,000 pieces.

With the foregoing parts, design changes required are insignificant, but instances are equally numerous wherein considerable difference in design is necessary. One such is shown in Fig. 5-9. Here the functional end use is identical, but utterly different basic processing is employed to obtain the major decrease in cost with identical or improved strength.

With the part as originally designed, shown in Fig. 5-9*a*, cost is established within rather firm limits. The quantity required usually indicates the process by which such a design can be most economically produced; in this case, 200,000 per year were produced on the screw machine. With large quantities, multiple-spindle machines can be used effectively, but on quantities under 10,000 pieces a single-spindle machine might be the necessary choice for production. If quantity dropped under

1,000 parts, a turret lathe might be the best means for turning. However, because quantity falls in the high-output bracket, processing by means of such high-speed methods as heading and thread rolling offers extremely attractive possibilities.

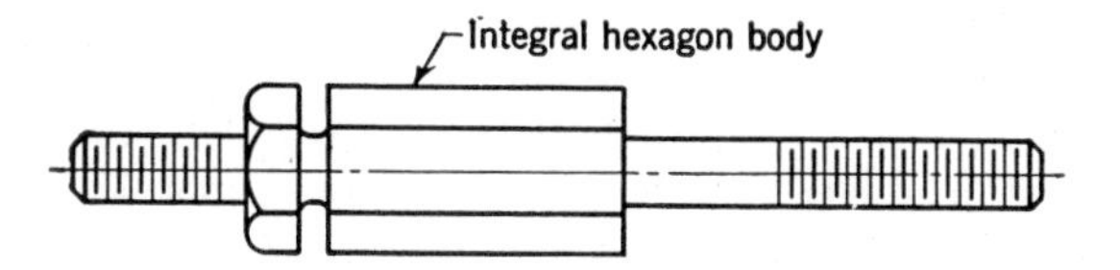

(*a*) Original screw-machine part cost $52.50 per thousand

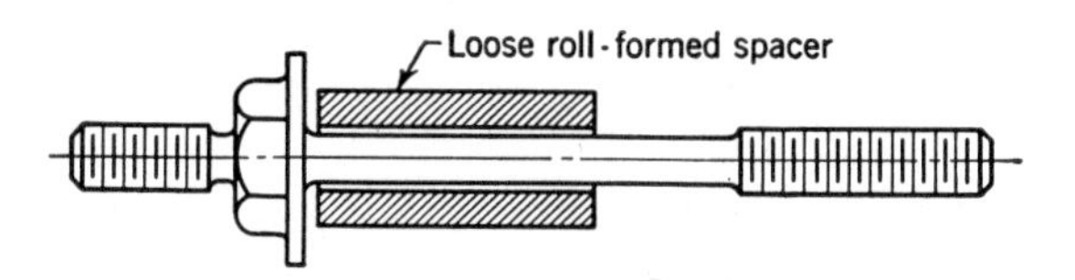

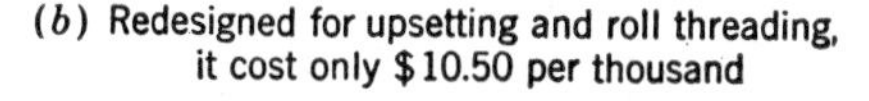
(*b*) Redesigned for upsetting and roll threading, it cost only $10.50 per thousand

FIG. 5-9. Cost reduction in a standoff stud by redesign.

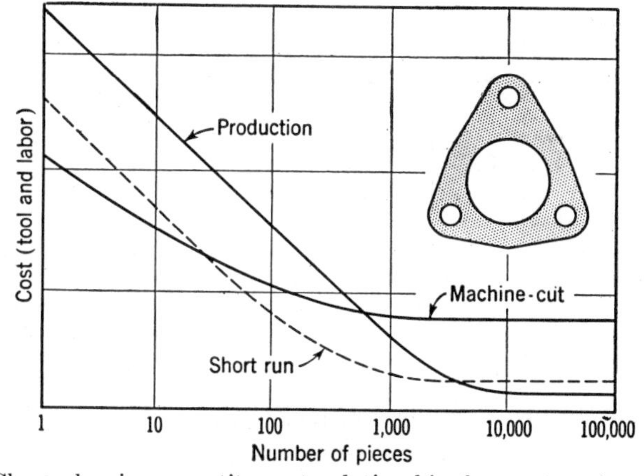

FIG. 5-10. Chart showing quantity-cost relationship for a stamping produced by machine-cutting, short-run, and high-production methods.

Effects of Quantity. Except for intermediate areas, quantity requirements are generally good indicators of suitable production methods. In these intermediate areas, all factors must be weighed carefully to assure clear-cut indication of where equal-cost points occur for the processes considered. For instance, where stamping operations are concerned, the range of possibilities runs from machine-cut through short-run to full production stamping on high-speed automatic presses. The chart shown in Fig. 5-10 indicates an area from 100 to 10,000 pieces in which this occurs.

As quantity increases from the category of machine-cut to fully automatic production, tool and setup costs increase rapidly but labor costs decrease. Tool costs are easily amortized over a large number of parts, and labor costs per part become negligible.

Tolerances. Among the effects of design specifications on costs, those of tolerances are perhaps most significant. Tolerances in design influence the producibility of the end product in many ways, from necessitating additional steps in processing to rendering a part completely impractical to produce economically. Tolerances may cover not only dimensional

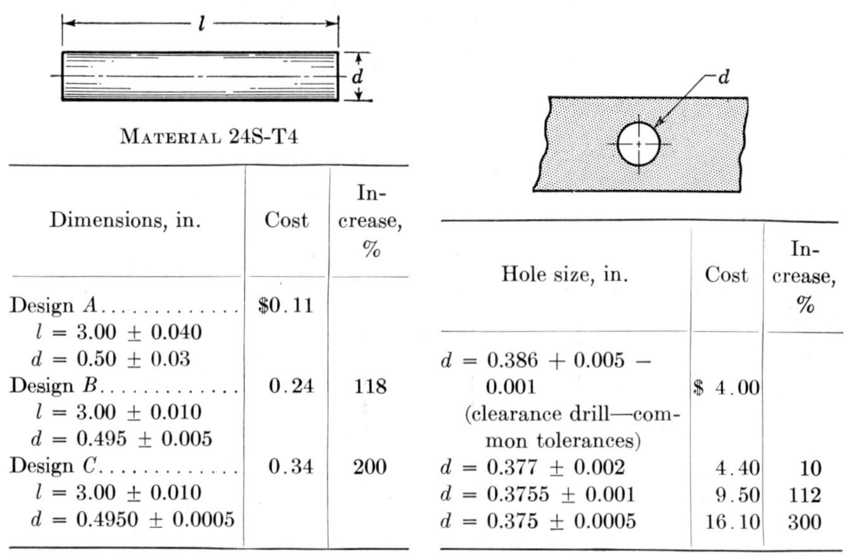

Dimensions, in.	Cost	Increase, %
Design *A*	\$0.11	
$l = 3.00 \pm 0.040$		
$d = 0.50 \pm 0.03$		
Design *B*	0.24	118
$l = 3.00 \pm 0.010$		
$d = 0.495 \pm 0.005$		
Design *C*	0.34	200
$l = 3.00 \pm 0.010$		
$d = 0.4950 \pm 0.0005$		

FIG. 5-11. Tolerances have a profound effect on costs. Design *A* permits use of stock as drawn, *B* requires turning, and *C* necessitates finish grinding.

Hole size, in.	Cost	Increase, %
$d = 0.386 + 0.005 - 0.001$ (clearance drill—common tolerances)	\$ 4.00	
$d = 0.377 \pm 0.002$	4.40	10
$d = 0.3755 \pm 0.001$	9.50	112
$d = 0.375 \pm 0.0005$	16.10	300

FIG. 5-12. Cost relationship of holes with varying tolerances. Cost shown was for 120 consecutive holes.

variation and surface-roughness range, but also the allowable variation in properties resulting from heat-treatment or other processing.

A simple example of how tolerances can increase cost is given in Fig. 5-11. Tolerances on dimensions specified at values smaller than functional requirements actually necessitate increased costs through additional machine time, checking and gauging time, rejections, and other procedures. In Fig. 5-11, design *A* can be made from bar stock by sawing to length, but tolerances for design *B* are too close for sawing. To hold the tolerances on design *B*, turning is required, and for design *C* grinding is necessary at a cost increase of 200 per cent over *A*.

In the same manner, holes are affected by specifications. The cost data in Fig. 5-12 were found from an actual study made to determine the

TABLE 5-2. PRICES OF MATERIALS (AS OF MAY 27, 1954)*

Material	Sheet	Rods (drawn)	Plate	Bars (rolled)	Extrusions	Tubing
Aluminum 2S, 3S	33.9	...	32.4	43.8	36.5 up	
Aluminum 63S-T5	...	...	...	...	...	31.6 up
Aluminum 11S-T3	...	46.6				
Magnesium FS1-O	94.0	...	56.0	...	51.5 up	59.0 up
Titanium and alloys	$15.00	...	$12.00	$6.00		
"A" nickel	86.5	82.5	84.5	82.5	...	$1.15½
Monel	67.5	65.5	66.5	65.5	...	$1.00½
Inconel	92.5	88.5	90.5	88.5	...	$1.37½
Copper	48.38	45.98	...	44.73	44.48	
Low brass	44.47	44.41				
Yellow brass	41.72	41.66				
Red brass	45.44	45.38				
Naval brass	45.76	40.07	...	...	41.33	
Leaded brass	...	...	...	...	39.11	
Commercial bronze	46.95	46.89				
Manganese bronze	49.48	43.62	...	...	45.18	
Phosphor bronze	66.58	67.08				
Muntz metal	43.96	39.77	...	...	41.02	
Nickel silver 10%	55.36	...	...	...	62.63	
HR steel	3.925	...	4.10	4.16	...	10.0
CD steel	4.775	5.22				
4615 steel	...	14.65	...	12.40		
4140 steel	...	14.58	...	12.28		
Spring steel 0.40C	...	5.45				
Spring steel 0.60C	...	7.65				
Spring steel 0.80C	...	8.60				
Spring steel 1.05C	...	10.55				
HR steel 2 in. OD	...	...	...	...	...	14.2
HR steel 3½ in. OD	...	...	...	...	...	11.5
CD steel 2 in. OD	...	...	...	...	...	17.1
CD steel 3½ in. OD	...	...	...	...	...	13.9
Tool steel Cr-V	...	$1.48				
Tool steel Hi-C, Cr	...	$0.70				
Tool steel Cr-V-Mo	...	$1.005				
Tool steel special C	...	$0.355				
Tool steel regular C	...	$0.25				
Stainless steel 301	38.25	35.25	37.25	35.25		
Stainless steel 321	50.50	42.00	45.75	42.00		
Stainless steel 410	34.25	28.75	30.00	28.75		
Stainless steel 430	34.75	29.75	30.50	29.75		
Cast-iron water pipe	...	...	...	...	...	5.60

* Compiled from *Iron Age*, vol. 173, no. 21, May 27, 1954. The prices given are in cents per pound unless otherwise indicated. These figures are approximate and are subject to correction for size and processing as well as freight costs.

relative effects of tightening hole tolerances. Some 120 holes were used in determining the cost factors, and these data do not include the additional costs of extra tooling and gauges necessary.

Materials. Table 5-2 can be used to find the relative prices of materials in different forms. In using this table, the reader should remember that prices are subject to change weekly, and since these prices are out of date they can be used only in a relative sense. Furthermore, the prices have been obtained for specific sizes and treatments or processes at producing centers scattered throughout the United States. Therefore corrections would be necessary for size, treatment, processing, and freight, in order to obtain the price at a given location.

PROBLEMS

NOTE: The first 10 problems are intended to be purely creative. Possible solutions should be shown by means of freehand or mechanical sketches. Since these problems will quickly become obsolete, the student is encouraged, with the advice and consent of his instructor, to state and solve other problems within the limitations of his academic program. The realization of the existence of a need and its statement are in themselves a creative act.

***5-1.** Make the preliminary sketches for the design of a new three-hole paper punch. The three-hole punch, as used in many classrooms for binding notes, sketches, and drawings, is subjected to so much abuse that a design for a rigid, long-wearing, well-built punch is needed. Students often jam as much paper between the jaws as possible and when it fails to operate they pound on the handle with a book or their fists. No punch is now available that will withstand this abuse. The punch should be capable of being mass-produced and should be made to sell at a reasonable price.

***5-2.** Describe a scheme for the design of simple self-opening and closing residence windows. The intelligence unit which dictates the opening and closing should be sensitive to temperature change. It would be desirable if it could also be made sensitive to wind and/or rain.

***5-3.** A wood screw has remarkable holding power but it is an expensive fastener because of the labor required for its use. As a substitute, design a self-clinching nail such that its presence is invisible from the far side of the joint.

***5-4.** Draw the preliminary sketches for the design of a hot- and cold-water mixing valve with automatic temperature control, capable of operating to any preset temperature, for use in residential baths and kitchens.

***5-5.** Describe a scheme to prevent mashing of fingers in automobile doors.

***5-6.** Design a base for a standard 115-volt incandescent light bulb such that it can be inserted in a standard threaded socket by a simple push and can be removed simply by pulling.

***5-7.** Describe a method for the design of a mechanism to be attached to a telephone book so that the proper page can be selected by a dialing operation.

***5-8.** Design a telescoping or folding slide rule.

***5-9.** Design a lever-operating drill chuck.

***5-10.** Describe a means for the design of a tire-deflation indicator. The indicator should be mounted on the dashboard so that the driver has a continuous visible check upon the condition of each tire.

*5-11. A one-piece 16-gauge (0.0598-in.) low-carbon sheet-steel shelf bracket with 8-in. legs is constructed as shown in the figure. Determine its strength by finding the total distributed load W which it can support.

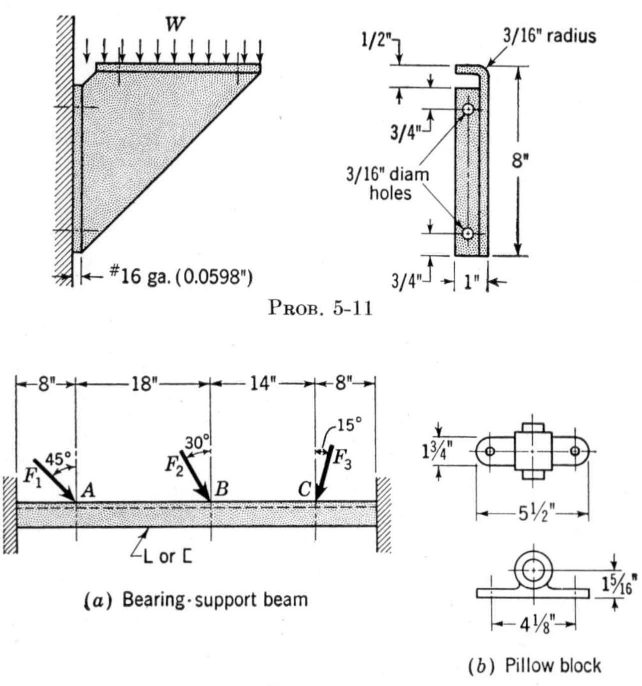

PROB. 5-11

(a) Bearing-support beam

(b) Pillow block

PROB. 5-12

*5-12. In the design of a special machine, of which only one will be built, it has been decided to use either a structural-steel angle or channel in a portion of the frame which acts as a bearing-support beam. In the figure, three pillow blocks are to be bolted to the beam at points A, B, and C. Each pillow block supports a rotating shaft having the bearing loads $F_1 = 225$ lb, $F_2 = 160$ lb, and $F_3 = 190$ lb. The forces act in the directions shown in the figure. The beam will be welded to the machine frame at the ends, and hence the ends are shown as fixed. The design of the welds is a separate problem and is not to be considered here. In order to keep the rotating components in proper relationship with each other, the deflection of the beam at points A, B, and C should not exceed $\frac{1}{32}$ in. No shock or impact loads are present. Select a standard-size angle or channel for the beam.

*5-13. In the figure a line drawing is used to illustrate the front view of a rack for the storage of stock-length pieces of steel. These racks are used in groups of two or three in warehouses and on the manufacturing floor for efficient handling of steel in lengths which may vary from 10 to 24 ft. A company desires to build 36 of these for its own use. Appearance is not important, but they must not tip over, sag, bend, or warp. The racks are to be portable and therefore no arrangements should be made for fastening them to the floor. Make whatever sketches and calculations are necessary to obtain an easily constructed, economical rack.

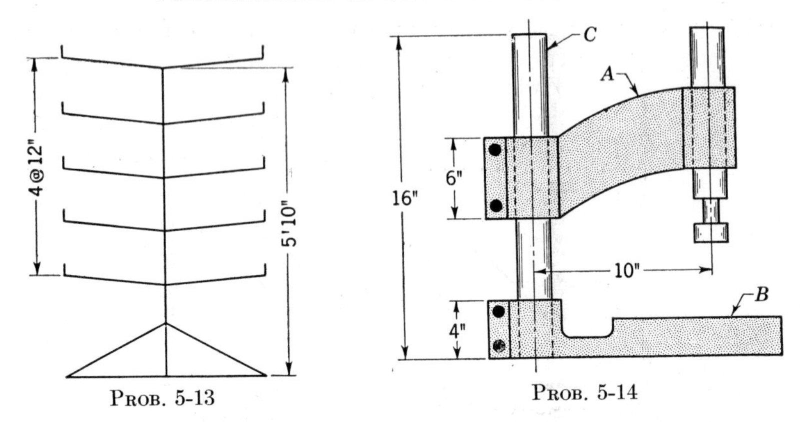

PROB. 5-13 PROB. 5-14

***5-14.** The figure illustrates a table-model pneumatic impact press. A power cylinder mounted in a guide bracket *A* may slide vertically on a base-supported column *C*. In use, a chuck on the piston rod holds a tool which may be a marking, riveting, staking, stamping, or swaging tool. Not shown in the figure is a mechanism in which a foot lever is pressed which causes the entire power cylinder to move downward in the bracket until the tool is in contact with the work. A slight additional pressure on the foot lever then "triggers" a valve so that sufficient air pressure is admitted to deliver the impact. The force of the impact is adjustable up to 7,000 lb by regulating the volume of air admitted. Design column *C* for manufacture in quantities of 1,000 units. Both the guide bracket and the base are clamped to the column.

***5-15.** The figure illustrates a 1-in. micrometer caliper. Select the material and determine the cross-sectional dimensions for the curved portion of the frame.

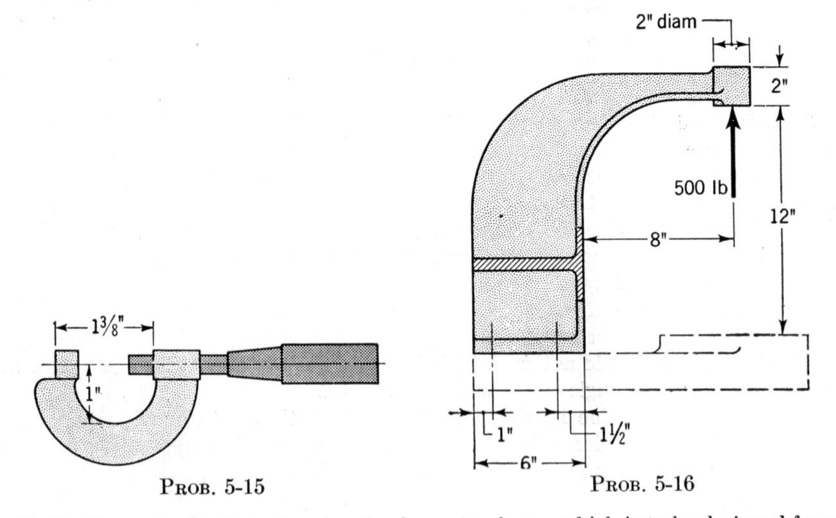

PROB. 5-15 PROB. 5-16

***5-16.** Shown in the figure is a small arbor-press frame which is to be designed for a name-plate load of 500 lb. The frame is to be attached to the base with four ⅝-in. bolts spaced as shown in the figure but with the spacing in the other direction to be specified by the designer. Make the decisions, calculations, and sketches necessary to specify the frame. Although a cast-iron T section is shown, there is no limitation on either the material or the shape. The frame is to be manufactured in quantities of 250 units at a time.

***5-17.** Shown in the figure is a bell-crank lever used on job-shop printing presses. The lever is shown in its central position, and it oscillates through a total angle of 24°, or 12° each way. The normal speed is $n = 160$ oscillations per minute, and

$$F_1 = 250 \cos 2\pi nt \text{ lb}$$

where t is the time in minutes. Hardened-steel pins ⅝ in. in diameter are used to transfer the load through nylon bushings A and B, which have an outside diameter of ⅞ in. and a length of 1¼ in. They are press-fitted into holes in the lever. The nylon bushing C has an outside diameter of 1⅛ in. and a length of 1¼ in. It is also press-fitted into the lever and works on a hardened-steel stud which is fastened to the frame of the press. It is to be manufactured in quantities of 50 to 100 pieces. Make a complete design of the lever.

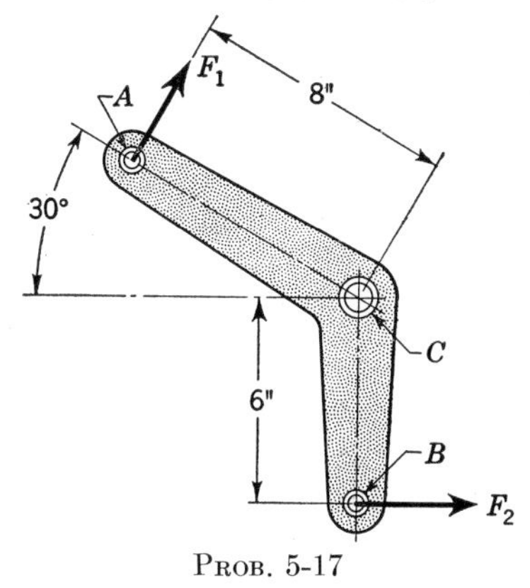

PROB. 5-17

***5-18.** Design a 24- × 36-in. surface plate of the type used in machine shops. It is to be supported uniformly along the four edges and must have a guaranteed flatness of ±0.0002 in.

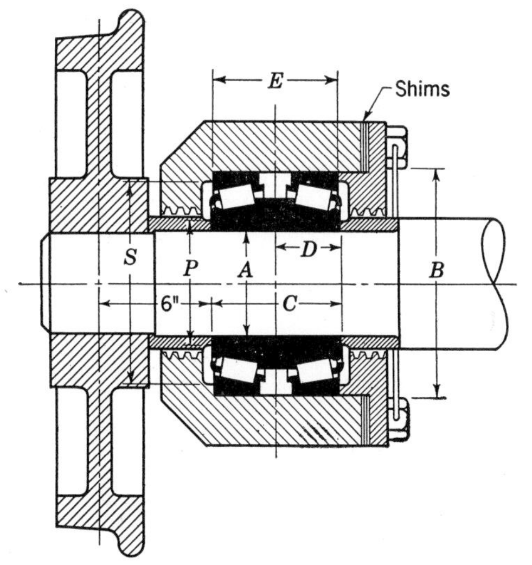

PROB. 5-19. (*Courtesy of The Timken Roller Bearing Company.*)

***5-19.** The figure shows the design of the inboard journals for an ingot car. The dimensions, in inches, are as follows: $A = 4.250$, $B = 6.500$, $C = 2⅞$, $D = 1\frac{7}{16}$, $E = 2⅞$, $P = 4\frac{17}{32}$, $S = 5¾$. The wheel load is 10,100 lb. Decide upon suitable values for those dimensions which are not given. Determine the stresses in the axle and specify a suitable material and heat-treatment.

PART 2

THE DESIGN AND SELECTION OF MACHINE ELEMENTS

CHAPTER 6

THE DESIGN OF SCREWS, FASTENERS, AND JOINTS

This book presupposes a knowledge of the elementary methods of fastening. Studies in engineering drawing and industrial processes ordinarily include instruction concerning typical fasteners such as bolts, nuts, cap screws, setscrews, rivets, spring retainers, locking devices, and keys. Instruction is also included on the various welds and welding symbols. Since the reader is expected to be familiar with the sources of this information, it will not be included in this book. On the other hand, we are interested in the selection of the proper fastener, in arranging or locating it with respect to the joint or assembly, and in studying rational methods of determining its size and material. New fastening products and processes are being introduced almost daily, and the designer must supplement his basic knowledge of them by a constant reading of the current literature. Since no single fastening method is the best, the choice of the most applicable and economical one requires a back ground knowledge of all those which are available.

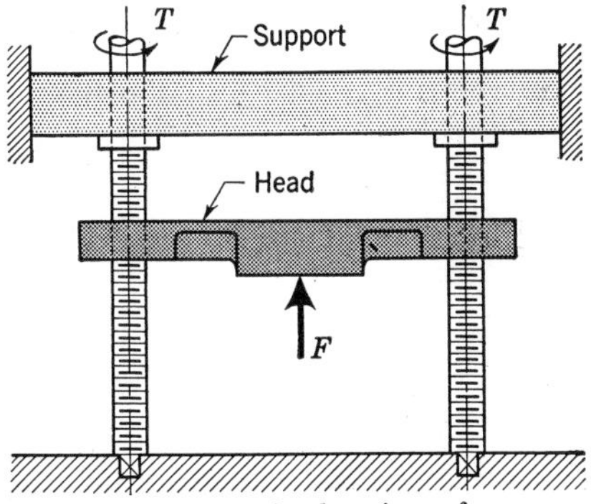

Fig. 6-1. Schematic drawing of a press driven by power screws.

6-1. Power Screws. A power screw is a device used in machinery to change rotary motion into linear motion. The more common types include the lead screws of lathes and screws for vises, presses, and jacks.

A schematic representation of the application of power screws to a power-driven press is shown in Fig. 6-1. In use, a torque T is applied to the ends of the screws through a set of gears, thus driving the head of the press downward against the load. The threads are generally *Acme* or 10° *modified square,* as listed in any reference handbook.

In designing a power screw, the material, treatment, and thread system are selected first. Although a power screw is usually loaded in torsion, this effect cannot be evaluated until all other calculations are complete. For this reason it is customary to estimate the diameter by considering the screw either as a column or as a tension member, depending upon which type of loading is present. Sometimes bending also exists, in which case the combined effects must be considered.

TABLE 6-1. THREADS PER INCH IN COMMON USE FOR POWER SCREWS

Major diameter, in.	$\frac{1}{4}$	$\frac{5}{16}$	$\frac{3}{8}$	$\frac{1}{2}$	$\frac{5}{8}$	$\frac{3}{4}$	1	$1\frac{1}{2}$
Threads per inch	16	14	12	10	8	6	5	4

After the tentative diameter has been obtained, a decision must be made regarding the pitch and lead. There is no standard for the pitch of power screws, but Table 6-1 lists the usual values. It is now necessary to obtain the torque required to drive the screw against the load.

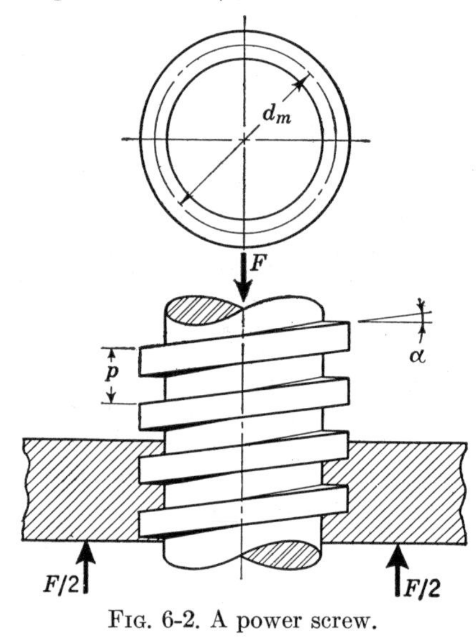

FIG. 6-2. A power screw.

Figure 6-2 shows a simplified square-threaded power screw with single thread having a mean diameter d_m, a pitch p, a helix angle α, and loaded by the axial compressive force F. In order to find the torque required to twist the screw against this load, let us imagine that a single thread is unrolled, or

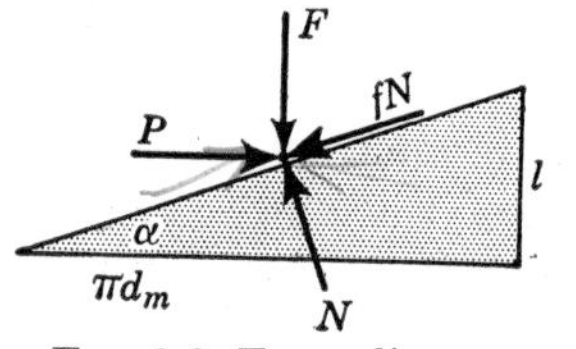

FIG. 6-3. Force diagram.

developed, producing the triangle shown in Fig. 6-3. The base of this triangle has a length which is equal to the circumference of the mean-thread-diameter circle. The angle is the helix angle α; the vertical side has a length l representing the lead, which is equal to the pitch for a single-threaded screw. The force F represents the summation of all the unit axial forces acting upon the normal-thread area. It is necessary to apply a force P parallel to the base in order to overcome the frictional force fN and push the load up the inclined plane. Since the system is in equilibrium under the action of these forces, we can write for the horizontal and vertical directions

$$\Sigma F_H = 0 \qquad P - N \sin \alpha - fN \cos \alpha = 0 \tag{a}$$
$$\Sigma F_V = 0 \qquad F + fN \sin \alpha - N \cos \alpha = 0 \tag{b}$$

Eliminating the normal force N and solving Eqs. (a) and (b) for the force P, we obtain

$$P = \frac{F(\sin\alpha + f\cos\alpha)}{\cos\alpha - f\sin\alpha} \tag{c}$$

Referring again to Fig. 6-3, we see that

$$\sin\alpha = \frac{l}{\sqrt{l^2 + \pi^2 d_m{}^2}} \qquad \text{and} \qquad \cos\alpha = \frac{\pi d_m}{\sqrt{l^2 + \pi^2 d_m{}^2}} \tag{d}$$

Substitution of these values in Eq. (c) yields

$$P = \frac{F(l + \pi f d_m)}{\pi d_m - fl} \tag{e}$$

Since the torque is $Pd_m/2$, we can write

$$T = \frac{Fd_m}{2}\,\frac{l + \pi f d_m}{\pi d_m - fl} \tag{6-1}$$

where T is the torque required to overcome the thread friction and raise the load and f is the coefficient of thread friction.

The previous equations have been developed for square threads where the normal thread loads are parallel to the axis of the screw. In the case of Acme or Unified threads the normal thread load is inclined to the axis by an amount β, which is equal to half the thread angle (Fig. 6-4). The effect of this is to increase the frictional force by the wedging action of the threads. Therefore the frictional terms in Eq. (6-1) must be divided by $\cos\beta$. This yields

$$T = \frac{Fd_m}{2}\,\frac{l + \pi f d_m \sec\beta}{\pi d_m - fl\sec\beta} \tag{6-2}$$

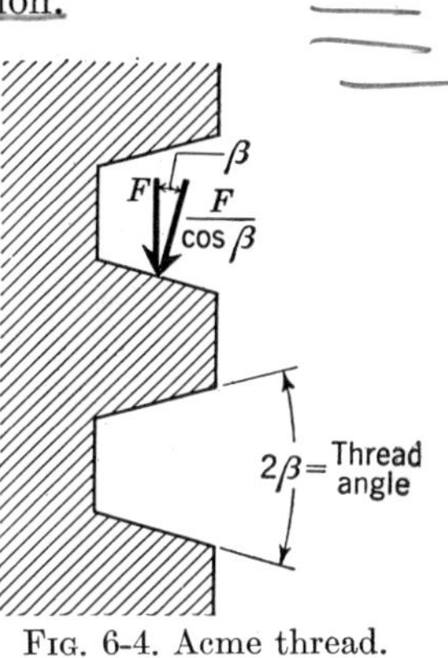

FIG. 6-4. Acme thread.

The Acme thread is preferred over the square thread for power screws because it is easier to machine and also because it permits the use of a split nut which can be used to take up for wear.

An expression for the efficiency is also useful. If we let $f = 0$ in Eq. (6-1) or (6-2), we obtain

$$T_0 = \frac{Fl}{2\pi} \tag{f}$$

which is the torque required to raise the load when no friction is present. The efficiency is, therefore,

$$e = \frac{T_0}{T} = \frac{Fl}{2\pi T} \tag{6-3}$$

It should be noted that Eq. (6-1) or (6-2) represents only the torque required to overcome thread friction and raise the load. Some additional torque must be applied to the screw in order to overcome the thrust or collar-bearing friction. Figure 6-5 shows a typical thrust collar in which the load is assumed to be concentrated at the mean collar diameter d_c. If f_c is the coefficient of collar friction, then the torque required is

$$T_c = \frac{Ff_cd_c}{2} \tag{6-4}$$

The total torque is then obtained by adding the results of Eq. (6-1) or (6-2) and Eq. (6-4). Knowing the total torque, the designer should next redetermine the strength of the screw, using the appropriate failure theory. In calculating this strength, the minor diameter will give a conservative figure. However, it has been demonstrated that the strength based upon the mean diameter of the threads most nearly approaches the strength of the original blank.[1]

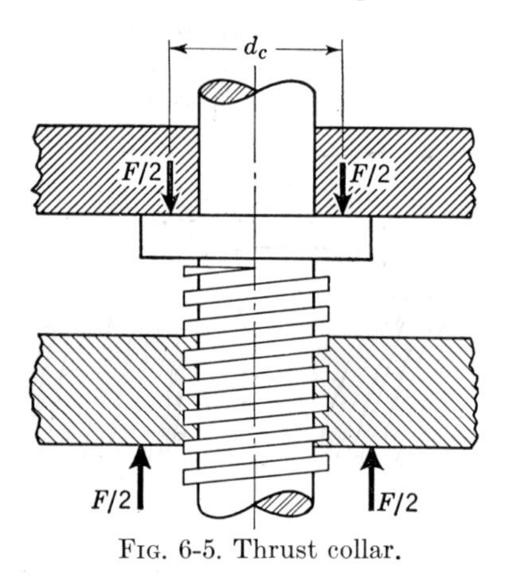

Fig. 6-5. Thrust collar.

Assumptions. It may be noted that the accuracy of the entire design depends upon a proper selection of the frictional coefficients. If the screw is normally operated very slowly, so that frictional characteristics approach statical conditions, then the coefficients may be as much as 30 per cent more than for running conditions. The accuracy with which the threads are cut, the thread finish, the expected lubrication conditions, the amount of run-in, and the rubbing materials all affect its value. In the absence of exact information, an average value of 0.13 is suggested. For poor conditions of lubrication, thread finish, or materials, this can be increased up to a maximum of 0.16. On the other hand, if these variables are such as to produce excellent frictional characteristics, then a value of f as low as 0.10 may be used. These values are applicable to both the thread friction and the collar friction for the stated conditions.

The suggested coefficients are necessarily empirical because they have been estimated from experimental data. The possibility of a comparatively large variation in these coefficients must be carefully considered, since this variation may be expected in a single power screw operated for a long period of time or in a group of power screws. This means that the

[1] E. M. Slaughter, Tests on Threaded Sections, *Metal Progr.*, vol. 26, p. 18, March, 1933.

exact values of the torques, forces, and stresses, which are calculated using frictional coefficients, must remain indefinite.

Thread Stresses. It is sometimes necessary to determine the thread stresses, as, for example, in the design of the nut. Figure 6-6 shows a square-threaded screw loaded by a nut. The thread on the screw tends to shear off on the minor diameter d_r. The average thread shearing stress for the screw is, therefore,

$$s_s = \frac{2F}{\pi d_r h} \tag{6-5}$$

where h is the height of the nut. Similarly, the average thread shearing stress for the nut is

$$s_s = \frac{2F}{\pi d h} \tag{6-6}$$

where d is the major diameter of the thread. The bearing pressure between the threads is

$$s_b = \frac{4pF}{\pi h(d^2 - d_r^2)} \tag{6-7}$$

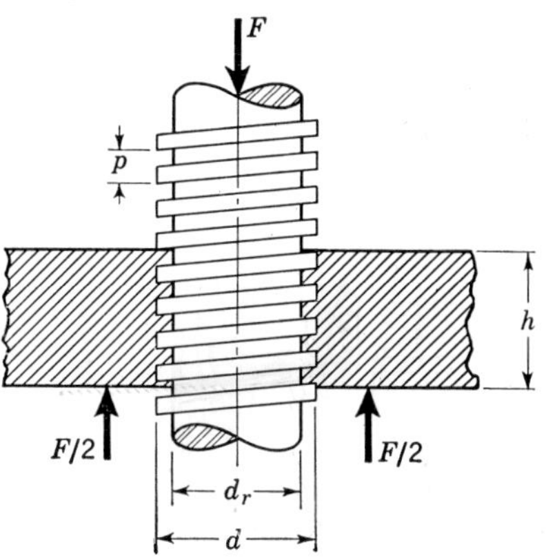

FIG. 6-6. Square-thread screw and nut.

A similar set of relations may be determined for Acme and V-type threads. In each case the stress is equal to the force divided by the area being stressed. In determining the bearing stress, both the force and the area would be increased by the same amount, thus canceling each other, and so this stress would not be changed.

Assumptions. The following assumptions are implied by the development of the thread-stress equations:

1. The load is equally divided among the threads. It will be shown in Sec. 6-3 that this is frequently *not true.*

2. Equations (6-5) and (6-6) are based upon the assumption that the threads are in direct shear. This assumption is seldom true because some bending (cantilever style) must exist in order that the threads have sufficient clearance for lubrication. We must therefore conclude that these are only *average* stresses.

3. Equation (6-7) implies that the bearing stress is the *average* stress, not the maximum.

The three thread-stress equations are easy to use, and they make it possible to calculate the stresses quickly. By employing a rather large factor of safety, a safe design is usually obtained. However, they are empirical equations because they do not give the actual maximum stress intensities. Their use is justified in a great deal of design work because of the simplification they bring about.

Decisions. The decisions which must be made in designing a power screw and nut depend upon the characteristics of the particular design. However, the following are usually required:

1. Select the tentative materials, heat-treatment if used, and manufacturing processes for the screw and nut.
2. Select the thread system to be used.
3. From a consideration of the loads, make the necessary design assumptions to calculate the diameters. This means that it is necessary to decide whether the screw is a column, a beam, a tension member, a torsion member, or a combination of these.
4. Decide on the factors of safety to use for each of the assumed methods of failure. If the screw may fail by two or more methods, then the factor of safety is *not* necessarily the same for each method, because the assumptions for each are different.
5. Select the pitch and lead of the thread.
6. Select the frictional coefficients.
7. Select the material properties which best define failure for each method of calculation. This might be the yield strength in tension or shear, the ultimate strength, or the fatigue strength.

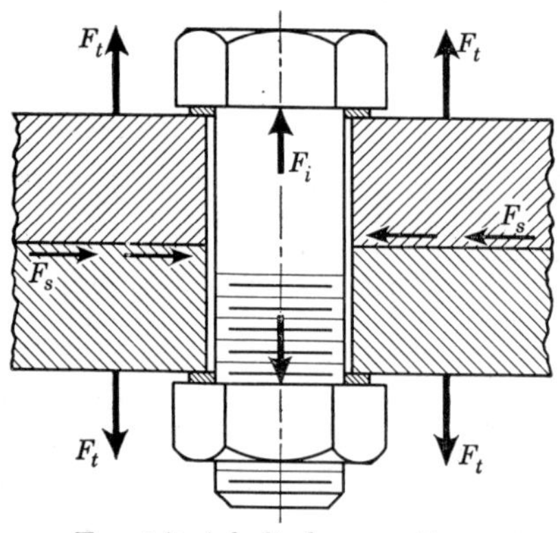

FIG. 6-7. A bolted connection.

6-2. Preloading of Bolts. When a connection is desired which can be disassembled without destructive methods and which is strong enough to resist both external tensile loads, shear loads, or a combination of these, then the simple bolted joint using hardened washers is a good solution. Such a joint is illustrated in Fig. 6-7 in which the bolt has first been tightened to produce an initial tensile preload F_i, after which the external tensile load F_t and the external shear load F_s are applied. The effect of the preload is to place the parts in compression for better resistance to the external tensile load and to create friction between the parts to resist the shear load.

The shear load does not affect the final bolt tension, and we shall neglect this load for the time being in order to study the effect of the external tensile load on the compression of the parts and the resultant bolt tension. In determining the portion of the external load taken by the connected parts and the portion taken by the bolt, it is necessary to define the term *stiffness constant.* The stiffness constant of a body is the ratio of the load applied to the body to the deflection produced by that load. Using the equation for deformation due to tensile or compressive loads, $\delta = Fl/AE$, and rearranging, we obtain

$$k = \frac{F}{\delta} = \frac{AE}{l} \tag{6-8}$$

where k is the stiffness constant in pounds per inch. When the external load is applied to the preloaded assembly there is a change in the deformations. Since the bolt is initially in tension, it must experience an increase in deformation; the increase is $\Delta\delta_b = F_b/k_b$. The subscript b refers to the bolt, and F_b is, therefore, the portion of the external load which is taken by the bolt. The connected members will experience a decrease in deformation amounting to $\Delta\delta_m = F_m/k_m$. The subscript m refers to the members or parts which are connected together. Since these changes in deformation must be equal, we can write

$$\frac{F_b}{k_b} = \frac{F_m}{k_m} \tag{a}$$

By substituting $F_m = F_t - F_b$ and rearranging, we have

$$F_b = \frac{k_b F_t}{k_b + k_m} \tag{b}$$

Therefore, the resultant load on the bolt is

$$F = F_b + F_i = \frac{k_b F_t}{k_b + k_m} + F_i \tag{6-9}$$

In the same manner, the resultant compression of the connected members is found to be

$$F = \frac{k_m F_t}{k_b + k_m} - F_i \tag{6-10}$$

Equations (6-9) and (6-10) hold only as long as some of the initial compression remains in the members. If the external force is large enough to remove completely this compression, then the members will separate and the entire load will be carried by the bolt. The importance of these equations is illustrated by the following example.

EXAMPLE 6-1. In Fig. 6-7 let the stiffness of the members relative to the bolt be $k_m = 3k_b$. If the initial preload on the bolt is $F_i = 1{,}200$ lb and the external tensile load is 1,200 lb, find the resultant tension in the bolt and the compression of the members.

Solution. The resultant tension in the bolt is found from Eq. (6-9). It is

$$F = \frac{k_b F_t}{k_b + k_m} + F_i = \frac{k_b(1{,}200)}{k_b + 3k_b} + 1{,}200 = 1{,}500 \text{ lb tension} \qquad \textit{Ans.}$$

The compression in the members is found from Eq. (6-10):

$$F = \frac{k_m F_t}{k_b + k_m} - F_i = \frac{3k_b(1{,}200)}{k_b + 3k_b} - 1{,}200 = -300 \text{ lb compression} \qquad \textit{Ans.}$$

This shows that the proportion of the load taken by the bolt is small and that it depends upon the relative stiffness of the two materials. Since the members are still in compression, there is no separation of the parts even though the external load, in this example, is equal to the bolt preload.

The importance of preloading of bolts cannot be overestimated. It has the following two desirable effects:

1. *Improvement of fatigue strength.* When a preloaded, bolted assembly is subjected to the action of fatigue loads only a small proportion of the total stress change is applied to the bolt. Therefore, the effect is to improve the fatigue resistance of the bolt. It should be noted that this resistance is due purely to preloading and does not include the effects of stress concentration or other surface irregularities which might cause failure.

2. *Improvement in the locking effect.* It has been demonstrated[1] that loosening of a nut is due to a variation of stress within the fastener. Preloading reduces the amount of stress change and therefore considerably improves the locking effect.

In order to obtain the beneficial effects of preloading, the assembled members must be rigid and the bolt must have a high preload. This condition is often achieved when metal-to-metal parts, that is, without a gasket, are bolted together. When the members which are bolted together are metal-to-metal, the stiffness of the members is often so much greater than the stiffness of the bolt that the proportion of the external load taken by the bolt may be neglected (see Sec. 6-5).

When a gasket is employed, the beneficial effects of preloading may be partly preserved by using a stiff gasket. A soft gasket, or the use of soft materials such as magnesium or aluminum, would completely destroy this effect and cause the bolt to take practically the entire load. When a gasket is employed, the stiffness constant of the members may often be neglected (since their stiffness is so much greater) and the constant calculated for the gasket alone. Equation (6-8) is employed, using l as the thickness of the gasket.

Shear Loading. Applications in which the bolt is loaded in shear occur quite frequently in design. The effect of preloading is to create sufficient friction between the assembled members so that no slippage occurs. Without slippage there are no shearing or bearing loads on the bolt shank, and the tension remains at its initial value. Maintenance of

[1] J. N. Goodier and R. J. Sweeney, Loosening by Vibration of Threaded Fasteners, *Mech. Eng.*, vol. 67, no. 12, pp. 798–802, December, 1945.

this condition means that even with fatigue loads the bolt remains statically loaded and thus is not subjected to fatigue. Another important effect of preloading is concerned with the compression of the material around the edge of the bolt hole. Since in shear loading the edge of the hole is a point of stress concentration which is loaded in tension, the effect of the preload is to neutralize this by placing the material initially in compression. This effect has been demonstrated in practice by a tendency for failure to occur in the gross-plate section rather than through the holes.[1]

Preloading Values. Bolts may be preloaded by heating them prior to assembly so that the resultant contraction upon cooling induces a preload, by a hydraulic jacking arrangement which stretches the bolt while the nut is tightened, by impact power-driving equipment, by a wrench equipped with a torque-measuring device, or by torquing the nut through a predetermined angle. Where accurate preloading is required it is necessary to resort to experimental methods of measurement. If torquing methods are used, then an estimate of the amount of torque required to produce a given preload is necessary. If Eqs. (6-2) and (6-4) are added together and rearranged, we obtain

$$T = F_i d_m \left(\frac{1}{2} \frac{l + \pi f d_m \sec \beta}{\pi d_m - fl \sec \beta} + 0.625 f_c \right) \tag{6-11}$$

where d_c has been replaced by $1.25d_m$ for a nut width of $1\frac{1}{2}$ diameters. We can obtain a solution to this equation if we substitute values for a particular bolt.

Using a $\frac{3}{4}$-10NC bolt as an example, we see that $l = 0.10$ in. and $\beta = 30°$. Using a coefficient of friction of 0.15 for both the thread friction and the friction between the nut and washer, the torque becomes

$$T = 0.205 F_i d_m \tag{c}$$

Substitution of values for other sizes of bolts will yield coefficients only slightly different from this.

In an experiment to determine the variation in the applied torque and the resulting preload, numerous bolts and nuts from various manufacturers, with both coarse and fine threads, were tried. The bolts were of low-carbon steel with the stresses relieved and with rolled threads; the nuts were American Standard, semifinished. The torque coefficient was determined, using the major diameter instead of the mean diameter as used above. For high torques the average coefficient was 0.191, and for medium torques it was 0.201. It was found that an extreme bolt would vary as much as 30 per cent from the average but the mean devia-

[1] "ASME Handbook, Metals Engineering—Design," sec. 6-16, p. 171, McGraw-Hill Book Company, Inc., New York, 1953.

tion was only 7 per cent.[1] Stewart[2] states that a fair estimate is

$$T = 0.20F_i d \tag{6-12}$$

where d is the size of the bolt and T is the torque required to produce the tensile preload F_i. Naturally, the coefficient may differ from this value up to 50 per cent, depending upon the thread-surface conditions which are present.

TABLE 6-2.* PROPERTIES OF VARIOUS GRADES OF BOLTS†

SAE grade	ASTM designation	Tensile strength, psi	Proof load or yield strength, psi	Material
0	...	...	...	Low carbon
1	A307	55,000	...	Low carbon
2	...	69,000	55,000	Low carbon, stress relieved
3	...	110,000	85,000	Medium carbon, cold-worked
5	...	120,000	85,000	Medium carbon, quenched and tempered
	A325	125,000	90,000	Medium carbon, quenched and tempered
6	...	140,000	110,000	Special medium carbon, quenched and tempered
7	...	130,000	105,000	Alloy steel, quenched and tempered
8	...	150,000	120,000	Alloy steel, quenched and tempered

* From "ASME Handbook, Metals Engineering—Design," p. 176, McGraw-Hill Book Company, Inc., New York, 1953.

† For ½-in. sizes and smaller. For larger bolts these values must be decreased. See ASTM Specifications.

The properties of various grades of bolts are listed in Table 6-2. These properties are for diameters of ½ in. and smaller and must be appropriately reduced for larger sizes. For example, the proof load[3] of an A325 bolt in the 1-in. size is 78,000 psi. The table can be used to select an appropriate bolt material. After the material is selected, the proof load and the tensile strength are used to determine the amount of preload. While the recommended minimum preload is 90 per cent of the

[1] G. A. Maney, Predicting Bolt Tension, *Fasteners*, vol. 3, no. 5, pp. 16–18, 1948.

[2] ASME Handbook, *op. cit.*, pp. 171–177.

[3] "The proof load of a bolt is roughly equivalent to terms such as elastic limit, yield strength, yield point, etc., but differs to some degree. Exactly, the proof load is the maximum load that can be applied to the bolt without getting a permanent set or permanent stretch. In testing a bolt for conformity to a specified proof load, the bolt length is measured accurately; the specified load is applied and then released. The bolt length is again accurately measured and, if it does not differ from the length before loading, the bolt conforms to requirement for proof load." From *Fasteners*, vol. 9, no. 5, Industrial Fasteners Institute, Cleveland, 1954.

proof load,[1] there is no maximum except failure of the bolt in tightening. The explanation for this is twofold. A typical stress-strain diagram for good bolt materials is shown in Fig. 6-8. It will be noticed that there is no clearly defined yield point and that the curve progresses smoothly up to the tensile strength. This means that, no matter how much preload is given the bolt, it will retain its load-carrying capacity. On the other hand, a bolt made with a material having a well-defined yield point would become plastic at the yield point and lose its ability to carry a load.

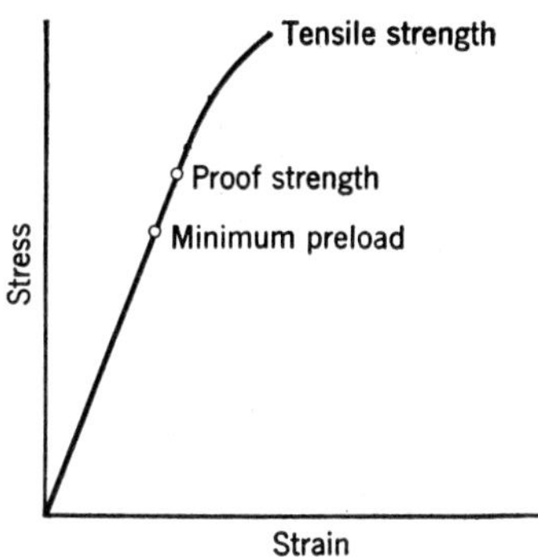

Fig. 6-8. Typical stress-strain diagram for bolt materials.

The second point is that, in tightening a nut, approximately 45 per cent of the torque is used in overcoming friction. This means that the bolt has not only a normal tensile stress but also a torsional shearing stress. These two combine to equal a resultant tensile stress which is approximately 20 per cent higher than the normal tensile stress. After tightening, the shearing stress disappears.[2] This means that, if the bolt does not fracture during tightening, a reserve strength of at least 20 per cent is present afterwards.

Table 6-3. Bolt-tension and Torque Values*

Bolt size, in.	Minimum bolt tension, lb	Equivalent torque, lb-ft
½	11,500	100
⅝	17,300	180
¾	25,600	320
⅞	32,400	470
1	42,500	710
1⅛	50,800	960
1¼	64,500	1,350

* From High Strength Bolting, *Machine Design*, vol. 25, no. 10, p. 384, October, 1953.

Table 6-3 lists values of the preload, on the basis of 90 per cent of the proof stress, and the corresponding torque values, as obtained from Eq.

[1] High Strength Bolting, *Fasteners*, vol. 9, no. 1, 1954.

[2] The initial torsion or shearing stress in a bolt may be held because of friction of the bolt head and nut. When the joint is subjected to dynamic loads, the flattening of high spots or of paint or dirt will often relieve this torsional friction, permitting the shearing stress to decrease. In particular cases it may be desirable to relieve the torsion by turning the nut back a small angle without decreasing the initial tension.

(6-12), for various bolt diameters. These values are based upon an ASTM A325 bolt. The importance of selecting a proper material should be emphasized. If the bolt material has a pronounced yield point, the bolt may twist off during tightening or be unable to retain a preload, because of plastic yielding.

6-3. Selection of the Nut. Figure 6-9 shows the loading conditions applied to a nut when the bolt is preloaded. If it is assumed that the same proportion of the load is taken by each thread, then the tension in the bolt is a maximum at the bottom of the nut and decreases uniformly to zero at the top. The opposite conditions prevail in the nut, with maximum compression occurring at the bottom, decreasing uniformly through the body, and becoming zero at the top. Since the bolt is in tension it will become longer; the nut, being in compression, will become shorter. The result of this assumption is that the pitch tends to decrease on the nut and increase on the bolt. This means that the threads move out of engagement with each other, which, of course, cannot be true. This leads to the conclusion that the bottom thread on the nut takes the entire load, with the remaining threads in contact but not transferring any load.

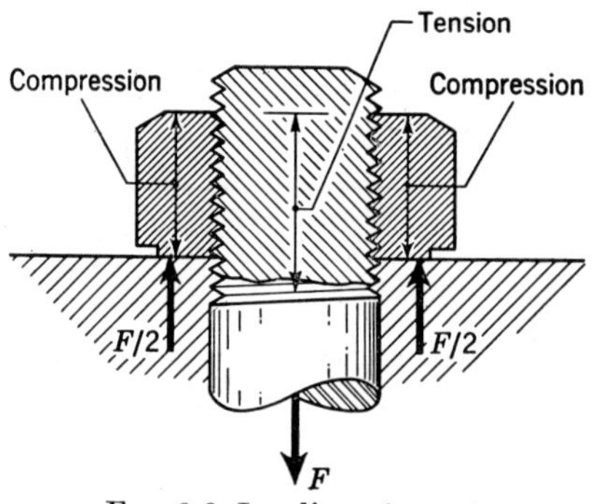

Fig. 6-9. Loading of a nut.

This tendency may be partially corrected by proportioning the nut so as to cause more deformation to exist at the bottom. Figure 6-10 shows two nut designs in which material has been removed from the lower portion of the nut in order to equalize the stress distribution.

In practice, conditions are not quite as severe as pictured, since yielding of the threads in the nut will permit the other threads to transfer some of the load. However, since such a tendency is present, it must be guarded against and knowledge of it used in selecting the nut.

Another factor which acts to reduce the tendency of the bottom thread to take the entire load is that the wedging action of the threads tends to spread or dilate the nut.

These conditions point to the fact that, when preloading is desired, careful attention should be given to the nut material. By selecting a soft nut, plastic yielding will enable the nut threads to divide the load more evenly.

Nuts are tested by determining their stripping strength. The test is made by threading a nut on a hardened-steel mandrel and pulling it through the nut. The strength is the load divided by the mean-thread area. Common nuts have a stripping strength of approximately 90,000 psi.

Another factor which must be considered in the design of bolted joints is the maintenance of the initial preload. This load may be relaxed by yielding of the clamped material, by extrusion of paint or plating from the contact surfaces, or by a compression of rough places. Extra contact area may be provided by hardened washers. This is especially necessary if the bolted parts are relatively soft and the bolt head or nut does not provide sufficient bearing area.

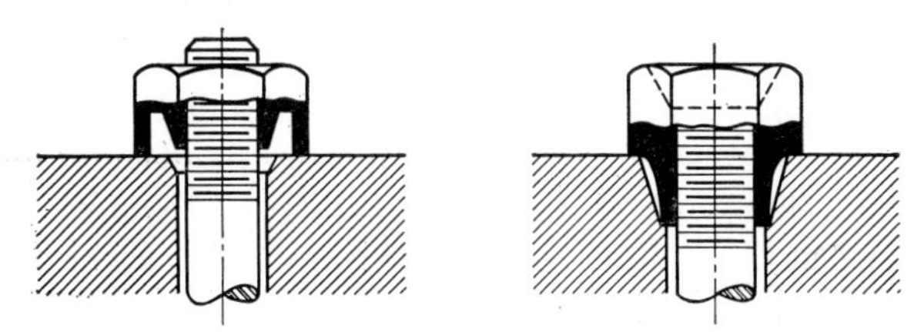

FIG. 6-10. Typical methods of distributing the thread load.

6-4. Bolted and Riveted Joints Loaded in Shear.[1] In designing bolted and riveted joints the machine designer is not limited by construction codes. He is thus able to use his ingenuity in selecting materials, stresses, and methods of calculation to produce strong economical connections with trim and pleasing appearances.

A satisfactory method of designing bolted joints is to design for rivets and then to substitute the same-size bolt for each rivet. With this method the bolted joint is stronger by approximately 50 per cent, which means that two bolts will carry as much shear load as three rivets.[2]

In Fig. 6-11*a* is shown a riveted connection loaded in shear. Let us now study the various means by which this connection might fail.

Figure 6-11*b* shows a failure by bending of the rivet or of the riveted members. The bending moment is approximately $M = Ft/2$, where F is the shearing force and t is the grip of the rivet, that is, the total thickness of the connected parts. The bending stress in the members or in the rivet is, neglecting stress concentration,

$$s = \frac{M}{I/c} \tag{6-13}$$

[1] The design of bolted and riveted connections for boilers, bridges, buildings, and other structures in which danger to human life is involved is strictly governed by various construction codes. When designing these structures the engineer should refer to the American Institute of Steel Construction Handbook, the American Railway Engineering Association specifications, or the Boiler Construction Code of the American Society of Mechanical Engineers.

[2] High Strength Bolting, *Machine Design*, vol. 25, no. 10, p. 388, October, 1953.

where I/c is the section modulus for the weakest member or for the rivet or rivets, depending upon which stress is to be found. The calculation of the bending stress in this manner is an assumption, because we do not know exactly how the load is distributed to the rivet nor the relative deformations of the rivet and the members. Although this equation can be used to determine the bending stress, it is seldom used in design; instead its effect is compensated for by an increase in the factor of safety.

The following modes of failure introduce a complicating factor in the determination of the stresses present. Some friction between the plates is always present in both riveted and bolted joints; in fact, when bolted joints are used and when the bolts are tightened to the recommended preload, the friction rather than the bolt is intended to carry the load. A determination of how much friction is present, and of what portion of the load it removes from the bolt or rivet, is difficult to make. It depends upon the nature of the contact surfaces, the amount of lubrication present and the surface finish, and the amount of relaxation of preload. Since the portion of the load supported by the friction between the plates cannot be calculated, it has been customary to design the joint as if no friction were present at all. This is on the conservative side, and the reader should remember that if friction is present the actual strength of the joint is much more than the calculations would indicate.

In Fig. 6-11*c* failure of the rivet by pure shear is shown; the stress in the rivet is

$$s_s = \frac{F}{A} \tag{6-14}$$

where A is the cross-sectional area of all the rivets in the group. It may be noted that it is standard practice in structural design to use the nominal diameter of the rivet rather than the diameter of the hole, even though a hot-driven rivet expands and nearly fills up the hole.

Rupture of one of the connected members or plates by pure tension is illustrated in Fig. 6-11*d*. The tensile stress is

$$s = \frac{F}{A} \qquad \text{or} \qquad s = k\frac{F}{A} \tag{6-15}$$

where A is the net area of the plate, that is, reduced by an amount equal to the area of all the rivet holes, and k is the stress-concentration factor for the holes. For brittle materials and static loads and for either ductile or brittle materials loaded in fatigue, the stress-concentration effects must be included. It is true that the use of a bolt with an initial preload and, sometimes, a rivet will place the area around the hole in compression and thus tend to nullify the effects of stress concentration, but, unless definite steps are taken to assure that the preload does not relax, it is on the conservative side to design as if the full stress-concentration effect were present. The stress-concentration effects are not considered in structural design because the loads are static and the materials ductile.

In calculating the area for Eq. (6-15) the designer should, of course, use the combination of rivet or bolt holes which gives the smallest area.

Figure 6-11e illustrates a failure by crushing of the rivet or plate. Calculation of this stress, which is usually called a *bearing stress,* is complicated by the distribution of the load on the cylindrical surface of the

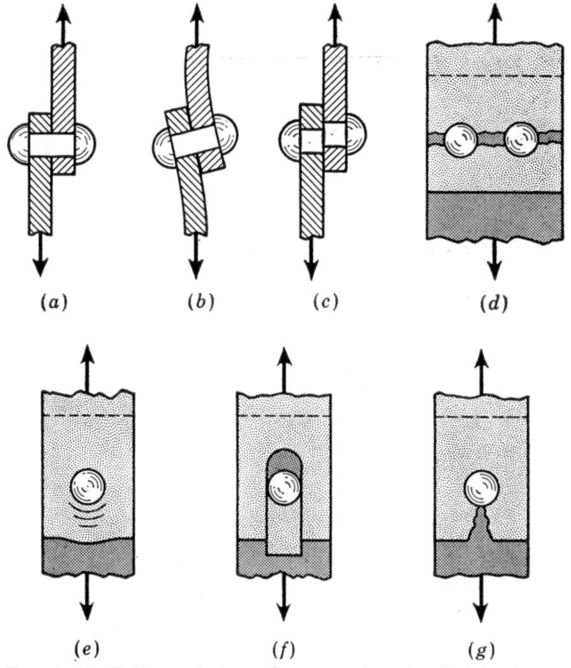

FIG. 6-11. Failure of riveted connections loaded in shear.

rivet. The exact values of the forces acting upon the rivet are unknown, and so it is customary to assume that the components of these forces are uniformly distributed over the projected contact area of the rivet. This gives for the stress

$$s = \frac{F}{A} \tag{6-16}$$

where the projected area for a single rivet is $A = td$. Here, t is the thickness of the thinnest plate and d is the rivet or bolt diameter.

Shearing or tearing of the margin is shown in Fig. 6-11f and g. In structural practice this failure is avoided by spacing the rivet at least 1½ diameters away from the margin. Bolted connections usually are spaced an even greater distance than this for satisfactory appearance, and hence this type of failure may usually be neglected.

In structural design it is customary to select in advance the number of rivets and their diameters and spacing. The strength is then determined for each method of failure. If the calculated strength is not satisfactory, a change is made in the diameter, spacing, or number of rivets used, to bring the strength in line with expected loading conditions. It is not usual, in structural practice, to consider the combined effects of the various methods of failure.

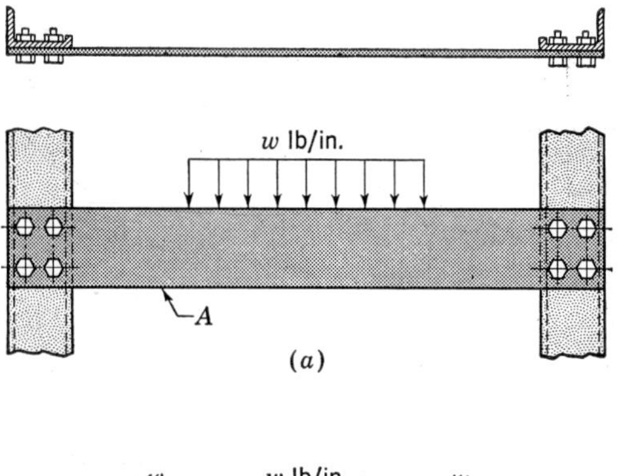

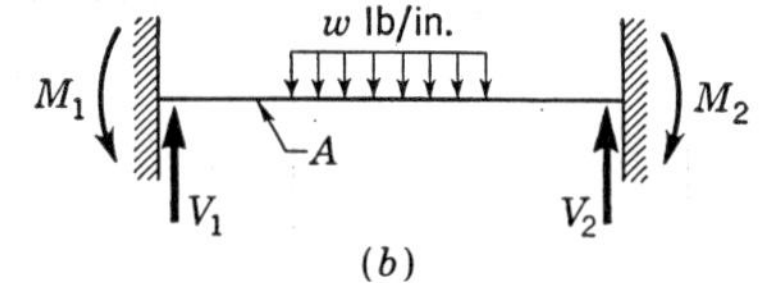

FIG. 6-12. Eccentric loading of bolts.

Eccentric Loading. An example of eccentric loading of fasteners is shown in Fig. 6-12. This is a portion of a machine frame containing a beam A subjected to the action of a bending load. In this case, the beam is fastened to vertical members at the ends with bolts. The reader will recognize the schematic representation in Fig. 6-12b as an indeterminate beam with both ends fixed and with the moment reaction M and the shear reaction V at the ends.

For convenience, the centers of the bolts at one end of the beam are drawn to a larger scale in Fig. 6-13. Point O represents the center of gravity of the group,[1] and it is assumed in this example that all the bolts are of the same diameter. The total load taken by each bolt will be calculated in three steps. In the first step the shear V is divided equally among the bolts so that each bolt takes $F' = V/n$ lb, where n refers to

[1] It should be noted that the center of gravity depends upon the size as well as the location of the bolts. For a review of center of gravity, see any elementary mechanics text.

the number of bolts in the group and the force F' is called the *direct load*, or *primary shear*.

It is noted that an equal distribution of the direct load to the bolts assumes an absolutely rigid member. The arrangement of the bolts or the shape and size of the members sometimes justify the use of another assumption as to the division of the load. The direct loads F' are shown as vectors on the loading diagram (Fig. 6-13).

The *moment load*, or *secondary shear*, is the additional load on each bolt due to the moment M. If r_A, r_B, r_C, etc., are the radial distances from the center of gravity to the center of each bolt, then the moment and moment load are related as follows:

$$M = F''_A r_A + F''_B r_B + F''_C r_C + \cdots \qquad (a)$$

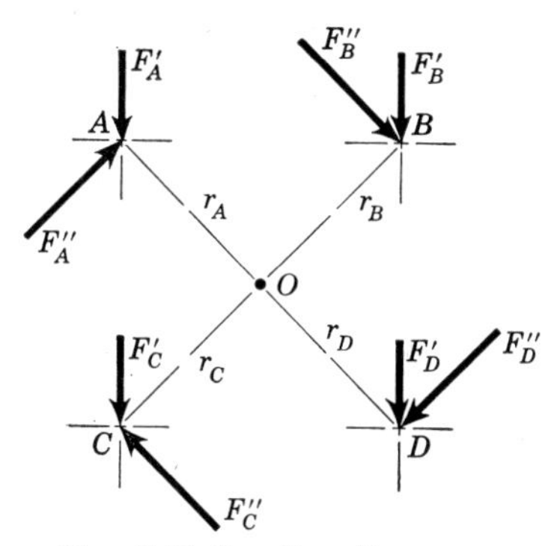

FIG. 6-13. Loading diagram.

where F'' is the moment load. The force taken by each bolt depends upon its radius; that is, the bolt farthest from the center of gravity takes the greatest load while the nearest bolt takes the smallest. We can therefore write

$$\frac{F''_A}{r_A} = \frac{F''_B}{r_B} = \frac{F''_C}{r_C} \qquad (b)$$

Solving Eqs. (a) and (b) simultaneously, we obtain

$$F''_n = \frac{M r_n}{r_A{}^2 + r_B{}^2 + r_C{}^2 + \cdots} \qquad (6\text{-}17)$$

where the subscript n refers to the particular bolt whose load is to be found. These moment loads are also shown as vectors on the loading diagram.

In the third step the direct and moment loads are added vectorially to obtain the resultant load on each bolt. Since all the bolts or rivets are usually the same size, only that bolt having the maximum load need be considered. When the maximum load is found, the strength may be determined, using the various methods already described.

EXAMPLE 6-2.[1] Design the fitting and fasteners for the end of the member shown in Fig. 6-14 to transfer the 40,000-lb load into the member.

[1] This example was obtained through the courtesy of the Glenn L. Martin Company. The original data and the method of solution have been adjusted to meet the requirements of this book.

Decisions. A yield strength of 38,000 psi is selected for the 14ST member. A female connection, as shown in Fig. 6-15, will be used with 2330 steel plates heat-treated to a yield strength of 100,000 psi. In order to keep the eccentric loading as

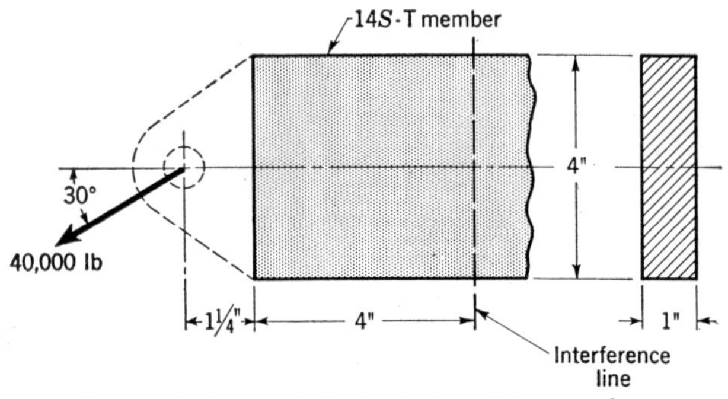

Fig. 6-14. Eccentrically loaded machine member.

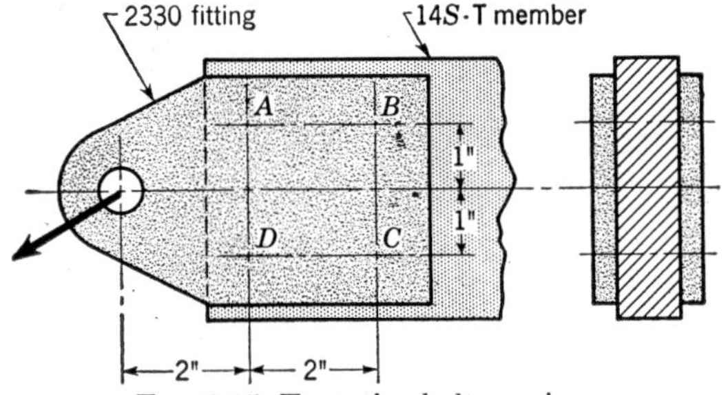

Fig. 6-15. Tentative bolt spacing.

small as possible, a wide bolt spacing will be tried; the tentative spacing is shown. ASTM A325 bolts with washers are chosen as the fasteners. Factors of safety are selected as follows: shear of bolts, 1.6; bearing on fitting, 1.3; bearing on member, 1.5; shear tearout of fitting, 1.5; strength of fitting, 1.3.

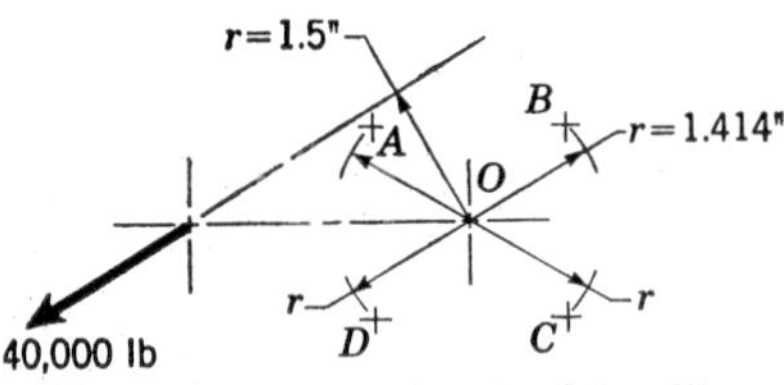

Fig. 6-16. Determination of radii.

Solution. 1. *Determination of the bolt loads.* The direct load is taken equally by the bolts and for each bolt is

$$F' = \frac{V}{n} = \frac{40,000}{4} = 10,000 \text{ lb}$$

In order to determine the moment load, the bolt group and the force are drawn to scale. The center of gravity is located by inspection and the radii determined by measurement (Fig. 6-16). The moment is

$$M = (40,000)(1.5) = 60,000 \text{ in.-lb}$$

The moment load on each bolt is determined by Eq. (6-17):

$$F''_A = \frac{Mr_A}{r_A^2 + r_B^2 + r_C^2 + r_D^2} = \frac{(60,000)(1.414)}{(4)(1.414)^2} = 10,600 \text{ lb}$$

Since the radii are equal, each bolt has the same moment load. In Fig. 6-17 the direct and moment loads are drawn to scale and the resultants obtained graphically.

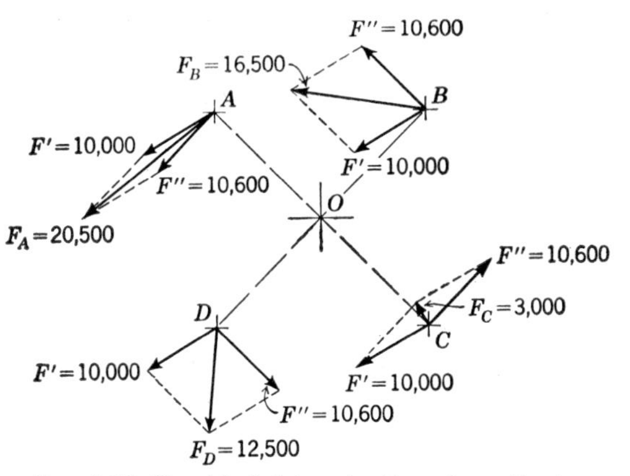

FIG. 6-17. Graphical determination of resultants.

2. *Determination of the bolt size.* Using the maximum-shear theory, the strength of the bolt in shear is

$$s_s = \frac{s_{yp}}{2} = \frac{90{,}000}{2} = 45{,}000 \text{ psi}$$

where the proof load from Table 6-2 is used for s_{yp}. The design stress is

$$s_d = \frac{s_s}{\text{f.s.}} = \frac{45{,}000}{1.6} = 28{,}200 \text{ psi}$$

Now, using the maximum bolt, and remembering that the bolt is in double shear, from Eq. (6-14) the area of the bolt is

$$A = \frac{F}{2s_d} = \frac{20{,}500}{(2)(28{,}200)} = 0.364 \text{ in.}^2$$

The theoretical bolt diameter is

$$d_r = \sqrt{\frac{4A}{\pi}} = \sqrt{\frac{(4)(0.364)}{\pi}} = 0.681 \text{ in.}$$

We will choose the next larger standard-size bolt, which is ¾ in.

The area of a ¾-in. bolt is 0.441 in.², and so the actual average shearing stress is

$$s_s = \frac{F}{2A} = \frac{20{,}500}{(2)(0.441)} = 23{,}200 \text{ psi}$$

The proof load for a ¾-in. bolt is 85,000 psi; this gives a value of 42,500 psi for the strength. Therefore, the true factor of safety is

$$\text{f.s.} = \frac{42{,}500}{23{,}200} = 1.83$$

and so the bolt selected is safe.

3. *Thickness of the fitting.* The thickness of the fitting will be found on the basis of the bearing stress. The design stress is

$$s_d = \frac{s_{yp}}{\text{f.s.}} = \frac{100{,}000}{1.3} = 77{,}000 \text{ psi}$$

Since each side takes one-half the load, the bearing load is

$$F = \frac{20{,}500}{2} = 10{,}250 \text{ lb}$$

From Eq. (6-16) the thickness of the fitting is

$$s_d = \frac{F}{td} \qquad t = \frac{F}{s_d d} = \frac{10{,}250}{(77{,}000)(0.75)} = 0.195 \text{ in.}$$

This will be manufactured from a cold-drawn-steel flat. The nearest standard size is ¼ in.

The next step is to check the bolt for bearing strength. From Eq. (6-16) the bearing stress on the bolt is

$$s = \frac{F}{td} = \frac{10{,}250}{(0.25)(0.75)} = 60{,}000 \text{ psi}$$

and the true factor of safety is

$$\text{f.s.} = \frac{s_{yp}}{s} = \frac{90{,}000}{60{,}000} = 1.5$$

which is safe for the bolt.

4. *Bearing strength of member.* The bearing stress on the member is also obtained from Eq. (6-16). It is

$$s = \frac{F}{td} = \frac{20{,}500}{(1)(0.75)} = 27{,}300 \text{ psi}$$

The true factor of safety is

$$\text{f.s.} = \frac{s_{yp}}{s} = \frac{38{,}000}{27{,}300} = 1.39$$

This is not safe because a factor of safety of 1.5 was selected for the member. It must therefore be redesigned. The design stress is

$$s_d = \frac{s_{yp}}{\text{f.s.}} = \frac{38{,}000}{1.5} = 25{,}300 \text{ psi}$$

Next, using Eq. (6-16) again and solving for the thickness,

$$t = \frac{F}{s_d d} = \frac{20{,}500}{(25{,}300)(0.75)} = 1.08 \text{ in.}$$

Therefore, the thickness of the member will be changed to the next larger size, which is 1⅛ in.

5. *Shear tearout.* This calculation is made to determine the distance from the bolt center line to the edge of the fitting. Three assumptions are made:

a. Since the bolts are spaced relatively far apart, it is assumed that no tearout will occur between the bolts.

b. It is assumed that the entire bolt load acts perpendicular to the nearest edge.

c. The tearout area is assumed to be based upon the closest distance from the edge to the bolt.

Using the maximum-shear theory, the design stress is

$$s_d = \frac{s_{yp}}{2(\text{f.s.})} = \frac{100{,}000}{(2)(1.5)} = 33{,}300 \text{ psi}$$

The loading is shown in Fig. 6-18. The equation for the shearing stress is

$$s_s = \frac{F}{A}$$

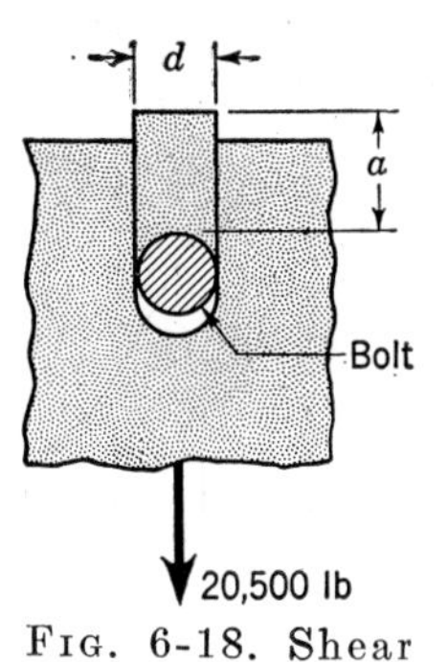

FIG. 6-18. Shear tearout.

where the tearout area is $A = 2at$. Solving for a, we obtain

$$a = \frac{F}{2ts_s} = \frac{10{,}250}{(2)(33{,}300)(0.25)} = 0.615 \text{ in.}$$

Therefore, the distance from the bolt center line to the edge will be

$$x = \frac{0.75}{2} + 0.615 = 0.990 \text{ in.}$$

We will make this distance 1 in.

6. *Strength of the fitting.* In Fig. 6-19 the load has been divided into its bending and tensile components. The fitting tends to fail by a combination of bending and tension on center line A-A. Using the transfer formula, the moment of inertia is $I = 0.940 \text{ in.}^4$ The bending stress at the outer fiber of a single fitting is

$$s = \frac{Mc}{I} = \frac{(20{,}000)(2)(2)}{(2)(0.940)} = 42{,}500 \text{ psi}$$

The tensile stress is

$$s = \frac{F}{A} = \frac{34{,}700}{2[(4)(0.25) - (2)(0.75)(0.25)]} = 27{,}800 \text{ psi}$$

The maximum combined stress is

$$s_{\max} = 42{,}500 + 27{,}800 = 70{,}300 \text{ psi}$$

Therefore, the true factor of safety is

$$\text{f.s.} = \frac{s_{yp}}{s_{\max}} = \frac{100{,}000}{70{,}300} = 1.42$$

Since a factor of safety of 1.30 was selected, the fitting is safe.

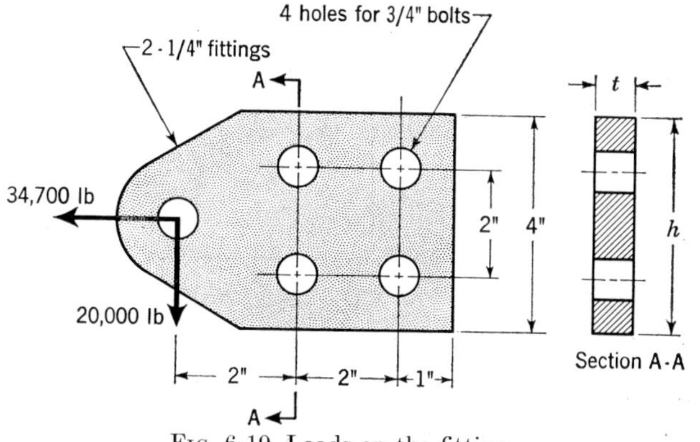

FIG. 6-19. Loads on the fitting.

Although the lug still remains to be designed, this completes the solution as far as the purposes of this example are concerned. The final dimensions are shown in Fig. 6-19.

6-5. Bolted Joints Loaded in Tension. The designer frequently has it in his power to design so that the fasteners are loaded in shear; he should do this whenever possible. When it becomes impossible to avoid tension loading, then, since rivets are not recommended, a bolted joint must be used.

Figure 6-20 shows a bolted joint in tension, employing a gasket. Equation (6-9), which gives the resultant bolt load when the initial preload and the external tensile load are known, can be arranged to give

$$F = CF_t + F_i \tag{6-18}$$

where

$$C = \frac{k_b}{k_b + k_m} \tag{6-19}$$

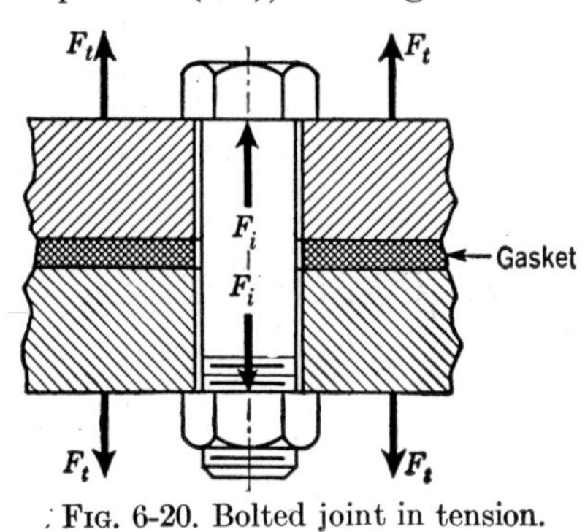

FIG. 6-20. Bolted joint in tension.

The quantity C, which may be called the *stiffness coefficient*, must have values between zero and 1. Doughtie and Carter[1] state that, when no gasket is employed, C may be taken equal to zero and that, in normal applications using the softest and most flexible gasket materials, tests show that C seldom exceeds 0.50. When the area, thickness, and modulus of elasticity of the gasket are known, the coefficient may be calculated from Eqs. (6-8) and (6-19). This makes it possible either to calculate C or, at most, to make a close guess as to its value.

TABLE 6-4. BOLT STRESS-CONCENTRATION FACTORS

Thread	Static loads with brittle materials			Fatigue loads, annealed steel			Fatigue loads, heat-treated steel		
	A	B	C	A	B	C	A	B	C
American Standard........	2.5	2.4	5.0	1.8	1.8	2.0	2.3	2.2	2.7
Whitworth...............	2.5	1.6	3.35	1.8	1.5	1.9	2.3	1.6	2.6

It has been shown that, when the bolt is properly preloaded, fatigue is not a serious problem in tension-loaded joints employing stiff materials. Since bolt materials are relatively ductile, this means that stress concentration is of minor importance too. However, when a relatively soft gasket is employed, the stress variation in the bolt is increased, and both fatigue and stress concentration must be considered.

[1] V. L. Doughtie and William J. Carter, Bolted Assemblies, *Machine Design*, vol. 22, no. 2, p. 127, February, 1950.

Vidosic[1] gives the form stress-concentration factors at three points on a bolted assembly for both American Standard and Whitworth threads. Using Fig. 4-24, we can obtain the corresponding fatigue stress-concentration factors. These are tabulated in Table 6-4 for convenience.

EXAMPLE 6-3. The bolted assembly in Fig. 6-21 employs a copper ring as a gasket. Calculate the stiffness coefficient of the assembly.

Solution. The area of the gasket is

$$A = \frac{\pi}{4}(D^2 - d^2) = \frac{\pi}{4}[(1.5)^2 - (1)^2] = 0.982 \text{ in.}^2$$

The length of the gasket is ¼ in., and, for copper, E = 17,000,000 psi. Solving Eq. (6-8), we obtain

$$k_m = \frac{AE}{l} = \frac{(0.982)(17)(10)^6}{0.25} = 66.7\,(10)^6 \text{ lb per in.}$$

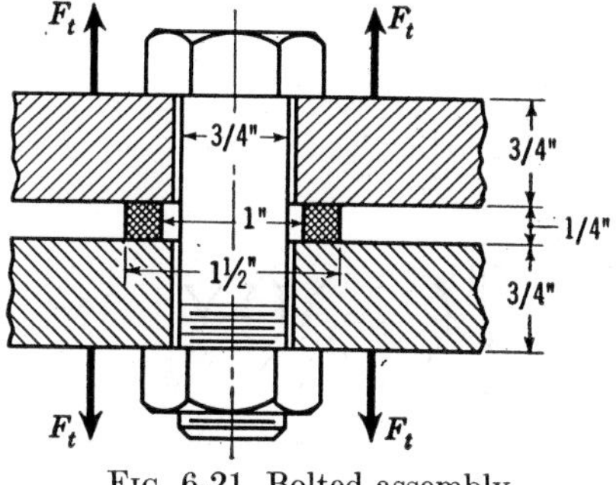

FIG. 6-21. Bolted assembly.

The area of the bolt is A = 0.441 in.² The stiffness constant of the bolt is found in a similar manner:

$$k_b = \frac{AE}{l} = \frac{(0.441)(30)(10)^6}{1.75} = 7.57\,(10)^6 \text{ lb per in.}$$

The stiffness coefficient is obtained from Eq. (6-19):

$$C = \frac{k_b}{k_b + k_m} = \frac{7.57}{7.57 + 66.7} = 0.102 \qquad Ans.$$

EXAMPLE 6-4. Figure 6-22 shows a cover-plate design for a treating cylinder. The treating process requires pressures varying from zero to 300 psi maximum. The gasket is copper-armored asbestos. Determine the specifications for the bolts to be used.

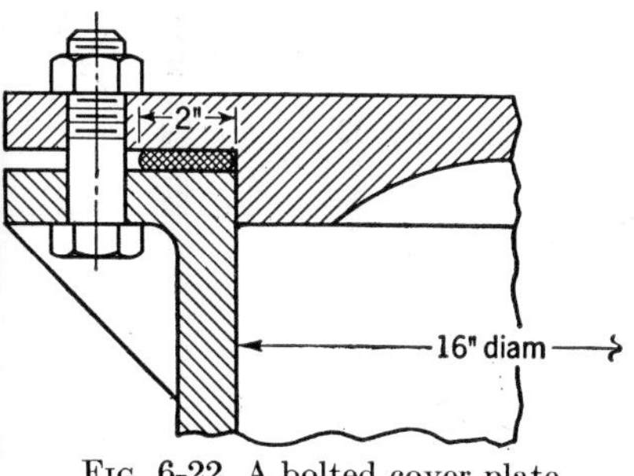

FIG. 6-22. A bolted cover plate.

Decisions. An SAE grade 7 bolt will be used (Table 6-2). The bolt will probably be larger than ½ in. in diameter, and so, in the absence of exact data, the yield point is estimated at 100,000 psi and the ultimate strength at 125,000 psi. In order to assure that the bolts will never be subjected to the full cover-plate load, the preload will be made 30 per cent larger than the maximum tensile load. The stiffness coefficient is estimated at 0.20, and a factor of safety of 1.5 is selected.

Solution. The sealing area is taken to the center of the gasket, giving an effective diameter of 18 in. Denoting the pressure by p, the maximum tensile load is

$$F_t = pA = 300\left[\frac{\pi(18)^2}{4}\right] = 76{,}400 \text{ lb}$$

[1] J. P. Vidosic, Improving Fatigue Resistance of Bolted Joints, *Product Eng.*, vol. 24, no. 4, pp. 190–191, April, 1953.

The preload must be

$$F_i = (76{,}400)(1.3) = 99{,}400 \text{ lb}$$

Therefore, the maximum bolt load is

$$F = CF_t + F_i = (0.20)(76{,}400) + 99{,}400 = 114{,}700 \text{ lb}$$

An SAE 7 volt is manufactured with rolled threads which corresponds to a machined finish. From Fig. 4-23, the endurance limit is 46,000 psi. The average bolt load is

$$F_{av} = \frac{F + F_i}{2} = \frac{114{,}700 + 99{,}400}{2} = 107{,}000 \text{ lb}$$

The fluctuating load is

$$F_r = F - F_{av} = 114{,}700 - 107{,}000 = 7{,}700 \text{ lb}$$

From Table 6-4, the stress-concentration factor is 2.7. This factor is applied to the fluctuating component of the load only, so that

$$F'_r = (2.7)(7{,}700) = 20{,}800 \text{ lb}$$

The maximum stress may be found graphically, using the Soderberg law (Sec. 4-8). In Fig. 6-23 the endurance limit is plotted at point A on the y axis, and the yield strength at point B on the x axis. It is noted that

$$\frac{s_r}{s_{av}} = \frac{F'_r}{F_{av}} = \frac{20{,}800}{107{,}000} = 0.195$$

so that a line OC must be constructed having a slope of 0.195. The coordinates corresponding to point C are the fluctuating and average stress components and are read directly from the diagram. This gives $s_r = 13{,}600$ psi and $s_{av} = 70{,}700$ psi. Therefore, the maximum stress is

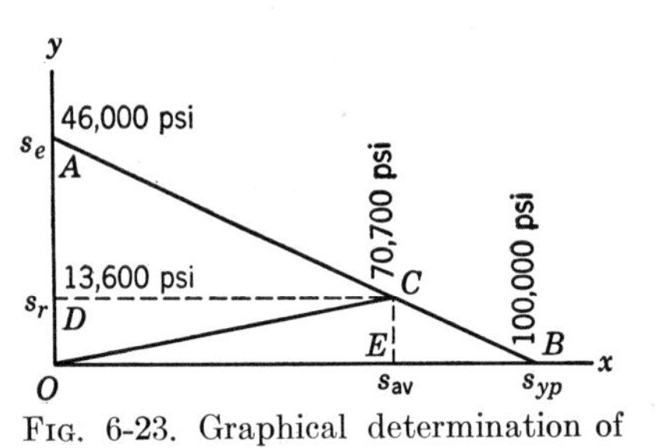

FIG. 6-23. Graphical determination of fatigue strength.

$$s_{max} = s_{av} + s_r = 70{,}700 + 13{,}600 = 84{,}300 \text{ psi}$$

The design stress is

$$s_d = \frac{s_{max}}{\text{f.s.}} = \frac{84{,}300}{1.5} = 56{,}200 \text{ psi}$$

The total area corresponding to the pitch diameter is

$$A = \frac{F}{s_d} = \frac{127{,}800}{56{,}200} = 2.27 \text{ in.}^2$$

A ¾" 10NC bolt has a pitch diameter of 0.683 in., which corresponds to an area of 0.366 in.² Six such bolts would have an area of 2.20 in.², which is satisfactory for strength considerations. With a bolt-circle diameter of approximately 21 in., the spacing would be 11 in., which seems large. A better selection would probably be eight ¾-in. bolts; this would give a spacing of 8¼ in.

It has been shown in Chap. 3 that, when bolts are to be subjected to the action of energy loads, improvement of stress distribution and increased ability to absorb these loads may be obtained by necking down the body. This necking down improves the fatigue resistance and flexibility of the bolt. The improvement in flexibility is especially important when using short preloaded bolts. There is always a certain amount of relaxation of initial tension which is the same regardless of the length of the bolt. Necking down of short bolts provides additional elasticity and, therefore, causes them to retain a greater percentage of the initial preload.

6-6. Effect of Assumptions. The character of the particular design problem will determine the degree of consideration which must be given to the assumptions used in the design of a bolted or riveted joint. When high strength or light weight is required, when the load is dynamic, and when failure may be dangerous or costly, the effect of the assumptions must be considered very carefully. On the other hand, design problems frequently arise in which none of these considerations is very important. It is a waste of engineering time and talent to spend hours investigating the stresses and deflections of a ½-in. bolt and to specify the hole tolerances and bolt finish in great detail, when a ¾-in. bolt will work just as well. Many times a fastener which is 75 per cent oversize will do very nicely. The machinist tightens it up until it "feels right," and the value of the preload remains completely unknown.

Occasions also arise in which the analysis must be more detailed than has been indicated here. The purpose of the assumptions is to simplify the analysis, but, at the same time, they make the results less exact. For this reason, the assumptions must be refined when a more careful analysis is indicated.[1]

6-7. Keys and Splines. Keys and splines are used to transfer torque from a shaft to a gear, pulley, or similar device, or vice versa (Fig. 6-24). Many types of keys such as the square, flat, round, or Woodruff keys, as well as others, are described in standard handbooks; the designer should use these information sources to select the type of key as well as to obtain the tentative cross-sectional

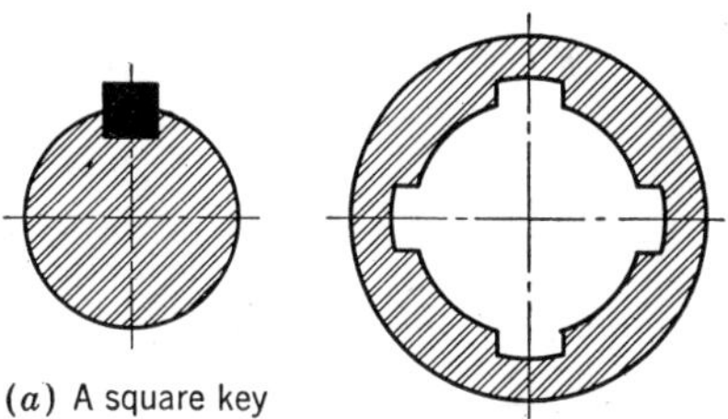

FIG. 6-24. Keys and splines.

[1] Engineering literature contains a great many different solutions, involving different sets of assumptions, to almost every design problem. The choice of a particular method of solution is one of the design decisions. Designers frequently differ on the one best method of design for a particular problem. The same situation arises in a textbook. It is obviously impossible to investigate all the methods of solving engineering problems. Teachers frequently know of alternate solutions which are even better than those presented here, or which result from study of new contributions to knowledge. The reader, too, should familiarize himself with many of the methods in use and be alert to the introduction of new ones.

dimensions. Splines are completely described and specified in the SAE Handbook.

The usual practice is to choose a key whose size is one-fourth of the shaft diameter. The length of the key is then adjusted according to the hub length and the strength required. It is sometimes necessary to use two keys in order to obtain the required strength.

In determining the strength of a key, the assumption may be made that the forces are uniformly distributed throughout the key length. This assumption is probably not true, since the torsional stiffness of the shaft will usually be less than that for the hub, causing large forces at one end of the key and small forces at the other end. This distribution may be still more complicated by the stiffening effect of the arms or web at the middle of the hub.

Having assumed a force distribution, it is customary to base the strength of the key on failure by crushing or by shearing. This is illustrated in the following example:

EXAMPLE 6-5. A C1035 steel shaft, heat-treated to a yield strength of 75,000 psi, has a diameter of $1\frac{7}{16}$ in. The shaft rotates at 600 rpm and transmits 40 hp through a gear. Select an appropriate key for the gear.

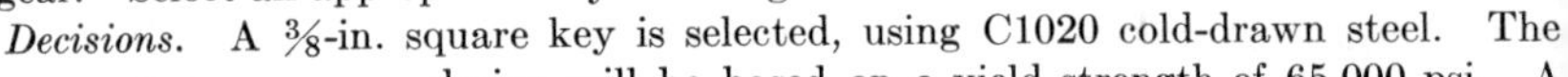

Decisions. A $\frac{3}{8}$-in. square key is selected, using C1020 cold-drawn steel. The design will be based on a yield strength of 65,000 psi. A factor of safety of 2.8 will be used in the absence of exact information of the nature of the load.

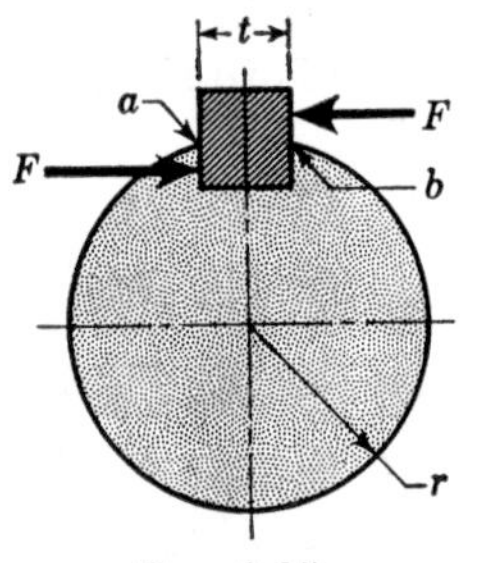

FIG. 6-25

Solution. The torque is obtained from the horsepower equation:

$$T = \frac{63{,}000 \text{ hp}}{n} = \frac{(63{,}000)(40)}{600} = 4{,}200 \text{ lb-in.}$$

Referring to Fig. 6-25, the force F at the surface of the shaft is

$$F = \frac{T}{r} = \frac{4{,}200}{0.719} = 5{,}850 \text{ lb}$$

Using the maximum-shear theory, the design shear stress is

$$s_d = \frac{s_{yp}}{(2)(\text{f.s.})} = \frac{65{,}000}{(2)(2.8)} = 11{,}600 \text{ psi}$$

In order to resist failure by shear across the area ab, the length of the key must be

$$s_s = \frac{F}{A} = \frac{F}{lt} \qquad l = \frac{F}{s_d t} = \frac{5{,}850}{(11{,}600)(0.375)} = 1.31 \text{ in.}$$

The design bearing stress is

$$s_d = \frac{s_{yp}}{\text{f.s.}} = \frac{65{,}000}{2.8} = 23{,}200 \text{ psi}$$

To resist crushing, the area of one-half the face of the key is used:

$$s = \frac{F}{A} = \frac{F}{lt/2} \qquad l = \frac{2F}{s_d t} = \frac{(2)(5{,}850)}{(23{,}200)(0.375)} = 1.34 \text{ in.}$$

The hub length of a gear is usually greater than the shaft diameter. If the key, in this example, is made equal in length to the hub, it would, therefore, have ample strength.

Splines are cut so that the area subjected to shear is greater than the bearing area. For this reason the bearing area should be used to select splines.

6-8. Pins, Cotters, and Retainers. A wide variety of pins, retainers, and miscellaneous locking devices are available. The designer must familiarize himself with these items and their applications. They can be found in most handbooks and in many commercial catalogues.

Some of these products are intended only for light loads. For example, they might be used to position a gear or pulley axially where no thrust loads are present. When loads are present, the designer should experience no difficulty in applying fundamental principles to their design.

6-9. Welded Joints. Although welding is used extensively in the fabrication of many machine members, there is a definite need for fundamental knowledge concerning the analysis and design of welded joints. The fact that factors of safety as high as 16 are recommended by the industry indicates that some of the present design methods are highly empirical. Even so, it is necessary for the student to understand existing methods of design, together with their limitations, before he can read new literature on the subject or make individual contributions of knowledge to the profession.

The usual welds are butt welds and fillet welds; they can be used to make butt and fillet joints between parallel bars, T joints between bars or plates joining each other at an angle, or corner joints. Stress concentrations are present in both butt and fillet joints. Fillet joints have stress concentrations at both the toe and root of the fillet, and these stress raisers are probably higher than in butt joints because of the inherent shape. A butt joint has stress raisers due to the reinforcement. In addition, all welded joints have stress concentrations due to internal flaws. It has been shown that for ductile materials subjected to static loads stress concentrations are not important, because of the ability of the material to yield plastically and obtain relief. In the case of welded joints this may not always be true, because of the tendency to produce a more brittle type of fracture.

Another point of uncertainty in the design of welded joints is concerned with the residual stresses which are developed in the joint and the welded members as a result of shrinkage of the weld metal during cooling. Depending upon the geometry of the part and the order of welding, many kinds of stresses may develop because of shrinkage. The fact that jigging, clamping, and other precautions are necessary during welding in order to minimize warpage is indicative of the presence of residual stresses. Experimental evidence is also available to indicate the presence of residual stresses in single welds, and values approaching the yield strength of the material have been measured. Butt welds seem to be the worst offenders in this respect.

Many investigators have determined the fatigue strength of welded joints and obtained considerable variation in results. Sometimes the results are given in terms of the parent member at the end of the weld and sometimes in terms of the deposited metal. In general, the fatigue strength will be affected by:

1. The stress history of the joint
2. The amount of stress concentrations present
3. The metallurgical changes due to welding
4. The surface condition of the joint

Design Formulas. Figure 6-26 shows a single-V groove weld loaded by the tensile force F. It is customary to calculate the stress by the equation

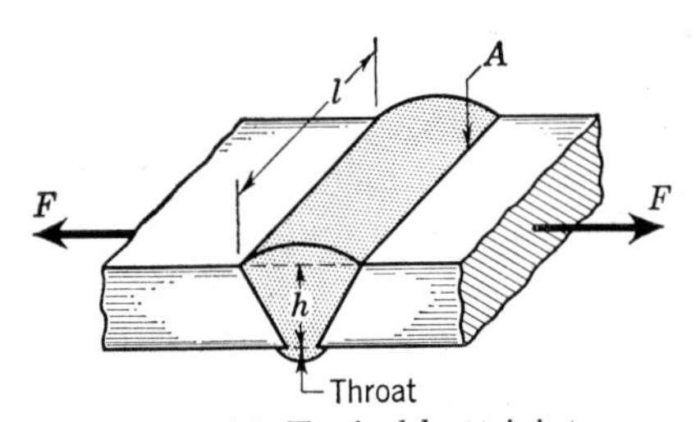

Fig. 6-26. Typical butt joint.

$$s = \frac{F}{hl} \tag{6-20}$$

where h is the weld throat and l is the length of the weld, as shown in the figure. It should be noted that the value of h does not consider the reinforcement of the welds. The reinforcement is desirable in order to compensate for flaws, but the amount varies throughout the length of the weld and it does produce stress concentration at point A in the figure. The stress in a butt weld due to shear loading is

$$s_s = \frac{F}{hl} \tag{6-21}$$

The equation for stress in a transverse fillet weld (Fig. 6-27) is based on the stress in the throat section which is assumed to be a normal tensile stress. This stress is

$$s = \frac{1.414F}{hl} \tag{6-22}$$

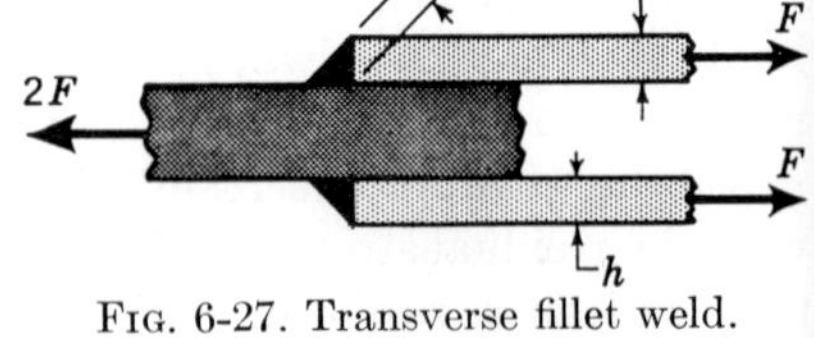

Fig. 6-27. Transverse fillet weld.

where $1.414 = 1/\cos 45°$.

When fillet welds are used on only one side of the plate (Fig. 6-28*a*), a bending moment is introduced because of the eccentricity of the forces. Referring to Fig. 6-28*b*, it is seen that the weld throat is acted upon by the tensile force F and a moment $M = Fh/4$. The bending stress is

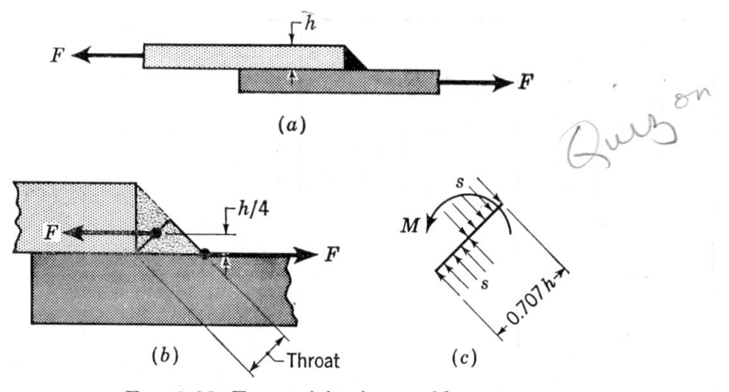

FIG. 6-28. Eccentricity in a weld.

assumed to have a rectangular distribution, as shown in Fig. 6-28c. Equating the bending moment to the internal couple, we obtain

$$M = sA\frac{0.707h}{2} = s\frac{0.707hl}{2}\frac{0.707h}{2}$$

or

$$s = \frac{4M}{(0.707h)^2l} = \frac{4Fh}{(4)(0.707h)^2l} = \frac{2F}{hl}$$

In this case the stress is a maximum at the root and is equal to the tensile stress plus the bending stress:

$$s = \frac{1.414F}{hl} + \frac{2F}{hl} = \frac{3.414F}{hl} \qquad (6\text{-}23)$$

It should be noted that this is over twice as much as the stress represented by Eq. (6-22).

Parallel fillet welds (Fig. 6-29) are assumed to fail in shear. The equation generally used is

$$s_s = \frac{0.707F}{hl} \qquad (6\text{-}24)$$

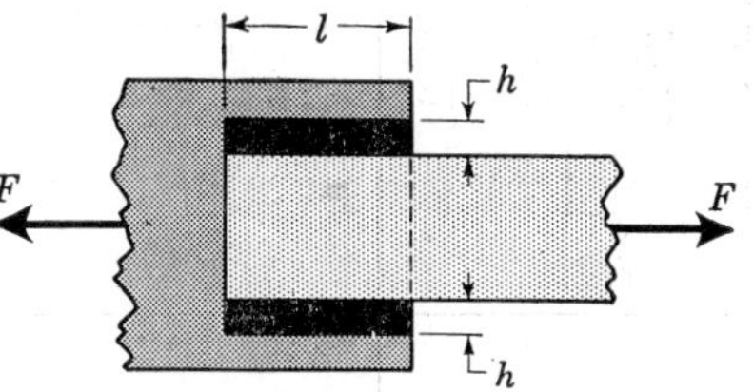

FIG. 6-29. A parallel fillet weld.

The stress distribution along such a weld is not uniform, being considerably higher at the ends.

A number of typical welded connections and their stress equations are shown in Fig. 6-30. These formulas have been developed using Eqs. (6-21) to (6-24), inclusive.[1]

A type of welded connection which occurs very frequently in machine design is illustrated by the cantilever beam of Fig. 6-31. The reactions at the support are a shear V and a moment M. The effect of these

[1] C. H. Hennings, Welding Design, *Trans. ASME*, vol. 58, pp. 497–509, 1936.

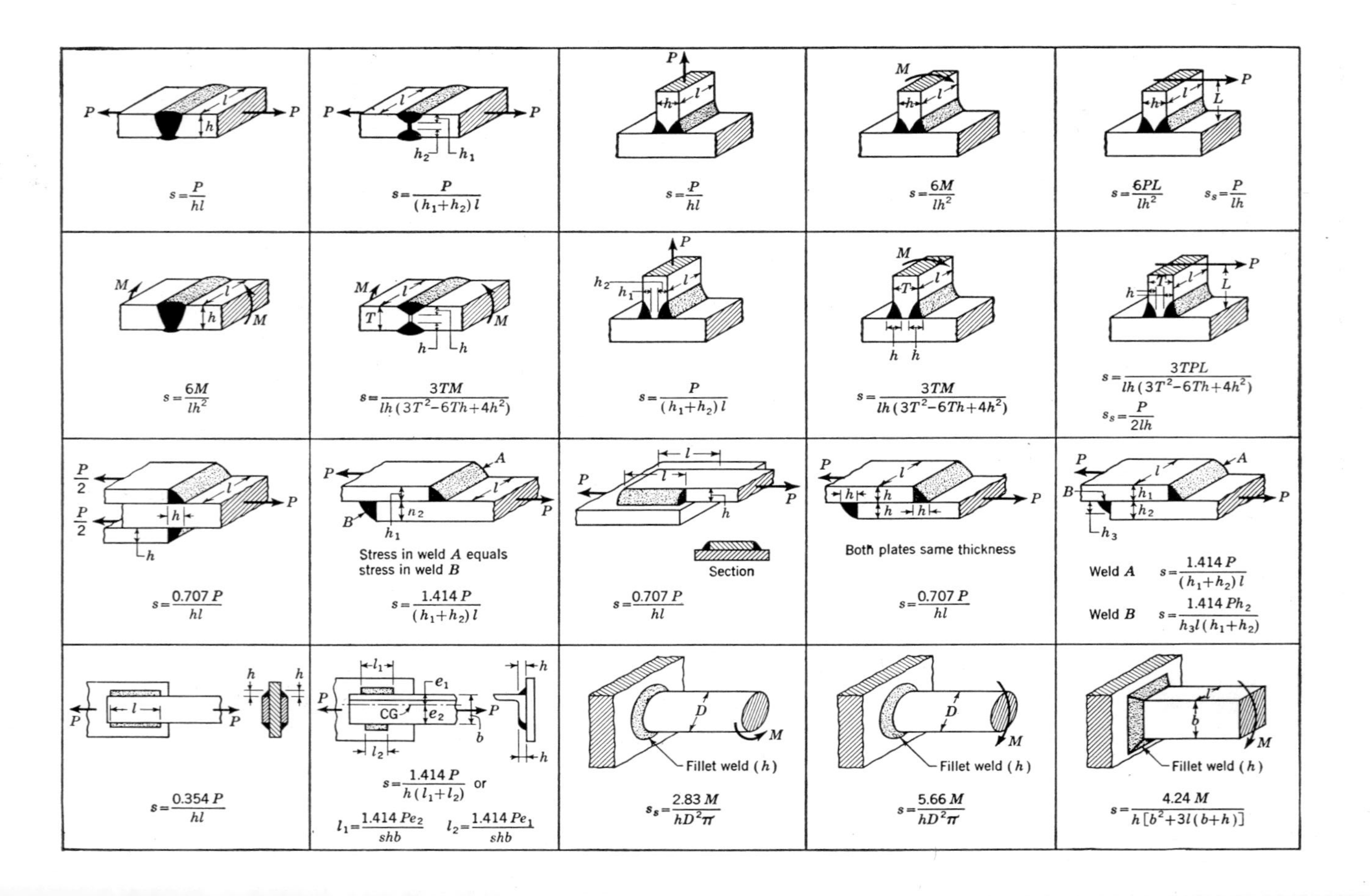

$s = \frac{P}{hl}$
$s = \frac{P}{(h_1+h_2)l}$
$s = \frac{P}{hl}$
$s = \frac{6M}{lh^2}$
$s = \frac{6PL}{lh^2}$ $s_s = \frac{P}{lh}$
$s = \frac{6M}{lh^2}$
$s = \frac{3TM}{lh(3T^2-6Th+4h^2)}$
$s = \frac{P}{(h_1+h_2)l}$
$s = \frac{3TM}{lh(3T^2-6Th+4h^2)}$
$s = \frac{3TPL}{lh(3T^2-6Th+4h^2)}$
$s_s = \frac{P}{2lh}$
$s = \frac{0.707P}{hl}$
Stress in weld A equals stress in weld B
$s = \frac{1.414P}{(h_1+h_2)l}$
Section
$s = \frac{0.707P}{hl}$
Both plates same thickness
$s = \frac{0.707P}{hl}$
Weld A $s = \frac{1.414P}{(h_1+h_2)l}$
Weld B $s = \frac{1.414Ph_2}{h_3l(h_1+h_2)}$
$s = \frac{0.354P}{hl}$
CG
$s = \frac{1.414P}{h(l_1+l_2)}$ or
$l_1 = \frac{1.414Pe_2}{shb}$ $l_2 = \frac{1.414Pe_1}{shb}$
Fillet weld (h)
$s_s = \frac{2.83M}{hD^2\pi}$
Fillet weld (h)
$s = \frac{5.66M}{hD^2\pi}$
Fillet weld (h)
$s = \frac{4.24M}{h[b^2+3l(b+h)]}$

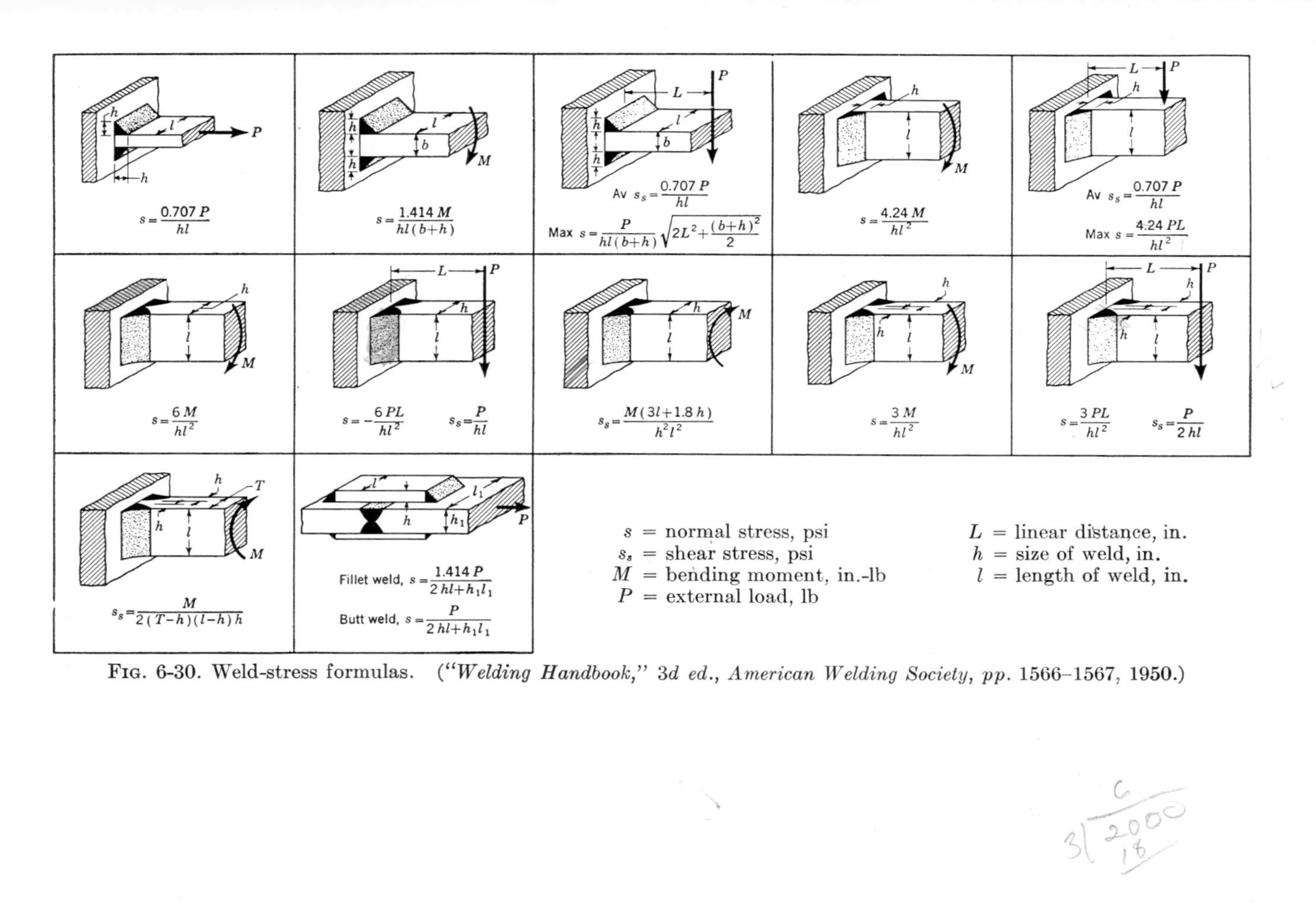

FIG. 6-30. Weld-stress formulas. (*"Welding Handbook,"* 3d *ed.*, *American Welding Society*, *pp.* 1566–1567, 1950.)

reactions is to produce primary and secondary shearing stresses in the welds. These stresses must be added vectorially, as in eccentrically loaded riveted connections, in order to obtain the resultant stress acting upon each weld.

The primary stresses are obtained as previously described. The secondary stress is obtained independently for each weld in the group. In Fig. 6-31 let point O be the center of gravity of the group, with r as the radius of any point on a single weld. The secondary stress is obtained

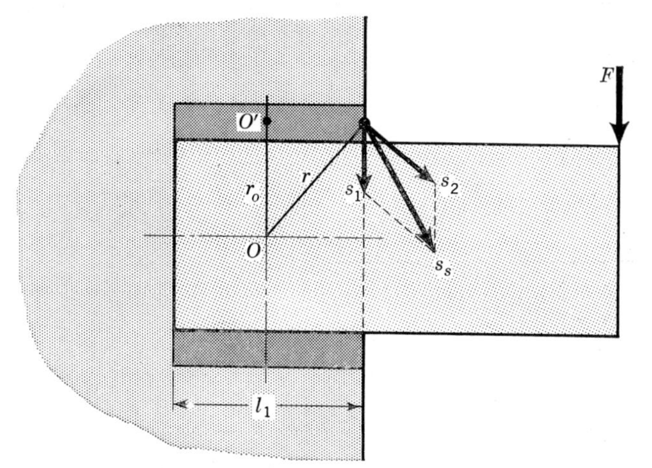

Fig. 6-31. A moment connection.

from the torsion formula [Eq. (2-18)] and is

$$s_2 = \frac{Mr}{J} \tag{6-25}$$

where J is the polar moment of inertia of the weld about point O. The maximum stress, of course, will occur when r is a maximum. The polar moment of inertia is obtained from the transfer formula and is

$$J = J_O + Ar^2 = \frac{Al^2}{12} + Ar_O{}^2 = A\left(\frac{l^2}{12} + r_O{}^2\right) \tag{6-26}$$

where A = throat area

J_O = polar moment of inertia of weld about its own center O'

r_O = radius from O' to center of gravity O of group

Design Stresses. The designer of machines is not required to use the design stresses specified by the various codes for structures, pressure vessels, and the like, unless he is engaged in their design. For this reason, he has a greater degree of freedom in designing to obtain a strong, economical, and well-constructed machine. The design stresses in Table 6-5, from the code for building construction, may be used as a guide in selecting suitable factors of safety in machine design. If the customary methods of design are employed, there is no reason why these exact stresses cannot be used. On the other hand, experiment or improved methods of analysis may reasonably justify a substantial increase in their values.

The design stresses listed in Table 6-5 depend upon the type of electrode used. They are based on the ultimate strength rather than the

TABLE 6-5. DESIGN STRESSES FOR WELDS MADE WITH MILD-STEEL ELECTRODES (AWS CODE FOR BUILDING CONSTRUCTION)

Type of load	Bare electrodes s_u = 40–55 kpsi		Covered electrodes s_u = 60–75 kpsi	
	Static loads	Dynamic loads	Static loads	Dynamic loads
Butt Welds				
Tension, psi	13,000	5,000	16,000	8,000
Compression, psi	15,000	5,000	18,000	8,000
Shear, psi	8,000	3,000	10,000	5,000
Fillet Welds				
Shear, psi	11,300	3,000	14,000	5,000

yield strength. If an ultimate strength of 45,000 psi is used for bare electrodes and butt welds, the factors of safety are found to be 3.5 for tension, 3.0 for compression, and 5.6 for shear. The design shearing stress is approximately 60 per cent of the tensile stress, which agrees closely with the distortion-energy failure theory.

Unless the welded members are themselves brittle, stress-concentration factors are not used for static loads. However, the stress-concentration factors are used for dynamic loads. When the dynamic load is composed of a varying stress superimposed on a steady stress, the stress-

TABLE 6-6. FATIGUE STRESS-CONCENTRATION FACTORS

Type of weld	Stress-concentration factor, k_f
Reinforced butt weld	1.2
Toe of transverse fillet weld	1.5
End of parallel fillet weld	2.7
T-butt joint with sharp corners	2.0

concentration factor is applied to the varying component only. Table 6-6 lists stress-concentration factors for various types of welds.

Weldable Materials. There are many factors which influence the weldability of various metals and alloys. When welding processes are being

TABLE 6-7. PROCESS CHART FOR WELDING FERROUS METALS*†

Material	Resistance	Oxyacetylene pressure	Gas	Arc	Submerged arc
Carbon steels:					
Low-carbon	A	A	A	A	A
Medium-carbon	A	A	A	A	A
High-carbon	B	A	B	A	B
Tool steel	B	A	B	B	B
Alloy steels:					
Ni	A	A	A	A	A
Ni-Cu	A	A	A	A	A
Mn-Mo	A	B	A	A	A
Ni-Cr	No	A	A	A	A
Cr-Mo	No	A	A	A	A
Ni-Cr-Mo	No	A	B	B	A
Ni-Mo	No	B	B	B	B
Cast iron:					
Gray	C	No	A	B	No
Malleable	C	No	B	B	No
Alloy	C	No	A	B	No
Stainless steels:					
Chromium	A	B	B	A	A
Chromium-nickel	A	A	A	A	A

* "ASM Metals Handbook," p. 370, 1948.

† A, commonly used; B, used occasionally under favorable conditions; C, no information available; No, not used.

considered, the designer should consult with the metallurgist and welding engineer regarding materials and weldability before making his final decisions. Table 6-7 indicates to a certain extent the weldability of ferrous metals and alloys and can be used as a rough guide in making preliminary decisions.

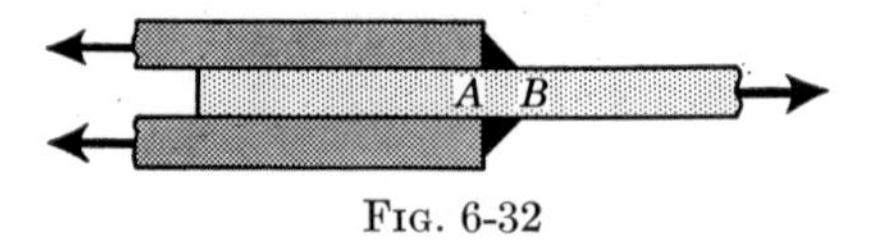

FIG. 6-32

Assumptions. The strength, especially the fatigue strength, of welded joints is a subject about which there has been much discussion, as well as some disagreement. Some of this disagreement is probably concerned with whether the fatigue strength of a welded joint is the strength of the weld metal or of the parent metal. For example, Fig. 6-32 shows a welded joint consisting of plates joined by fillet welds. When this joint is loaded in fatigue, stress raisers cause failure of the outer plates at A or of the inner plate at B, with the weld metal remaining intact. The result of the weld is to reduce seriously the fatigue strength of the plates themselves.

In general, the following uncertainties must be considered in the design of welded joints:

1. Stress concentration. These effects are present at the toe and root of a fillet weld, at the ends of welds, at the reinforcement of butt welds, and at internal flaws in welds.

2. Metallurgical changes due to welding. The welding process may produce brittleness within a certain area of the joint or produce an abrupt change in the physical properties. If the weld metal and the parent metal are of different compositions, then stress concentration may occur at the junction between the two.

3. Surface conditions. The welding process may produce slag inclusions or surface irregularities, both of which reduce the fatigue strength of the joint.

4. Residual stresses. Residual stresses resulting from shrinkage or warping may seriously affect the strength of the joint.

6-10. Closure. Strength considerations in the selection of fasteners and joints have been emphasized in this chapter because of their academic value. It is important to realize that, in general, only a small proportion of the joints to be designed have strength as a primary consideration. In fact, a very large number of connections in machines have no loads on them at all! When this is the case, no calculations are necessary, and the designer is free to base his decisions upon economy and appearance factors. His judgment and experience in making these decisions will be materially assisted by frequent surveys of current literature and advertisements and by a critical examination of new products.

BIBLIOGRAPHY

Almen, J. O.: On the Strength of Highly Stressed, Dynamically Loaded Bolts and Studs, *Trans. SAE*, vol. 52, no. 4, pp. 151–158, April, 1944. Also see Torquing of Nuts in Aircraft Engines, *SAE Special Publ.* 23.

"Procedure Handbook of Arc Welding Design and Practice," The James F. Lincoln Arc Welding Foundation, Cleveland, 1950.

Rossi, B. E.: "Welding Engineering," McGraw-Hill Book Company, Inc., New York, 1954.

Spotts, M. F.: "Design of Machine Elements," Prentice-Hall, Inc., New York, 1953.

Univ. Illinois Eng. Expt. Sta. Bull. 302, 327, 344, 350.

Vallance, A., and V. L. Doughtie: "Design of Machine Members," McGraw-Hill Book Company, Inc., New York, 1951.

"Welding Handbook," 3d ed., American Welding Society, New York, 1950.

PROBLEMS

6-1. Find the torque required to turn a $\frac{5}{8}$″–8 single-square-thread power screw. The coefficient of thread friction is 0.15. The load is 400 lb. The collar has a mean diameter of 1 in. and a coefficient of friction of 0.13. *Ans.:* 51.2 lb-in.

6-2. A $\frac{3}{4}$″-6 double-square-thread power screw drives a load of 600 lb at a speed of 2 fpm. The thrust is taken by an antifriction bearing so that the collar friction may be neglected. Find the horsepower required if the coefficient of thread friction is 0.11.

6-3. A $\frac{5}{8}$″-12 square-thread power screw has triple threads and is required to move a load of 320 lb. The frictional coefficients are 0.10 for the threads and 0.12 for the collar. The collar has a frictional diameter of $1\frac{5}{16}$ in. Find the total torque and the combined efficiency.

6-4. A C clamp uses a $\frac{3}{8}$″-12 square-thread screw. The frictional coefficients are 0.15 for the threads and for the collar. If the mean collar diameter is $\frac{5}{8}$ in. and the normal capacity of the clamp is 150 lb, find the torque required.

6-5. Find the horsepower required to drive a $1\frac{1}{2}$″-4 square-thread power screw with double threads against a load of 2,400 lb. The nut is to move at a velocity of 8 fpm. The frictional coefficients are 0.10 for the threads and for the collar. The mean diameter of the collar is 3 in.

6-6. A 1″-5 power screw has Acme 29° threads and is to raise a load of 1,000 lb. The frictional coefficients are 0.12 for the threads and for the collar. If the frictional radius of the collar is $1\frac{3}{4}$ in., find the total torque required to raise the load and the combined efficiency.

6-7. A single-square-thread power screw is to raise a load of 15,000 lb. The screw has a major diameter of $1\frac{1}{2}$ in. and a pitch of $\frac{1}{4}$ in. The frictional coefficients are 0.13 for the threads and 0.10 for the collar. If the mean collar diameter is $3\frac{1}{2}$ in. and the screw turns at a speed of 60 rpm, find (*a*) the horsepower input to the screw and (*b*) the combined efficiency of the screw and collar. *Ans.:* (*a*) 4.3 hp, (*b*) 0.132.

6-8. The nut for the screw in Prob. 6-7 transfers the load as shown in the figure. It is to be made of ASTM 25 gray cast iron. Using a factor of safety of 4 for both shear and bearing, determine the height h of the nut. *Ans.:* 2.44 in.

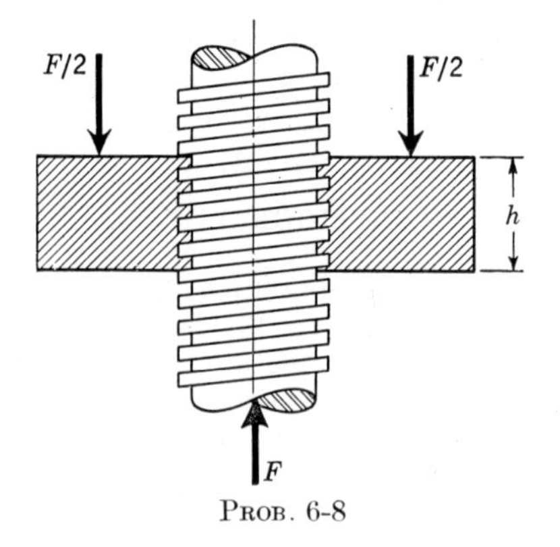

PROB. 6-8

6-9. A $2\frac{1}{2}$″-3 power screw has Acme 29° threads. It is to lift a load of 35,000 lb, which places the screw in tension. The frictional coefficients are 0.15 for the threads and 0.10 for the collar. The collar has a mean diameter of 5 in. Find the maximum combined normal and shear stresses in the screw.

6-10. A $1\frac{1}{4}''$-6 square-thread power screw is required to raise and lower a load of 10,000 lb. The frictional coefficients are 0.13 for the threads and for the collar. The collar has a frictional diameter of 2 in. Determine the values of both the steady and the varying components of shearing stress in the screw.

6-11. A power screw is loaded eccentrically so that it is required to lift a load of 12,000 lb, placing the screw in tension and also producing a constant bending moment of 7,500 in.-lb on the screw. The threads are 2″-4 single-square. The coefficient of thread friction is 0.14. The screw is supported by tapered roller bearings so that the collar friction is negligible. The material is C1042 carbon steel, heat-treated to a yield strength of 90,000 psi. Determine the maximum combined normal and shearing stresses in the screw.

***6-12.** Determine the diameter and pitch of a single-square-thread power screw to raise a dead load of 8,000 lb. The mechanism is arranged so as to place the screw in tension. The coefficient of thread friction is 0.12. An antifriction thrust bearing is used instead of a collar, so that this friction may be neglected. The screw is to be made of hot-rolled C1018 steel. The factor of safety for all types of failure is 3.

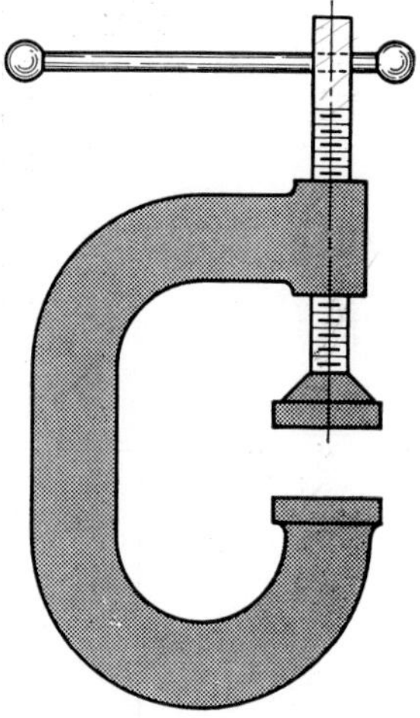

PROBS. 6-13 TO 6-20

***6-13 to 6-20.** Design a C-clamp screw according to the data in the accompanying table. The clamp is to be manufactured in large quantities and will be sold in a competitive market. The design should include the selection of a tentative material for the frame and specification of the minimum length of the threaded portion. Instructions to be packaged with the clamps will caution the user against employing a long bar to secure additional clamping force and will suggest that the screw be lubricated frequently.

Prob. No.	Maximum opening, in.	Throat depth, in.	Extreme depth, in.	Load limit, lb
6-13	2	2	$2\frac{3}{8}$	2,700
6-14	3	$2\frac{1}{4}$	$2\frac{3}{4}$	3,200
6-15	4	$2\frac{1}{2}$	$3\frac{1}{8}$	3,400
6-16	5	3	$3\frac{5}{8}$	3,500
6-17	6	$3\frac{1}{4}$	$3\frac{7}{8}$	3,700
6-18	8	$3\frac{3}{4}$	$4\frac{1}{2}$	4,500
6-19	10	4	$4\frac{3}{4}$	5,000
6-20	12	$4\frac{1}{4}$	5	5,400

***6-21 to 6-27.** Design the screws, threaded bushings, and the collar bearings for the bench-type press shown in the figure. Use the specifications given in the table on page 218. The press is to be mounted upon a small stand or bench. Only one press will be manufactured. Details concerning the collar bearings, the threaded bushings, and the ends of the screws have been purposely omitted from the sketch.

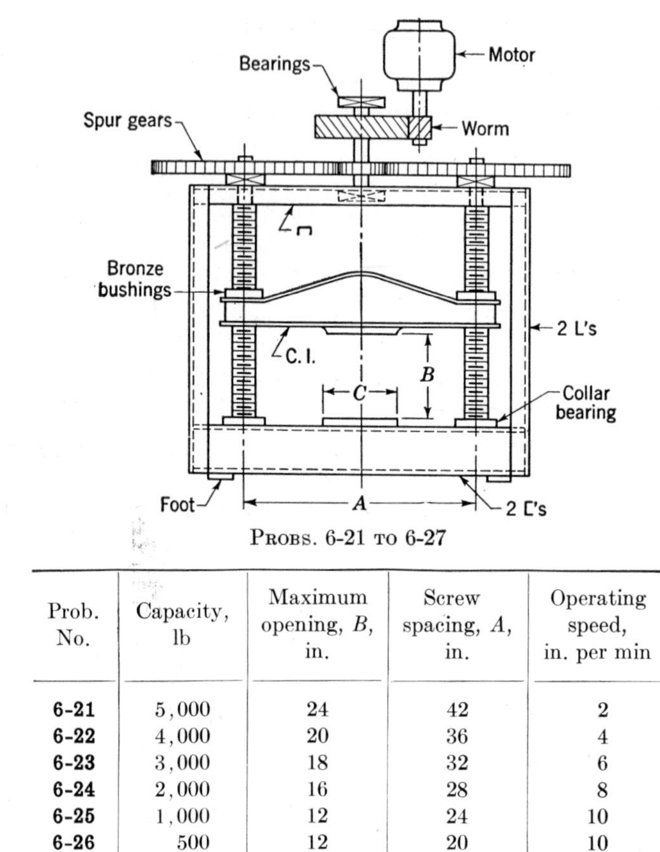

PROBS. 6-21 TO 6-27

Prob. No.	Capacity, lb	Maximum opening, B, in.	Screw spacing, A, in.	Operating speed, in. per min
6-21	5,000	24	42	2
6-22	4,000	20	36	4
6-23	3,000	18	32	6
6-24	2,000	16	28	8
6-25	1,000	12	24	10
6-26	500	12	20	10
6-27	250	12	18	10

6-28. The connection shown in the figure carries a static tensile load F. The bolt and nut are American Standard, semifinished. The bolt has a yield strength of 60,000 psi, and the members have a strength of 70,000 psi. Determine the strength of the connection if (a) the members are made of ductile materials and (b) if they are made of brittle materials. 7500 b) 10,700

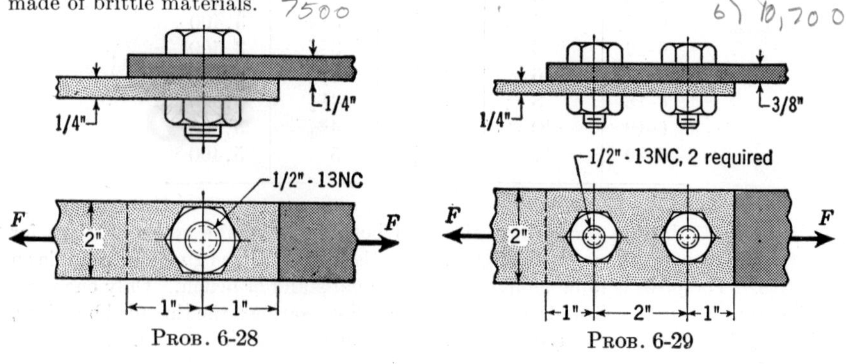

PROB. 6-28 PROB. 6-29

6-29. ASTM A325 bolts and American Standard nuts compose the connection shown in the figure. The members are C1020 cold-drawn steel. Determine the strength of the connection if the load is (*a*) a static tensile load, (*b*) a completely reversed axial load, and (*c*) a repeated tensile load.

6-30. The figure shows a bolted tensile connection using a C1040 finished-steel bolt, heat-treated to a yield strength of 86,000 psi. The members are of C1137 cold-drawn steel. Find the strength of the connection.

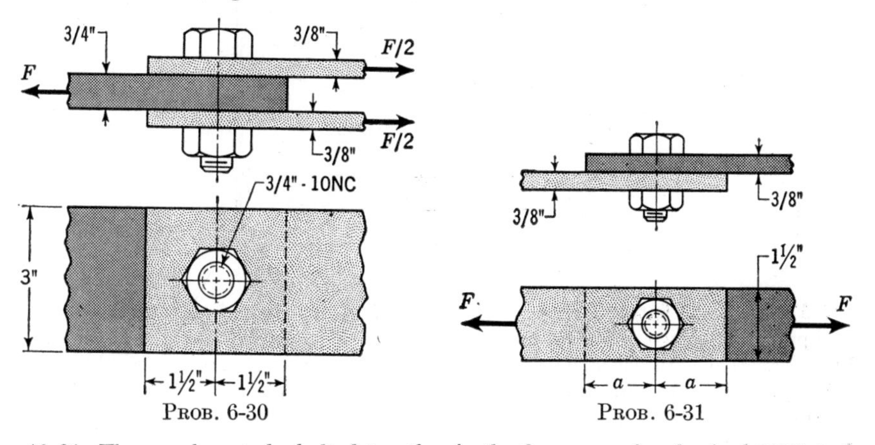

PROB. 6-30 PROB. 6-31

***6-31.** The members to be bolted together in the figure are of carburized 2317 steel having a ground finish. Specify a suitable bolt and the dimension *a* such that the bolt will have approximately the same strength as the members. How much torque should be used in tightening? T = 470 lbf (minimum)

***6-32.** The members shown in the figure are of C1020 cold-drawn steel. The load *F* is a completely reversed axial load. Select suitable fasteners and specify dimensions *a*, *b*, and *c* so that the fasteners will carry as much load as the members.

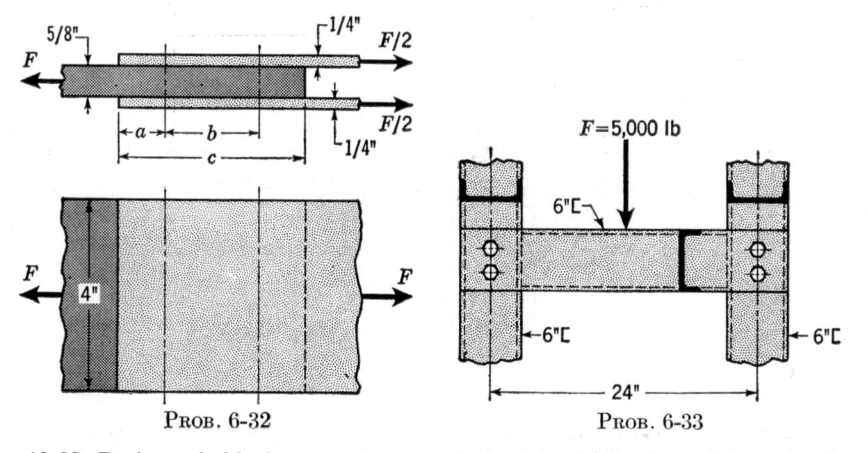

PROB. 6-32 PROB. 6-33

***6-33.** Design suitable fasteners to connect the 6-in. 8.2-lb channel beam to the columns. The channels are made from C1015 hot-rolled steel. The load is static.

***6-34.** The same as Prob. 6-33 except that the channel beam is 3-in. 4.1-lb, and the load is 3,500 lb.

***6-35.** The same as Prob. 6-33 except that all the channels are 8-in. 18.75-lb, the load is 12,000 lb, and the distance between column centers is 42 in.

***6-36.** Select suitable fasteners to connect the low-carbon, hot-rolled steel angles shown in the figure. The loading is repeated, and the supporting angles are braced against rotation.

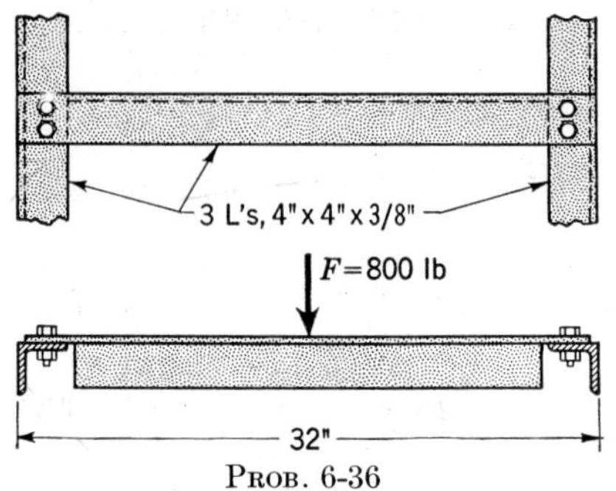

PROB. 6-36

***6-37.** A typical fixture for clamping slidable devices to round columns, such as in drill presses, is shown. The load is 50 lb and acts, either up or down, along the center line *A-A*. The fixture is made of forged 1018 steel, and the column is 1018 cold-drawn tubing, 2 in. OD × ¼ in. Specify the fastenings and design the portion of the fixture shown. Use a sketch to show all dimensions required. Specify the tightening-up torque for the fasteners. Use a factor of safety of 3 for all methods of failure.

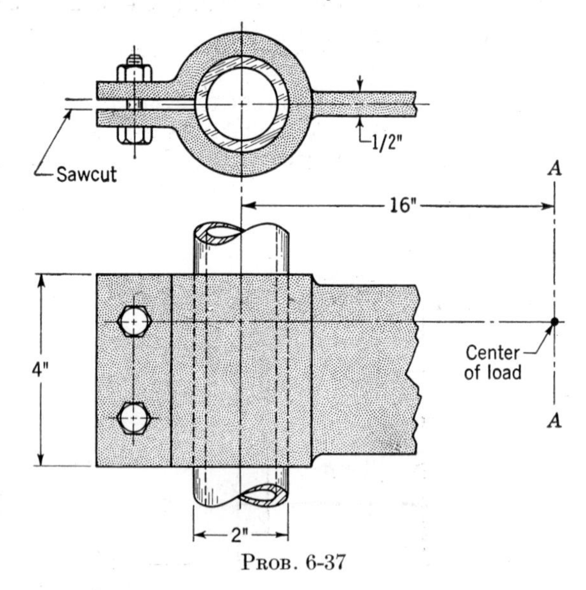

PROB. 6-37

***6-38.** The welded-steel bracket in the figure supports a rotating shaft which loads the bracket as shown. The bracket is to be secured to the support with four through bolts having a grip of 1½ in. Using SAE grade 7 bolt material, specify the size of bolts and torque-wrench setting required.

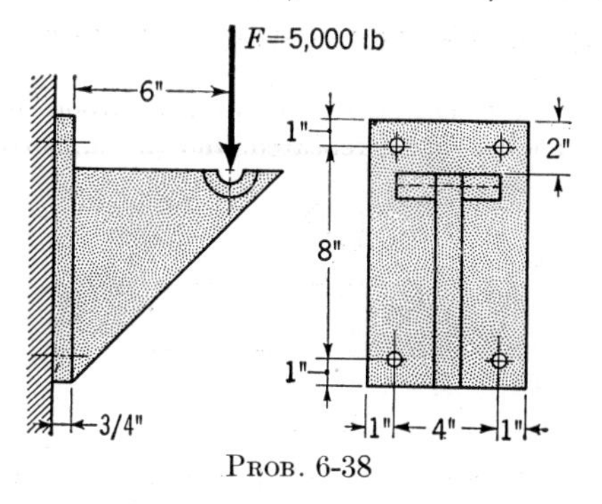

PROB. 6-38

6-39. A 16-in. steam-engine cylinder head uses a gasket having a stiffness coefficient of 0.15. The steam pressure is 200 psi. Select ASTM A325 National Coarse–thread through bolts, using a preload 25 per cent more than the maximum tensile load. Use a factor of safety of 2.

***6-40.** A cover is to be bolted to a 12-in.-diameter pressure vessel. The maximum pressure is 100 psi. Using a hard gasket material, specify completely the bolts to be used. If possible, the bolts should be mounted on a 13½-in. bolt circle.

***6-41.** A 24-in.-diameter pressure vessel is to be used for the preservative treatment of lumber. The treating cycle employs pressures up to 180 psi and vacuums to 26 in. Hg. The vessel is to use a head fastened with through bolts which must be removed at the end of each treating cycle in order to unload the treated lumber and reload with green lumber. The time of treatment is dependent upon the lumber size; for small sizes it may be as short as 12 hours. The bolts should be designed for a life of 10 years. To assure a good seal, at least eight bolts should be used, and they should be mounted on a 30-in. bolt circle. The weight of the head may be neglected because it is supported by hinges attached to the side of the vessel. Specify the bolt size, number, material, heat-treatment, and proper tightening torque. Specify the gasket material, and also write any instructions which may be necessary to the operating personnel.

6-42. Find the safe static load F for the joint shown in the figure, if the design stress is 13,000 psi. *Ans.:* 13,800 lb.

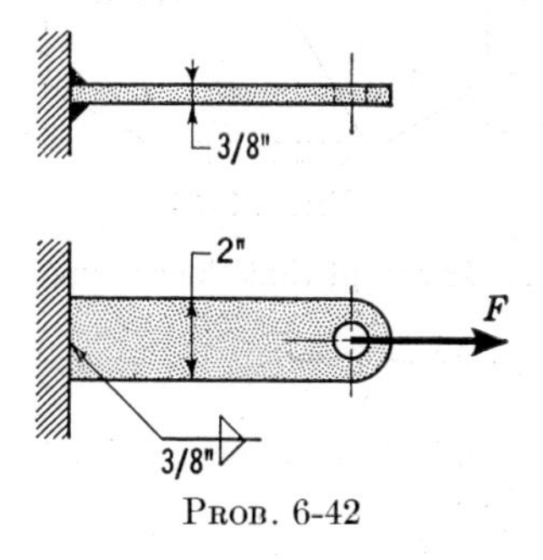

PROB. 6-42

6-43. Repeat Prob. 6-42 for a T butt weld instead of the fillet weld which is shown. *Ans.:* 9,750 lb.

6-44. Find the maximum stress in the weld shown in the figure. *Ans.:* 6,040 psi.

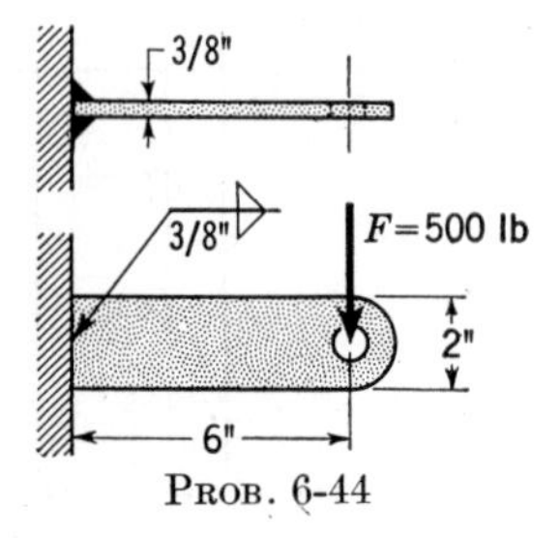

PROB. 6-44

6-45. Repeat Prob. 6-44 for a T butt weld instead of the fillet weld which is shown.

6-46. Find the maximum stress in the welds shown in the figure.

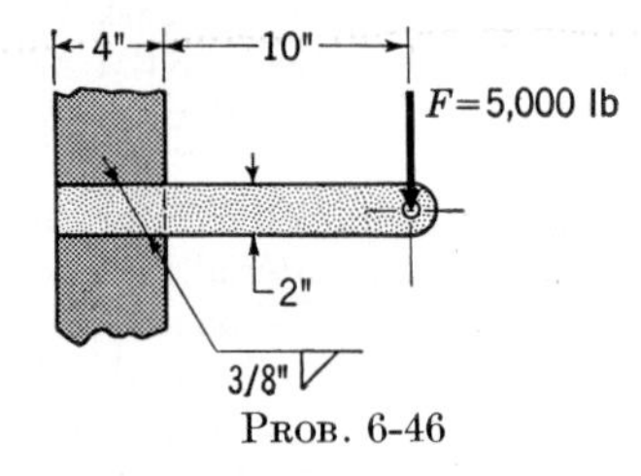

PROB. 6-46

6-47. Repeat Prob. 6-46 if the 5,000-lb load places the bar in axial tension instead of bending.

***6-48.** The 6-in. channel beam shown in the figure is to be welded to the channel columns at the ends to produce a beam with fixed ends. All members shown are of low-carbon steel. Specify suitable welds.

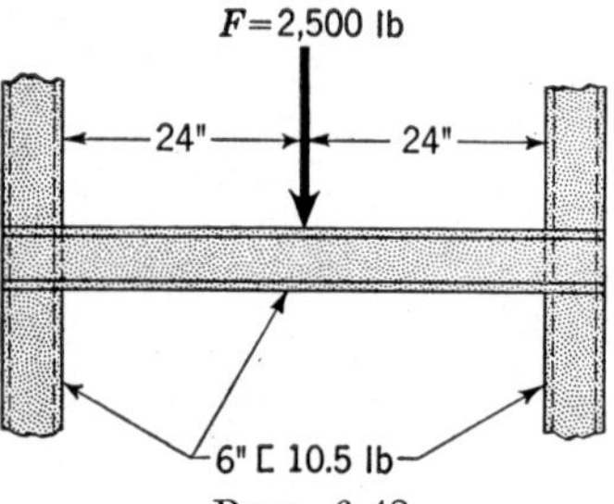

PROB. 6-48

***6-49.** The same as Prob. 6-48 except that the channels are 3-in. 4.1-lb and the load is 500 lb.

***6-50.** The same as Prob. 6-48 except that the channels are 10-in. 15.3-lb and the load is 7,000 lb.

***6-51.** Specify suitable welds, instead of bolts, and determine the resulting strength of the connection of Prob. 6-28.

***6-52.** Repeat Prob. 6-51 for Prob. 6-29.

***6-53.** Repeat Prob. 6-51 for Prob. 6-30.

***6-54.** Specify suitable welds for the connection of Prob. 6-33.

CHAPTER 7

MECHANICAL SPRINGS

Mechanical springs are used in machines to exert force, to provide flexibility, and to store or absorb energy. In general, springs may be classified as either wire springs or flat springs, although there are variations within these divisions. Wire springs include helical springs of round, square, or special-section wire and are made to resist tensile, compressive, or torsional loads. Under flat springs are included the cantilever and elliptical types, the wound motor- or clock-type power springs, and the flat spring washers which are usually called Belleville springs.

7-1. Stresses in Helical Springs. In Chap. 3 the term *spring constant*, which is also called the *scale*, was defined as

$$K = \frac{F}{y} \tag{7-1}$$

in which y is the deflection in inches produced by the force F. The spring constant K thus has the units of pounds per inch. Equation (7-1) is valid for any type of spring, provided that the elastic limit of the material is not exceeded.

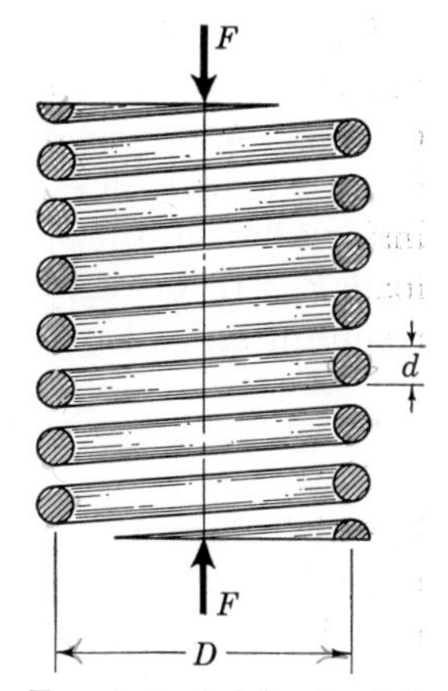

FIG. 7-1. Axially loaded helical spring.

Figure 7-1 shows a helical spring loaded axially by the compressive force F, having a mean spring diameter D and a wire diameter d. The effect of the axial force F is to twist the wire. The reader can visualize this effect by picturing a thread being pulled axially off a spool; as each turn of thread is pulled off the spool, the thread receives one additional twist or turn. If the stresses in a spring were exactly like the stresses in the twisted thread, they could be calculated by Eq. (2-18) for the shearing stress in a straight bar loaded in torsion.

There are two factors which cause the shearing stress to differ from a torsionally loaded straight bar. First, it should be noted that the fiber length on the inside of the coiled wire is shorter than on the outside. This means that, for a given angular rotation of adjacent cross sections of the wire, the inner fiber has a higher shearing stress. Secondly, the direct shearing stress due to the load F is additive to the torsional shearing stress on the inner fiber and subtractive on the outer fiber.

Wahl[1] demonstrates analytically that the fundamental torsion formula may be used if a stress-concentration factor is employed. The equation then becomes

$$s_s = k\frac{Tr}{J} = k\frac{8FD}{\pi d^3} \tag{7-2}$$

where $J = \pi d^3/32$
$r = d/2$
$T = FD/2$
k = stress-concentration factor, called the *Wahl correction factor*

The value of k may be obtained from the following equation:

$$k = \frac{4C - 1}{4C - 4} + \frac{0.615}{C} \tag{7-3}$$

where $C = D/d$ and is called the *spring index.*

Equation (7-3) is obtained from theoretical considerations in which the spring is treated somewhat as a curved beam. Wahl's factor k corrects for two conditions: the stress concentration due to the curvature of the wire, which exists because of the smaller radius of curvature of the inside fibers of the spring; and the direct shearing stress due to the axial load F. If we ignore the stress concentration due to curvature, the resultant stress is

$$s_s = \frac{Tr}{J} \pm \frac{F}{A} = \frac{8FD}{\pi d^3} \pm \frac{4F}{\pi d^2} \tag{a}$$

in which the stress is obtained using the plus sign for the inner fiber and the minus sign for the outer fiber. Therefore, the stress on the inner fiber is a maximum, and Eq. (a) can be rearranged to give

$$s_s = \frac{8FD}{\pi d^3}\left(1 + \frac{0.5}{C}\right) \tag{b}$$

This permits us to define a *shear-stress multiplication factor* by the equation

$$k_s = 1 + \frac{0.5}{C} \tag{7-4}$$

which accounts for the effects due to direct shear but not for the curva-

[1] A. M. Wahl, "Mechanical Springs," p. 37, Penton Publishing Company, Cleveland, 1944.

ture of the bar. The values of this factor have been calculated for various values of the spring index and are shown in Fig. 7-2.

When springs are subjected to static loads, the effect of curvature may be neglected, because yielding of the material will relieve the stresses. Equation (7-2) then becomes

$$s_s = k_s \frac{8FD}{\pi d^3} \tag{7-5}$$

which is valid only for ductile spring materials.

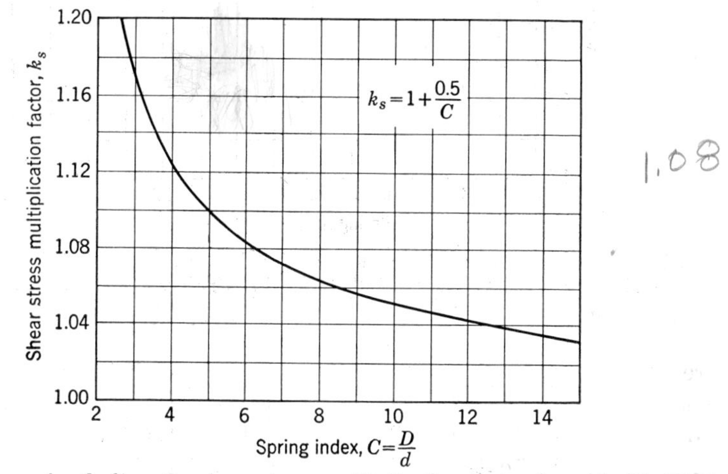

FIG. 7-2. Curve for finding the shear-stress multiplication factor k_s. (*A. M. Wahl, "Mechanical Springs," p. 101, Penton Publishing Company, Cleveland,* 1944.)

The stress-concentration factor for curvature is

$$k_c = \frac{k}{k_s} \tag{7-6}$$

which must be true because the product of k_c and k_s must equal k. Fatigue loads will be treated in a subsequent portion of this chapter. In Fig. 7-3 is shown a curve which was obtained by calculating values of the Wahl correction factor k for various values of the spring index. The effects of these corrections are shown graphically in Fig. 7-4.

Special-section Springs. The use of square or rectangular wire is not recommended for springs[1] unless space limitations make it necessary. Special-wire shapes are not made in large quantities, as are those of round wire; they have not had the benefit of refining development and hence are not as strong as those of round wire. Square wire is used to

[1] "Mechanical Spring Design," p. 15, Associated Spring Corporation, Bristol, Conn., 1949.

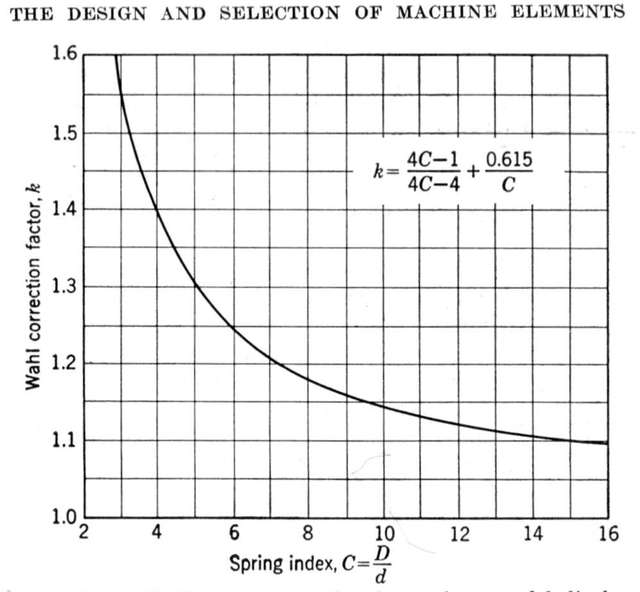

Fig. 7-3. Values of the Wahl stress-correction factor for round helical extension or compression springs. (*A. M. Wahl, "Mechanical Springs," p.* 101, *Penton Publishing Company, Cleveland,* 1944.)

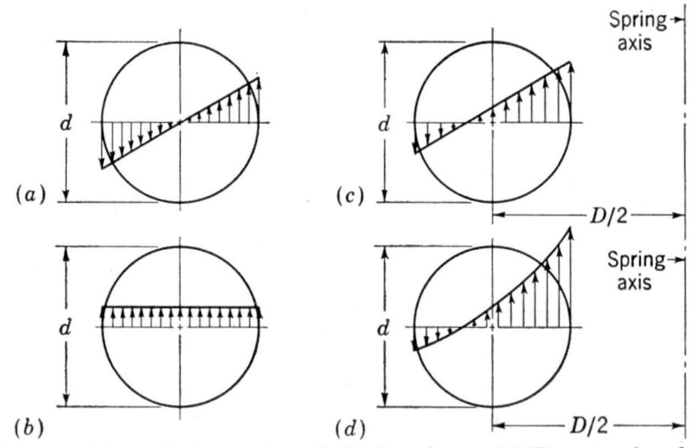

Fig. 7-4. Superposition of stresses in a helical spring. (*a*) Pure torsional stress. (*b*) Direct shearing stress. (*c*) Resultant of direct and torsional shearing stresses. (*d*) Resultant of direct, torsional, and curvature shearing stresses.

obtain the greatest load capacity in the smallest space, but this means that these springs are highly stressed.

An accurate determination of the stresses in a special-section helical spring is difficult and will not be considered in this book.[1]

[1] Charts for the calculation of stresses in square and rectangular helical springs may be found in the current literature. See also Wahl, *op. cit.*, p. 214.

7-2. Deflection of Helical Springs. In order to obtain the equation for the deflection of a helical spring, we shall consider an element of wire formed by two adjacent cross sections. Figure 7-5 shows such an element, of length dx, cut from wire of diameter d. Let us consider a line ab on the surface of the wire which is parallel to the spring axis. After deformation it will rotate through the angle γ and occupy the new position ac. From Eq. (3-4), which is the expression of Hooke's law for torsion, we have

$$\gamma = \frac{s_s}{G} = \frac{8FD}{\pi d^3 G} \tag{a}$$

where the value of s_s is obtained from Eq. (7-2), using unity for the value of k.* The distance bc is $\gamma\, dx$, and the angle $d\alpha$, through which one section rotates with respect to the other, is

$$d\alpha = \frac{\gamma\, dx}{d/2} = \frac{2\gamma\, dx}{d} \tag{b}$$

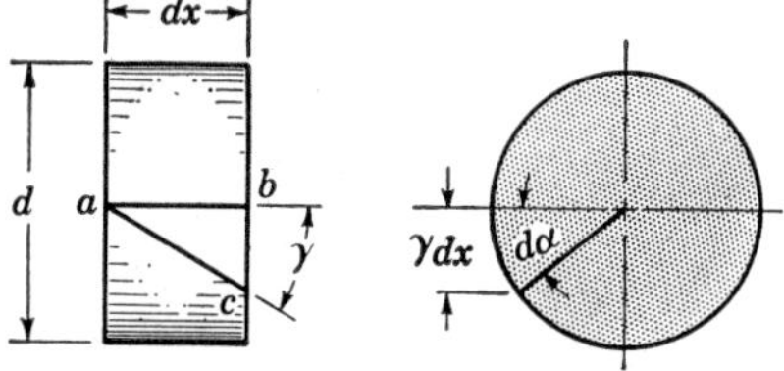

FIG. 7-5. Cross-sectional element of a helical spring.

If the number of active coils is denoted by N, the total length of the wire is πDN. Substituting γ from Eq. (a) into Eq. (b) and integrating, the angular deflection of one end of the wire with respect to the other is

$$\alpha = \int_0^{\pi DN} \frac{2\gamma}{d}\, dx = \int_0^{\pi DN} \frac{16FD}{\pi d^4 G}\, dx = \frac{16FD^2N}{d^4G} \tag{c}$$

The load F has a moment arm of $D/2$, and so the deflection is

$$y = \alpha \frac{D}{2} = \frac{8FD^3N}{d^4G} \tag{7-7}$$

Using Eq. (7-1) and substituting the value of y from Eq. (7-7), the spring constant is found to be

$$K = \frac{d^4G}{8D^3N} \tag{7-8}$$

The equations demonstrated in this section are valid for both compression and extension springs. Long coil springs compressively loaded may be subject to column action and so fail by buckling. This condition may be corrected by mounting the spring in a tube or over a round bar.

7-3. Extension Springs. Extension springs necessarily must have some means of transferring the load from the support to the body of the spring. Although this can be done with a threaded plug or a swivel hook, both of

* Wahl quotes the results of tests to show that k can be made unity for calculating deflections with very accurate results. See Wahl, *op. cit.*, p. 29.

these add to the cost of the finished product, and so one of the methods shown in Fig. 7-6 is usually employed. In designing a spring with a hook end the stress-concentration effect must be considered.

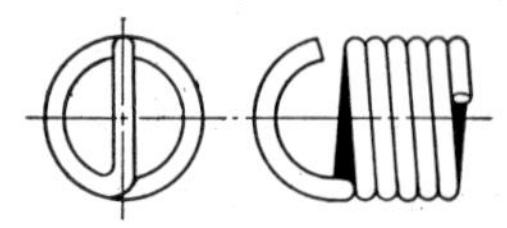

Machine half loop - open

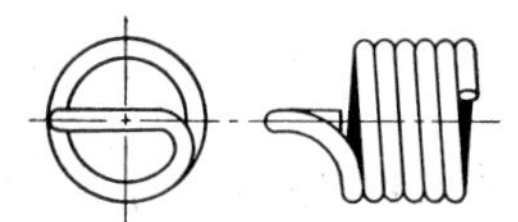

Short twisted loop

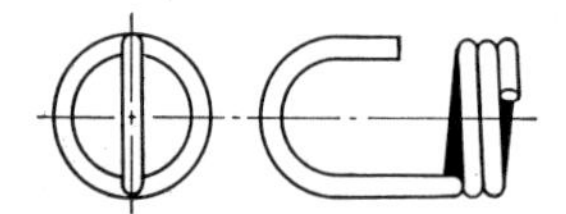

Raised hook

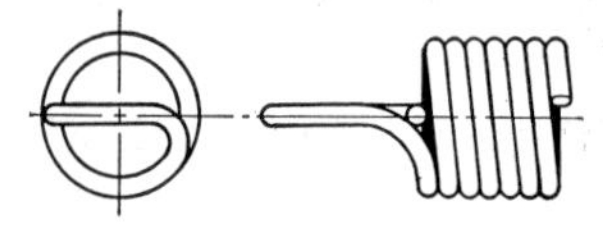

Full twisted loop

FIG. 7-6. Types of ends used on extension springs. (*Courtesy of Associated Spring Corporation.*)

In Fig. 7-7*a* is shown a much used method of designing the end. Stress concentration due to the sharp bend makes it impossible to design the hook as strong as the body. Tests show that the stress-concentration factor is given approximately by

$$k = \frac{r_0}{r_i} \tag{7-9}$$

which holds for bending stress and occurs when the hook is offset and for torsional stress. Figure 7-7*b* shows an improved design due to a reduced coil diameter, not to elimination of stress concentration. The reduced coil diameter results in a lower stress because of the shorter moment arm.

Initial Tension. Close-wound springs are frequently made so that a load must be applied in order to separate the coils, one from another. The separating load is called the initial tension. Spring manufacturers prefer some initial tension in close-wound springs in order to hold the free length more accurately. However, the designer should specify the amount desired. The stress due to initial tension may be obtained from the equations in Sec. 7-2.

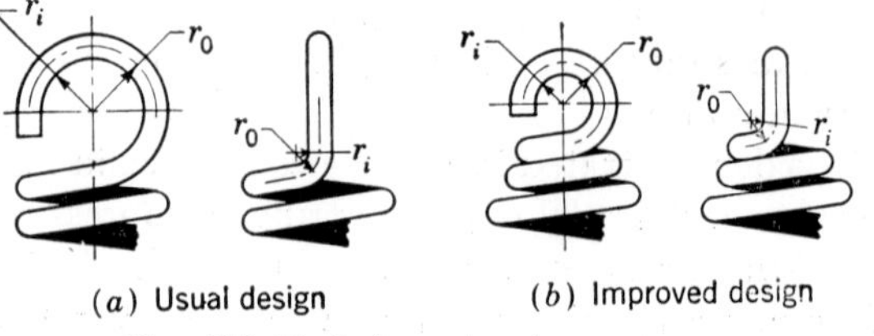

FIG. 7-7. Ends for extension springs.

7-4. Compression Springs. The type of end should be specified as follows: (1) plain ends; (2) plain ends, ground; (3) squared ends; or (4) squared and ground ends. The type of end used results in dead or inactive turns at each end of the spring, and these must be subtracted from the total number of turns in order to obtain the number of active turns. There is no hard and fast rule, but the following, when subtracted from the total number of turns, will give the approximate number of active coils:

Plain ends—subtract one-half turn
Plain and ground ends—subtract one turn
Squared ends—subtract one turn
Squared and ground ends—subtract two turns

It is customary in the design of springs to neglect the effects of eccentricity of loading due to the end turns. It is also customary to neglect

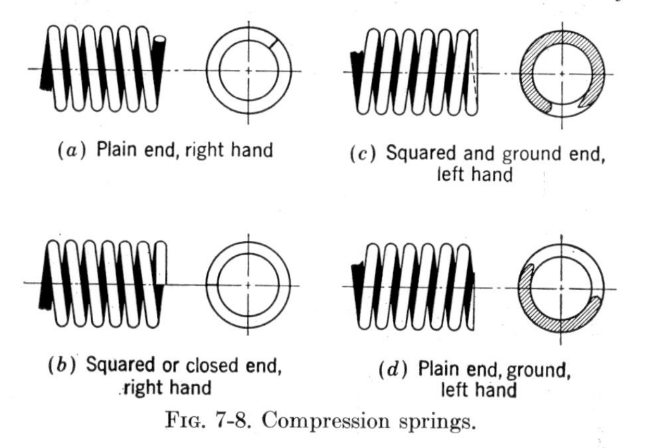

FIG. 7-8. Compression springs.

the effect of residual stresses caused by heat-treatment or overstressing. Instead, these two effects are usually accounted for by an increase in the factor of safety. It is the usual practice, in the manufacture of compression springs, to close them to their solid height; this induces a residual stress opposite in direction to the working stress and has the effect of improving the strength of the spring.

7-5. Fatigue Loading. In the case of shafts and other machine members, fatigue loading in the form of completely reversed stresses is quite ordinary. Helical springs, on the other hand, are almost never used as both compression and extension springs and for this reason are not subject to completely reversed loads. Figure 7-9 shows the usual stress variation encountered in the design of helical springs. The worst condition will occur when $s_{s,\min}$ is zero. Since springs are usually assembled in place, with initial tension in the case of extension springs and initial compression of compression springs, the worst condition is seldom obtained. If we assume the worst condition is obtained, then $s_{s,\min}$ is zero, and the average stress s_{av} (static component) is $s_{s,\max}/2$. This means that on the fatigue-stress diagram (Fig. 7-10) only points to the right of point A need be considered.

Wahl suggests two methods of treating fluctuating stresses in the design of helical springs. In the first method, which employs the fatigue-stress diagram of Fig. 7-10, the varying component of stress s_r is figured, using a reduced value of the Wahl correction factor. The Wahl factor is reduced because some materials are less sensitive to stress concentration when subjected to fatigue loads (see Chap. 4, Sec. 4-9). The method is applied by calculating the curvature factor k_c from Eq. (7-6), after which

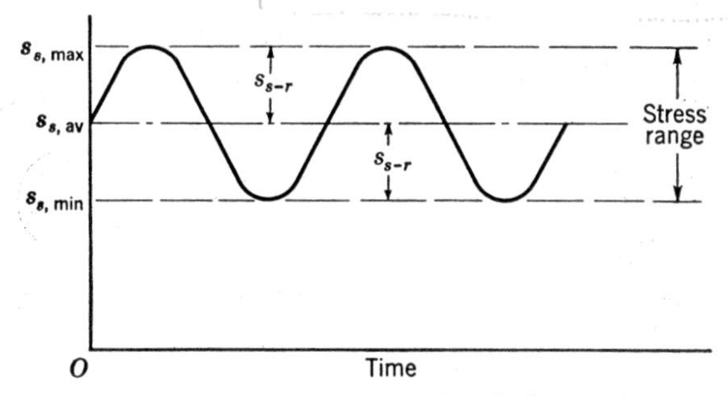

FIG. 7-9. Fluctuating stresses in a helical spring.

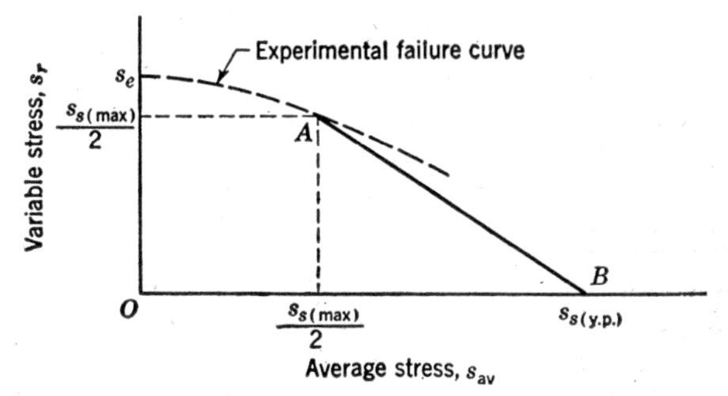

FIG. 7-10. Fatigue-stress diagram for springs.

k_c is adjusted for fatigue, employing Fig. 4-24. The variable stress s_r is then obtained from Eq. (7-2) as follows:

$$s_r = k_f k_s \frac{8D}{\pi d^3} \frac{F_{max} - F_{min}}{2} \tag{7-10}$$

where k_f is the reduced value of k_c obtained from Fig. 4-24. The average stress s_{av} is calculated from Eq. (7-5), because this is the static component:

$$s_{av} = k_s \frac{8D}{\pi d^3} \frac{F_{max} + F_{min}}{2} \tag{7-11}$$

We may now define an endurance range of stress by the equation

$$R = s_{s,max} - s_{s,min} \tag{7-12}$$

Table 7-1 gives experimental values of R as obtained by various investigators. By selecting $s_{s,max}/2 = R/2$ we may locate point A on Fig. 7-10. The problem is then solved by applying the methods of Sec. 4-8

TABLE 7-1. ENDURANCE STRESS RANGE R FOR HELICAL SPRINGS* ($s_{s,min}$ NEAR ZERO)

Material	Approximate wire diameter, in.	Index, $C = D/d$	Limiting stress range R, psi	Notes
Cold-drawn wire	0.13–0.16	10–11	41,000	Tension
Cold-drawn wire	0.16	6	60,000	Compression
Cold-drawn wire	0.135	14	46,000	Compression
Music wire	0.25	8	56,000	Compression
Music wire	0.063	7	76,000	Compression
Music wire	0.148	6–7	70,000	Compression
Music wire	0.148	6–7	115,000	Compression, shot-blasted
Valve-spring wire	0.162	6.5	75,000	Compression
Valve-spring wire	0.162	6.5	115,000	Compression, shot-blasted
Valve-spring wire	0.135	14	68,000	Compression
C steel, cold-wound	0.148	7.4	60,000	Compression
C steel, cold-wound	0.148	7.4	52,000	Compression
C steel, cold-wound	0.135	14	53,000	Compression
C steel, cold-wound	0.25	8	56,000	Compression
SAE 6150 steel	0.148	7.4	70,000	Compression
SAE 6150 steel	0.148	7.4	115,000	Compression, shot-blasted
18-8 stainless	0.148	6–7	45,000	Compression
18-8 stainless	0.148	6–7	90,000	Compression, shot-blasted
Phosphor bronze	0.148	6–7	15,000	Compression
Phosphor bronze	0.148	6–7	30,000	Compression, shot-blasted
Open-hearth carbon steel	0.56	4.8	68,000	Compression
Open-hearth carbon steel	0.75	5.0	72,700	Compression
Chromium-vanadium steel	0.56	4.8	77,000	Compression
Beryllium bronze	0.56	4.8	33,000	Compression

* A. M. Wahl, "Mechanical Springs," pp. 91–92, Penton Publishing Company, Cleveland, 1944.

to the right-hand portion of Fig. 7-10. This is illustrated in the following example:

EXAMPLE 7-1. A helical compression spring is made of music wire having a diameter of 0.063 in. The spring has a mean diameter of 3/16 in. The material has a torsional yield strength of 120,000 psi. Determine F_{max} and F_{min} for a ratio of $F_{max}/F_{min} = 4$ and a factor of safety of 1.8, employing the method described above.

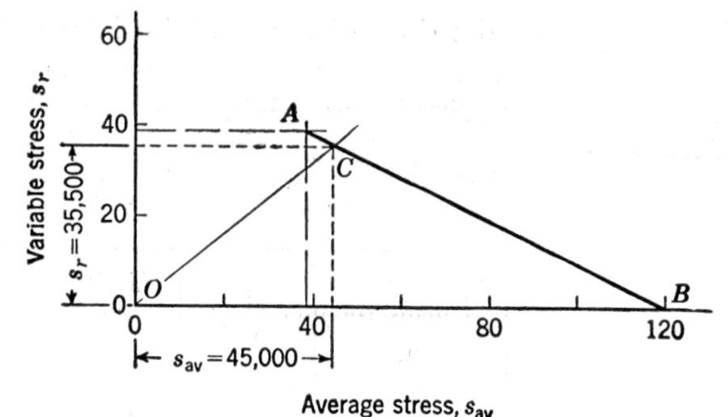

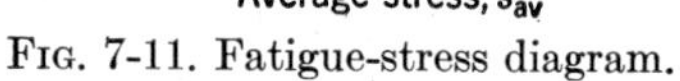

Fig. 7-11. Fatigue-stress diagram.

Solution. The spring index is $C = D/d = 0.1875/0.063 = 2.98$, say 3. From Eqs. (7-3), (7-4), and (7-6), the correction factors are

$$k = \frac{4C - 1}{4C - 4} + \frac{0.615}{C} = \frac{(4)(3) - 1}{(4)(3) - 4} + \frac{0.615}{3} = 1.575$$

$$k_s = 1 + \frac{0.5}{C} = 1 + \frac{0.5}{3} = 1.167$$

$$k_c = \frac{k}{k_s} = \frac{1.575}{1.167} = 1.35$$

Applying $k_c = 1.35$ to Fig. 4-24, the curvature factor corrected for fatigue is $k_f = 1.31$. From Eq. (7-10), the variable stress is

$$s_r = k_f k_s \frac{8D}{\pi d^3} \frac{F_{\max} - F_{\min}}{2} = k_f k_s \frac{8D}{\pi d^3} \frac{3F_{\max}}{8} \tag{a}$$

since $F_{\min} = F_{\max}/4$. Substituting the given data in Eq. (*a*) yields

$$s_r = (1.31)(1.167) \frac{(8)(0.1875)}{\pi (0.063)^3} \frac{3F_{\max}}{8} = 1{,}100F_{\max} \tag{b}$$

Similarly, from Eq. (7-11), the average stress is

$$\begin{aligned} s_{av} &= k_s \frac{8D}{\pi d^3} \frac{F_{\max} + F_{\min}}{2} = k_s \frac{8D}{\pi d^3} \frac{5F_{\max}}{8} \\ &= 1.167 \frac{(8)(0.1875)}{\pi (0.063)^3} \frac{5F_{\max}}{8} = 1{,}400F_{\max} \end{aligned} \tag{c}$$

From Table 7-1 the endurance stress range is 76,000 psi. Therefore,

$$\frac{s_{s,\max}}{2} = \frac{76{,}000}{2} = 38{,}000 \text{ psi}$$

This is located as point A on the fatigue-stress diagram (Fig. 7-11), and the torsional yield strength, $s_{s(yp)} = 120{,}000$ psi, as point B. The ratio of the variable and average components is

$$\frac{s_r}{s_{av}} = \frac{1{,}100F_{\max}}{1{,}400F_{\max}} = 0.785$$

The line OC is now constructed with a slope of 0.785. Its intersection with AB gives the limiting values of s_r and s_{av}. They are found by scaling the diagram:

$$s_r = 35{,}500 \text{ psi} \qquad s_{av} = 45{,}000 \text{ psi}$$

Applying the factor of safety and solving Eq. (*b*), we obtain

$$F_{max} = \frac{s_r}{(1{,}100) \text{ f.s.}} = \frac{35{,}500}{(1{,}100)(1.8)} = 18.0 \text{ lb} \qquad Ans.$$

The same value may be obtained by using the factor of safety and solving Eq. (*c*) for F_{max}. The minimum load is

$$F_{min} = \frac{F_{max}}{4} = \frac{18.0}{4} = 4.50 \text{ lb} \qquad Ans.$$

It is also desirable to check the maximum stress against the yield strength. This is obtained from Eq. (7-5):

$$s_{s,max} = k_s \frac{8F_{max}D}{\pi d^3} = 1.167 \frac{(8)(18)(0.1875)}{\pi(0.063)^3} = 40{,}000 \text{ psi}$$

Since this is well below the yield strength of 120,000 psi, the design is safe.

The second method suggested by Wahl applies the factor of safety directly to the endurance range of stress. The stress range, however, is calculated using the full value of the Wahl correction factor; that is, the stress-concentration factor is not adjusted for notch sensitivity. In applying this method, Wahl also sets up a second condition which is that the peak stress calculated using only k_s shall not exceed the yield strength divided by a suitable factor of safety. This method is applied to Example 7-1 as follows:

A statement of the first condition of Wahl's alternative method is

$$s_{s,max} - s_{s,min} = \frac{R}{\text{f.s.}} \tag{7-13}$$

The left-hand side of this equation is obtained from Eq. (7-2) as

$$s_{s,max} - s_{s,min} = k \frac{8D}{\pi d^3} (F_{max} - F_{min}) = k \frac{8D}{\pi d^3} \frac{3}{4} F_{max}$$

$$= 1.575 \frac{(8)(0.1875)}{\pi(0.063)^3} \frac{3}{4} F_{max} = 3{,}000 F_{max}$$

Applying the factor of safety of 1.8 to the endurance range of 76,000 psi, we obtain

$$\frac{76{,}000}{1.8} = 42{,}200 \text{ psi}$$

Therefore, $$F_{max} = \frac{42{,}200}{3{,}000} = 14.1 \text{ lb} \qquad Ans.$$

so that $$F_{min} = \frac{F_{max}}{4} = \frac{14.1}{4} = 3.52 \text{ lb} \qquad Ans.$$

The second condition states that the peak stress must not exceed the yield strength divided by the factor of safety. The peak stress is calculated as if it were a static stress. Thus, from Eq. (7-5)

$$s_{s,\max} = k_s \frac{8F_{\max}D}{\pi d^3} = 1.167 \frac{(8)(14.1)(0.1875)}{\pi(0.063)^3} = 31{,}400 \text{ psi} \qquad \textit{Ans.}$$

The design stress is

$$s_d = \frac{s_{yp}}{\text{f.s.}} = \frac{120{,}000}{1.8} = 66{,}600 \text{ psi}$$

Therefore, the spring is safe for the second condition.

7-6. Assumptions and Decisions. *Assumptions.* The assumptions used in the preceding analysis are:

1. Stress concentration due to curvature is neglected in calculating the static component of stress. In the case of springs with static loads, yielding of the material is assumed to relieve these stresses. When the load is fluctuating, the curvature factor is still not applied to the static component; this is in accordance with Soderberg's recommendation (Sec. 4-8). The alternative method is not subject to this limitation.

In addition, there is some feeling among spring designers that the use of the full value of the Wahl factor gives stresses which are too high. This has been partially verified by experiment.

2. For a given wire size the endurance range of a material is assumed to be the same for all values of the spring index. This may not be true because of the additional cold working experienced by small-index springs when they are wound.

3. Residual stresses are neglected. Residual stresses may be produced by heat-treatment, by cold working, or by prestressing.

4. The additional stress at the ends of the spring due to any eccentric loading and the possibility of column action are neglected.

Decisions. The design of a helical spring is usually accomplished on a trial-and-error basis because stress and deflection are both important. A tentative material, wire size, and spring diameter are selected. The stress and deflection are calculated and the results used to alter the tentative selection. Several trials will ordinarily serve to reveal an optimum design.

7-7. Helical Torsion Springs. The torsion springs illustrated in Fig. 7-12 are used in door hinges, automobile starters, and, in fact, for any application where torque is required. They are wound in the same manner as extension or compression springs but have the ends shaped to transmit torque. A torsion spring should always be loaded so as to cause the spring to wind up when the load is applied. The reason for this is that the springs are wound cold; this sets up residual stresses which will oppose the load if it is applied so as to wind up the spring.

A torsion spring is subjected to the action of a bending moment $M = Fr$, as shown in Fig. 7-13. The bending stress may be obtained using curved-beam theory as explained in Sec. 3-12.[1] The expression reduces to

$$s = k\frac{Mc}{I} \tag{a}$$

where the value of k depends upon the shape of the wire and upon whether or not the stress is desired on the inner fiber of the coil or on the outer

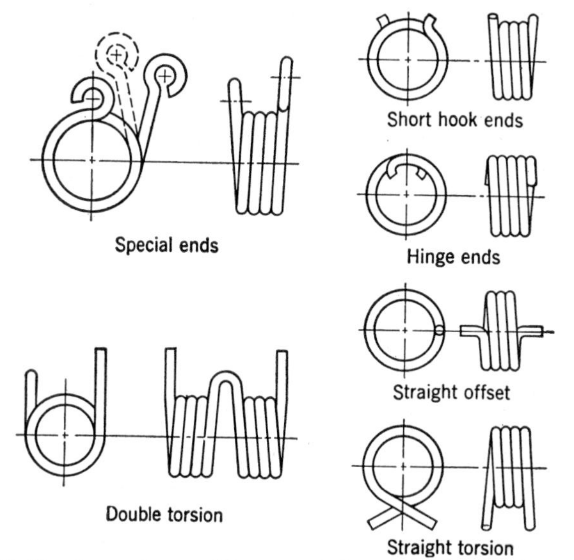

FIG. 7-12. Torsion springs. (*Courtesy of Associated Spring Corporation.*)

fiber. Wahl has analytically determined the following values of k for round wire:

$$k_i = \frac{4C^2 - C - 1}{4C(C - 1)} \qquad k_o = \frac{4C^2 + C - 1}{4C(C + 1)} \tag{7-14}$$

where C is the spring index and the subscripts i and o refer to the inner and outer fibers, respectively. When the bending moment $M = Fr$ and the section modulus $I/c = \pi d^3/32$ are substituted in Eq. (a), we obtain

$$s_{max} = k_i \frac{32Fr}{\pi d^3} \tag{7-15}$$

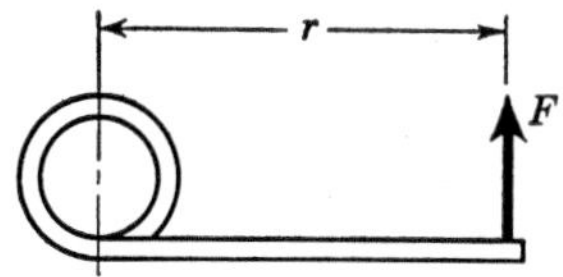

FIG. 7-13. A loaded torsion spring.

which gives the maximum bending stress for a round-wire torsion spring.

Deflection. In elementary strength of materials it is shown that

$$\theta = \int \frac{M\,ds}{EI} \tag{b}$$

[1] See also Wahl, *op. cit.*, pp. 317–326, and S. P. Timoshenko, "Strength of Materials," pt. II, pp. 73–75, D. Van Nostrand Company, Inc., New York, 1941.

where θ is the slope or angular deflection and ds is the length of an element of the spring. Integrating over the total length of the spring, πDN, we obtain

$$\theta = \int_0^{\pi DN} \frac{M\,ds}{EI} = \frac{\pi MDN}{EI} \tag{c}$$

We can now substitute the moment of inertia, $I = \pi d^4/64$, and the moment, $M = Fr$. This gives

$$\theta = \frac{64FrDN}{d^4E} \tag{7-16}$$

where θ is the angular deflection in radians.

It should be noted that Eq. (7-16) has been developed without regard to the curvature of the wire. Comparison of the results of this equation with the exact results obtained by considering curvature shows that the difference is negligible.

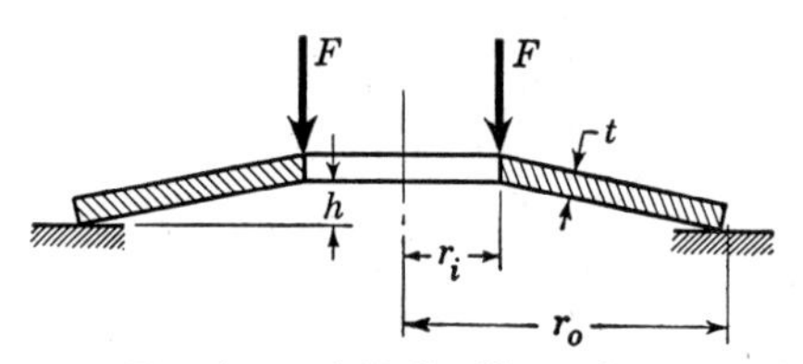

FIG. 7-14. A Belleville spring.

7-8. Belleville Springs. Figure 7-14 shows a coned-disk spring which is commonly called a *Belleville spring*. Although the mathematical treatment is beyond the purposes of this book, the reader should at least be familiar with the remarkable characteristics of these springs.

Aside from the obvious advantage of occupying a small space, a variation of the h/t ratio will produce a wide variety of load-deflection curve shapes, as illustrated in Fig. 7-15. For example, using an h/t ratio of 2.83 or larger gives an S curve which might be useful for snap-acting mechanisms. By reducing the ratio to a value between 1.41 and 2.1 the central portion of the curve becomes horizontal, which means that the load is constant over a considerable deflection range.

A higher load for a given deflection may be obtained by nesting, that is, by stacking the springs in parallel. On the other hand, stacking in series provides a larger deflection for the same load, but in this case there is danger of instability.

7-9. Leaf Springs. The design of multiple-leaf springs, such as are used in automotive applications, is a highly specialized art combining both theory and experiment[1] and is used only in certain industries. The following discussion may be considered as fundamental to their design.

Flat springs are basically beams, as shown in Fig. 7-16, and their

[1] Faires has an excellent short discussion of leaf springs. See Virgil Moring Faires, "Design of Machine Elements," 3d ed., pp. 189–195, The Macmillan Company, New York, 1955.

stresses and deflections may be calculated using the ordinary beam equations. These springs, however, are inefficient in their use of material because of the fact that the stress is not constant throughout the length.

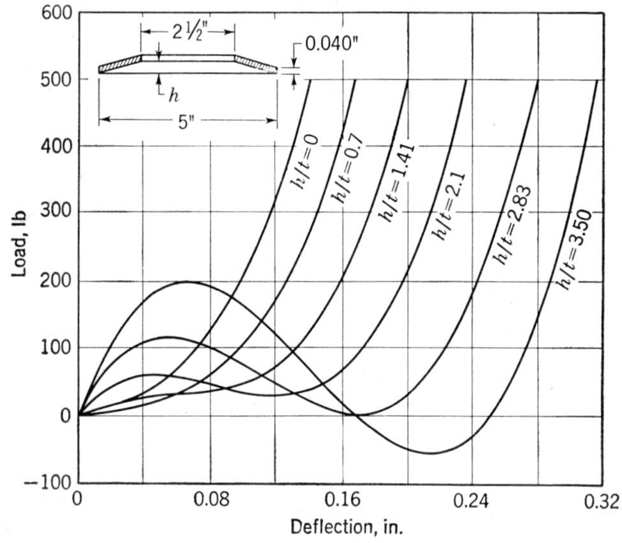

FIG. 7-15. Load-deflection curves for Belleville springs. (*Courtesy of Associated Spring Corporation.*)

A better arrangement of material, from this consideration, would be one of the two methods shown in Fig. 7-17. The dimensions of each section may be obtained as follows: Using the fundamental equation for bending stress, $s = Mc/I$, and solving for the section modulus, we obtain

$$\frac{I}{c} = \frac{M}{s_d} = \frac{Fx}{s_d} \qquad (a)$$

where s_d is the design stress and the origin of coordinates is as shown in the figure. For a rectangular section, the section modulus is $bh^2/6$. Equating this to (a) gives

$$\frac{bh^2}{6} = \frac{Fx}{s_d} \qquad (b)$$

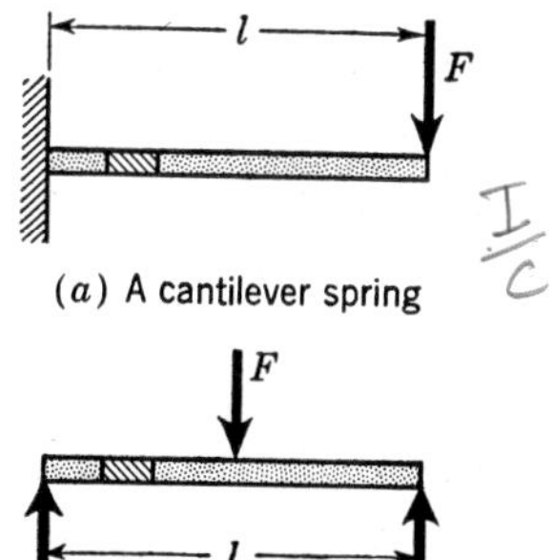

FIG. 7-16. Types of flat springs.

For the triangular beam shown in Fig. 7-17a the width b is variable. Solving Eq. (b) for the width gives

$$b = \frac{6Fx}{h^2 s_d} \qquad \text{and} \qquad b_0 = \frac{6Fl}{h^2 s_d} \qquad (7\text{-}17)$$

The height h is variable in the parabolic beam shown in Fig. 7-17b, and so, solving Eq. (b) for h,

$$h = \sqrt{\frac{6Fx}{bs_d}} \quad \text{and} \quad h_o = \sqrt{\frac{6Fl}{bs_d}} \tag{7-18}$$

The values of h_o and b_o were each obtained by substituting the length l for x. These equations may be used for the design of constant-strength

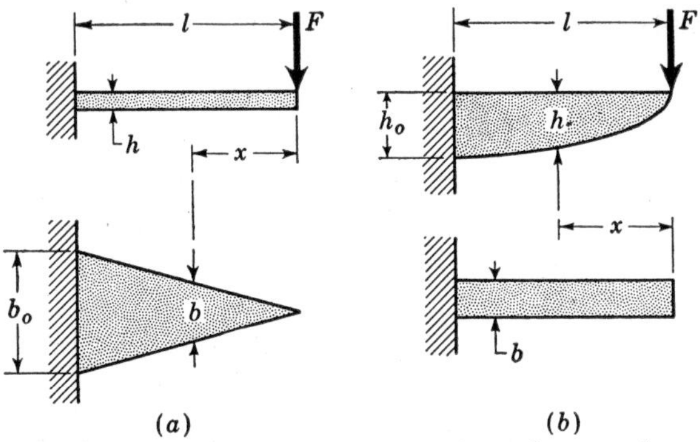

FIG. 7-17. Improved arrangements of cantilever springs.

springs. Since the moments of inertia are variable, the graphical-integration method described in Sec. 3-5 should be used to determine the deflection.

It is not difficult to imagine either of the springs of Fig. 7-17 being sliced or cut so as to produce the leaf spring of Fig. 7-18. Such a spring will have approximately the same stress as that given by Eq. (7-17) or (7-18), although the deflection may be somewhat different. There are a number of considerations which contribute to the inaccuracy of this method. These are:

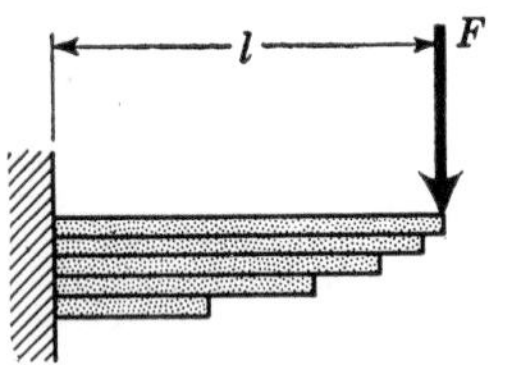

FIG. 7-18. A simplified leaf spring.

1. The moment of inertia is no longer continuously variable.
2. The possibility of friction between the leaves.
3. Stress-concentration effects.

In addition, in the manufacture of leaf springs, the ends of the leaves are often tapered, and the leaves are sometimes curved, with the various leaves having different radii of curvature. The addition of U bolts and clips also complicates the determination of the stresses and deflections.

7-10. Critical Frequency of Helical Springs. Coil springs are frequently used in applications imposing a very rapid reciprocating motion upon the coils, as, for example, in automotive valve springs. In these cases, the designer must assure himself that the physical dimensions of the spring are not such as to create a natural vibratory frequency close to the frequency of the applied force. Such a condition would mean that the spring would resonate at the same frequency as the applied motion. Since helical springs are relatively free of damping forces, the internal stresses at resonance would be high.

Wahl[1] has shown that the critical frequency of a helical spring is

$$f = \frac{m}{2}\sqrt{\frac{Kg}{W}} \tag{7-19}$$

where the fundamental frequency is found for $m = 1$, the second harmonic for $m = 2$, and so on, and where K is the spring constant as defined by Eq. (7-8). The frequency f is given in cycles per second. The weight of the spring is

$$W = AL\rho = \frac{\pi d^2}{4}(\pi DN)(\rho) = \frac{\pi^2 d^2 DN\rho}{4} \tag{7-20}$$

where ρ is the wire density (0.285 lb per in.^{3} for steel) and the other quantities are as previously defined.

The fundamental critical frequency should be from fifteen to twenty times the frequency of the force in order to avoid resonance with the harmonics. If the frequency is not high enough, then the spring should be redesigned to increase K or decrease W.

7-11. Energy Considerations. Springs may be used for the storage of energy and for absorbing and slowly releasing the energy from shock or impact loads. The energy-storage capacity of a spring is, therefore, an important consideration in design. It has been shown in Chap. 3 that strain energy may be computed from one of the two following equations:

$$U = \frac{Fy}{2} \qquad U = \frac{M\theta}{2} \tag{7-21}$$

where y and θ = linear and angular deflections, respectively
F = force
M = torque, or bending moment

By substitution of the moment or force and the proper deflection, these equations may be used to find the energy capacity of any spring in which the deflection is directly proportional to the load.

The capacity of a statically loaded spring is limited by the stress approaching the yield point. The capacity of a spring loaded in fatigue is limited by the stress approaching the endurance limit. If the maximum energy capacity is to be determined, one of these two strengths must, therefore, be used.

The procedure is to substitute in the appropriate stress formula a

[1] Wahl, *op. cit.*, p. 231. The reader should compare this result with Eq. (3-40).

Table 7-2. Physical Properties of Spring Materials*

	Material	Analysis		Tensile properties			Rockwell hardness	Torsional properties of wire			Process of manufacture, chief uses, special properties
		Element	%	Ultimate strength, psi	Elastic limit, psi	Modulus of elasticity		Ultimate strength, psi	Elastic limit, psi	Modulus in torsion	
Flat cold-rolled spring steel	Watch-spring steel	C Mn	1.10–1.19 0.15–0.25	330,000–350,000	310,000–330,000	32,000,000	C50–55	Not used	Not used	Not used	Cold-rolled and heat-treated before forming; mainsprings for watches and similar uses
	Clock-spring steel	C Mn	0.90–1.05 0.30–0.50	180,000–340,000	150,000–310,000	30,000,000	C40–52	Not used	Not used	Not used	Cold-rolled and heat-treated before forming; clock and motor springs, miscellaneous flat springs for high stress
	Flat-spring steel	C Mn	0.65–0.80 0.50–0.90	160,000–320,000	125,000–280,000	30,000,000	Annealed, B70–85; tempered, C38–50	Not used	Not used	Not used	Cold-rolled or annealed or tempered; miscellaneous flat springs
Carbon steel wires	High-carbon wire	C Mn	0.85–0.95 0.25–0.60	200,000–250,000	160,000–210,000	30,000,000	C44–48	160,000–200,000	110,000–150,000	11,500,000	Cold-rolled or drawn; high-grade helical springs or wire forms
	Oil-tempered wire (ASTM A229-41)	C Mn	0.60–0.70 0.60–0.90	155,000–300,000	120,000–250,000	29,000,000	C42–46	115,000–200,000	80,000–130,000	11,500,000	Cold-drawn and heat-treated before coiling; general spring use
	Music wire (ASTM A228-41)	C Mn	0.70–1.00 0.30–0.60	250,000–500,000	150,000–350,000	30,000,000	. . .	150,000–300,000	90,000–180,000	11,500,000–12,000,000, depending on size	Patented and cold-drawn; miscellaneous small springs of various types—high quality
	Hard-drawn spring wire (ASTM A227-41)	C Mn	0.60–0.70 0.90–1.20	150,000–300,000	100,000–200,000	29,000,000	. . .	120,000–220,000	75,000–130,000	11,500,000	Patented and cold-drawn; same uses as music wire but lower-quality wire

Hot-rolled special steel	Hot-rolled bars (SAE 1095, ASTM A14-42)	C Mn	0.90–1.05 0.25–0.50	175,000–200,000	105,000–140,000	28,500,000	C40–46	110,000–140,000	75,000–110,000	10,500,000	Hot-rolled heavy coil or flat springs
	Chrome-vanadium alloy steel (SAE 6150)	C Mn Cr V	0.45–0.55 0.50–0.80 0.80–1.10 0.15–0.18	200,000–250,000	180,000–230,000	30,000,000	C42–48	140,000–175,000	100,000–130,000	11,500,000	Cold-rolled or drawn; special applications
	Silico-manganese alloy steel (SAE 9260)	C Mn Si	0.55–0.65 0.60–0.90 1.80–2.20	About the same as chrome-vanadium				About the same as chrome-vanadium			Hot- or cold-rolled or drawn; in some applications may be used as a lower-cost material in place of chrome-vanadium
Alloy and stainless spring materials	Type 18–8 stainless (Type 302, SAE 30915)	C Ni C Mn Si	17–20 7–10 0.08–0.15 2 max 0.30–0.75	160,000–330,000	60,000–260,000	28,000,000	C35–45	120,000–240,000	45,000–140,000	10,000,000	Cold-rolled or drawn; best corrosion resistance; fair temperature resistance
	Cutlery-type stainless (Type 420)	Cr C	12–14 0.25–0.40	170,000–250,000	130,000–200,000	28,000,000	C42–47	120,000–180,000	80,000–120,000	11,000,000	Cold-rolled or drawn; heat-treated after forming; resists corrosion when polished; good temperature resistance
	Spring brass	Cu Zn	64–72 Balance	100,000–130,000	40,000–60,000	15,000,000	B90	45,000–90,000	30,000–60,000	5,500,000	Cold-rolled or drawn; for electrical conductivity at low stresses; for corrosion resistance
Nonferrous spring materials	Nickel silver	Cu Zn Ni	56 25 18	130,000–150,000	80,000–110,000	16,000,000	B95–100	85,000–100,000	60,000–70,000	5,500,000	Cold-rolled or drawn; better quality than brass; also used for its color; corrosion-resistant
	Phosphor bronze	Cu Sn or Cu Sn	91–93 7–9 94–96 4–6	100,000–150,000	60,000–110,000	15,000,000	B90–100	80,000–105,000	50,000–85,000	6,250,000	Cold-rolled or drawn; used for corrosion resistance and electrical conductivity

TABLE 7-2. PHYSICAL PROPERTIES OF SPRING MATERIALS (*Continued*)

	Material	Analysis		Tensile properties			Rockwell hardness	Torsional properties of wire			Process of manufacture, chief uses, special properties
		Element	%	Ultimate strength, psi	Elastic limit, psi	Modulus of elasticity		Modulus strength, psi	Elastic limit, psi	Modulus of torsion	
Nonferrous spring materials	Silicon bronze (made under various trade names)	Si Sn or Mn Cu	2–3 Small amounts Balance	Properties similar to phosphor bronze				Properties similar to phosphor bronze			Cold-rolled or drawn; used as substitute for phosphor bronze where lower cost is necessary
	Monel	Ni Cu Mn Fe	64 26 2.5 2.25	100,000–140,000	80,000–120,000	26,000,000	C23–28	75,000–110,000	45,000–70,000	9,500,000	Cold-rolled or drawn; resists corrosion; moderate stresses to 400°F
	Inconel	Ni Cr Fe	80 14 Balance	140,000–175,000	110,000 135,000	31,000,000	C30–40	95,000–120,000	55,000–80,000	11,000,000	Cold-rolled or drawn; resists corrosion; high stresses to 650°F
	K-monel	Ni Cu Al Fe	66 29 2.75 0.90	160,000–180,000	115,000–145,000	26,000,000	C33–40	105,000–125,000	65,000–85,000	9,500,000	Cold-rolled or drawn; precipitation hardened by heat-treatment; resists corrosion; high stresses to 450°F
	Z-nickel	Ni Cu, Mn, Fe, Si	98 Small amounts	180,000–230,000	130,000–170,000	30,000,000	C36–46	120,000–150,000	60,000–90,000	11,000,000	Cold-rolled or drawn; precipitation hardened by heat-treatment; resists corrosion; high stresses to 550°F
	Beryllium-copper	Cu Be	98 2	160,000–200,000	100,000–150,000	16,000,000–18,500,000, subject to heat-treatment	C35–42	100,000–130,000	65,000–95,000	6,000,000–7,000,000, subject to heat-treatment	Cold-rolled or drawn; corrosion resistance like copper; high physicals for electrical work; low hysteresis

* Courtesy of Associated Spring Corporation. The values given are intended to provide a comparison of various materials. They are only typical, must be adjusted for size and heat-treatment, and should not be used to specify minimum properties.

strength which will give the maximum force or moment corresponding to the strength used. The value of this force or moment is then used to obtain the deflection, after which Eq. (7-21) can be solved.

EXAMPLE 7-2. A flat spring, in the form of a simply supported beam centrally loaded, is made of 1095 steel and heat-treated to a yield strength of 110,000 psi. The spring is statically loaded and has the dimensions shown in Fig. 7-19. Find the energy-storage capacity.

Solution. The maximum force, corresponding to the yield-point strength, must first be obtained. For a rectangular section, the section modulus is

$$\frac{I}{c} = \frac{bh^2}{6} = \frac{(1)(0.25)^2}{6} = 0.0104 \text{ in.}^3$$

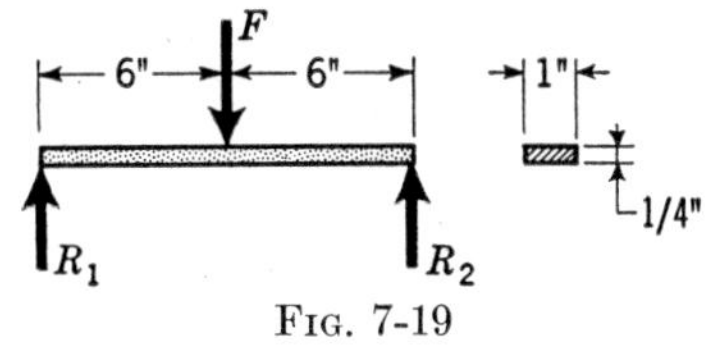

FIG. 7-19

For a simply supported beam, loaded at the center, the maximum bending moment is $M_{\max} = Fl/4 = 3F$. Using the yield strength and solving for the force from the bending-stress equation $s = Mc/I$, we obtain

$$M = 3F = s_{yp}\frac{I}{c} = (110{,}000)(0.0104)$$
$$F = 382 \text{ lb}$$

The moment of inertia is $I = bh^3/12 = 0.0013$ in.^{4} The deflection equation is obtained from Table A-2. Solving it, we find

$$y_{\max} = \frac{Fl^3}{48EI} = \frac{(382)(12)^3}{(48)(30)(10)^6(0.0013)} = 0.353 \text{ in.}$$

This deflection corresponds to the maximum force, and we can now solve Eq. (7-21) for the energy capacity:

$$U = \frac{Fy_{\max}}{2} = \frac{(382)(0.353)}{2} = 67.5 \text{ lb-in.} \qquad \textit{Ans.}$$

7-12. Spring Materials. Springs are manufactured either by hot- or cold-working processes, depending upon the size of the material and the properties desired. Table 7-2 lists typical physical properties of some of the various spring materials. The word *patented*, as used in this table, refers to a continuous annealing process.

The variation in properties as given in the table corresponds to different wire sizes; that is, the maximum properties are for very fine material sizes and the minimum properties for coarse sizes. The spring designer should have access to a table of properties based upon the exact material sizes, because of the large variation in these.

Music Wire. This is a very-high-quality, high-carbon-steel (0.70 to 1.00 per cent carbon), cold-drawn wire which has been reduced in area about 80 per cent by cold working in from 8 to 10 passes. It is usually used for cold-wound springs in wire diameters up to ⅛ in. Music wire will withstand moderate temperatures; the tensile strength increases up to 400°F and drops off slightly at 700°F.

Oil-tempered Spring Wire. This is a good-quality, high-carbon-steel wire, corresponding to about an SAE 1065 composition. It has a high endurance limit which is principally due to the care in heat-treatment and the maintenance of a smooth, scratch-free surface. It is produced by cold-drawing followed by the heat-treatment. The springs are made by cold winding followed by a mild thermal treatment to relieve winding stresses.

Hard-drawn Spring Wire. This corresponds approximately to an SAE 1066 composition and is one of the cheapest materials available. It is satisfactory for unimportant springs, but because of its poor surface finish it is not recommended where a long life is required. Springs made of this material are wound cold, followed, sometimes, by a thermal treatment.

SAE 1095. Materials of approximately this composition are used in the cold-drawn condition for thin flat springs. They may also be used for hot-worked, heavy-coil, or flat springs. It is a poor hardening steel for sections much thicker than ⅛ in.

Alloy Steels. The alloy steels commonly used for springs are the chrome-vanadium SAE 6150, the chrome-silicon SAE 9254, and the silicon-manganese SAE 9260. In general, these materials are employed where a high endurance limit and a high shock resistance are required.

Nonferrous Materials. Phosphor bronze, spring brass, beryllium copper, and various nickel alloys are also used as spring materials. They are employed where corrosion resistance, electrical conductivity, or temperature resistance is required.

PROBLEMS

7-1. A helical compression spring is made of No. 18 (0.047-in.) music wire having a torsional yield strength of 108,000 psi. It has an outside diameter of ½ in. and has 14 active coils. (*a*) Find the maximum static load corresponding to the yield point of the material. (*b*) What deflection would be caused by the load in (*a*)? (*c*) Calculate the scale of the spring. (*d*) If the spring has one dead turn at each end, what is the solid height? (*e*) What should be the pitch of the wire so that when it is compressed solid the stress will not exceed the yield point?

Ans.: (*a*) 9.25 lb, (*b*) 1.73 in., (*c*) 5.35 lb per in., (*d*) 0.752 in., (*e*) 0.170 in.

7-2. The same as Prob. 7-1 except that the wire is No. 13 (0.092-in.), the outside spring diameter is ¾ in., and the torsional strength is 90,000 psi.

7-3. A compression coil spring of No. 10 (0.135-in.) music wire, having an outside diameter of ⅞ in., has eight active coils. Determine the stress and deflection caused by a static load of 60 lb. *Ans.:* 50,200 psi, 0.408 in.

7-4. A helical compression spring uses No. 14 (0.080-in.) oil-tempered wire and has six active coils. If the spring has an outside diameter of 5⁄16 in., what should be the free length of the active coils in order that, when it is compressed solid, the stress will not exceed 115,000 psi?

7-5. Determine the scale of a spring made of No. 25 (0.020-in.) hard-drawn steel wire and having an outside diameter of $\frac{3}{16}$ in., if there are six active coils.

7-6. The same as Prob. 7-5 except that there are 12 active coils.

7-7. The same as Prob. 7-5 except that the outside diameter is $\frac{3}{8}$ in.

7-8. If the stress is not to exceed 75,000 psi, what maximum static load can be applied to a compression coil spring made of No. 20 (0.035-in.) music wire and having an outside diameter of $\frac{9}{32}$ in.?

7-9. An extension coil spring is $\frac{5}{8}$ in. OD, is made of 16-gauge (0.063-in.) wire, and has an initial tension of 5 lb. Find the stress corresponding to the initial tension. *Ans.:* 30,200 psi.

7-10. A 12-gauge (0.105-in.) extension spring has an outside diameter of $1\frac{1}{8}$ in. The spring is to be given an initial tension corresponding to a stress of 18,000 psi. Calculate the initial load in pounds.

7-11. A 30-gauge (0.014-in.) extension spring, made of music wire, has an outside diameter of $\frac{1}{4}$ in. and has 60 active coils. The spring has an initial tension corresponding to a stress of 12,000 psi. What is the maximum deflection of the spring if the stress is not to exceed 120,000 psi. The load is static. *Ans.:* 6.82 in.

7-12. A 22-gauge (0.028-in.) extension spring, made of hard-drawn steel wire, has an outside diameter of $\frac{1}{2}$ in. The spring has 48 active coils and is wound with an initial tension of $\frac{1}{6}$ lb. What is the stress in the spring if it is extended 2 in.?

7-13. An extension spring is made of 24-gauge (0.023-in.) music wire and has an outside diameter of $\frac{3}{16}$ in. The spring is wound with an initial tension of 0.25 lb, and the load fluctuates between this value and a maximum of 1.5 lb. Since this is a fatigue load, calculate the stress range.

7-14. A compression coil spring is made of No. 14 (0.080-in.) music wire. The outside diameter is $\frac{1}{2}$ in. The maximum and minimum values of the fatigue load to which the spring is subjected are 20 and 10 lb, respectively. If the endurance range of stress is 75,000 psi and the torsional strength is 110,000 psi, find the factors of safety corresponding to the fatigue loading and the maximum loading. Use the alternative method. *Ans.:* fatigue, 2.78; static, 2.40.

7-15. A helical compression spring has eight active turns. It is made of 5-gauge (0.207-in.) oil-tempered wire and has an outside diameter of $1\frac{1}{2}$ in. Calculate the critical frequency. *Ans.:* 13,000 cycles per min.

7-16. A compression coil spring is made of $\frac{1}{2}$-in.-diameter oil-tempered wire and has an outside diameter of 4 in. Calculate the critical frequency if there are six active coils.

7-17. A flat cantilever spring is 6 in. long, has a concentrated load at the end, and is made of $\frac{1}{8} \times 1\frac{1}{2}$-in. 1095 steel, properly heat-treated. Calculate the spring constant. K = 95.4 lbf/in

7-18. A flat spring is made in the form of a simply supported beam with a concentrated load at the center. The material is hot-rolled 1095 steel, 14 in. long, $1\frac{1}{2}$ in. wide, and $\frac{1}{4}$ in. thick. Calculate the spring constant. K = 980 lbf/in

7-19. An extension spring, made of 8-gauge (0.162-in.) oil-tempered wire, is $1\frac{1}{2}$ in. in outside diameter and has 20 active coils. Find the maximum static-energy storage capacity corresponding to a torsional yield strength of 80,000 psi.

7-20. A compression coil spring is made from 0000-gauge (0.394-in.) SAE 1095 steel. The spring is to have eight active coils of round wire and a mean diameter of $1\frac{3}{4}$ in. Find the energy-storage capacity corresponding to an endurance stress range of 40,000 psi.

***7-21.** A machine requires a steel compression spring to exert a force of 150 lb when the deflection is $\frac{3}{4}$ in. The spring is subject to severe service, and the application is such that breakdowns are expensive. However, the load is static. An outside diameter of up to 1¾ in. may be used. There is no limitation on the length. The unit is to be made in quantities of 100. Make a complete design of the spring.

***7-22.** A steel coil compression spring is to be manufactured in quantities of 100,000. The spring is subjected to a fluctuating force of 8 lb maximum and 2 lb minimum, at a speed of 600 cycles per min. It is to deflect ⅜ in. under the action of this force variation. There is no limitation on the length. The spring operates in a lubricated atmosphere whose temperature does not exceed 300°F. The service may be described as mild. Cost is a primary consideration. Specify the material, treatment, and the complete dimensions of the spring.

***7-23.** Design an extension coil spring, made of steel, to exert a force of 40 lb when the length between supports is 8 in. and 60 lb when the spring is extended to 10 in. The ends should have a double-twisted-loop design with both ends in the same plane. The spring is to be operated out of doors, in a cold climate, and, since the loads are accurately known, the service may be described as mild. The use of the springs indicates that they will only be operated several times a day, but they are continually under tension. They are easy to replace on the machine, and breakdowns are not expensive. They will be manufactured in quantities of 1,000.

***7-24.** A compression coil spring is to operate in a 4-in.-diameter chamber whose length varies from 4 to 4½ in. The spring should exert an average compressive force of 500 lb. Fatigue loading is present. The application is such that breakdowns cost approximately $20,000 per hour of down time. The springs are difficult to replace. They will be manufactured in quantities of 10. The service may be described as mild. Design the spring. Specify the material in sufficient detail.

CHAPTER 8

ANTIFRICTION BEARINGS

The term *antifriction bearing* is used to describe that class of bearing in which the main load is transferred through elements in rolling contact rather than in sliding contact. In a rolling bearing the starting friction and the running friction are about the same, and the effects of load, speed, and temperature variation on the friction are small. It is probably a mistake to describe a rolling bearing as "antifriction" since some friction does exist, but the term is used generally throughout the industry.

From the machine designer's standpoint, the study of antifriction bearings differs in several respects when compared with the study of other topics. The specialist in antifriction-bearing design is confronted with the problem of designing a group of elements which compose a rolling bearing; these elements must be designed to fit into a space whose dimensions are specified; they must be designed to receive a load having certain characteristics; and, finally, these elements must be designed to have a satisfactory life when operated under the specified conditions. The bearing specialist must therefore consider such matters as fatigue loading, friction, heat, corrosion resistance, kinematic problems, material properties, lubrication, machining tolerances, assembly, use, and cost. From a consideration of all these factors he arrives at a compromise which, in his judgment, is a good solution to the problem as stated. The reader has, by now, already been introduced to a good many of the topics with which the antifriction-bearing specialist must be familiar.

Antifriction-bearing manufacturers have made available an almost countless number of sizes and types of rolling bearings. They have tabulated these sizes and types in handbooks, together with recommended loads and speeds. Thus the problem of the specialist in machine design is *not* how to design a rolling bearing but, rather, how to select one. This problem of selection has been made very simple by the bearing manufacturers, and the reader should have no difficulty in understanding their handbooks.

However, we cannot dismiss the subject so simply. The study of machine design would be incomplete without at least a brief discussion of antifriction bearings. In addition, there are certain fundamentals, not always mentioned in bearing handbooks, which will materially assist the designer in making an intelligent selection.

8-1. Bearing Types. Bearings are manufactured to take pure radial loads, pure thrust loads, or a combination of these two. The nomenclature of a ball bearing is illustrated in Fig. 8-1 which also shows the four essential parts of a bearing. These are the outer ring, the inner ring, the balls or rolling elements, and the separator. In low-priced bearings the separator is sometimes omitted, but it has the important function of

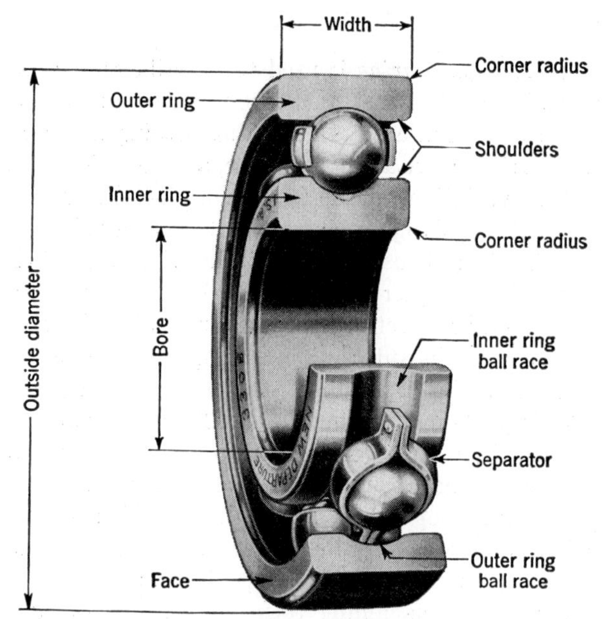

Fig. 8-1. Nomenclature of a ball bearing. *(Courtesy of New Departure, Division of General Motors Corporation.)*

separating the elements so that rubbing contact will not occur. Some of the various types of standardized bearings which are manufactured are shown in Fig. 8-2.

Types of Ball Bearings. The single-row deep-groove bearing will take radial load as well as some thrust load. The balls are inserted into the grooves by moving the inner ring to an eccentric position. The balls are separated after loading, and the separator is then assembled.

The use of a filling notch (Fig. 8-2*b*) in the inner and outer rings enables a greater number of balls to be inserted, thus increasing the load capacity. The thrust capacity is decreased, however, because of the bumping of the balls against the edge of the notch when thrust loads are present.

The angular-contact bearing (Fig. 8-2*c*) provides a greater thrust capacity. All these bearings may be obtained with shields on one or both sides. The shields are not a complete closure but do offer a measure of protection against dirt.

A variety of bearings are manufactured with seals on one or both sides. When the seals are on both sides, the bearings are lubricated at the factory. Although a sealed bearing is supposed to be lubricated for life, a method of relubrication is sometimes provided.

Single-row bearings will withstand a small amount of shaft misalignment or deflection, but where this is severe, self-aligning bearings may be used.

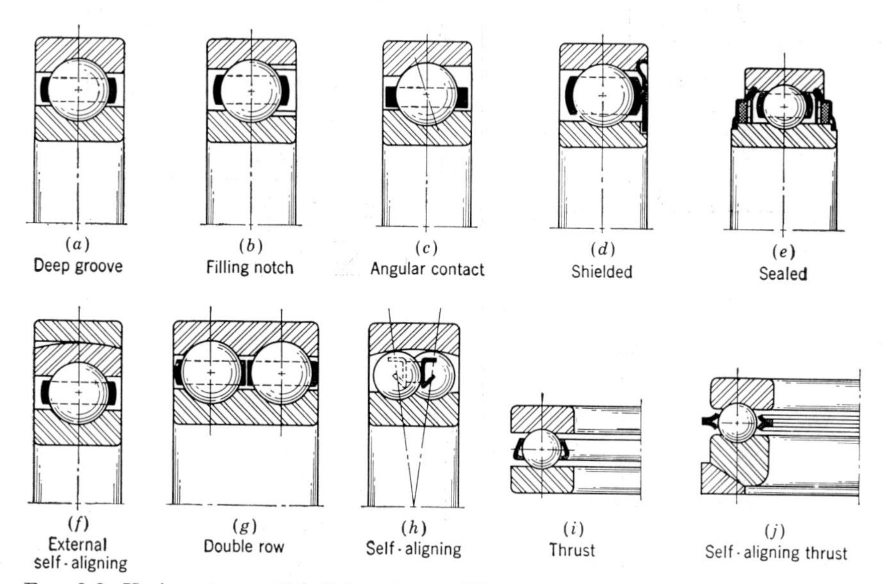

FIG. 8-2. Various types of ball bearings. (*Courtesy of The Timken Roller Bearing Company.*)

Double-row bearings are made in a variety of types and sizes to carry heavier radial and thrust loads. Sometimes two single-row bearings are used together for the same reason, although the use of a double-row bearing will usually require fewer parts and occupy less space.

The one-way ball thrust bearings (Fig. 8-2*i*) are made in many types and sizes.

Types of Roller Bearings. Some of the large variety of standard roller bearings available are illustrated in Fig. 8-3. Straight roller bearings will carry a greater load than ball bearings of the same size because of the greater contact area. However, they have the disadvantage of requiring almost perfect geometry of the raceways and rollers. A slight misalignment will cause the rollers to skew and get out of line. For this

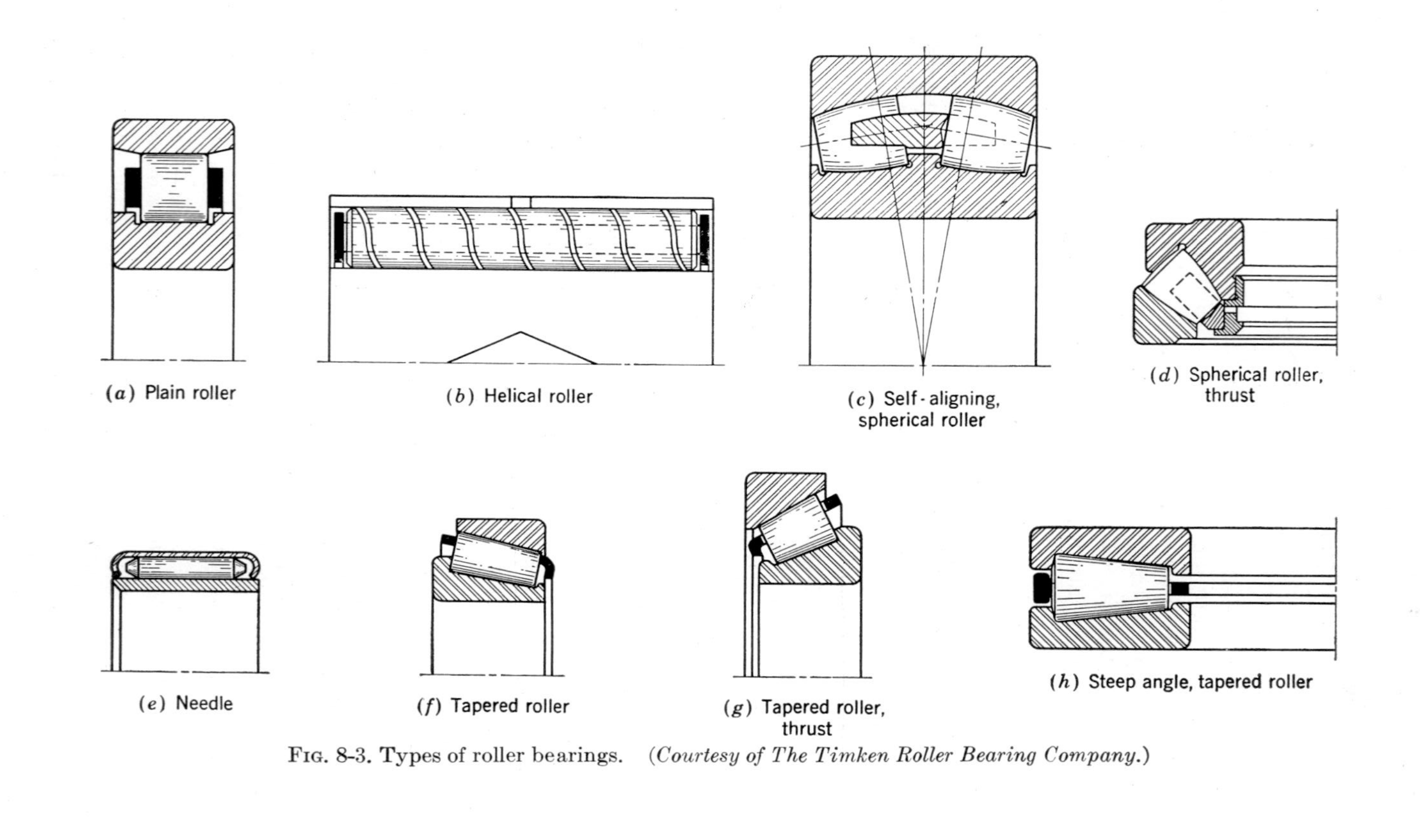

FIG. 8-3. Types of roller bearings. *(Courtesy of The Timken Roller Bearing Company.)*

reason, the retainer must be heavy. Straight roller bearings will not, of course, take thrust loads.

Helical rollers (Fig. 8-3*b*) are made by winding rectangular material into rollers, after which they are hardened and ground. Because of the inherent flexibility, they will take considerable misalignment. If necessary, the shaft and housing can be used for raceways instead of separate inner and outer races. This is especially important if radial space is limited.

The spherical-roller thrust bearing (Fig. 8-3*d*) is useful where heavy loads and misalignment occur. The spherical elements have the advantage of increasing their contact area as the load is increased.

Needle bearings (Fig. 8-3*e*) are very useful where radial space is limited. They have a very high load capacity when separators are used, but may be obtained without separators. They are furnished both with and without races.

Tapered roller bearings (Fig. 8-3*f*, *g*, and *h*) combine the advantages of ball and straight roller bearings since they can take either radial or thrust loads or any combination of the two, and, in addition, they have the high load-carrying capacity of straight roller bearings. The tapered roller bearing is designed so that all elements in the roller surface and the raceways intersect at a common point on the bearing axis.

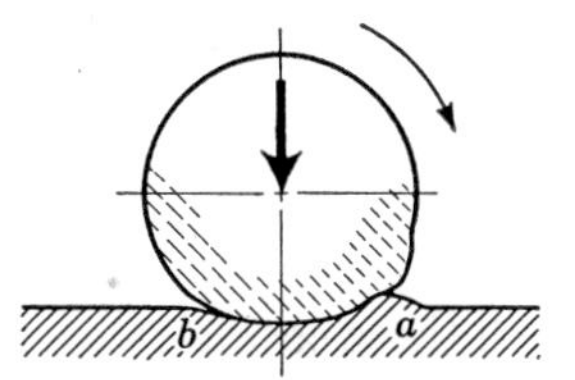

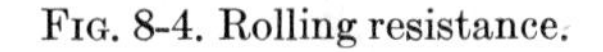
Fig. 8-4. Rolling resistance.

8-2. Bearing Theory. There are many factors which contribute to the total friction in an antifriction bearing, and, in fact, the problem has not been completely solved.

When two elastic bodies roll on one another (Fig. 8-4) with normal forces existing between them, the action can be compared to the rolling of a soft wheel across, say, a thick rug. Since forces exist between them, the surfaces are deformed, and a definite contact area exists. Referring to the figure, region *a* is in compression while region *b* is in less compression or possibly in tension. For a given point on the rolling elements, this is equivalent to an elastic hysteresis, since it is well known that, for given deformations, the stress is higher for increasing loads than for decreasing loads.

In addition to the rolling resistance, other factors which contribute to the friction are as follows:

1. Sliding between the rolling elements and the race. When the rolling elements are curved, all points in contact do not have the same linear velocity, because of their differing radii of rotation. In Fig. 8-5, for example, a point *A* on the ball will have a definite linear velocity if no sliding occurs. However, a second point *B* on the ball will have less

linear velocity than A because of its smaller radius of rotation. But point B on the race actually has a slightly greater linear velocity than A. This introduces sliding in both backward and forward directions. Other factors which introduce sliding are the inevitable inaccuracies in geometry and other deviations from true rolling.

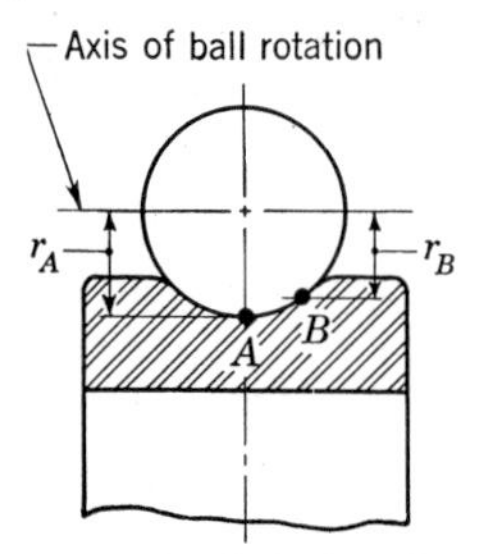

FIG. 8-5. Friction between rolling elements because the velocity at all contact points is not the same.

2. The sliding action between the rolling elements and the separator. Although contact takes place at the poles, where the velocity is lowest, some sliding action is present.

3. In roller bearings, the sliding action between the rolling elements and the guide flanges.

4. The losses between the bearings parts and the lubricant and between the different particles of the lubricant.

Palmgren[1] gives the following frictional coefficients for antifriction bearings:

Self-aligning ball bearings	$f = 0.0010$
Cylindrical roller bearings	$f = 0.0011$
Thrust ball bearings	$f = 0.0013$
Single-row deep-groove ball bearings	$f = 0.0015$
Tapered and spherical roller bearings	$f = 0.0018$
Needle bearings	$f = 0.0045$

All these coefficients are referred to the bearing bore. They are for run-in bearings, under normal conditions, with good lubrication. When determining the total losses in a given application, the seal friction must not be ignored since it may be considerable.

Bearing Life. In Sec. 2-7 on Hertz contact stresses it was shown that, when two bodies having curved surfaces are pressed together, the bodies deform, an area of contact is developed, and a high compressive stress is obtained. In Hertz's original work he shows that the shearing stress is zero at the surface but that at a very small distance below the surface the difference between the principal stresses becomes large and consequently a large shearing stress is obtained.[2] In a loaded antifriction bearing these contact stresses occur in the rolling elements and in the raceways each time an element rolls into the area of load application. It was shown in Sec. 2-7 that the surface stress is proportional to the load

[1] Arvid Palmgren, "Ball and Roller Bearing Engineering," p. 39, SKF Industries, Philadelphia, 1945.

[2] From the maximum-shear theory $s_s = \frac{1}{2}(s_1 - s_2)$. See Sec. 4-10. Also see S. P. Timoshenko and J. N. Goodier, "Theory of Elasticity," 2d ed., pp. 372–382, McGraw-Hill Book Company, Inc., New York, 1951.

and to the area of contact. In an antifriction bearing the load is usually distributed over several rolling elements.

We see, then, that an antifriction bearing is subjected to a very large number of applications of contact stresses whose magnitude is dependent upon the number of rolling elements, the shape of the elements and raceways, and the applied load. These stresses may be calculated when the design of the bearing is specified. The number of times the stresses are applied to given areas of the raceways and to the rolling elements is a function of the speed of the bearing, the design, and the number of hours of running time. Thus it is possible, in a bearing of a given design, to calculate the exact stresses and the number of times these stresses have been applied.

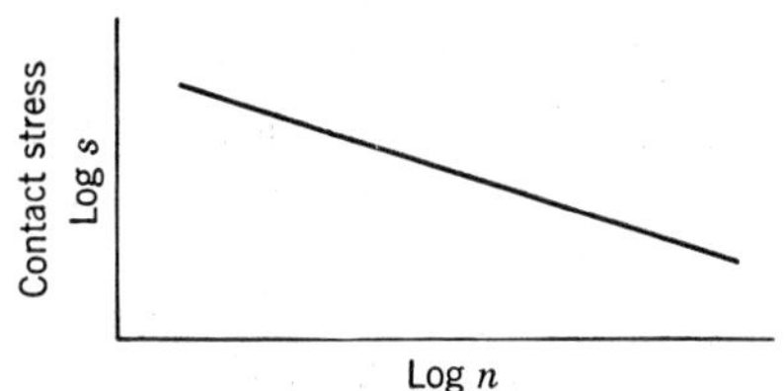

Fig. 8-6. An s-n diagram for antifriction bearings.

Since the stresses may be calculated and the number of applications may be counted, it is possible to construct an s-n diagram (see Sec. 4-6) for antifriction bearings. This may be done experimentally by subjecting a large group of bearings of the same size and design to different loads and counting the number of cycles required for failure. When this is done, the s-n diagram of Fig. 8-6 results. In obtaining such a curve there is a considerable amount of scatter, as is to be expected in any fatigue test, and the curve shown represents a statistical analysis of the results. This curve may be represented by the following equation:

$$n = \frac{C}{s^k}$$

where n = number of stress cycles required for failure

s = stress

k = slope of failure line in s-n diagram

The constant C is obtained from the Hertz equations and is corrected for the surface finish, the quality of the material, and the residual stresses. The constant k varies from 3 to 4 for different manufacturers.

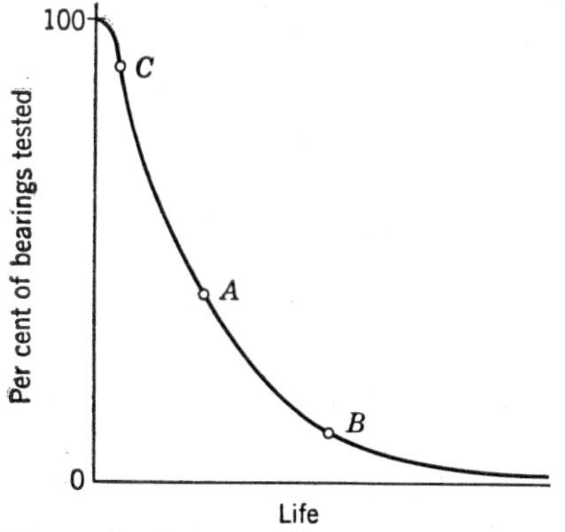

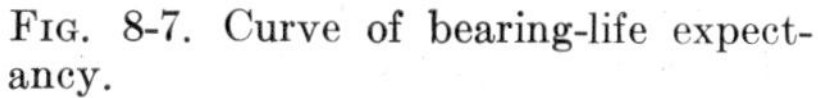

Fig. 8-7. Curve of bearing-life expectancy.

If a large number of bearings are tested to failure they will exhibit a considerable amount of life scatter. Figure 8-7 is a graph showing the relative life expectancy of such a group of bearings. Point A represents the average life of the entire group. Point B shows that approximately 10 per cent of those tested will have a life over twice as long as the average. It has been found that the longest life will seldom exceed four times the average. Failure of 10 per cent of the bearings tested is represented by point C, and it is seen that the average life is about five times as long.

8-3. Bearing Selection. Bearing ratings are indicated by giving either the radial or the thrust load for a specified number of hours of life, based upon a certain inner-race rpm. Bearing manufacturers have not established standards for hours of life or for the inner-race rpm. For example, the Timken base is 3,000 hr at 500 rpm, but New Departure uses 3,800 hr and specifies the load rating at various speeds.

Neither is there any agreement among manufacturers as to which point on the life-expectancy curve should be used to establish the ratings. New Departure, for example, bases the load ratings upon the average life expectancy of a bearing (point A, Fig. 8-5). On the other hand, all Timken ratings are based upon the time after which 90 per cent of the bearings will still be in operation (point C, Fig. 8-7) and calls this the *B-10 life*. Other manufacturers use various points between A and C to establish their ratings. For this reason, even when the number of hours of life is the same, bearing ratings from different manufacturers are not comparable. In fact, the only method by which they can be compared is to choose a point on the life-expectancy curve and then to calculate a comparative rating based upon a common speed and life.

In selecting a bearing for a particular application, since catalogue ratings are usually based upon a single life and speed, it is necessary to correct the actual life and speed to the catalogue base. This is done by employing factors which are used to correct the actual load to an equivalent load. The equivalent load is then used to select the proper bearing from the catalogue. Each bearing manufacturer uses a slightly different method, but the methods described in the two following sections are typical.[1]

8-4. Selection of Ball Bearings.[2] Reproduced as Tables 8-1 and 8-2 are two pages from the New Departure Handbook, giving the dimensions, numbering, and radial-load ratings of the 3000-series bearings. This is the light- and medium-series, single-row radial bearing, with no loading groove. The dimensions are in the metric system; this is standard practice for all ball bearings except for a few aircraft bearings which use English units.

[1] Most bearing manufacturers will provide students of machine design with copies of their handbooks giving the dimensions and load ratings of their products.

[2] Extracted from "New Departure Handbook," vol. 1, New Departure, Division of General Motors Corporation, Bristol, Conn.

TABLE 8-1. DIMENSIONS OF BALL BEARINGS*

SINGLE ROW RADIAL — TYPE 3000

Dimensions and Numbering

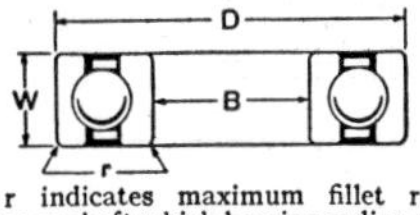

* Radius r indicates maximum fillet radius in housing or on shaft which bearing radius will clear.

Brg. No. Plain	Bore B		Diameter D		Width W		Balls		* Radius r	Bearing Numbers			R	T	S
	mm	inch	mm	inch	mm	inch	Dia.	No.		ONE SHIELD	TWO SHIELDS	SNAP RING			
3200	10	.3937	30	1.1811	9	.3543	7/32	7	.025	**7500**	**77500**	**43200**	1 23/64	.042	.120
3300			35	1.3780	11	.4331	1/4	7		**7600**	**77600**	**43300**	1 35/64	.042	.120
3201	12	.4724	32	1.2598	10	.3937	.210	8	.025	**7501**	**77501**	**43201**	1 7/16	.042	.120
3301			37	1.4567	12	.4724	9/32	7	.04	**7601**	**77601**	**43301**	1 39/64	.042	.120
3202	15	.5906	35	1.3780	11	.4331	.235	8	.025	**7502**	**77502**	**43202**	1 35/64	.042	.120
3302			42	1.6535	13	.5118	5/16	7	.04	**7602**	**77602**	**43302**	1 13/16	.042	.120
3203	17	.6693	40	1.5748	12	.4724	9/32	8	.025	**7503**	**77503**	**43203**	1 3/4	.042	.120
3303			47	1.8504	14	.5512	11/32	7	.04	**7603**	**77603**	**43303**	2 1/16	.042	.136
3204	20	.7874	47	1.8504	14	.5512	5/16	8	.04	**7504**	**77504**	**43204**	2 1/16	.042	.136
3304			52	2.0472	15	.5906	13/32	7		**7604**	**77604**	**43304**	2 17/64	.042	.136
3205	25	.9843	52	2.0472	15	.5906	5/16	9	.04	**7505**	**77505**	**43205**	2 17/64	.042	.136
3305			62	2.4409	17	.6693	13/32	8		**7605**	**77605**	**43305**	2 21/32	.065	.190
3206	30	1.1811	62	2.4409	16	.6299	3/8	9	.04	**7506**	**77506**	**43206**	2 21/32	.065	.190
3306			72	2.8346	19	.7480	15/32	8		**7606**	**77606**	**43306**	3 5/64	.065	.190
3207	35	1.3780	72	2.8346	17	.6693	7/16	9	.04	**7507**	**77507**	**43207**	3 5/64	.065	.190
3307			80	3.1496	21	.8268	17/32	8	.06	**7607**	**77607**	**43307**	3 13/32	.065	.190
3208	40	1.5748	80	3.1496	18	.7087	15/32	9	.04	**7508**	**77508**	**43208**	3 13/32	.065	.190
3308			90	3.5433	23	.9055	19/32	8	.06	**7608**	**77608**	**43308**	3 51/64	.095	.220
3209	45	1.7717	85	3.3465	19	.7480	15/32	10	.04	**7509**	**77509**	**43209**	3 19/32	.065	.190
3309			100	3.9370	25	.9843	21/32	8	.06	**7609**	**77609**	**43309**	4 3/16	.095	.220
3210	50	1.9685	90	3.5433	20	.7874	15/32	11	.04	**7510**	**77510**	**43210**	3 51/64	.095	.220
3310			110	4.3307	27	1.0630	23/32	8	.08	**7610**	**77610**	**43310**	4 37/64	.095	.220
3211	55	2.1654	100	3.9370	21	.8268	17/32	11	.06	**7511**	**77511**	**43211**	4 3/16	.095	.220
3311			120	4.7244	29	1.1417	25/32	8	.08	**7611**	**77611**	**43311**	5 3/32	.109	.265
3212	60	2.3622	110	4.3307	22	.8661	19/32	10	.06	**7512**	**77512**	**43212**	4 37/64	.095	.220
3312			130	5.1181	31	1.2205	27/32	8	.08	**7612**	**77612**	**43312**	5 1/2	.109	.265
3213	65	2.5591	120	4.7244	23	.9055	21/32	10	.06	**7513**	**77513**	**43213**	5 3/32	.109	.265
3313			140	5.5118	33	1.2992	29/32	8	.08	**7613**	**77613**	**43313**	5 57/64	.109	.297
3214	70	2.7559	125	4.9213	24	.9449	21/32	11	.06	**7514**	**77514**	**43214**	5 19/64	.109	.265
3314			150	5.9055	35	1.3780	31/32	8	.08	**7614**	**77614**	**43314**	6 9/32	.109	.297
3215	75	2.9528	130	5.1181	25	.9843	21/32	11	.06	**7515**	**77515**	**43215**	5 1/2	.109	.265
3315			160	6.2992	37	1.4567	1	8	.08	**7615**	**77615**	**43315**	6 43/64	.109	.297
3216	80	3.1496	140	5.5118	26	1.0236	11/16	11	.08	**7516**	**77516**	**43216**	5 57/64	.109	.297
3316			170	6.6929	39	1.5354	1 1/16	8		**7616**	**77616**	**43316**	7 3/16	.120	.339
3217	85	3.3465	150	5.9055	28	1.1024	25/32	11	.08	**7517**	**77517**	**43217**	6 9/32	.109	.297
3317			180	7.0866	41	1.6142	1 1/8	8	.10	**7617**	**77617**	**43317**	7 19/32	.120	.339
3218	90	3.5433	160	6.2992	30	1.1811	27/32	11	.08	**7518**	**77518**	**43218**	6 43/64	.109	.297
3318			190	7.4803	43	1.6929	1 3/16	8	.10			**43318**	7 63/64	.120	.339
3219	95	3.7402	170	6.6929	32	1.2598	29/32	11	.08	**7519**	**77519**	**43219**	7 3/16	.120	.339
3319			200	7.8740	45	1.7717	1 5/16	8	.10			**43319**	8 3/8	.120	.339
3220	100	3.9370	180	7.0866	34	1.3386	31/32	11	.08	**7520**	**77520**	**43220**	7 19/32	.120	.339
3320			215	8.4646	47	1.8504	1 3/8	8	.10			**43320**	8 31/32	.120	.339
3221	105	4.1339	190	7.4803	36	1.4173	1	10	.08	**7521**	**77521**	**43221**	7 63/64	.120	.339
3321			225	8.8583	49	1.9291	1 7/16	8	.10			**43321**	9 23/64	.120	.339
3222	110	4.3307	200	7.8740	38	1.4961	1 1/16	11	.08	**7522**	**77522**	**43222**	8 3/8	.120	.339
3322			240	9.4488	50	1.9685	1 1/2	8	.10			**43322**	9 61/64	.120	.339
3224	120	4.7244	215	8.4646	40	1.5748	1 1/8	11	.08						
3226	130	5.1181	230	9.0551	40	1.5748	1 3/16	11	.10						
3228	140	5.5118	250	9.8425	42	1.6535	1 5/16	11	.10						

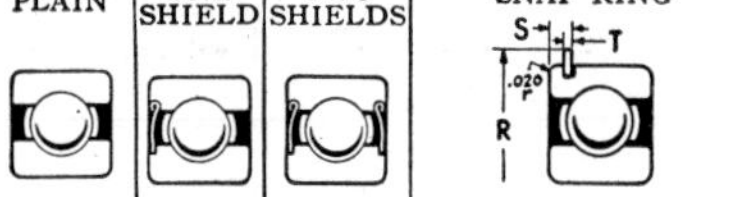

* Courtesy of New Departure, Division of General Motors Corporation.

TABLE 8-2. LOAD RATINGS OF BALL BEARINGS*

SINGLE ROW RADIAL—TYPE 3000

Radial Load Ratings

Based on Average Life of 3800 Hours

Bearing Number	Revolutions per Minute												
	50	**100**	**200**	**300**	**400**	**500**	**600**	**800**	**1000**	**1500**	**2000**	**3000**	**5000**
3200	570	480	405	365	340	320	305	285	270	245	225	205	180
3300	760	640	540	485	450	430	410	380	360	325	300	275	240
3201	570	480	405	365	340	320	305	285	270	245	225	205	180
3301	985	825	695	630	585	555	530	490	465	420	390	355	310
3202	725	610	515	465	430	410	390	360	345	310	290	260	230
3302	1230	1040	870	785	730	695	660	615	580	525	490	440	390
3203	1080	905	760	685	640	605	580	540	510	460	430	385	340
3303	1500	1260	1060	960	890	845	805	750	710	640	595	540	475
3204	1350	1130	950	860	800	755	725	675	635	575	535	485	425
3304	2150	1800	1520	1370	1280	1210	1150	1070	1010	915	855	770	680
3205	1460	1220	1030	930	865	820	785	730	690	620	580	525	460
3305	2350	1970	1660	1500	1400	1320	1260	1170	1110	1000	935	845	740
3206	2150	1810	1520	1370	1280	1210	1150	1070	1020	920	855	770	680
3306	3110	2620	2200	1990	1850	1750	1670	1560	1470	1330	1240	1120	985
3207	2940	2480	2080	1880	1750	1660	1580	1470	1390	1260	1170	1060	930
3307	3850	3240	2720	2460	2290	2170	2070	1930	1820	1650	1530	1380	1220
3208	3370	2830	2380	2150	2000	1890	1810	1680	1590	1440	1340	1210	1060
3308	4650	3910	3290	2970	2760	2610	2500	2320	2200	1990	1850	1670	1470
3209	3610	3040	2560	2310	2150	2030	1940	1810	1710	1540	1440	1300	1140
3309	5440	4580	3850	3480	3240	3060	2930	2720	2570	2330	2160	1960	1720
3210	3850	3240	2720	2460	2290	2170	2070	1920	1820	1650	1530	1380	
3310	6350	5340	4490	4060	3770	3570	3410	3170	3000	2710	2520	2280	
3211	4760	4000	3370	3040	2830	2680	2560	2380	2250	2030	1890	1710	
3311	7170	6030	5070	4580	4270	4040	3860	3590	3390	3070	2850	2580	
3212	5390	4540	3810	3450	3210	3030	2900	2700	2550	2310	2140	1940	
3312	7990	6720	5650	5100	4750	4490	4290	3990	3780	3410	3180	2870	
3213	6320	5310	4470	4040	3760	3550	3400	3160	2990	2700	2510	2270	
3313	8860	7450	6260	5660	5270	4980	4760	4430	4190	3790	3520	3180	
3214	6730	5660	4760	4300	4000	3790	3620	3370	3180	2880	2680	2420	
3314	9760	8210	6900	6240	5800	5490	5250	4880	4620	4170	3880	3510	
3215	6730	5660	4760	4300	4000	3790	3620	3370	3180	2880	2680	2420	
3315	10175	8560	7200	6510	6060	5730	5470	5090	4810	4350	4050	3660	
3216	7250	6100	5130	4640	4310	4080	3900	3630	3430	3100	2880	2610	
3316	11125	9360	7870	7110	6620	6260	5980	5560	5260	4760	4430		
3217	8870	7460	6270	5670	5280	4990	4770	4440	4190	3790	3530		
3317	12050	10125	8520	7700	7160	6780	6480	6020	5700	5150	4790		
3218	9870	8300	6980	6310	5870	5550	5310	4940	4670	4220	3930		
3318	13050	10975	9230	8340	7760	7340	7020	6530	6170	5580	5190		
3219	10950	9210	7750	7000	6510	6160	5890	5480	5180	4680	4360		
3319	15125	12700	10700	9660	8990	8500	8120	7560	7150	6460	6010		
3220	12075	10150	8540	7710	7180	6790	6490	6030	5710	5160	4800		
3320	16100	13525	11375	10275	9570	9050	8650	8050	7610	6880	6400		
3221	12600	10600	8900	8050	7490	7080	6770	6290	5950	5380	5010		
3321	17300	14550	12225	11050	10275	9730	9300	8650	8180	7390	6880		
3222	13750	11575	9730	8790	8180	7740	7400	6880	6510	5880	5470		
3322	18350	15425	12975	11725	10900	10325	9860	9170	8680	7840	7300		
V3224	14900	12525	10525	9520	8860	8380	8010	7450	7040	6370	5920		
V3226	16150	13575	11425	10325	9600	9080	8680	8070	7630	6900	6420		
3228	18700	15725	13225	11950	11125	10525	10050	9340	8840	7990			

* Courtesy of New Departure, Division of General Motors Corporation.

To make the bearing selection the following equation is used:

$$R_R = \frac{RF_C F_L}{F_S} \tag{8-1}$$

where R_R = radial rating at catalogue rpm or radial rating required at given speed
R = computed radial load
F_C = combined load factor for conversion of both thrust and radial load to equivalent radial load
F_L = life-modifying factor
F_S = speed factor for use when actual speed is not same as tabulated values

The life-modifying factor for any desired average life is found from the graph of Fig. 8-8. If the speed is listed in the load-rating table (Table

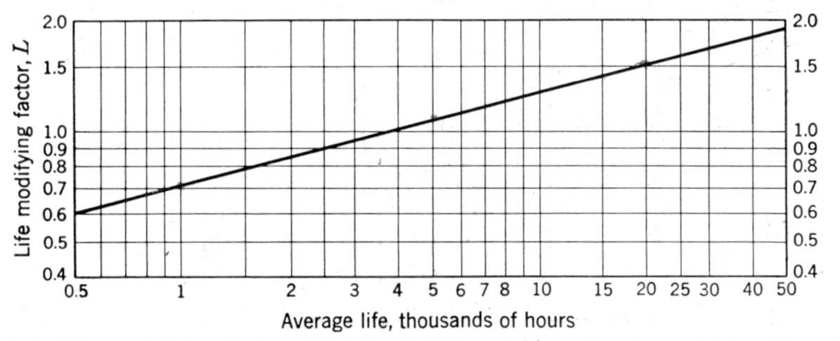

FIG. 8-8. Life-modifying factors (F_L) for ball bearings. (*Courtesy of New Departure, Division of General Motors Corporation.*)

8-2), then F_S is equal to unity. If the speed is not listed, F_S should be obtained from Fig. 8-9, which converts the equivalent radial load to a speed of 1,000 rpm.

Since the rating table is for radial loads, an adjustment is made only if thrust is present. The combined load factor F_C is obtained from Table 8-3 for any value of the T/R ratio (thrust load divided by radial load) up to 10. For values of T/R greater than 10 the thrust load is used in place of R, and the radial component is neglected. The values of F_C have been computed so as to produce the same endurance life as would be obtained if the thrust and radial loads were acting together. Since the value of F_C depends upon the design of the bearing, Table 8-3 cannot be used for double-row or angular-contact bearings, for example, since their design will produce different load factors. Values of F_C for other bearing types may be found in the New Departure Handbook.

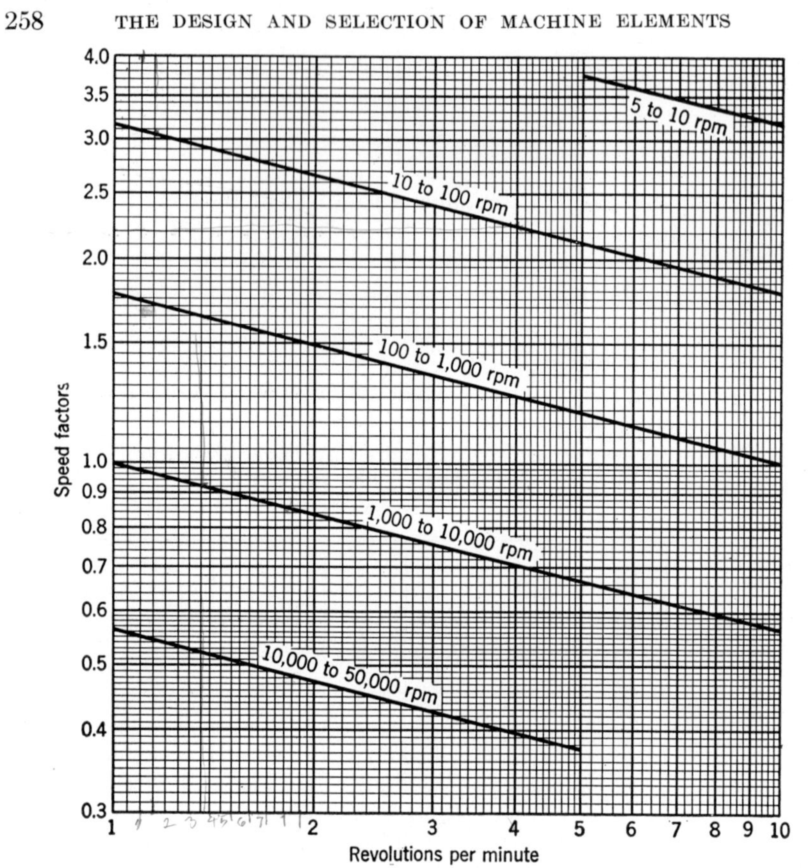

FIG. 8-9. Speed factors (F_S) for ball bearings for conversion of any speed to 1,000-rpm base. (*Courtesy of New Departure, Division of General Motors Corporation.*)

TABLE 8-3. COMBINED LOAD FACTORS FOR 3000-SERIES (NEW DEPARTURE) BEARINGS

T/R	F_C	T/R	F_C
0.05	1.01	0.80	1.56
0.10	1.02	0.90	1.67
0.15	1.04	1.00	1.77
0.20	1.06	1.25	2.02
0.25	1.09	1.50	2.27
0.30	1.12	1.75	2.52
0.35	1.16	2.00	2.77
0.40	1.20	3.00	3.77
0.45	1.24	4.00	4.76
0.50	1.28	5.00	5.77
0.60	1.37	7.50	8.27
0.70	1.46	10.00	10.77

EXAMPLE 8-1. Select a 3000-series bearing for an expected average life of 18,000 hr at 1,800 rpm. The radial load is 800 lb, and the thrust load is 1,000 lb.

Solution. The T/R ratio is

$$\frac{T}{R} = \frac{1,000}{800} = 1.25$$

Entering Table 8-3 with this ratio, the combined load factor is $F_C = 2.02$. From Fig. 8-9 the speed factor is $F_S = 0.86$. The life-modifying factor, from Fig. 8-8, is $F_L = 1.475$. Using Eq. (8-1), the radial rating is

$$R_R = \frac{RF_CF_L}{F_S} = \frac{(800)(2.02)(1.475)}{0.86} = 2,770 \text{ lb}$$

Entering Table 8-2 at 1,000 rpm, it is found that a 3213 light-series or a 3310 in the medium series is closest to this rating. The choice between these two would probably depend upon the shaft size. Either one, however, would have an average life of better than 18,000 hr for the load and speed given.

The effective speed of a ball bearing is the speed of the inner ring relative to a stationary outer ring. If the outer ring rotates and the inner ring is stationary, then the radial load capacity is reduced 20 per cent. Thrust load is not affected by ring rotation.

8-5. Selection of Tapered Roller Bearings.[1] The selection of a tapered roller bearing, a barreled roller bearing, and a straight roller bearing is similar and differs only in that the straight roller bearing cannot take thrust loads. The nomenclature of a tapered roller bearing differs in some respects from a ball bearing; the inner ring is called the cone and the outer ring is called the cup, as shown in Fig. 8-10. It can also be seen that a tapered roller bearing is separable in that the cup can be removed from the cone and roller assembly. Since the tapered roller bearing is an American invention, the dimensions are in the English system.

In the equations to follow, the radial and thrust ratings are based on a cone speed of 500 rpm and a B-10 life of 3,000 hr. This corresponds to point C in Fig. 8-7 and represents the life after which 90 per cent of the bearings will still be in operation. When the load is predominantly radial, the following equation applies:

$$RRR = \frac{RE \times LF \times AF}{SF} \tag{8-2}$$

where RRR = required radial rating at 500 rpm
RE = radial equivalent load from combination of radial and thrust loads or effective radial load

[1] This material is extracted from the *Timken Engineering Journal*, The Timken Roller Bearing Company, Canton, Ohio.

LF = life factor corresponding to desired B-10 hours of life expectancy
AF = application factor to compensate for shock, continuous duty, or inequality of loading
SF = speed factor

If only thrust loads are present, Eq. (8-2) becomes

$$RTR = \frac{T \times LF \times AF}{SF} \tag{8-3}$$

where RTR = required thrust rating at 500 rpm and T = imposed thrust load.

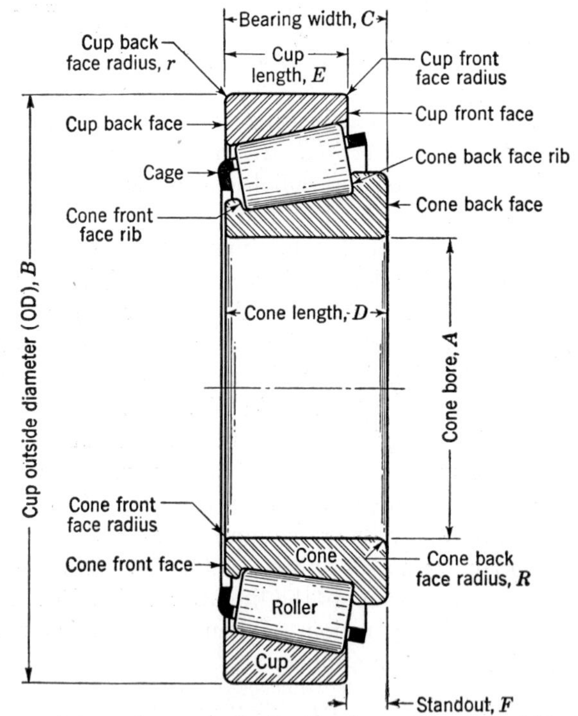

FIG. 8-10. Nomenclature of a tapered roller bearing. (*Courtesy of The Timken Roller Bearing Company.*)

The application factors are generally unity, but where there is doubt the *Timken Engineering Journal* should be consulted. The speed and life factors may be obtained from Fig. 8-11.

When the cup rotates, the number of stress applications increases, and the radial equivalent load is

$$RE = 1.7R \tag{8-4}$$

where R is the calculated radial load. The coefficient 1.7 is the rotating-cup factor and has been obtained on the basis of experience and theoretical considerations.

Because of the tapered roller design, a pure radial load R will produce a thrust component whose magnitude is

$$T_r = \frac{0.47R}{K}$$

where $K = \dfrac{\text{radial rating of bearing}}{\text{thrust rating of bearing}}$

The constant 0.47 is derived from a summation of the thrust components from the individual rollers supporting the load. The value of K is approximately 1.5 for plain bearings and 0.75 for steep-angle bearings. These values may be used for a preliminary bearing selection, after which the exact values may be obtained in order to verify the selection.

The induced thrust T_r due to the radial load is available to counteract any external thrust. Because of this induced thrust, the net thrust on the bearing is

$$T - \frac{0.47R}{K}$$

For both radial and thrust loads, the radial equivalent load becomes

$$\begin{aligned} RE &= R + K\left(T - \frac{0.47R}{K}\right) \\ &= 0.53R + KT \end{aligned} \qquad (8\text{-}5)$$

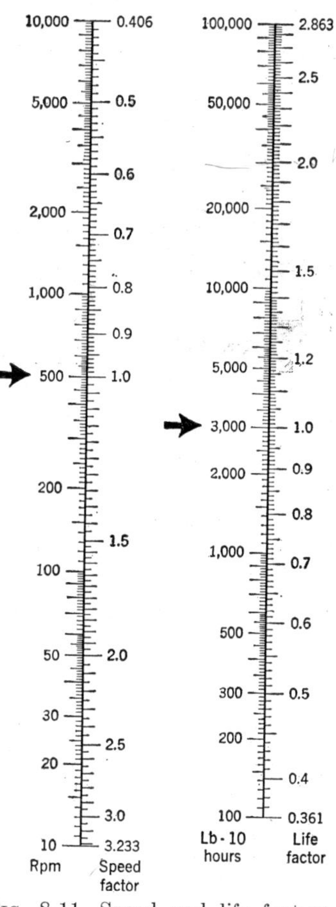

FIG. 8-11. Speed and life factors for tapered roller bearings. (*Courtesy of The Timken Roller Bearing Company.*)

which is valid for a rotating cone. When the cup rotates, the equation is

$$\begin{aligned} RE &= 1.7R + K\left(T - \frac{0.47R}{K}\right) \\ &= 1.23R + KT \end{aligned} \qquad (8\text{-}6)$$

EXAMPLE 8-2.[1] The gear-reduction unit shown in Fig. 8-12 is arranged so as to cause the cup to rotate while the cone is stationary. Bearing A takes the thrust load of 250 lb and, in addition, has a radial load of 875 lb. Bearing B has a pure radial

[1] *Timken Eng. J.*, pp. 1–33, 1950.

load of 625 lb. The speed is 150 rpm. The desired B-10 life is 11,500 hr. The desired shaft diameters are 1⅜ in. at A and 1¼ in. at B. Select suitable bearings. Use an application factor of unity.

Solution. From Fig. 8-11, the life factor is 1.5 and the speed factor is 1.435 for 150 rpm. Since B carries only radial load, the thrust on A is augmented by the induced thrust due to B. Equation (8-6) then becomes

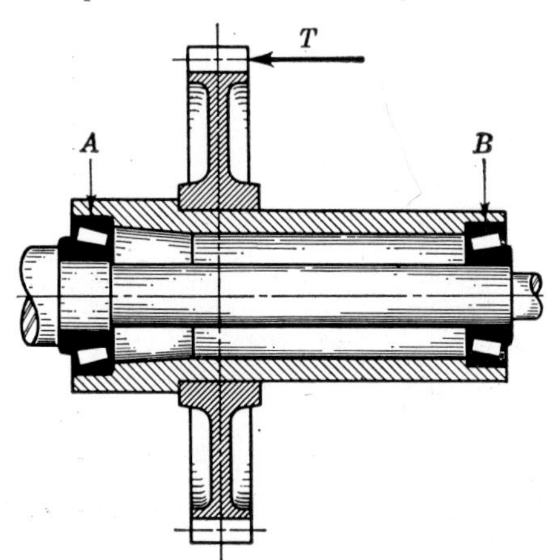

Fig. 8-12. Tapered roller bearings applied to a gear-reduction unit. (*Courtesy of The Timken Roller Bearing Company.*)

$$RE_A = 1.23R_A + K_AT_A + \frac{K_A}{K_B}(0.47R_B) \tag{8-7}$$

Using a value of 1.5 for K, the radial equivalent loads are

For A, $RE_A = (1.23)(875) + (1.5)(250) + (0.47)(625) = 1{,}745$ lb

For B, $RE_B = 1.7R_B = (1.7)(625) = 1{,}063$ lb

The required radial rating for bearing B is, from Eq. (8-2),

$$RRR_B = \frac{RE_B \times LF \times AF}{SF} = \frac{(1{,}063)(1.5)(1)}{1.435} = 1{,}111 \text{ lb}$$

A portion of the dimension sheets is shown in Fig. 8-13. From this figure, bearing B is selected as type TS, cone 15123, cup 15245. The bearing has a radial rating of 1,395 lb, a bore of 1.250 in., and $K = 1.45$. Substituting the basic radial rating (BRR) for the required radial rating (RRR) in Eq. (8-2) and solving for the actual life factor, we find

$$LF_B = \frac{BRR_B \times SF}{RE_B \times AF} = \frac{(1{,}395)(1.435)}{(1{,}063)(1)} = 1.88$$

From Fig. 8-11, we see that this corresponds to a B-10 life of 24,500 hr, which is satisfactory.

Equation (8-2) is now used for A:

$$RRR_A = \frac{RE_A \times LF \times AF}{SF} = \frac{(1{,}745)(1.5)(1)}{1.435} = 1{,}825 \text{ lb}$$

The bearing assembly selected is (Fig. 8-13) type TS, cone 02877, cup 02820. We also find for this bearing

$$BRR = 1{,}760 \text{ lb}$$
$$\text{Bore} = 1.375 \text{ in.}$$
$$K = 1.12$$

Since the rating is slightly low, it is necessary to check the life factor. Solving Eq. (8-7) again, we find

$$RE_A = (1.23)(875) + (1.12)(250) + \frac{1.12}{1.45}(0.47)(625) = 1{,}583 \text{ lb}$$

The life factor is

$$LF = \frac{BRR_A \times SF}{RE_A \times AF} = \frac{(1{,}760)(1.435)}{(1{,}583)(1)} = 1.59$$

This corresponds to a B-10 life of 14,250 hr, which is satisfactory.

BEARING TABLES—TYPE TS THE TIMKEN ENGINEERING JOURNAL

Single Row Bearings—Straight Bore—Type TS

Arranged according to cone bore

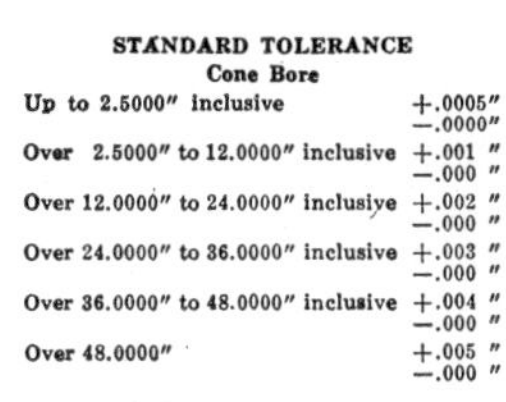

STANDARD TOLERANCE
Cone Bore

Up to 2.5000″ inclusive	+.0005″ −.0000″
Over 2.5000″ to 12.0000″ inclusive	+.001″ −.000″
Over 12.0000″ to 24.0000″ inclusive	+.002″ −.000″
Over 24.0000″ to 36.0000″ inclusive	+.003″ −.000″
Over 36.0000″ to 48.0000″ inclusive	+.004″ −.000″
Over 48.0000″	+.005″ −.000″

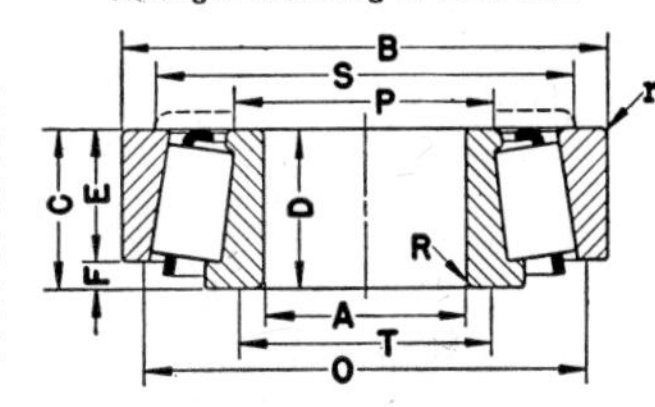

STANDARD TOLERANCE
Cup Outside Diameter

Up to 12.0000″ inclusive	+.001″ −.000″
Over 12.0000″ to 24.0000″ inclusive	+.002″ −.000″
Over 24.0000″ to 36.0000″ inclusive	+.003″ −.000″
Over 36.0000″ to 48.0000″ inclusive	+.004″ −.000″
Over 48.0000″	+.005″ −.000″

COMPLETE BEARING									CONE					CUP				
Bore	Outside Diam.	Width	Rating at 500 RPM		Factor	Part Number		Page or Assembly Drawing Number	Radius	Length	Standout	Shoulder Diam.		Radius	Length	Shoulder Diam.		Remarks
			Radial Lbs.	Thrust Lbs.		Cone	Cup											
A	B	C			K				R	D	F	T	P	r	E	S	O	
1.1895	2.5000	.8125	1395	960	1.45	15120	15250X	2-26	.031	.8125	.1875	1 7/16	1 25/64	.062	.6250	2 1/8	2 5/16	
1.1895	2.5000	.8125	1395	960	1.45	15119	15250	2-26	.060	.8125	.1875	1 1/2	1 25/64	.046	.6250	2 5/32	2 5/16	
1.1895	2.5000	.8125	1395	960	1.45	15119	15250X	2-26	.060	.8125	.1875	1 1/2	1 25/64	.062	.6250	2 1/8	2 5/16	
1.1895	2.5000	.8125	1395	960	1.45	15118	15250	2-26	.140	.8125	.1875	1 5/8	1 25/64	.046	.6250	2 5/32	2 5/16	
1.1895	2.5000	.8125	1395	960	1.45	15118	15250X	2-26	.140	.8125	.1875	1 5/8	1 25/64	.062	.6250	2 1/8	2 5/16	
1.1900	2.7170	.7813	1520	1140	1.33	14116	14276	2-40	.031	.7710	.1563	1 7/16	1 7/16	.046	.6250	2 5/16	2 1/2	
1.1900	2.7170	.7813	1520	1140	1.33	14116	14274	2-40	.031	.7710	.1563	1 7/16	1 7/16	.125	.6250	2 1/4	2 1/2	
1.1900	2.7170	.8813	1520	1140	1.33	14116	14277	2-40	.031	.7710	.1563	1 7/16	1 7/16	.093	.7250	2 3/16	2 1/2	
1.1900	2.8380	.8813	1520	1140	1.33	14116	14283	2-40	.031	.7710	.1563	1 7/16	1 7/16	.093	.7250	2 1/4	2 9/16	
1.2450	2.6250	.8125	1460	1065	1.37	1674	1620	2-30	.062	.8125	.1875	1 9/16	1 15/32	.062	.6250	2 7/32	2 7/16	
1.2500	2.3125	.5781	825	770	1.07	08125	08231	2-25	.040	.5937	.1562	1 7/16	1 27/64	.040	.4219	2 1/32	2 11/64	
1.2500	2.4410	.7150	1395	960	1.45	15123	15245	2-26	Spec.	.7500	.1525	1 11/16	1 7/16	.046	.5625	2 3/32	2 9/32	
1.2500	2.4410	.7500	1395	960	1.45	15126	15245	2-26	.031	.8125	.1875	1 7/16	1 7/16	.046	.5625	2 3/32	2 9/32	
1.2500	2.4410	.7500	1395	960	1.45	15125	15245	2-26	.140	.8125	.1875	1 11/16	1 7/16	.046	.5625	2 3/32	2 9/32	
[illegible]	2.4410	.7775	1395	960	1.45	15123	15244	2-26	Spec.	[illegible]	[illegible]	1 11/16	1 7/16	.046	.6250	2 1/8	2 9/32	
[illegible]	[illegible]	[illegible]	1395	960	1.45	15126	[illegible]	[illegible]	[illegible]	[illegible]	[illegible]	[illegible]	[illegible]	[illegible]	.6250	2 1/8	[illegible]	
1.3750	2.8345	[illegible]	[illegible]	[illegible]	[illegible]	[illegible]	[illegible]	[illegible]	.140	[illegible]	[illegible]	[illegible]	[illegible]	[illegible]	[illegible]	[illegible]	[illegible]	
1.3750	2.8380	.8813	1520	1140	1.33	14137A	14283	2-40	.062	.7710	.1563	1 11/16	1 9/16	.093	.7250	2 1/4	2 9/16	
1.3750	2.8380	.8813	1520	1140	1.33	14138A	14283	2-40	.140	.7710	.1563	1 13/16	1 9/16	.093	.7250	2 1/4	2 9/16	
1.3750	2.8440	.8125	1460	1150	1.27	16137	16284	2-46	.140	.8125	.1875	1 7/8	1 19/32	.046	.6250	2 7/16	2 5/8	
1.3750	2.8440	.9375	1460	1150	1.27	16137	16283	2-46	.140	.8125	.1875	1 7/8	1 19/32	.093	.7500	2 5/16	2 5/8	
1.3750	2.8750	.8750	1760	1570	1.12	02878	02830	2-37	.031	.8750	.1875	1 5/8	1 19/32	.031	.6875	2 1/2	2 11/16	
1.3750	2.8750	.8750	1760	1570	1.12	02878	02820	2-37	.031	.8750	.1875	1 5/8	1 19/32	.125	.6875	2 5/16	2 11/16	
1.3750	2.8750	.8750	1760	1570	1.12	02877	02830	2-37	.140	.8750	.1875	1 7/8	1 19/32	.031	.6875	2 1/2	2 11/16	
1.3750	2.8750	.8750	1760	1570	1.12	02877	02820	2-37	.140	.8750	.1875	1 7/8	1 19/32	.125	.6875	2 5/16	2 11/16	
1.3750	2.8750	.8750	1960	1415	1.39	2878	2821	2-42	.031	.9375	.1875	1 5/8	1 19/32	.031	.6875	2 1/2	2 11/16	
1.3750	2.8750	.8750	1960	1415	1.39	2878	2820	2-42	.031	.9375	.1875	1 5/8	1 19/32	.125	.6875	2 3/8	2 11/16	
1.3750	2.8750	.8750	1960	1415	1.39	2877	2821	2-42	.140	.9375	.1875	1 7/8	1 19/32	.031	.6875	2 1/2	2 11/16	
1.3750	2.8750	.8750	1960	1415	1.39	2877	2820	2-42	.140	.9375	.1875	1 7/8	1 19/32	.125	.6875	2 3/8	2 11/16	
1.3750	2.8750	.9375	2255	1285	1.75	25877	25821	2-38	.062	.9688	.1875	1 11/16	1 19/32	.031	.7500	2 17/32	2 21/32	
1.3750	2.8750	.9375	2255	1285	1.75	25877	25820	2-38	.062	.9688	.1875	1 11/16	1 19/32	.093	.7500	2 13/32	2 21/32	
1.3750	2.8750	.9375	2255	1285	1.75	25878	25821	2-38	.140	.9688	.1875	1 13/16	1 19/32	.031	.7500	2 17/32	2 21/32	
1.3750	2.8750	.9375	2255	1285	1.75	25878	25820	2-38	.140	.9688	.1875	1 13/16	1 19/32	.093	.7500	2 13/32	2 21/32	
1.3750	2.8750	.9375	2230	1330	1.68	2793	2735X	2-50	.031	1.0100	.1875	1 5/8	1 5/8	.031	.7500	2 19/32	2 23/32	
1.3750	2.8750	.9375	2230	1330	1.68	2796	2735X	2-50	.140	1.0100	.1875	1 7/8	1 5/8	.031	.7500	2 19/32	2 23/32	
1.3750	2.8750	.9375	2230	1330	1.68	2786	2735X	2-50	.203	1.0100	.1875	2	1 5/8	.031	.7500	2 19/32	2 23/32	
1.3750	2.8750	.0625	2410	1750	1.38	23690	23621	2-41	.140	1.0620	.1875	1 13/16	1 9/16	.031	.8750	2 1/2	2 21/32	
1.3750	2.8750	1.0625	2410	1750	1.38	23690	23620	2-41	.140	1.0620	.1875	1 13/16	1 9/16	.062	.8750	2 7/16	2 21/32	
1.3750	2.9375	.9375	2230	1330	1.68	2793	2736	2-50	.031	1.0100	.1875	1 5/8	1 5/8	.031	.7500	2 19/32	2 23/32	
1.3750	2.9375	.9375	2230	1330	1.68	2796	2736	2-50	.140	1.0100	.1875	1 7/8	1 5/8	.031	.7500	2 19/32	2 23/32	
1.3750	2.9375	.9375	2230	1330	1.68	2786	2736	2-50	.203	1.0100	.1875	2	1 5/8	.031	.7500	2 19/32	2 23/32	
1.3750	3.0000	.8125	1660	1310	1.27	28137	28300	2-52	.062	.8244	.2020	1 3/4	1 5/8	.046	.6105	2 5/8	2 25/32	
1.3750	3.0000	.9375	2230	1330	1.68	2793	2729	2-50	.031	1.0100	.1875	1 5/8	1 5/8	.031	.7500	2 5/8	2 3/4	
1.3750	3.0000	.9375	2230	1330	1.68	2793	2729X	2-50	.031	1.0100	.1875	1 5/8	1 5/8	.062	.7500	2 9/16	2 3/4	
1.3750	3.0000	.9375	2230	1330	1.68	2793	2720	2-50	.031	1.0100	.1875	1 5/8	1 5/8	.125	.7500	2 1/2	2 3/4	

FIG. 8-13

8-6. Thrust Bearings. The ball thrust bearing of Fig. 8-14 is typical of pure thrust bearings, that is, bearings which will take no radial load. Each rolling element takes an equal share of the thrust load only if the axis of the load coincides with the axis of the bearing bore (d). In the usual case, the load is eccentric, and the elements on one side of the bearing are loaded more heavily than those on the other side. However, pure thrust bearings are usually employed in combination with radial bearings.

Thrust bearings are made with the rolling elements as balls or tapered rollers in both English and metric sizes. Their selection generally follows the procedure outlined for radial bearings.

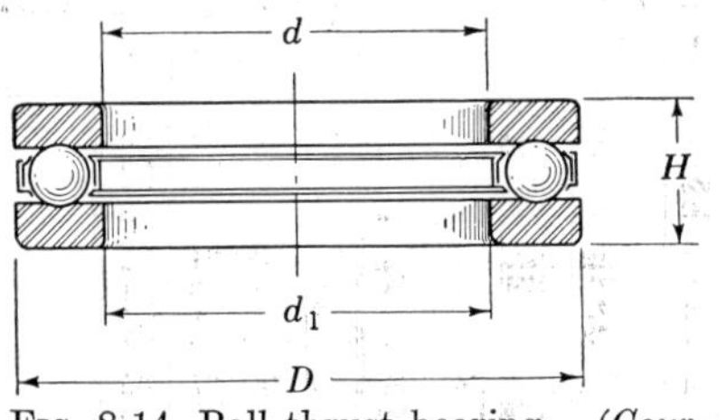

FIG. 8-14. Ball thrust bearing. (*Courtesy of SKF Industries.*)

8-7. Lubrication. The primary purpose of lubrication in a sliding bearing is to separate the load-bearing surfaces during operation by the maintenance of a film of lubricant between them. If this film is broken for any reason, considerable sliding friction is generated which may rapidly lead to overheating and scoring or seizing. In the case of antifriction bearings, the pressure between the rolling surfaces is so high that the formation of a film is impossible, and the loads must be supported by rolling surfaces in metal-to-metal contact. It would appear, therefore, that lubrication plays only a minor rôle in the action of antifriction bearings. This is very definitely not the case.

It has already been shown that, when an antifriction bearing is subjected to an external load, the raceways and rolling elements experience a deformation. This deformation takes place at a frequency depending upon the number of elements and their speed. Heat is generated during each deformation because of the hysteresis effect, and it must be distributed and carried away. This is one of the purposes of the lubricant. This lubrication is especially important at high bearing speeds where particular precautions must be taken in order to dispose of the excess heat.

The fact that some sliding friction takes place between the separator and the rolling elements has already been demonstrated. Although the loading between these elements is small, lubrication is necessary at these points in order to reduce the friction.

The purposes of an antifriction-bearing lubricant may be summarized as:

1. To provide a film of lubricant between the sliding surfaces
2. To help dissipate heat

3. To prevent corrosion of the bearing surfaces
4. To assist the seals in keeping the lubricant and to protect the parts from the entrance of foreign matter

Either oil or grease may be employed as a lubricant. The following rules may help in deciding between them:

Use grease when:

1. The temperature is not over 200°F.
2. The speed is low.
3. Unusual protection is required from the entrance of foreign matter.
4. Simple bearing enclosures are desired.
5. Operation for long periods without attention is desired.

Use oil when:

1. Speeds are high.
2. Temperatures are high.
3. Oiltight seals are readily employed.
4. Bearing type is not suitable for grease lubrication.
5. The bearing is lubricated from a central supply which is also used for other machine parts.

8-8. Enclosure. In order to exclude dirt and foreign matter and to retain the lubricant, the bearing mountings must include a seal. The

(*a*) Felt seal

(*b*) Commercial seal

(*c*) Labyrinth seal

FIG. 8-15. Typical sealing methods. (*Courtesy of New Departure, Division of General Motors Corporation.*)

three principal methods of sealing are the felt seal, the commercial seal, and the labyrinth seal (Fig. 8-15).

Felt seals may be used with grease lubrication when the speeds are low. The rubbing surfaces should have a high polish. Felt seals should be protected from dirt by placing them in machined grooves or by using metal stampings as shields.

The commercial seal is an assembly consisting of the rubbing element and, generally, a spring backing, which are retained in a sheet-metal jacket. These seals are usually made by press-fitting into a counterbored hole in the bearing cover. Since they obtain the sealing action by rubbing, they should not be used for high speeds.

The labyrinth seal is especially effective for high-speed installations and may be used with either oil or grease. It is sometimes used with flingers. At least three grooves should be used, and they may be cut on either the bore or the outside diameter. The clearance may vary from 0.010 to 0.040 in., depending upon the speed and temperature.

8-9. Shaft and Housing Details. There are so many methods of mounting antifriction bearings that each new design is a real challenge to the ingenuity of the designer. The housing bore and shaft outside diameter must be held to very close limits, which, of course, is expensive. There are usually one or more counterboring operations, several facing operations, and drilling, tapping, and threading operations, all of which must be performed on the shaft, housing, or cover plate. Each of these operations contributes to the cost of production, so that the designer, in ferreting out a trouble-free and low-cost mounting, is faced with a difficult

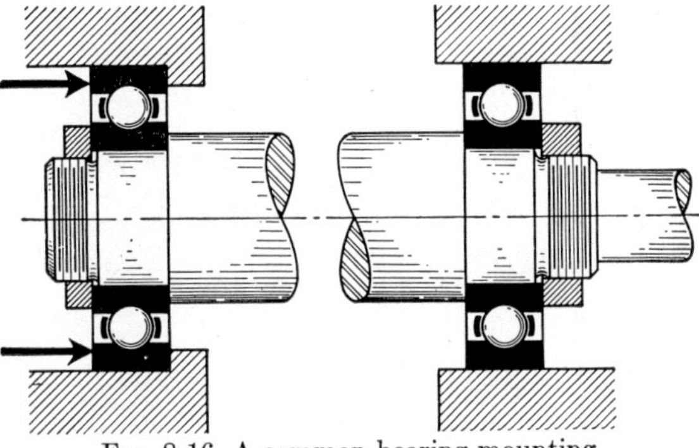

FIG. 8-16. A common bearing mounting.

and important problem. The various bearing manufacturers' handbooks give many mounting details in almost every design area. In a text of this nature, however, it is possible to give only the barest details.

The most frequently encountered mounting problem is that which requires one bearing at each end of a shaft. Such a design might use one ball bearing at each end, one tapered roller bearing at each end, or a ball bearing at one end and a straight roller bearing at the other. One of the bearings usually has the added function of positioning or axially locating the shaft. Figure 8-16 shows a very common solution to this problem. The inner rings are backed up against the shaft shoulders and are held in position by round nuts threaded onto the shaft. The outer ring of the left-hand bearing is backed up against a housing shoulder and is held in position by a device which is not shown. The outer ring of the right-hand bearing floats in the housing.

There are many variations possible to the method shown in Fig. 8-16. For example, the function of the shaft shoulder may be replaced by retaining rings, by the hub of a gear or pulley, or by spacing tubes or rings. The round nuts may be replaced by retaining rings or by washers locked in position by screws, cotters, or taper pins. The housing shoulder may be replaced by a retaining ring; the outer ring of the bearing may be grooved for a retaining ring, or a flanged outer ring may be used. The force against the outer ring of the left-hand bearing is usually applied by the cover plate, but if no thrust is present the ring may be held in place by retaining rings.

Figure 8-17 shows an alternative method of mounting in which the inner races are backed up against the shaft shoulders as before but no retaining devices are required. With this method the outer races are completely retained. This eliminates the grooves or threads, which cause stress concentration on the overhanging end, but it requires accurate dimensions in an axial direction or the employment of adjusting means. This method has the disadvantage that, if the distance between the bearings is great, the temperature rise during operation may expand the shaft enough to wreck the bearings.

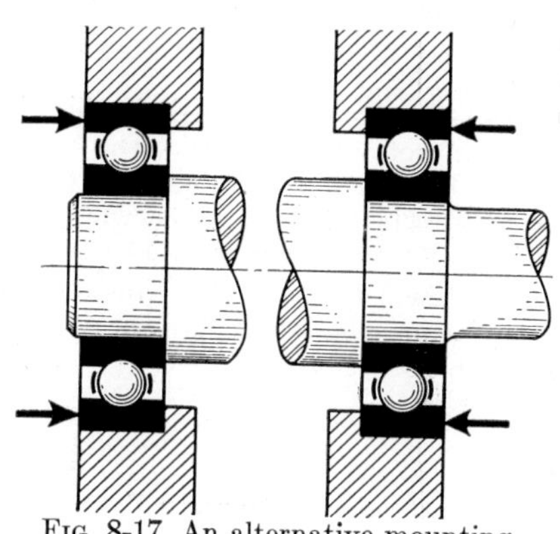

FIG. 8-17. An alternative mounting.

It is frequently necessary to use two or more bearings at one end of a shaft. For example, two bearings could be used to obtain additional rigidity or increased load capacity or to cantilever a shaft. Several two-bearing mountings are shown in Fig. 8-18. These may be used with

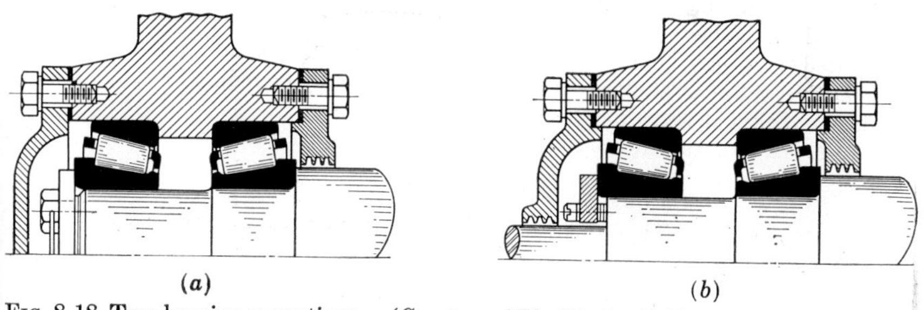

FIG. 8-18. Two-bearing mountings. (*Courtesy of The Timken Roller Bearing Company.*)

tapered roller bearings, as shown, or with ball bearings. In either case it should be noted that the effect of the mounting is to preload the bearings in an axial direction.

PROBLEMS

8-1. A 3000-series ball bearing is subjected to a radial load of 1,800 lb and a thrust load of 900 lb. The inner ring rotates at 900 rpm. The average expected life is to be 5,000 hr. Determine the required radial rating at 1,000 rpm. *Ans.:* 2,400 lb.

8-2. The B-10 life is approximately one-fifth the average life. Determine the required radial rating of the bearing in Prob. 8-1 for a B-10 life of 5,000 hr at 1,000 rpm. *Ans.:* 3,580 lb.

8-3. A shaft is to be supported by two 3000-series bearings. The shaft rotates at 1,725 rpm. The radial load on each bearing is 600 lb. For convenience, both bearings are to be the same size, but one of them will be required to take 250 lb of thrust load in addition to the radial component. The average expected life is to be 5,000 hr. The shaft diameter is to be 1⅛ in. or more. Select suitable bearings.

8-4. A 3000-series ball bearing is to be used on a shaft whose speed is 400 rpm. The computed loads are 400 lb radial and 400 lb thrust. The bearing is to have a B-10 life of 5,000 hr. Select suitable bearings if the shaft diameter is to be not less than ¾ in.

***8-5.**[1] The figure shows a shaft which is to be supported by bearings at R_1 and R_2. The shaft rotates at 720 rpm. The loads, F_1 and F_2, are only estimated average values and are subject to probably a 30 per cent variation with light shock included. The assembly is to fit into a machine which is to be used for 12 hr per day and which should have a useful life of at least 10 years. While the bearings are not too difficult to replace, there is the possibility that bearing failure would cause other, more expensive components to be damaged. The minimum shaft diameter should be 1¾ in. Specify a suitable set of bearings.

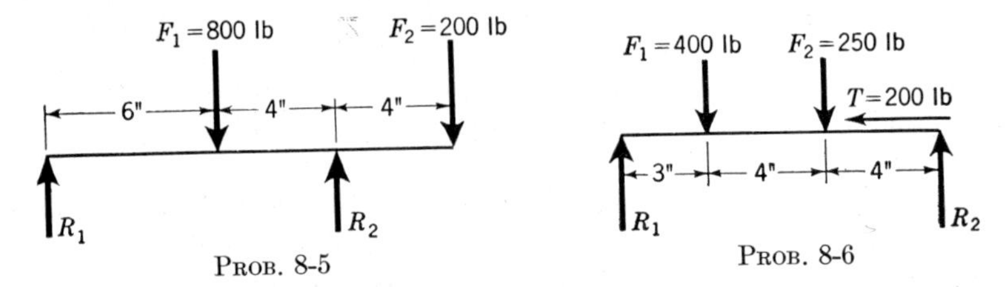

PROB. 8-5 PROB. 8-6

***8-6.** The figure shows the radial and thrust loads on a shaft which rotates at 1,200 rpm. The shaft is to be supported in bearings at R_1 and R_2. The life may be computed on the basis of 4 hr per day for 6 years. The loads have been accurately calculated, and only minor shock loads are present. The price situation is highly competitive. The shaft diameter is 1⅜ in., but this may be reduced at points of low moment. Select the antifriction bearings.

***8-7.** A shaft rotating at a speed of 600 rpm is to support a uniform load of

$$w = 200 \text{ lb per in.}$$

for a distance of 16 in. between the inner sides of the housing. Bearings are to be mounted as close to points A and B, in the figure, as is practical. The shaft is hollow

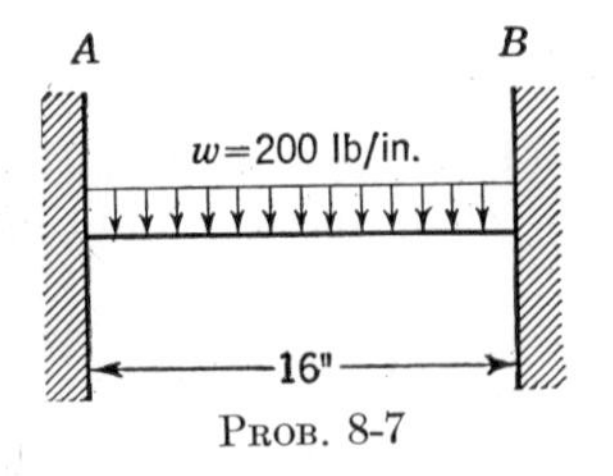

PROB. 8-7

and has an outside diameter of 2½ in. and an inside diameter of 2 in. The shaft is to be mounted as rigidly as possible, and it is suggested, therefore, that the bearings

[1] A bearing handbook is required for the solution of the remaining problems in this chapter.

be selected and mounted so as to secure the effect of built-in ends. The bearings should be chosen for continuous duty for a period of 3 years. Select appropriate bearings, and make a sketch showing the proposed shaft mounting. It should be remembered that a built-in beam has a high moment at the ends, and, therefore, stress-concentration effects must be carefully avoided. The design should be conservative.

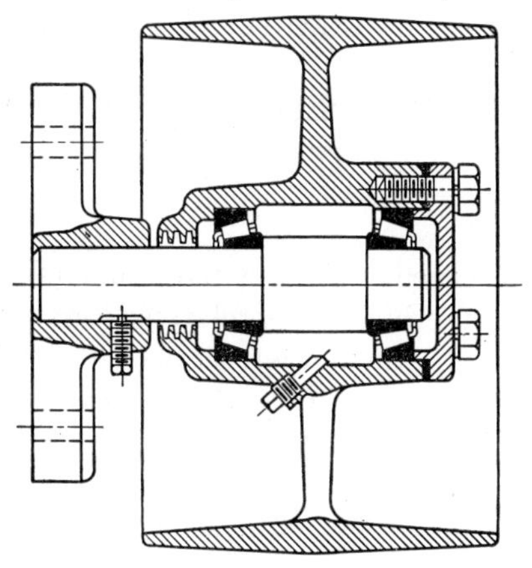

PROB. 8-8. (*Courtesy of The Timken Roller Bearing Company.*)

***8-8.** The flat-belt-idler pulley assembly shown in the figure has the following dimensions: pulley, $7\frac{1}{2} \times 11$ in. OD; center line of belt to back of bracket, 6 in.; bracket hub, $2\frac{1}{2}$ in. long; bracket base, 8 in. square. The pulley runs at a speed of 600 rpm. The bearings should be selected for a life of 6,000 hr. The assembly is to be used on agricultural machinery. Regarding the figure as a preliminary design sketch, design the shaft and specify appropriate bearings.

CHAPTER 9

LUBRICATION AND JOURNAL BEARINGS

Lubrication is concerned with the reduction of friction, wear, and heating of machine parts which move relative to each other. A lubricant is any substance which, when inserted between the moving surfaces, accomplishes these purposes. In a *sleeve bearing* a shaft, or *journal*, rotates or oscillates within a sleeve, or *bearing*, and the relative motion is sliding. In an antifriction bearing the main relative motion is rolling. A follower may either roll or slide on the cam. Gear teeth mate with each other by a combination of rolling and sliding. Pistons slide within their cylinders. All these applications require lubrication to reduce friction, wear, and heating.

Journal bearings are often a very satisfactory answer to a bearing-selection problem. Thousands of applications exist in which the loads are light and the service relatively unimportant. A simple, easily installed bearing is required, using little or no lubrication. In such cases an antifriction bearing might be a poor answer because of the cost, the elaborate enclosures, the close tolerances, the radial space required, the high speeds, or the increased inertial effects. Instead, a nylon bearing requiring no lubrication, a powder-metallurgy bearing with the lubrication "built in," or a bronze bearing with ring-oiled, wick-feed, or grease lubrication might be a very satisfactory solution. Recent metallurgical developments in bearing materials, combined with an increased knowledge of the lubrication process, now make it possible to design journal bearings with a very satisfactory life. Nevertheless, there is still a need for additional knowledge and a simplification of the analysis procedures. The assumptions and the analysis to be demonstrated can only suggest avenues for additional investigation.

FIG. 9-1. A water skier is supported by the pressure of the water against the inclined moving skis.

9-1. Fundamentals. The principle of lubrication is illustrated in Fig. 9-1. Thus, for lubrication, there must exist:

1. A surface
2. A lubricant
3. Motion of the surface relative to the lubricant
4. Wedging of the lubricant against the surface to create pressure

No matter how highly finished a surface may be, if it is examined under a microscope it shows many irregularities. When any two such dry surfaces are pressed together by a load (Fig. 9-2), the contacting points, by one theory, become welded together by the tremendous pressures. In order to move one surface relative to another it is necessary to shear these welds apart. The amount of force required is a measure of the friction between the surfaces. This is called *dry friction*, and its magnitude depends upon the nature of the materials and their surfaces.

Lubrication is simply a means of separating these two surfaces so that their "peaks" will not contact or interfere with one another during relative motion. This is illustrated in Fig. 9-3, in which a wedge-shaped

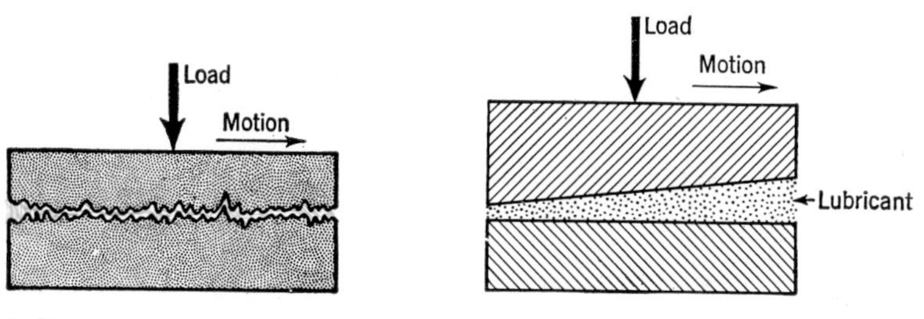

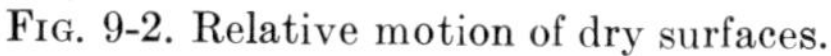

Fig. 9-2. Relative motion of dry surfaces.

Fig. 9-3

lubricant separates the relatively moving surfaces. Since the surfaces are not in contact, the force necessary to produce motion is only the force required to shear the lubricant. Notice that all the requirements of lubrication exist. There is a surface, a lubricant, motion of the surface relative to the lubricant, and pressure created by the wedging of the lubricant.

When all the requirements for lubrication are met, then *thick-film lubrication* is obtained. This is not to imply that the film is thick except in a relative sense. It does imply that the surfaces are separated and that the frictional forces are due to the internal resistance of the lubricant. It also implies that the action can be explained by the laws of hydrodynamics. Thick-film lubrication is also called *fluid, hydrodynamic, complete*, or *perfect* lubrication.

Thin-film lubrication is obtained when some of the requirements are not wholly met. For example, sufficient surface area may not exist or the supply of lubricant may be inadequate, or the relative velocity may not be sufficient to pump in the lubricant. Any one of these inadequacies will create a situation which is intermediate between the conditions for dry friction and those for thick-film lubrication.

Although thin-film lubrication obviously exists widely, its exact nature has not been satisfactorily explained. It is possible that the explanation may lie partly in the chemistry of the lubricant and the surfaces.[1] It is certainly true that the character of the surfaces is more important with thin-film than with thick-film lubrication. Thin-film lubrication is also called *imperfect*, *partial*, or *boundary* lubrication.

9-2. Viscosity. Figure 9-4 shows a plate A moving with a velocity U on a film of lubricant of thickness h. Because of the internal resistance of the fluid, a force F is required to move the plate. If the film is imagined as a series of horizontal layers, then the force F causes these layers to deform or slide on one another just like a deck of cards. The layers in contact with the moving plate move with a velocity U equal to the velocity of the plate. Those in contact with the stationary surface have zero velocity. Intermediate layers have velocities which depend upon their distances y from the stationary surface. Newton's law of viscous flow states that the shearing stress in the fluid is proportional to the rate of change of the velocity. Thus

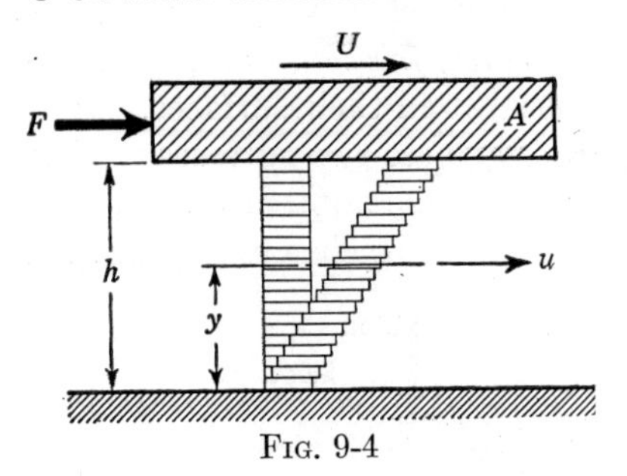

FIG. 9-4

$$s_s = \frac{F}{A} = \mu \frac{du}{dy} \tag{9-1}$$

where μ is the constant of proportionality and defines *absolute viscosity*. The derivative du/dy is the rate of change of velocity with distance and may be called the rate of shear, or the velocity gradient. The viscosity μ is thus a measure of the internal frictional resistance of the fluid. If the assumption is made that the rate of shear is a constant, then $du/dy = U/h$, and from Eq. (9-1)

$$s_s = \frac{F}{A} = \mu \frac{U}{h} \tag{9-2}$$

Substituting units of inches, pounds, and seconds into Eq. (9-2), we find that the units of viscosity are pound-seconds per square inch. This is called the *reyn* in honor of Osborne Reynolds.

In the metric system, the units of centimeters, dynes, and seconds are used, and the viscosity is expressed in dyne-seconds per square centime-

[1] A. E. Norton, "Lubrication," p. 6, McGraw-Hill Book Company, Inc., New York, 1942.

ter. This unit is called a *poise*. A more convenient value is the *centipoise*, which is one-hundredth of a poise. When the viscosity is expressed in centipoises it is designated by Z. The relation between the absolute viscosities in the English and metric systems is

$$\mu \text{ (reyns)} = \frac{Z \text{ (centipoises)}}{(6.9)(10)^6}$$

In the United States, viscosity is usually determined with an instrument called the *Saybolt Universal viscometer* or *viscosimeter*. The determination is accomplished by measuring the time in seconds for 60 cm^3 of fluid to pass through a standard capillary tube at a given temperature. The resulting time is called the viscosity in *seconds Saybolt*, or the *Saybolt Universal viscosity* (SUV) in seconds. The viscosity which is thus determined is called the *kinematic viscosity* and is in contrast to the absolute viscosity as defined by Eq. (9-1). The kinematic viscosity must be multiplied by the specific gravity corresponding to the given temperature in order to obtain the absolute viscosity. The following equation applies:

$$Z_k = \left(0.22\tau - \frac{180}{\tau}\right) \tag{9-3}$$

where Z_k is the kinematic viscosity in centistokes and τ is the number of seconds Saybolt. The absolute viscosity is

$$Z = \rho Z_k \tag{9-4}$$

where ρ is the specific gravity at the temperature considered and Z is, as before, the viscosity in centipoises. Combining Eqs. (9-3) and (9-4), we have

$$Z = \rho\left(0.22\tau - \frac{180}{\tau}\right) \tag{9-5}$$

which is useful in converting from seconds Saybolt to absolute viscosities in centipoises.

The specific gravity is usually specified at 60°F but at any other temperature may be obtained from the equation

$$\rho_t = \rho_{60} - 0.00035(t - 60) \tag{9-6}$$

where ρ_t is the specific gravity at t°F referred to water at 60°F.

The American Petroleum Institute (API) has adopted arbitrary hydrometer scales for the measurement of specific gravity. When the API gravity is specified, the specific gravity may be obtained from the relation

$$\rho_{60} = \frac{141.5}{131.5 + {}^\circ\text{API}} \tag{9-7}$$

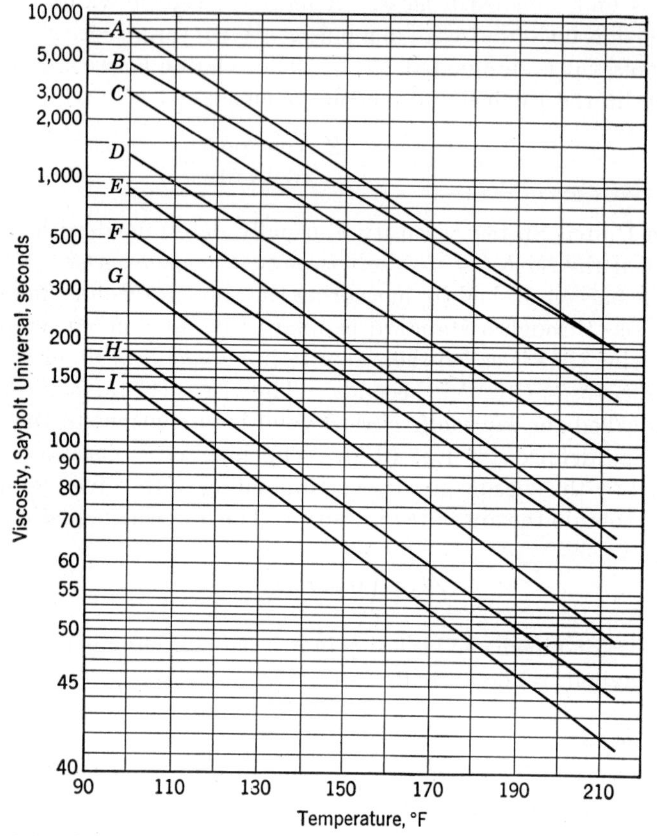

Fig. 9-5. Viscosity-temperature chart. These are average values compiled from several sources.

Table 9-1. Specific Gravities of Lubricating Oils at 60°F

Oil	Chart letter	Specific gravity, at 60°F
SAE 160	A	0.9365
Gear oil	B	0.9153
SAE 110	C	0.9328
Airplane 100G	D	0.8927
SAE 40	E	0.9275
SAE 30	F	0.9185
SAE 20	G	0.9254
SAE 10	H	0.8894
Turbine oil	I	0.8877

The Saybolt Universal viscosities of a number of lubricating oils are shown in Fig. 9-5. These oils are identified in Table 9-1 which also lists their specific gravities at 60°F. Charts similar to Fig. 9-5 are available from the ASTM for plotting purposes.[1] They are convenient for determining the viscosity at any temperature when the viscosities at two temperatures are known.

9-3. Statement of the Problem. Let us now consider a vertical shaft rotating in a guide bearing. It is assumed that the bearing carries a very small load, that the clearance space c is completely filled with oil, and that leakage is negligible (Fig. 9-6). We denote the radius of the shaft by r, the radial clearance by c, and the length of the bearing by l, all dimensions being in inches. If the shaft rotates at N rpm, then its surface velocity U is

$$U = \frac{2\pi r N}{60} \qquad (a)$$

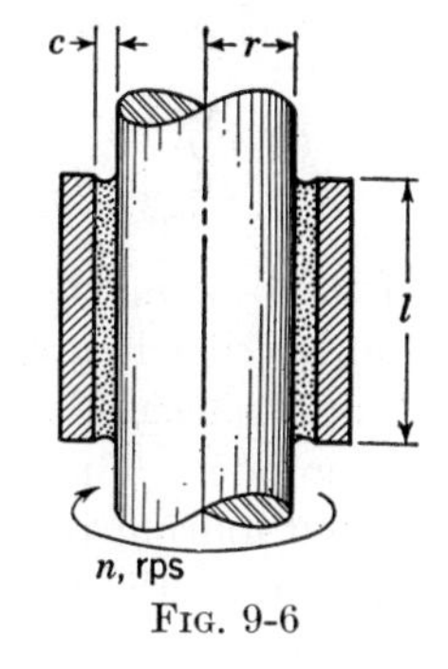

FIG. 9-6

where U is in inches per second. Since the shearing stress in the lubricant is equal to the velocity gradient times the viscosity, from Eq. (9-2) we have

$$s_s = \mu \frac{U}{h} = \frac{2\pi r}{c} \frac{\mu N}{60} \qquad (b)$$

where the radial clearance c has been substituted for the distance h. The force required to shear the film is the stress times the area. The torque is the force times the lever arm. Thus

$$T = (s_s A)(r) = \left(\frac{2\pi r}{c} \frac{\mu N}{60}\right)(2\pi r l)(r) = \frac{4\pi^2 r^3 l}{c} \frac{\mu N}{60} \qquad (c)$$

If we now designate a small force on the bearing by W, in pounds, then the pressure (unit force) P, in pounds per square inch of projected area, is $P = W/2rl$. The frictional force is fW, where f is the coefficient of friction, and so the frictional torque is

$$T = fWr = (f)(2rlP)(r) = 2r^2 flP \qquad (d)$$

Substituting the value of the torque from Eq. (d) into Eq. (c) and solving for the coefficient of friction, we find

$$f = \frac{\pi^2}{30} \frac{\mu N}{P} \frac{r}{c} \qquad (9\text{-}8)$$

Equation (9-8) is called *Petroff's law* and was first published in 1883. The two quantities $\mu N/P$ and r/c are very important parameters in

[1] Available from American Society for Testing Materials, Philadelphia.

lubrication. Substitution of the appropriate dimensions in each parameter will show that they are dimensionless or can be made so.

Journal Bearing with Perfect Lubrication. Petroff's law fails in several respects. For example, let us examine the formation of an oil film in a journal bearing. Figure 9-7*a* shows a journal which is beginning to rotate in a clockwise direction. If the bearing is dry, as it would be under starting conditions, the journal will climb up the right-hand side of the bearing, and equilibrium will be obtained when the frictional force is balanced by the tangential component of the load. Now if a lubricating oil is introduced into the top of the bearing the action of the rotating journal is to pump the oil around the bearing in a clockwise direction, as shown in Fig. 9-7*b*. The journal is again located eccentrically in the bearing, but this time it is on the other side. The minimum oil-film thickness h_o occurs not at the bottom of the journal but displaced clockwise from the bottom, as shown. This can be explained by the fact that a positive oil-film pressure develops in the converging half of the film and reaches a maximum somewhere between the bottom of the bearing and the location of h_o. The remaining half of the film may then have a zero or negative pressure. All the requirements for lubrication are met. There is a surface, a lubricant, relative motion of the two, and a wedging action between the lubricant and the surface to create pressure.

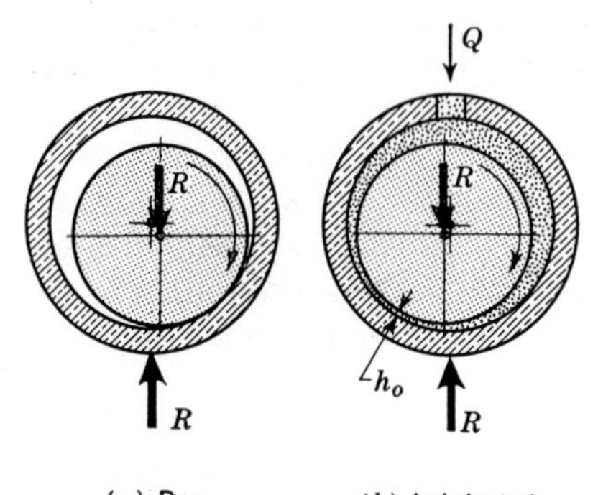

FIG. 9-7. Formation of a film.

The pressure distribution in such a bearing is shown in Fig. 9-8 as a polar diagram. Petroff's law not only fails to account for the effect of varying pressure but does not consider the eccentricity of the journal.

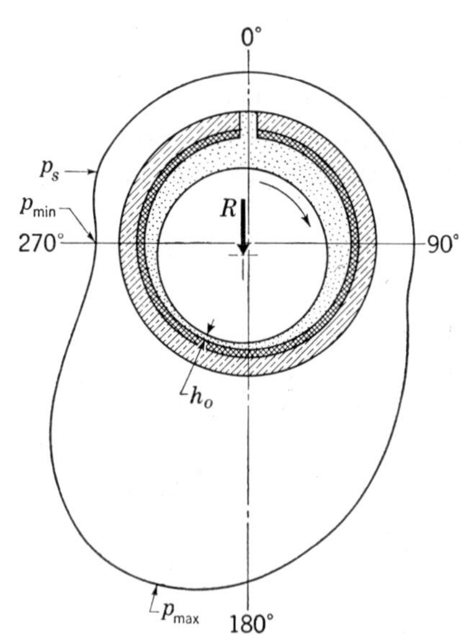

FIG. 9-8. Distribution of oil pressure in a journal bearing.

Stability of Lubrication. The distinction between thin-film and thick-film lubrication has been mentioned. The requirements of lubrication have been emphasized and a picture of perfect lubrication, for the case of journal bearings, obtained. We must now ask ourselves the question, Under what conditions is lubrication perfect and under what conditions is it imperfect? In other words, is there a unique boundary between the two? The answer to this question was obtained by the McKee brothers in a test of friction.[1] The results are shown in Fig. 9-9. Point C represents the value of $\mu N/P$ for which the coefficient of friction is a minimum. It is a unique point and evidently represents a transition from one type of phenomenon to another. Examination of Petroff's law reveals that the frictional coefficient ought to increase with increasing values of $\mu N/P$. We therefore conclude that the region to the right of AB represents thick-film lubrication while that to the left represents thin-film lubrication.

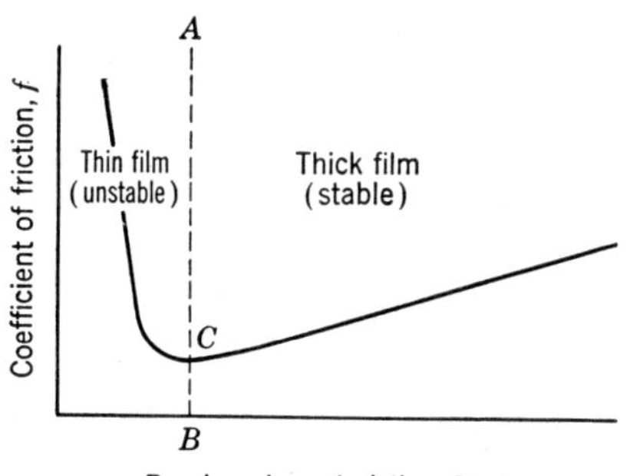

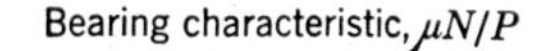

FIG. 9-9. Variation of the coefficient of friction with $\mu N/P$.

Figure 9-9 also defines stability of lubrication. Suppose that a bearing is operating to the right of line AB and that the coefficient of friction is caused to increase slightly. The increase in friction will create a higher temperature. But temperature increase causes a viscosity decrease. This reduces $\mu N/P$ and causes a reduction in friction. We have *stable lubrication*, then, because variations in the quantities are self-correcting. To the left of line AB a decrease in viscosity would increase the friction. A temperature rise would ensue and the viscosity be reduced still more. The result would be compounded. Thus the region to the left of line AB represents *unstable lubrication*.

Nomenclature. The nomenclature of a journal bearing is shown in Fig. 9-10. The dimension c is the radial clearance and is the difference in the radii of the bearing and journal. In Fig. 9-10 the center of the journal is at O and the center of the bearing at O'. The distance between these centers is the eccentricity and is denoted by e. The minimum oil-film thickness is designated by h_o, and it occurs at the line of centers. The oil-film thickness at any other point is designated by h. We also define an *eccentricity ratio* λ as

$$\lambda = \frac{e}{c}$$

The bearing shown in the figure is known as a *partial bearing*. If the radius of the bearing is the same as the radius of the journal, it is known

[1] S. A. McKee and T. R. McKee, Journal Bearing Friction in the Region of Thin Film Lubrication, *SAE Journal*, vol. 31, pp. (T) 371–377, 1932.

as a *fitted bearing*. If the bearing encloses the journal, as indicated by the dashed lines, it becomes a *full bearing*. The requirements of lubrication may be completely satisfied by a partial bearing. The angle β describes the angular length of a partial bearing. For example, a 120° partial bearing has the angle β equal to 120°.

The Fundamental Problem. Petroff's law states that the friction in a sliding bearing depends upon the parameters $\mu N/P$ and r/c. In addition, we can expect that the length of the bearing will affect the frictional

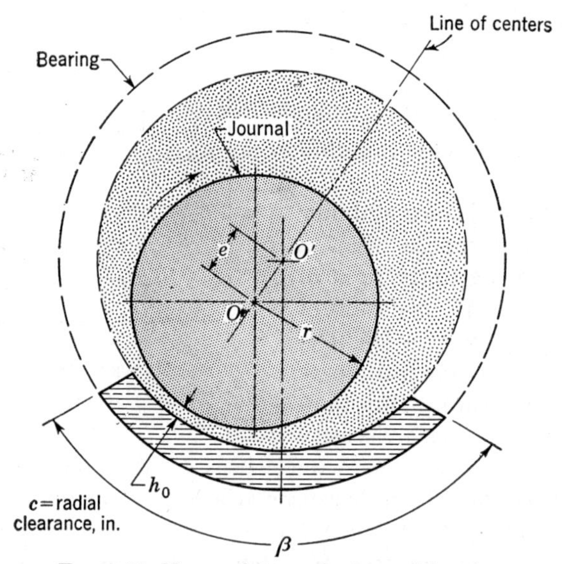

FIG. 9-10. Nomenclature of a journal bearing.

characteristics. But the viscosity is a function of temperature and pressure. We have seen that the pressure varies; there will also be temperature variation. A bearing has a finite length; how do the pressure and oil flow vary in the axial direction? What is the effect of oil grooves? What is the effect of varying the eccentricity ratio or of the minimum oil-film thickness? The shaft may deflect because of load variations or thermal deformations, or it may not be aligned properly in the first place. Suppose that the speed is not constant or that the surfaces are not quite cylindrical or smooth. These and other variables must all be considered in the design of sliding bearings.

The fundamental problem in sliding bearings is to find a relation or a group of relations which will describe the individual and combined effects of all these variables. With such a relation or set of relations available, we can find the effect of separately changing each variable and so arrive at an optimum bearing for any group of conditions.

9-4. Hydrodynamic Theory. The irregularities which occurred in a series of experiments with journal bearings (reported in 1883 and 1884) induced the experimenter, Beauchamp Tower, to include experiments with the surfaces completely immersed in oil. The results he obtained had such regularity that Osborne Reynolds concluded that there must exist a definite law relating the friction, the pressure, and the velocity. The present mathematical theory of lubrication is based upon Reynolds' work following the experiments by Tower.[1]

We shall develop this theory, using a plane slider bearing for one-dimensional flow; that is, side leakage is to be neglected. The equation

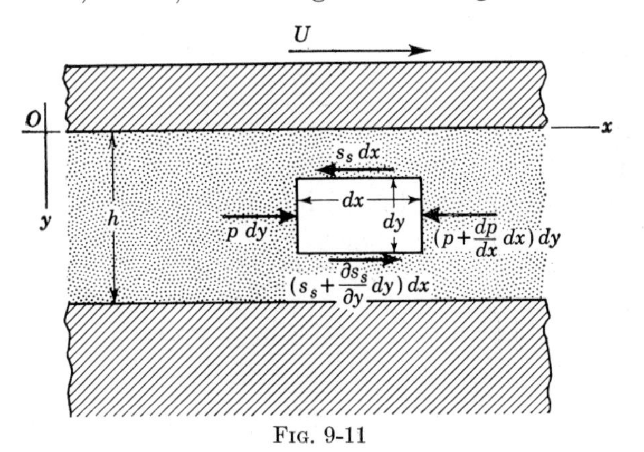

FIG. 9-11

may be developed for two-dimensional flow in a similar manner. The following assumptions will be made:

1. The lubricant obeys Newton's law of viscous flow.
2. The forces due to supply pressure and the inertia of the lubricant are neglected.
3. The pressure is assumed to be constant throughout the film thickness.
4. The lubricant is assumed to be incompressible.
5. The viscosity is assumed to be constant throughout the film.
6. The pressure is assumed to be constant on any line perpendicular to the direction of sliding.

Referring to Fig. 9-11, we choose a coordinate system with the x axis in the direction of motion and the y axis defining a point at any depth in the film. An element of lubricant is selected with unit thickness in the z direction. We must first determine the forces acting upon this element. There exists within the film a pressure p whose value depends upon x. The pressure on the left side of the element is $p\,dy$ acting in a positive direction. The force on the right side of the element is $(p + dp/dx)\,dy$,

[1] Osborne Reynolds, Theory of Lubrication, pt. I, *Trans. Roy. Soc. London*, 1886.

and it acts in a negative direction. The shearing force on the top face of the element acts in a negative direction and is $s_s\,dx$. The shearing force on the bottom face of the element is $[s_s + (\partial s_s/\partial y)\,dy]\,dx$ acting in a positive direction. The partial derivative is used because s_s depends upon both x and y. Writing the equation for static equilibrium gives

$$p\,dy - \left(p + \frac{dp}{dx}\,dx\right)dy - s_s\,dx + \left(s_s + \frac{\partial s_s}{\partial y}\,dy\right)dx = 0 \qquad (a)$$

This reduces to

$$\frac{dp}{dx} = \frac{\partial s_s}{\partial y} \qquad (b)$$

From Eq. (9-1), we have

$$s_s = \mu\,\frac{\partial u}{\partial y} \qquad (c)$$

where the partial derivative is used since the velocity u depends upon both x and y. Substituting Eq. (c) into Eq. (b), we obtain

$$\frac{dp}{dx} = \mu\,\frac{\partial^2 u}{\partial y^2} \qquad (d)$$

Holding x constant, we now integrate this expression twice with respect to y. This gives

$$\frac{\partial u}{\partial y} = \frac{1}{\mu}\frac{dp}{dx}\,y + C_1$$

$$u = \frac{1}{2\mu}\frac{dp}{dx}\,y^2 + C_1 y + C_2 \qquad (e)$$

We now assume that there is no slip between the oil and the boundary surfaces. This gives two sets of initial conditions to be used for evaluating the constants of integration. The boundary conditions are

$$\begin{matrix} y = 0 \\ u = U \end{matrix} \quad \text{and} \quad \begin{matrix} y = h \\ u = 0 \end{matrix} \qquad (f)$$

It is noted in the second condition that h may be a function of x. Substituting these conditions in Eq. (e) and solving for the constants give

$$C_2 = U$$

$$C_1 = -\frac{h}{2\mu}\frac{dp}{dx} - \frac{U}{h}$$

or

$$u = U\,\frac{h - y}{h} - \frac{y(h - y)}{2\mu}\,\frac{dp}{dx} \qquad (g)$$

Differentiating Eq. (g) with respect to y obtains

$$\frac{\partial u}{\partial y} = -\frac{U}{h} - \frac{h - 2y}{2\mu}\,\frac{dp}{dx} \qquad (h)$$

We next define Q as the volume of oil flowing in the x direction per unit time. Using a width of unity in the z direction, the volume may be obtained by the expression

$$Q = \int_0^h u\, dy \tag{i}$$

Substituting the value of u from Eq. (g) and integrating give

$$Q = \frac{Uh}{2} - \frac{h^3}{12\mu}\frac{dp}{dx} \tag{j}$$

The next step is to make the mathematical statement that the flow of oil in the x direction is the same at all points. Thus

$$\frac{dQ}{dx} = 0$$

From Eq. (j),

$$\frac{dQ}{dx} = \frac{U}{2}\frac{dh}{dx} - \frac{d}{dx}\left(\frac{h^3}{12\mu}\frac{dp}{dx}\right) = 0$$

or

$$\frac{d}{dx}\left(\frac{h^3}{\mu}\frac{dp}{dx}\right) = 6U\frac{dh}{dx} \tag{9-9}$$

Equation (9-9) is the classical Reynolds equation for one-dimensional flow. It neglects side leakage, that is, flow in the z direction. A similar development is used when side leakage is not neglected. The resulting equation is

$$\frac{\partial}{\partial x}\left(\frac{h^3}{\mu}\frac{\partial p}{\partial x}\right) + \frac{\partial}{\partial z}\left(\frac{h^3}{\mu}\frac{\partial p}{\partial z}\right) = 6U\frac{dh}{dx} \tag{9-10}$$

When side leakage is neglected, $\partial p/\partial z = 0$, and Eq. (9-10) reduces to (9-9). The equations are therefore identical except for the additional term involving z.

Although Eqs. (9-9) and (9-10) have been developed for slider bearings, they may be applied to journal bearings by employing the additional assumption that the curvature may be neglected. This implies that the films are to be developed or "unwrapped" so as to cause them to lie flat.

Equation (9-10) has been integrated for a number of conditions. Most of these integrations are complex and difficult to read. One of the most important is due to Sommerfeld and may be expressed as

$$\frac{r}{c}f = \phi\left[\left(\frac{r}{c}\right)^2 \frac{\mu n}{P}\right] \tag{9-11}$$

where ϕ indicates a functional relationship. Sommerfeld found the values of ϕ for half bearings and full bearings, using the assumption of no side leakage.

9-5. Design Factors. We may distinguish between two groups of variables in the design of sliding bearings. In the first group are those whose values are either given or are under the control of the designer. These are:

1. The viscosity μ
2. The load per unit of projected bearing area, P
3. The speed N
4. The bearing dimensions r, c, β, and l

Of these four variables, the designer usually has no control over the speed, because it is specified by the over-all design of the machine. Sometimes the viscosity is specified in advance, as, for example, when the oil is stored in a sump and is used for lubricating and cooling a variety of bearings. The remaining variables, and sometimes the viscosity, may be controlled by the designer and are therefore the *decisions* he makes. In other words, when these four variables are defined the design is complete.

In the second group are the dependent variables. The designer cannot control these except indirectly by changing one or more of the first group. These are:

1. The coefficient of friction f
2. The temperature rise ΔT
3. The flow of oil Q
4. The minimum film thickness h_o

We may regard this group as *design factors*, because it is necessary to set up limitations on their values. These limitations are specified by the characteristics of the bearing materials and the lubricant. The fundamental problem in bearing design, therefore, is to define satisfactory limits for the second group of variables and then to decide upon values for the first group such that these limitations are not exceeded.

9-6. The Relation of the Variables. Before proceeding to the problem of design, it is necessary to establish the relationships between the variables.[1] In this book these relations are given in the form of charts (Figs. 9-12 to 9-15, inclusive) and are the results of calculation from formulas, using the assumption of no side leakage. Figures 9-16 to 9-18 are correction factors to be used when side leakage is to be considered.[2]

[1] These relationships are obtained from theoretical considerations in this book because of the fundamental nature of the text. The reader is urged to use experimental evidence when it is available for a particular class of bearings.

[2] These charts are from John Boyd and Albert A. Raimondi, Applying Bearing Theory to the Analysis and Design of Journal Bearings, pts. I and II, *Trans. ASME*, vol. 73, pp. 298–316, 1951, and are reproduced with the permission of the authors from material furnished by the Westinghouse Electric Corporation, Research Laboratories, East Pittsburgh, Pa.

Figure 9-12 relates the viscosity to the temperature for several SAE oils without the necessity for conversion.

The *bearing characteristic number*, or the *Sommerfeld number*, is defined by the equation

$$S = \left(\frac{r}{c}\right)^2 \frac{\mu N}{P} \tag{9-12}$$

where S = Sommerfeld number, sec per min
r = journal radius, in.
c = radial clearance, in.
μ = absolute viscosity, reyns
N = relative speed of journal and bearing, rpm
P = load per unit of projected bearing area, psi

The advantage of the Sommerfeld number is that it contains all the variables to be specified by the designer. For this reason it has been used as the abscissa in the charts which follow.

The *friction variable* $(r/c)f$ is plotted against S for various values of the bearing arc β in Fig. 9-13. This chart is used as follows:

A 360° bearing has the following quantities specified:
$\mu = (4)(10)^{-6}$ reyn
N = 1,750 rpm
W = 600-lb bearing load
r = 0.75 in.
c = 0.0015 in.
l = 2.0 in.

The unit load is

$$P = \frac{W}{2rl} = \frac{600}{(2)(0.75)(2.0)} = 200 \text{ psi}$$

From Eq. (9-12), the Sommerfeld number is

$$S = \left(\frac{r}{c}\right)^2 \frac{\mu N}{P} = \left(\frac{0.75}{0.0015}\right)^2 \frac{(4)(10)^{-6}(1{,}750)}{200} = 8.73 \text{ sec per min}$$

From Fig. 9-13, the friction variable FV is

$$FV = \frac{r}{c} f = 3.0$$

or

$$f = FV \frac{c}{r} = 3.0 \frac{0.0015}{0.75} = 0.006 \qquad \textit{Ans.}$$

The friction torque is

$$T = fWr = (0.006)(600)(0.75) = 2.70 \text{ lb-in.} \qquad \textit{Ans.}$$

The power loss may be expressed in horsepower or in Btu per minute. Thus

$$\text{hp} = \frac{TN}{63{,}000} = \frac{(2.70)(1{,}750)}{63{,}000} = 0.075 \qquad \textit{Ans.}$$

$$H = \frac{2\pi TN}{(778)(12)} = \frac{2\pi(2.70)(1{,}750)}{(778)(12)} = 2.30 \text{ Btu per min} \qquad \textit{Ans.}$$

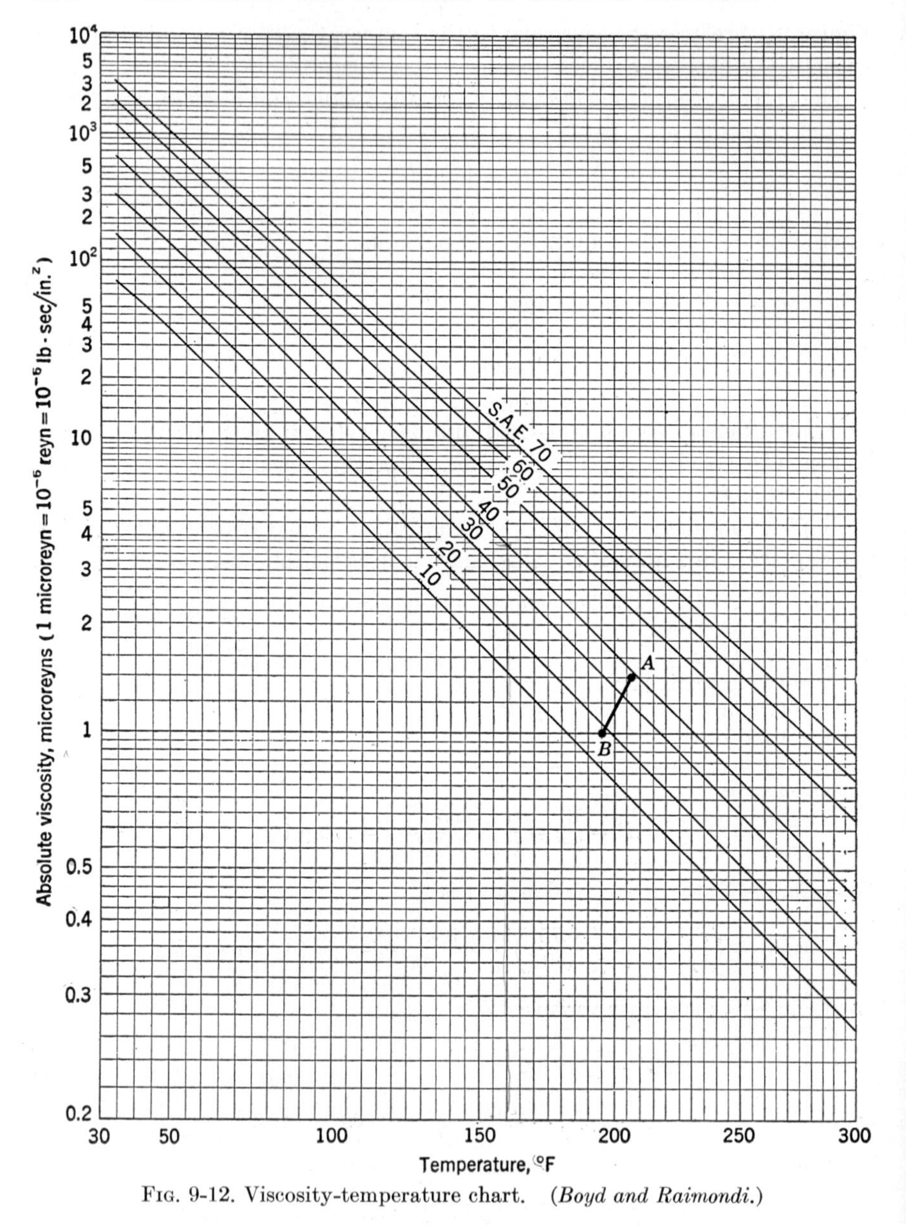

FIG. 9-12. Viscosity-temperature chart. *(Boyd and Raimondi.)*

One of the important variables in bearing design is the minimum film thickness h_o. Should h_o be less than a certain safe value, then there is danger of metal-to-metal contact during overloads or of the film being so thin that any dirt contained in the oil cannot pass. In addition, the flow of oil depends upon the film thickness; with a small flow, the temperature rise may be excessive.

The *minimum-film-thickness variable*, designated as MFT, is h_o/c and is found from Fig. 9-14.

For the preceding example, and corresponding to $\beta = 360°$ and $S = 8.73$, we find from Fig. 9-14

$$MFT = \frac{h_o}{c} = 0.88$$

so that the minimum film thickness is

$$h_o = MFT(c) = (0.88)(0.0015) = 0.00132 \text{ in.} \qquad Ans.$$

Figure 9-15 is used to find the oil flow; this is often necessary when the temperature rise is to be found. Again, as with the friction and film-

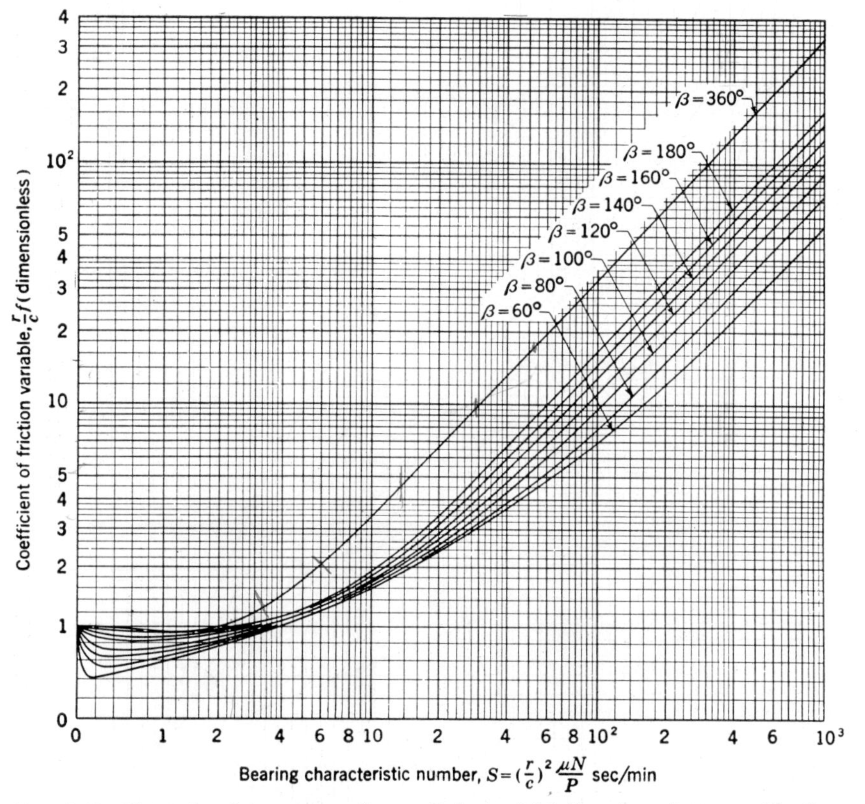

FIG. 9-13. Chart for determining the coefficient of friction, based on no side flow. (*Boyd and Raimondi.*)

thickness variables, we assume no side leakage. The *flow variable* is dimensionless and is defined as

$$FLV = \frac{Q}{rcNl}$$

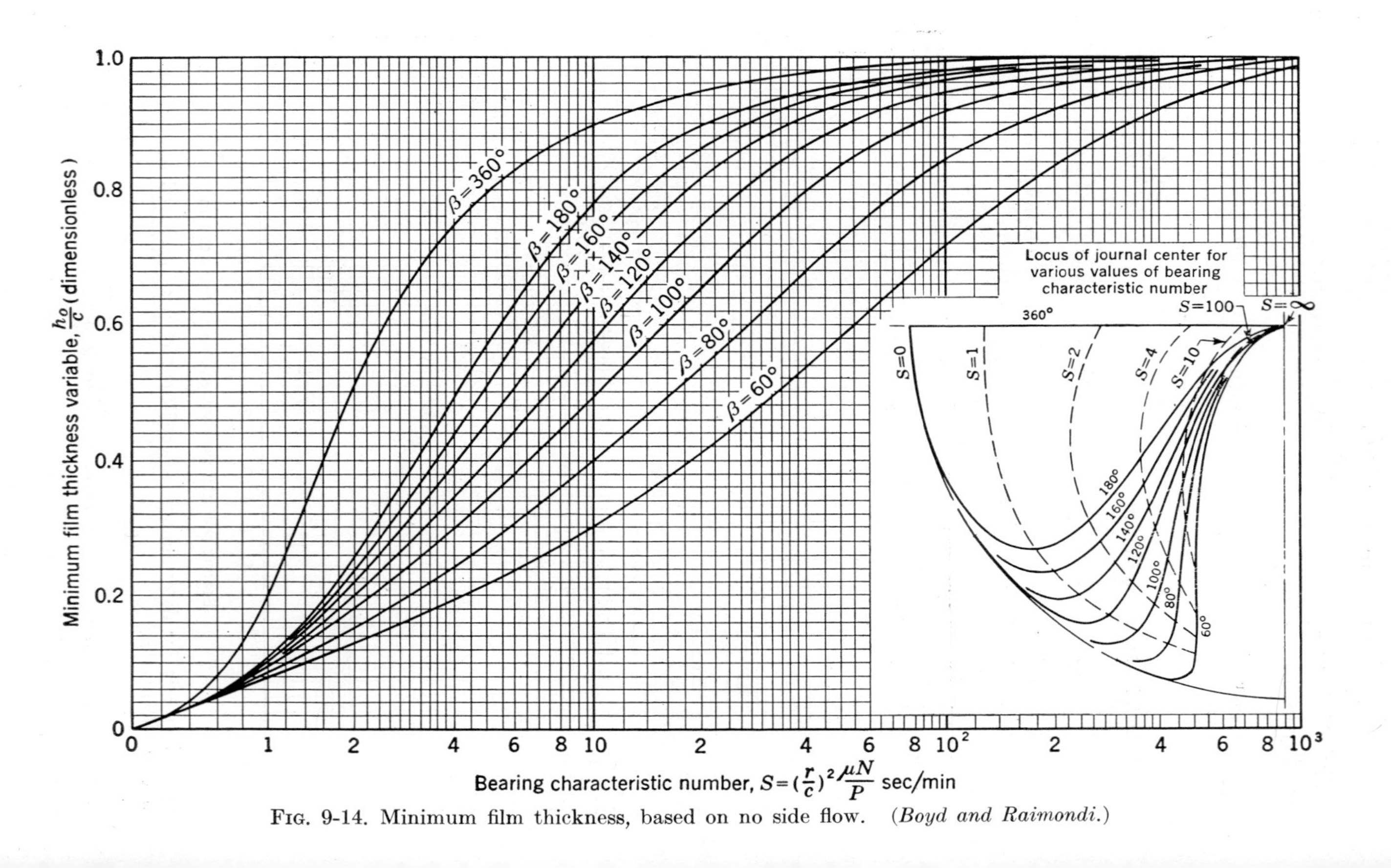

FIG. 9-14. Minimum film thickness, based on no side flow. (*Boyd and Raimondi.*)

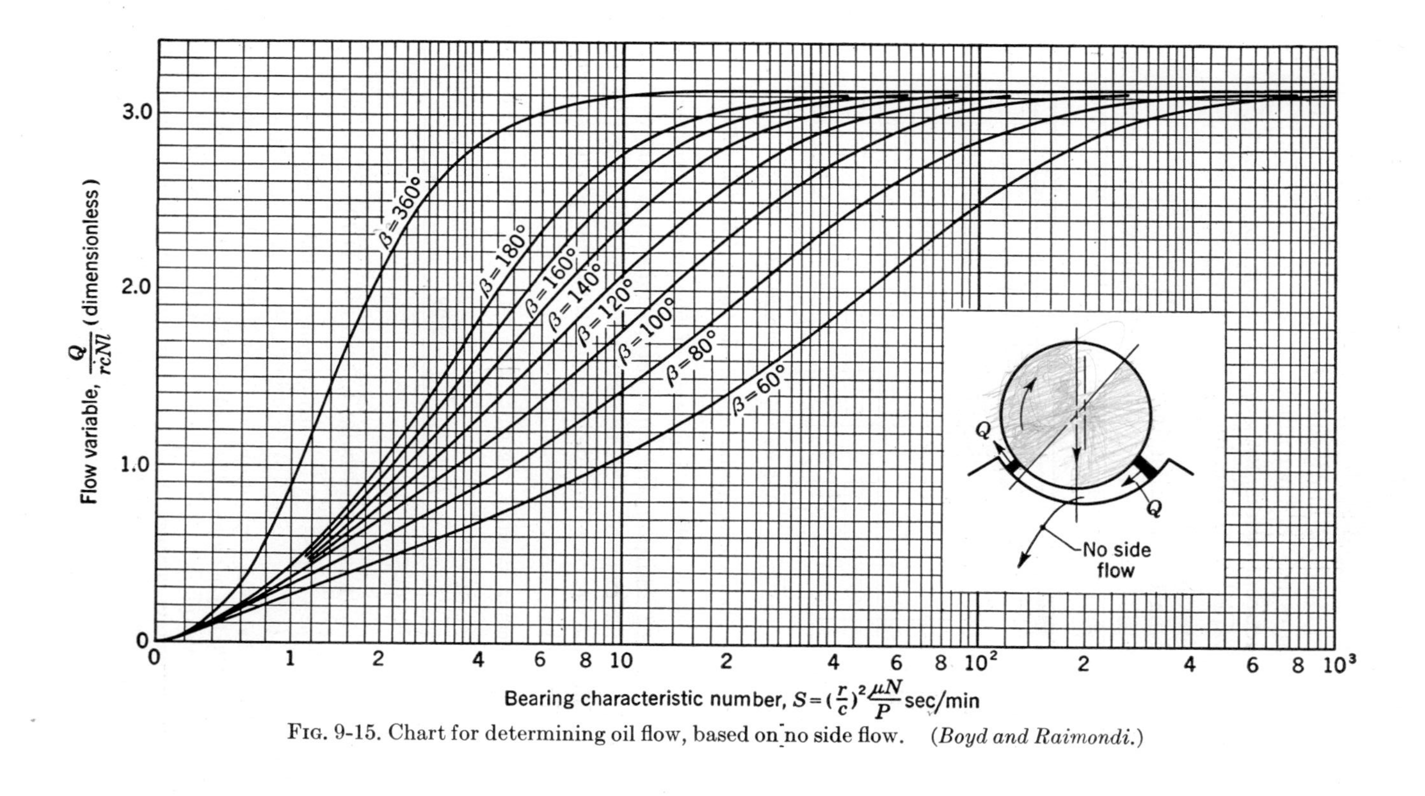

FIG. 9-15. Chart for determining oil flow, based on no side flow. (*Boyd and Raimondi.*)

where FLV = flow variable, dimensionless
Q = amount of lubricant entering bearing arc at atmospheric pressure, in.^{3} per min
r = journal radius, in.
c = radial clearance, in.
N = speed, rpm
l = length of bearing, in.

It is noted that the lubricant flow Q is only the oil which is carried around by the journal, and the assumption is made that a sufficient quantity is

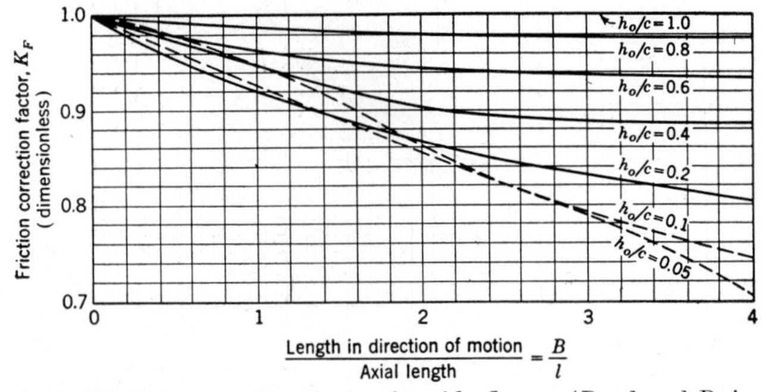

Fig. 9-16. Friction correction factor for side flow. *(Boyd and Raimondi.)*

available. The flow will be increased if the supply pressure is above atmospheric. In addition, the flow variable does not consider the effect of grooving. For example, if a central groove is used, then l is one-half the length of the bearing; in this case, the total flow should be found for two half bearings.

Using the preceding example, we enter Fig. 9-15 with $S = 8.73$ and $\beta = 360°$. This gives

$$FLV = \frac{Q}{rcNl} = 2.98$$

The flow is

$$Q = FLV(rcNl) = (2.98)(0.75)(0.0015)(1{,}750)(2.0) = 11.70 \text{ in.}^3 \text{ per min} \qquad Ans.$$

or

$$Q = \frac{11.70}{231} = 0.0509 \text{ gpm} \qquad Ans.$$

Since the journal does work on the lubricant, heat is produced, as we have seen, at the rate of 2.30 Btu per min. This heat must be dissipated by conduction, convection, radiation, and oil flow. The rate of heat flow by each method of dissipation is extremely difficult to calculate with any accuracy. This problem will be treated subsequently in more detail, but, for the present, if we make the assumption that the oil flow carries away all the heat, then at least we shall be on the conservative side. With this assumption, the heat-balance equation is

$$H = 231 \frac{62.4}{1{,}728} C_H \rho Q (\Delta T)$$

where C_H is the specific heat and ΔT is the temperature rise in degrees Fahrenheit. We are not justified in using anything but average values for the specific heat and the specific gravity, because of the assumption involved. Most SAE oils have a specific gravity of about 0.86 at the operating temperature. The specific heat is about

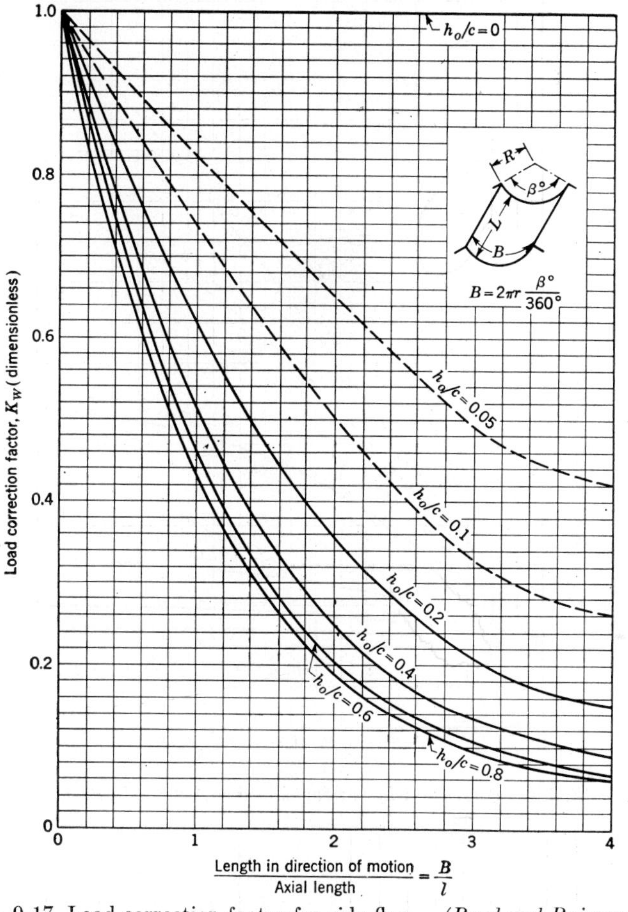

FIG. 9-17. Load correction factor for side flow. (*Boyd and Raimondi.*)

0.42 Btu per lb per deg. Therefore,

$$H = 3Q(\Delta T) \tag{9-13}$$

where Q is in gallons per minute. Thus, for this example,

$$\Delta T = \frac{H}{3Q} = \frac{2.30}{(3)(0.0509)} = 15.1°\text{F} \qquad \textit{Ans.}$$

Side Leakage. When the lubricant flows from the end of the bearing, the same pressure distribution is not obtained (Fig. 9-19), and the values of the quantities are changed. One method of accounting for endwise flow of oil is to apply correction factors. Figures 9-16, 9-17, and 9-18 give these factors for the friction, the load, and the flow, which are designated K_f, K_W, and K_Q, respectively.

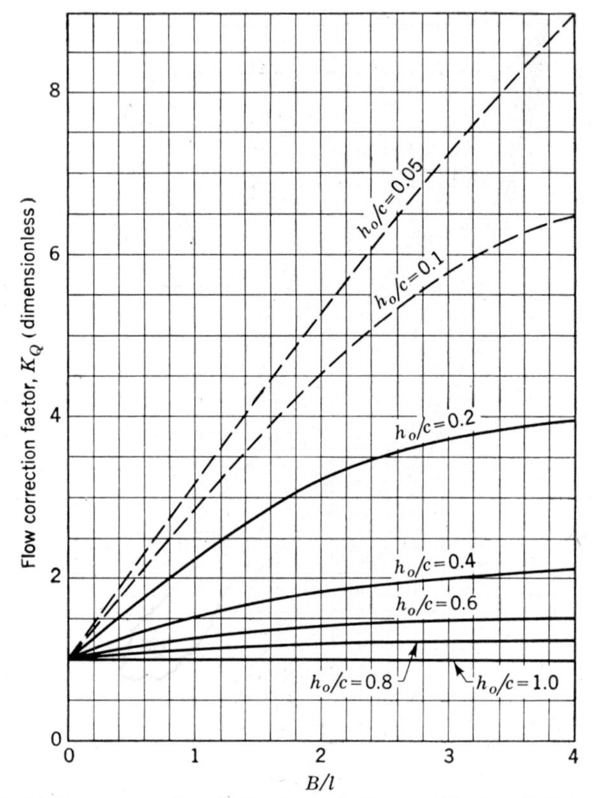

FIG. 9-18. Flow correction factor for side flow. (*Boyd and Raimondi.*)

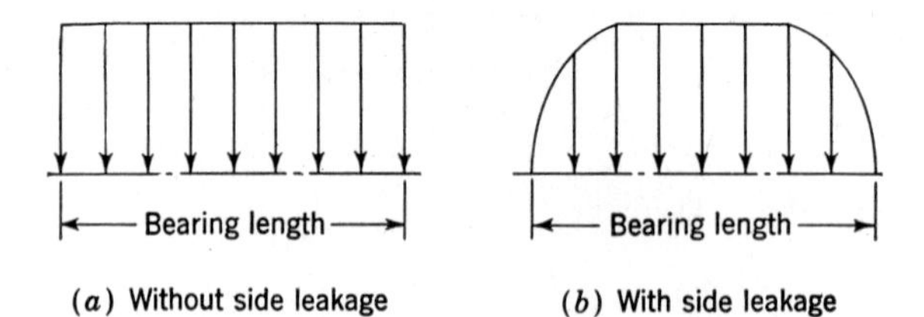

FIG. 9-19. Pressure distribution along the bearing length with and without side leakage.

The problem of side leakage is complicated still more by the fact that the Sommerfeld number must also be corrected for pressure distribution. Thus, the equation

$$S_o = \left(\frac{r}{c}\right)^2 \frac{\mu N}{P} K_W \tag{9-14}$$

where K_W is the load correction factor and S_o is the Sommerfeld number for side leakage, should be used in entering the charts, instead of Eq. (9-12). Since S_o cannot be found directly, it must be determined by a trial-and-error method.

Employing the previous example again, the following quantities were determined for no side leakage:

$$S = 8.73 \text{ sec per min} \qquad h_o/c = 0.88$$

In order to obtain the load correction factor K_W, we must first calculate the ratio B/l, where B is the length of the bearing arc in inches. Thus

$$B = 2\pi r \frac{\beta}{360°} = 2\pi(0.75)\frac{360}{360} = 4.71 \text{ in.}$$

and so

$$\frac{B}{l} = \frac{4.71}{2} = 2.36$$

From Fig. 9-17, for $B/l = 2.36$ and $h_o/c = 0.88$, we obtain $K_W = 0.14$, so that

$$S_o = SK_W = (8.73)(0.14) = 1.23$$

and corresponding to $S_o = 1.23$ we find from Fig. 9-14 that $h_o/c = 0.28$. But the assumption of no side leakage gave $h_o/c = 0.88$. Therefore we must estimate a new value for h_o/c and continue this process until agreement is obtained. In beginning this trial-and-error process, a value of 0.4 for h_o/c is a good value to try. Thus, using $h_o/c = 0.4$ and $B/l = 2.36$ in Fig. 9-17, we find $K_W = 0.19$. The Sommerfeld number is

$$S_o = SK_W = (8.73)(0.19) = 1.67$$

Entering Fig. 9-14 again, we find $h_o/c = 0.42$, which is close enough. Therefore, when considering side leakage, Figs. 9-13 and 9-15 are used with a value for the Sommerfeld variable of

$$S_o = 1.67$$

Thus, from Fig. 9-13, the friction variable is $FV = (r/c)f = 0.95$, and from Fig. 9-16 the friction correction factor K_f is 0.90. Therefore the coefficient of friction is

$$f = FV\frac{c}{r}\frac{K_f}{K_W} = 0.95\frac{(0.0015)(0.90)}{(0.75)(0.19)} = 0.00898 \qquad \textit{Ans.}$$

The friction torque is

$$T = fWr = (0.00898)(600)(0.75) = 4.04 \text{ lb-in.} \qquad \textit{Ans.}$$

The loss in horsepower is

$$\text{hp} = \frac{TN}{63{,}000} = \frac{(4.04)(1{,}750)}{63{,}000} = 0.112 \qquad \textit{Ans.}$$

The power loss in Btu per minute is

$$H = \frac{2\pi TN}{(778)(12)} = \frac{(2\pi)(4.04)(1{,}750)}{(778)(12)} = 4.75 \text{ Btu per min} \qquad \textit{Ans.}$$

Entering Fig. 9-15 with $S_o = 1.67$ and $\beta = 360°$, we find the flow variable is 1.8. Entering Fig. 9-18 with $B/l = 2.36$ and $h_o/c = 0.40$, we find the flow correction factor K_Q is 1.9. The flow is

$$Q = FLV(rcNl)K_Q = (1.8)(0.75)(0.0015)(1{,}750)(2)(1.9) = 13.50 \text{ in.}^3 \text{ per min} \qquad Ans.$$

or

$$Q = \frac{13.50}{231} = 0.0584 \text{ gpm} \qquad Ans.$$

Then, assuming that all the heat generated is carried away by the oil, the temperature rise is

$$\Delta T = \frac{H}{3Q} = \frac{4.75}{(3)(0.0584)} = 27.1°\text{F} \qquad Ans.$$

Summary. The formulas used in the preceding discussion are tabulated in Table 9-2 for convenience. The various quantities and their units are as follows:

B = length of bearing arc, in.
c = radial clearance, in.
f = coefficient of friction
h_o = minimum film thickness, in.
H = power loss, Btu per min
K_f = friction correction factor for side leakage
K_Q = flow correction factor for side leakage
K_W = load correction factor for side leakage
l = length of bearing, in.
N = speed, rpm
P = unit load on projected area, psi
r = journal radius, in.
S = Sommerfeld number without side leakage, sec per min
S_o = Sommerfeld number with side leakage, sec per min
ΔT = temperature rise, °F
T = friction torque, lb-in.
Q = flow, in.^{3} per min or gpm
W = bearing load, lb
β = angular length of bearing, deg
μ = absolute viscosity, reyns

Assumptions.[1] 1. *Side flow.* The assumption of no side leakage makes the bearing much easier to analyze but does not duplicate actual conditions.

[1] Boyd and Raimondi, *loc. cit.*, state that Figs. 9-13 to 9-15 were obtained by direct calculation from the formulas given by Kingsbury.* They also state that Figs. 9-16 to 9-18 are based upon Needs's† results for a 120° bearing with side flow and are assumed to be applicable to bearings of other arcs.

* A. Kingsbury, Optimum Conditions in Journal Bearings, *Trans. ASME*, vol. 54, pp. 123–148, 1932.

† S. J. Needs, Effect of Side Leakage in 120° Centrally Supported Journal Bearings, *Trans. ASME*, vol. 56, pp. 721–732, 1934; vol. 57, pp. 135–138, 1935.

2. *Viscosity.* It has been assumed that the viscosity of the lubricant is constant as it passes through the bearing. Actually it is not constant but varies with both temperature and pressure. Since the oil temperature rises as it passes through the bearing, the viscosity used should probably be that which corresponds to the average of the inlet and outlet

TABLE 9-2. SUMMARY OF BEARING FORMULAS

Quantity	Symbol	Formula or figure number: Without side leakage	Formula or figure number: With side leakage
Sommerfeld number, sec per min	S	$S = \left(\frac{r}{c}\right)^2 \frac{\mu N}{P}$	$S_o = \left(\frac{r}{c}\right)^2 \frac{\mu N}{P} K_W$
Unit load, psi	P	$P = \frac{W}{2rl}$	$P = \frac{W}{2rl}$
Friction variable, dimensionless	FV	$FV = \frac{r}{c} f$, Fig. 9-13	$FV = \frac{r}{c} f$, use S_o, Fig. 9-13
Coefficient of friction, dimensionless	f	$f = FV \frac{c}{r}$	$f = FV \frac{c}{r} \frac{K_f}{K_W}$
Friction torque, lb-in.	T	$T = fWr$	$T = fWr$
Horsepower loss, hp	hp	$\text{hp} = \frac{TN}{63{,}000}$	$\text{hp} = \frac{TN}{63{,}000}$
Power loss, Btu per min	H	$H = \frac{2\pi TN}{(778)(12)}$	$H = \frac{2\pi TN}{(778)(12)}$
Minimum-film-thickness variable, dimensionless	MFT	$MFT = \frac{h_o}{c}$, Fig. 9-14	$MFT = \frac{h_o}{c}$, use S_o, Fig. 9-14
Minimum film thickness, in.	h_o	$h_o = MFT(c)$	$h_o = MFT(c)$
Flow variable, dimensionless	FLV	$FLV = \frac{Q}{rcNl}$, Fig. 9-15	$FLV = \frac{Q}{rcNl}$, Fig. 9-15
Flow, in.³ per min	Q	$Q = FLV(rcNl)$	$Q = FLV(rcNl)K_Q$
Flow, gpm	Q	$Q = \frac{FLV}{231} rcNl$	$Q = \frac{FLV}{231} (rcNl)K_Q$
Temperature rise, °F	ΔT	$\Delta T = \frac{H}{3Q}$	$\Delta T = \frac{H}{3Q}$

temperatures. In other words, the equation

$$T_{av} = T_1 + \frac{\Delta T}{2}$$

gives the value of the temperature to be used in finding the viscosity when the oil flow is assumed to carry away all the generated heat.

3. *Pressure distribution.* The oil-pressure distribution shown in Fig. 9-8 shows a supply pressure p_s, a minimum pressure p_{min}, and a maximum

pressure p_{max}. The bearing-performance curves have been plotted on the basis of atmospheric supply pressure. If the supply and discharge pressures are varied, then an equivalent increase or decrease is produced throughout the film, but the positions are not changed. For small values of S, that is, where the speed or viscosity is low and the bearing pressure high, there is a possibility of a large difference between p_s and p_{min}. This raises the possibility of negative pressures. Ordinarily, liquids cannot withstand negative pressures, and, since the analysis does not exclude this possibility, it must be noted that the graphs are in error for low values of S. In general, this error is not large for values of S greater than 2.

4. *Oil flow.* For the assumption of no side leakage the flow of oil is that which is chargeable to the pumping action of the journal. When side leakage is not neglected, the flow of oil is the sum of the side leakage and that pumped by the journal. The supply and discharge pressures are atmospheric. Therefore, the flow given by the charts will be altered if force feed is used, if insufficient lubrication is available, or if special grooving is used.

9-7. Pressure-fed Bearings. *Oil Flow.*[1] We have seen that oil flow is an important quantity because of the heat which it carries away from

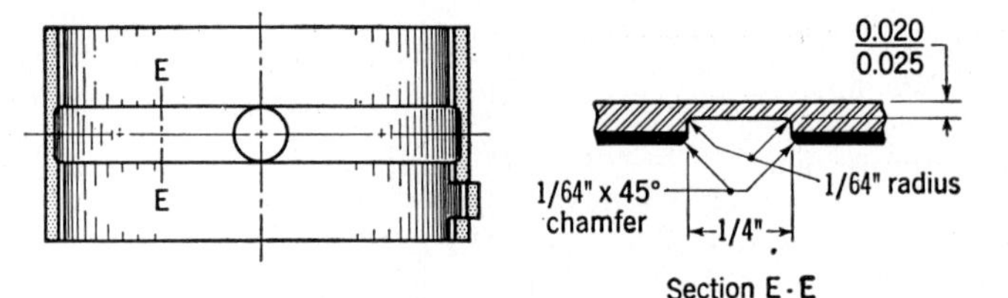

FIG. 9-20. Centrally located, full annular groove. (*Courtesy of The Cleveland Graphite Bronze Company, Division of Clevite Corporation.*)

the bearing. In the case of pressure-fed bearings, Fig. 9-15 does not apply, and it is necessary to determine the flow from other considerations.

In general, the amount of oil flowing through a bearing depends upon the supply and discharge pressures, the journal speed, the clearance and eccentricity, the bearing diameter and length, the load, the viscosity, and the method of grooving. Space does not permit solving the problem for all types of grooving and so we will select a full annular groove, as shown in Fig. 9-20, which has had wide acceptance among lubrication engineers. It may be noted that the groove divides the pressure-distribution curve into two lobes and reduces the film thickness, but, according to Slaymaker, it interferes less with bearing performance than any other type of groove.

In order to set up a method of solution, we will assume a groove ample

[1] This treatment is from Robert R. Slaymaker, "Design and Lubrication of Pressure Fed Bearings," pp. 7–10, Case Institute of Technology, Cleveland, 1953.

enough that the pressure drop in the groove itself is small. Initially we will neglect eccentricity and then apply a correction factor for this condition. The oil flow, then, is the amount which flows out of the two halves of the bearing in the direction of the concentric shaft. If we neglect the rotation of the shaft, we obtain the force situation shown in Fig. 9-21. Here we designate the supply pressure by p_s and the pressure at any point by p. Laminar flow is assumed, and we are interested in the statical equilibrium of an element of width dx, thickness $2y$, and unit depth. The pressure is $p + dp$ on the left face, p on the right face, and the upper

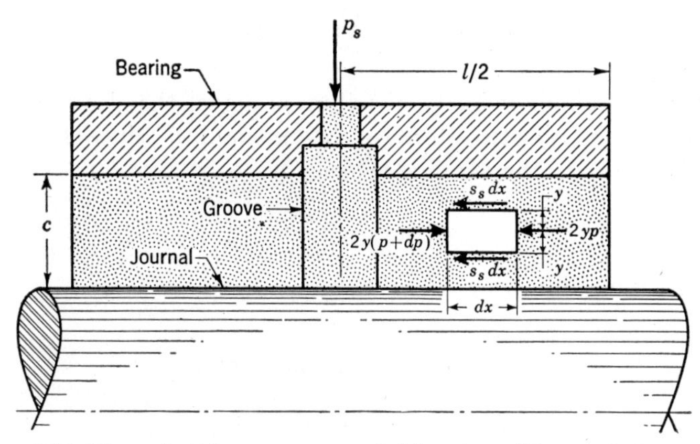

FIG. 9-21. Flow of oil from a pressure-fed bearing with a central groove.

and lower surfaces are acted upon by shearing stresses s_s. The origin of coordinates is chosen at the center of the clearance space. Equilibrium requires

$$2y(p + dp) - 2s_s\,dx - 2yp = 0 \tag{a}$$

Applying Newton's law for viscous flow [Eq. (9-1)], we have

$$s_s = -\mu \frac{du}{dy} \tag{b}$$

where the negative sign is used because the origin of y is at the center of the film instead of the boundary. Substituting Eq. (b) into Eq. (a) gives

$$\frac{du}{dy} = -\frac{1}{\mu}\frac{dp}{dx}\,y \tag{c}$$

Integrating with respect to y gives

$$u = -\frac{1}{\mu}\frac{dp}{dx}\frac{y^2}{2} + C \tag{d}$$

The constant of integration is evaluated using the condition that $u = 0$ at either boundary, that is, when $y = \pm c/2$. This gives

$$C = \frac{1}{\mu}\frac{dp}{dx}\frac{c^2}{8}$$

and

$$u = \frac{1}{8\mu}\frac{dp}{dx}(c^2 - 4y^2) \tag{e}$$

If we assume a linear pressure distribution with respect to x, then $dp/dx = 2p_s/l$, and Eq. (e) becomes

$$u = \frac{p_s}{4\mu l}(c^2 - 4y^2) \tag{f}$$

This gives a parabolic velocity distribution across the clearance space c. The average velocity is two-thirds of the maximum. Since the maximum occurs where $y = 0$, the average velocity is

$$u_{av} = \frac{p_s c^2}{6\mu l} \tag{g}$$

The quantity of oil flowing is

$$Q = Au_{av}$$

where A is the area of the clearance space. Thus

$$Q = (2\pi rc)u_{av} \tag{h}$$

Substitution of Eq. (g) in Eq. (h) gives

$$Q = \frac{\pi p_s c^3 r}{3\mu l} \tag{i}$$

Equation (i) gives the flow from one end of the bearing in cubic inches per second (because μ is in reyns). Therefore, the flow from both ends in gallons per minute is

$$Q = 2\,\frac{60}{231}\,\frac{\pi p_s c^3 r}{3\mu l} = 0.544\,\frac{p_s c^3 r}{\mu l} \qquad \text{gpm} \tag{9-15}$$

Dennison[1] gives the eccentricity correction factor as $1 + \frac{3}{2}e/c$. Thus Eq. (9-15) becomes

$$Q = 0.544\left(1 + \frac{3}{2}\frac{e}{c}\right)\frac{p_s c^3 r}{\mu l} \tag{9-16}$$

The eccentricity ratio e/c may be obtained from the equation

$$\frac{e}{c} = 1 - \frac{h_o}{c} \tag{9-17}$$

[1] E. S. Dennison, Film-lubrication Theory and Engine-bearing Design, *Trans. ASME*, vol. 58, p. 25, 1936.

Analysis. It is customary in the analysis of pressure-fed bearings to determine the coefficient of friction from Petroff's law by applying an eccentricity correction factor. Thus, from Eq. (9-8) we have

$$f = k_1 \frac{\pi^2}{30} \frac{\mu N}{P} \frac{r}{c} \tag{9-18}$$

Dennison gives the value of the eccentricity correction factor as

$$k_1 = \frac{1}{\sqrt{1 - (e/c)^2}} \tag{9-19}$$

We must now make use of the following equations:

Oil flow, $$Q = 0.544 k_2 \frac{p_s c^3 r}{\mu l} \quad \text{gpm} \tag{9-20}$$

where $$k_2 = 1 + \frac{3}{2} \frac{e}{c} \tag{9-21}$$

Power loss, $$H = \frac{2\pi f W r N}{(778)(12)} \quad \text{Btu per min} \tag{9-22}$$

Temperature rise, $$\Delta T = \frac{H}{3Q} \tag{9-13}$$

The coefficient of friction may be eliminated by substituting f from Eq. (9-18) into Eq. (9-22). We may now obtain an expression for ΔT by substituting the values of Q and H [from Eqs. (9-20) and (9-22)] into Eq. (9-13). This gives

$$\Delta T = \frac{4\pi^3}{(0.544)(778)(12)(3)(30)} \frac{k_1}{k_2} \left(\frac{Nrl}{c^2} \right)^2 \frac{\mu^2}{p_s} \tag{j}$$

where $W/2rl$ has been substituted for P. Multiplication of the numerical terms gives

$$\Delta T = \frac{272}{10^6} \frac{k_1}{k_2} \left(\frac{Nrl}{c^2} \right)^2 \frac{\mu^2}{p_s} \tag{9-23}$$

The eccentricity factors k_1 and k_2 in the above equation are functions of the Sommerfeld number. These could be obtained from Fig. 9-14 by applying the correction factors of Fig. 9-17. However, this method is somewhat unwieldy in this case, and, in addition, the charts do not include the length-diameter ratios ordinarily found in pressure-fed bearings. For this reason we will employ the Dennison relations which were specifically derived for these bearing types. They are tabulated in Table 9-3.

The usual problem in journal-bearing analysis is to determine the temperature rise and minimum film thickness when the dimensions of the

TABLE 9-3. VALUES OF THE SOMMERFELD VARIABLE FOR VARIOUS h_o/c AND L/d RATIOS*

L†$/d$ \ h_o/c	1	0.2	0.1	0.067	0.05	0.04	0.033	0.0286	0.025
0.1	0	43.5	8.76	4.35	2.50	1.79	1.37	1.10	0.962
0.2	0	18.9	4.39	2.20	1.32	0.970	0.775	0.649	0.581
0.3	0	11.6	2.96	1.52	0.952	0.714	0.585	0.503	0.452
0.4	0	8.27	2.22	1.18	0.770	0.595	0.495	0.438	0.396
0.5	0	6.21	1.81	1.00	0.680	0.537	0.452	0.406	0.369
0.6	0	5.12	1.60	0.909	0.640	0.510	0.436	0.390	0.357
0.8	0	3.98	1.40	0.833	0.599	0.483	0.416	0.377	0.346
1.0	0	3.41	1.29	0.787	0.568	0.467	0.403	0.366	0.338
1.2	0	3.12	1.21	0.752	0.549	0.450	0.394	0.357	0.330
1.5	0	2.86	1.12	0.715	0.526	0.435	0.380	0.347	0.321
2.0	0	2.53	1.06	0.681	0.505	0.420	0.370	0.339	0.314
∞	0	2.07	0.922	0.611	0.465	0.394	0.352	0.322	0.301

* From E. S. Dennison, *Trans. ASME*, vol. 58, p. 25, 1936. It is noted that Dennison found it more convenient to tabulate the reciprocals of S and h_o/c.

† L = effective bearing length. For a central annular groove

$$L = \frac{l - w}{2} = \frac{\text{bearing length} - \text{groove width}}{2}$$

bearing are given, the oil is specified, and the supply pressure and inlet temperature are given. An easy way to solve this problem is to make several calculations and plot the results on Fig. 9-12. A line is then constructed crossing the SAE line for the given oil. Its intersection gives the viscosity corresponding to the average temperature. The Sommerfeld number may then be calculated and the minimum film thickness obtained from Table 9-3. This is illustrated in the following example.

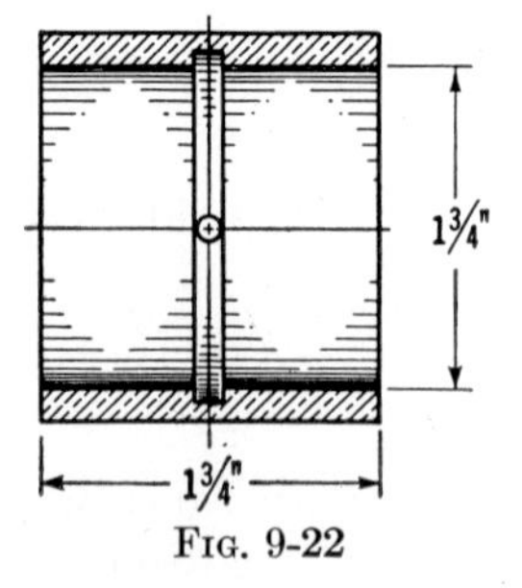

FIG. 9-22

EXAMPLE 9-1. Figure 9-22 shows the dimensions of a pressure-fed bearing with an annular central groove. The oil is SAE 30 at 180°F inlet temperature and a supply pressure of 20 psi. The bearing supports a load of 980 lb at a journal speed of 1,000 rpm. For a radial clearance of 0.001 in., determine the temperature rise and the minimum oil-film thickness.

Solution. The constants are

$$\frac{L}{d} = \frac{1.75}{(2)(1.75)} = 0.50 \qquad \frac{r}{c} = \frac{0.875}{0.001} = 875$$

$$P = \frac{W}{2rl} = \frac{980}{(2)(0.875)(1.75)} = 320 \text{ psi}$$

The next step is to select a viscosity. We will select $\mu = (1.4)(10)^{-6}$ reyn. This gives for the Sommerfeld number

$$S = \left(\frac{r}{c}\right)^2 \left(\frac{\mu N}{P}\right) = \frac{(875)^2(1.4)(10)^{-6}(1{,}000)}{320} = 3.35 \text{ sec per min}$$

It is now necessary to determine the value of h_o/c corresponding to this value of S and an L/d ratio of 0.50. This is done by interpolation. From Table 9-3 we see that h_o/c is between 0.20 and 0.10. Interpolation gives

$$\frac{h_o}{c} = 0.135$$

The eccentricity ratio is

$$\frac{e}{c} = 1 - \frac{h_o}{c} = 1 - 0.135 = 0.865$$

The eccentricity factors are calculated from Eqs. (9-19) and (9-21):

$$k_1 = \frac{1}{\sqrt{1 - (e/c)^2}} = \frac{1}{\sqrt{1 - (0.865)^2}} = 1.99$$

$$k_2 = 1 + \frac{3}{2}\frac{e}{c} = 1 + \frac{3}{2}(0.865) = 2.30$$

Solving Eq. (9-23) for the temperature rise gives

$$\begin{aligned} \Delta T &= \frac{272}{10^6}\frac{k_1}{k_2}\left(\frac{Nrl}{c^2}\right)^2 \frac{\mu^2}{p_s} \\ &= \frac{272}{10^6}\frac{1.99}{2.30}\left[\frac{(1{,}000)(0.875)(1.75)}{(0.001)^2}\right]^2 \frac{[(1.4)(10)^{-6}]^2}{20} \\ &= 54.2°\text{F} \end{aligned}$$

The average bearing temperature is

$$T_{av} = T_1 + \frac{\Delta T}{2} = 180 + \frac{54.2}{2} = 207.1°\text{F}$$

Referring to Fig. 9-12, point A is plotted corresponding to $T_{av} = 207.1°$F and the assumed viscosity of $(1.4)(10)^{-6}$ reyn.

For a second point we will choose a viscosity slightly lower than the expected value. Let us choose $\mu = (1.0)(10)^{-6}$ reyn. The previous analysis is repeated for the second value of μ. When this is done, the following values are obtained:

$$S = 2.40 \text{ sec per min} \qquad \frac{h_o}{c} = 0.113 \qquad \frac{e}{c} = 0.887 \qquad T = 29.6°\text{F}$$

$$T_{av} = T_1 + \frac{\Delta T}{2} = 180 + \frac{29.6}{2} = 194.8°\text{F}$$

The viscosity $\mu = (1.0)(10)^{-6}$ reyn and the average temperature $T_{av} = 194.8°$F are located as point B on Fig. 9-12. A line drawn from A to B crosses the SAE 30 line at $\mu = (1.27)(10)^{-6}$ reyn and $T_{av} = 203°$F. Therefore, the temperature rise is

$$\Delta T = 2(T_{av} - T_1) = 2(203 - 180) = 46°\text{F} \qquad \textit{Ans.}$$

The Sommerfeld number corresponding to the average temperature is

$$S = \left(\frac{r}{c}\right)^2 \frac{\mu N}{P} = \frac{(875)^2(1.27)(10)^{-6}(1{,}000)}{320} = 3.04 \text{ sec per min}$$

From Table 9-3, we find $h_o/c = 0.127$, so that the minimum film thickness is

$$h_o = (0.127)(c) = (0.127)(0.001) = 0.000127 \text{ in.} \qquad \textit{Ans.}$$

It will be noted in the preceding example that the eccentricity factors k_1 and k_2 are very nearly equal. They both depend upon the eccentricity ratio and increase when the eccentricity ratio increases, although not at the same rate. This fact suggested to Slaymaker the idea of equating these constants and solving Eq. (9-23) as follows:

$$\frac{\Delta T}{\mu^2} = \frac{272}{10^6}\left(\frac{Nrl}{c^2}\right)^2 \frac{1}{p_s} \tag{9-24}$$

Now it will be noticed that everything on the right-hand side of this equation is known or can be specified. Thus, for every value of μ, there is a corresponding value of ΔT. Of course, the assumption that $k_1 = k_2$ is not exact. But, when the assumptions and inaccuracies which are present in nearly every lubrication problem are considered, it is seen that this assumption is often completely justified. In any event, it establishes a temperature trend which is very useful in design.

9-8. Heat Dissipation of Bearings. The case in which the lubricant carries away all the generated heat has already been discussed. We shall now investigate the case in which the bearing housing itself is to dissipate the heat generated. The heat given up by the bearing may be approximated by the equation

$$H = \frac{CA(T_2 - T_1)}{60} \tag{9-25}$$

where H = heat to be dissipated, Btu per min
C = combined coefficient of radiation and convection, Btu per hr per ft² per °F
A = area of housing, ft²
$T_2 - T_1$ = difference in temperature between bearing housing and surrounding air

In using Eq. (9-25), the area of the case can be calculated with accuracy, and the heat generated in the bearing may be obtained by the methods of Sec. 9-6. It is very difficult, however, to arrive at a figure for the coefficient C. The value of C depends upon the material, color, and roughness of the housing, the velocity of the air around the housing, the temperature drop between the housing and its surroundings, and upon the objects which the housing sees. An approximation for this coefficient may be obtained from Table 9-4. As an additional guide, Norton[1] uses a value of 2 for C for still air. Since a bearing supports a shaft which is presumed to be rotating, the effect would be to create some air movement; if there

[1] Norton, *op. cit.*, p. 187.

existed nearby rotating masses, this movement might be quite rapid. In addition, there will be some conduction of heat along the shaft. It therefore seems that a C of about 2.7 could be used for general design.

TABLE 9-4. COEFFICIENT OF HEAT DISSIPATION (FOR ROUGH DARK SURFACES)*

Air velocity, fps	0	20	40	60	80	100
Coefficient C	0.47	2.49	3.32	3.95	4.50	5.10

* From Lionel S. Marks (ed.), "Mechanical Engineers' Handbook," 5th ed., p. 378, McGraw-Hill Book Company, Inc., New York, 1951.

Although the housing may be dissipating heat at the rate indicated by Eq. (9-25), giving a housing surface temperature of T_2, the actual oil-film temperature may be much higher. Its actual value may be difficult to estimate because it depends upon the construction of the bearing, the materials used, the surface finish, and how well the oil distributes the heat to all portions of the housing. Karelitz[1] found on 4-in. ring-oiled bearings an oil-film temperature rise of about twice the housing temperature rise. This may be expressed in equation form as

$$T_{av} = T_1 + 2(T_2 - T_1) \tag{9-26}$$

where T_{av} = average oil-film temperature, °F
T_1 = air temperature, °F
T_2 = surface temperature of bearing housing, °F

9-9. Practical Range of the Variables. We have seen that the fundamental problem in journal-bearing design is to select suitable values for the independent variables so as to create a favorable operating situation with respect to the dependent variables. Having investigated the relationships between these variables, it is now necessary to determine the practical operating range for each variable. The assumptions used in bearing design limit the accuracy of the solution, and it is necessary to restrict the operating range of each variable to a degree which will practically warrant a successful bearing design.

9-10. The Independent Variables. The independent variables are the viscosity, the unit bearing load, the speed, and the bearing dimensions.

The Lubricant. The selection of a lubricant depends upon the characteristics of the load and machine and upon the lubricant feeding system. The viscosities listed in Table 9-5 for various machines are given

[1] G. B. Karelitz, Performance of Oil Ring Bearings, *Trans. ASME*, vol. 52, pp. 57–70, 1930.

by Thomsen[1] as representative of current practice. The values are only approximate and may be altered for a particular design situation.

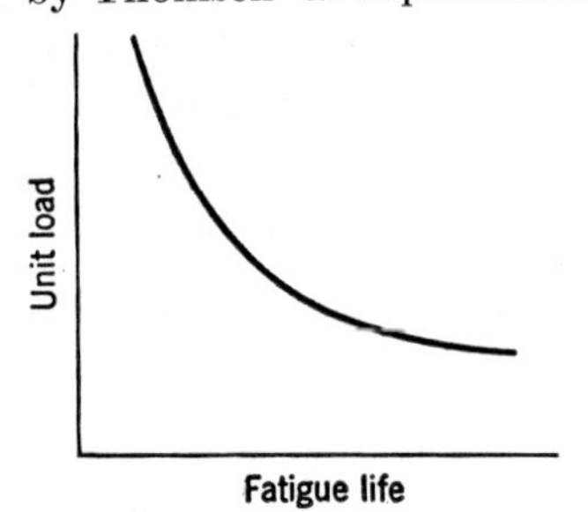

FIG. 9-23. Endurance curve for a typical sliding bearing.

The Bearing Load. The magnitude of the unit bearing load selected is dependent upon the desired bearing life. The relation between the unit load and the life of a bearing is somewhat as shown in Fig. 9-23. For a given load the life depends upon the materials and construction of the bearing, the bearing temperature, the contaminants in the lubricant, and upon the alignment, distortion, and other service conditions. Materials and bearing construction will be discussed in Sec. 9-13. The unit loads given in Table 9-5 represent current practice with standard materials and for normal conditions of operation.

TABLE 9-5. OIL VISCOSITIES AND PERMISSIBLE UNIT LOADS IN CURRENT USE*

Type of bearing	Viscosity, SUS at 100°F	Unit load, psi of projected area
Diesel engines:		
Main bearings	250–850	800–1,500
Crankpin	250–850	1,000–2,000
Wristpin	250–850	1,800–2,000
Electric-motor bearings	122–180	100–200
Marine diesel engines:		
Main bearings	250–500	400–600
Crankpin	250–500	1,000–1,400
Steam turbines and reduction gears	122–470	100–220
Automotive engines:		
Main bearings	150–850	500–600
Crankpin	150–850	1,500–2,000
Air compressors:		
Main bearings	150–1,700	120–240
Crankpin	150–1,700	240–400
Aircraft-engine crankpin	150–500	700–2,000
Centrifugal pumps	122–180	80–100
Miscellaneous bearings	122–250	80–150
Automotive transmissions	800–1,500	

* The unit loads are from Lionel S. Marks (ed.), "Mechanical Engineers' Handbook," 5th ed., p. 967, McGraw-Hill Book Company, Inc., New York, 1951.

[1] T. C. Thomsen, "The Practice of Lubrication," 4th ed., McGraw-Hill Book Company, Inc., New York, 1951.

The Bearing Dimensions. The bearing dimensions are the journal radius r, the radial clearance c, the angular length β, and the bearing length l. Since grooves affect the performance of the bearing, their dimensions and location must also be considered and included with the dimensions.

The radial clearance used depends somewhat upon the materials. The following figures may be used in preliminary design:

Material	*Minimum radial clearance c per inch of shaft diameter*
Lead and tin-base........	0.0005–0.00075
Copper-lead.............	0.00075–0.001
Aluminum...............	0.001–0.00125

The length-diameter ratio (l/d) of a bearing depends upon whether it is expected to run under thin-film-lubrication conditions. A long bearing (large l/d ratio) reduces the coefficient of friction and the side flow of oil and therefore is desirable where thin-film or boundary-value lubrication is present. On the other hand, where force-feed or positive lubrication is present, then the l/d ratio should be relatively small. The short bearing results in a greater flow of oil out of the ends and thus keeps the bearing cooler. Current practice is to use an l/d ratio of about unity, in general, and then to increase this ratio if thin-film lubrication may occur and to decrease it for thick-film lubrication or high temperatures. If shaft deflection is likely to be severe, a short bearing should be used in order to prevent metal-to-metal contact at the ends of the bearings. Usual values of the l/d ratio seem to run from about 0.5 for force-feed-lubricated bearings up to 2 and over.

9-11. The Dependent Variables. The dependent variables are the coefficient of friction, the temperature rise, the flow of oil, and the minimum film thickness. Before establishing limitations on these values, it is necessary to consider their relation to the clearance.

The importance of selecting a proper clearance is illustrated graphically in Fig. 9-24.[1] This graph shows the effect of clearance on the bearing temperature and the minimum oil-film thickness. It is seen that if the clearance is too tight the temperature will be too high and the film thickness low. High temperatures may cause the bearing to fail by fatigue. If the oil film is too thin, dirt particles may not pass without scoring or may imbed themselves in the bearing. In either event, there will be excessive wear and friction, resulting in high temperatures and possible seizure.

[1] From the paper by E. Crankshaw and R. C. Savage, Latest Engineering Techniques in the Bearing Industry, delivered before the Chicago Section, SAE, 1953, and distributed by The Cleveland Graphite Bronze Company, Cleveland.

It would seem that a large clearance will permit the dirt to pass through and also will permit a large flow of oil. This lowers the temperature and increases the life of the bearing. However, if the clearance becomes too large, the bearing becomes noisy and the film thickness begins to decrease again.

When both the production tolerance and the future wear on the bearing are considered, it is seen that the best compromise is a clearance range slightly to the left of the point where both curves begin to flatten out. In this way, future wear will move the operating point to the right

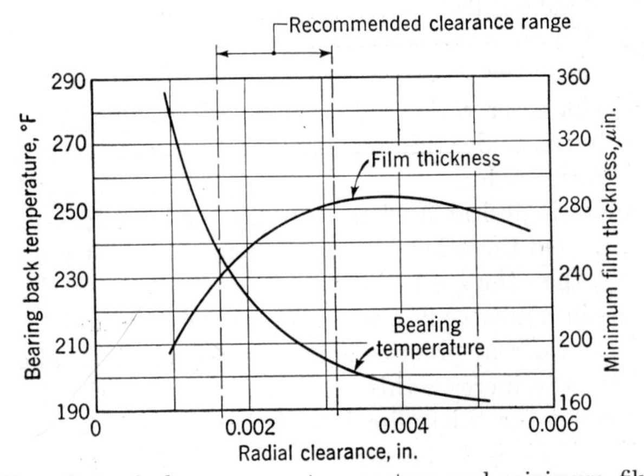

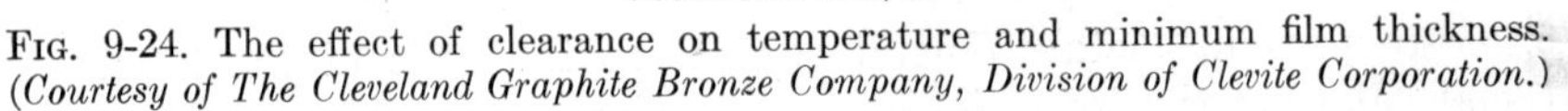
FIG. 9-24. The effect of clearance on temperature and minimum film thickness. (*Courtesy of The Cleveland Graphite Bronze Company, Division of Clevite Corporation.*)

and tend to increase the film thickness and decrease the operating temperature.

Slaymaker[1] suggests that these two curves should be used in bearing design to fix the clearance and the production tolerance. The data for the curves may be calculated after the dimensions of the bearing have been established for the given load, speed, oil viscosity, and oil-sump temperature. The procedure is to calculate the minimum film thickness and the temperature rise for various values of the radial clearance. The bearing temperature is taken equal to the oil-sump temperature plus the temperature rise. Enough points should be taken to define the hump on the film-thickness curve.

Tolerance. The permissible variation in a dimension is called the *tolerance.* The clearance range is the production tolerance after the parts are assembled. The diametral clearance and clearance range are calculated as shown in Fig. 9-25. These values must be divided by 2 in order to obtain the radial clearance for use in the formulas. The tol-

[1] Slaymaker, *op. cit.*, pp. 11–13.

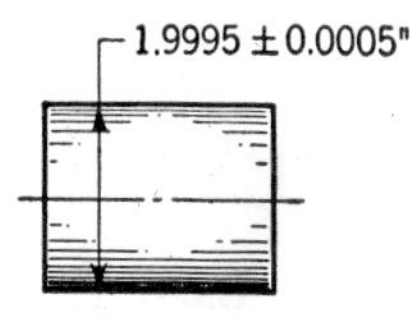

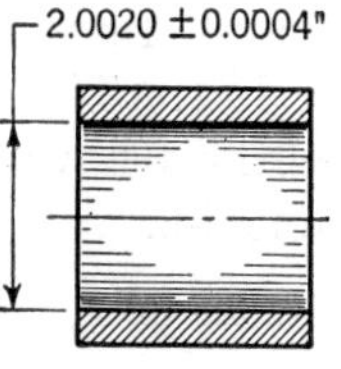

(a) Shaft (b) Hole

Tolerance = (2)(0.0005) = 0.0010 in. Tolerance = (2)(0.0004) = 0.0008 in.

Maximum clearance = (2.0020 + 0.0004) [Largest hole] − (1.9995 − 0.0005) [Smallest shaft] = 0.0034 in.

Minimum clearance = (2.0020 − 0.0004) [Smallest hole] − (1.9995 + 0.0005) [Largest shaft] = 0.0016 in.

Clearance range = 0.0034 − 0.0016 = 0.0018 in.

FIG. 9-25. Determination of diametral clearance range.

erance is fixed by manufacturing considerations. In general, the following represent reasonable values of tolerances for dimensions up to 4 in.:[1]

Grinding	0.0005–0.001 in.
Broaching and reaming	0.001 –0.002 in.
Turning and boring	0.001 –0.003 in.

The effect of temperature on bearing life is shown in Fig. 9-26. This curve shows that a great deal is to be gained if the bearing can be operated at a relatively low temperature. This agrees with the experience of bearing manufacturers who have established the fact that if a bearing can be kept cool it will usually operate successfully. Therefore it would seem that temperature is one of the most important considerations in bearing design, with friction, oil flow, and film thickness important only as they affect the heating of the bearing.

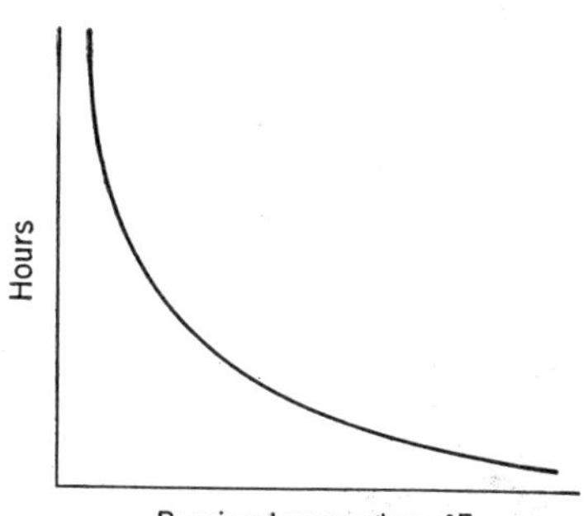

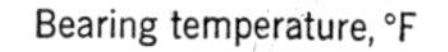

FIG. 9-26. Bearing life as a function of temperature.

However, the film thickness is important not only as it affects oil flow and heating of the bearing but also because it may indicate the degree of safety of a design. Should the minimum film thickness become too low, there is danger of thin-film lubrication. Norton[2] suggests a value of $h_0/r = 0.0005$ for general bearing design where data concerning current practices are not available.

[1] Additional information may be obtained from American Standards Association (ASA) tables on classification of cylindrical fits or recommended allowances and tolerances. These are to be found in many handbooks and are also available from the ASME.

[2] Norton, *op. cit.*, p. 191.

Another design criterion which is frequently used is maximum load or minimum power loss. The values of the minimum film thickness for both these conditions have been determined by Kingsbury[1] and are tabulated in Table 9-6.

TABLE 9-6. VALUES OF h_o/c FOR MAXIMUM LOAD CAPACITY OR MINIMUM POWER LOSS*

	Bearing arc, deg			
	360	180	150	120
For maximum load capacity, h_o/c =	0.662	0.655	0.605	0.530
For minimum power loss, h_o/c =	0.634	0.630	0.590	0.510

* Values determined by A. Kingsbury, Optimum Conditions in Journal Bearings, *Trans. ASME*, vol. 54, pp. 123–148, 1932.

9-12. Bearing Types. A bearing may be as simple as a hole machined into a cast-iron machine member. It may still be simple yet require

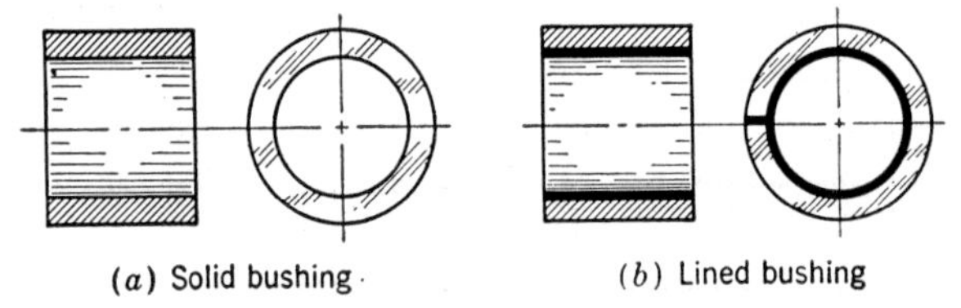

FIG. 9-27. Bearings.

detailed design procedures, as, for example, the two-piece, grooved, pressure-fed, connecting-rod bearing in an automotive engine. Or it may be as elaborate as the large water-cooled, ring-oiled bearings with built-in oil reservoirs used on heavy machinery.

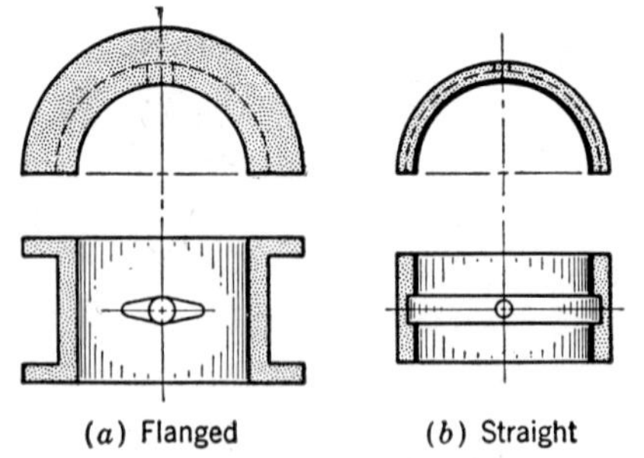

FIG. 9-28. Two-piece bearings.

Figure 9-27 shows two types of bearings which are often called bushings. The solid bushing is made by casting, by drawing and machining, or by using a powder-metallurgy process. The lined bushing is usually a split type. In one method of manufacture the molten lining material is cast continuously on thin strip steel. The babbitted strip is then processed through presses, shavers, and broaches, resulting in a lined bushing. Any

[1] Kingsbury, *loc. cit.*

type of grooving may be cut into the bushings. Bushings are assembled as a press fit and finished by boring, reaming, or burnishing.

Flanged and straight two-piece bearings are shown in Fig. 9-28. These are available in many sizes in both thick- and thin-wall types with or without lining material. A locking lug positions the bearing and effectively prevents axialwise or rotationalwise movement of the bearing in the housing.

The principle of the thrust bearing is shown in Fig. 9-29. This consists essentially of a runner sliding over a fixed pad. Oil is brought into the radial grooves and pumped into the wedge-shaped space by the motion of the runner. Thus all the requirements of lubrication are satisfied.[1]

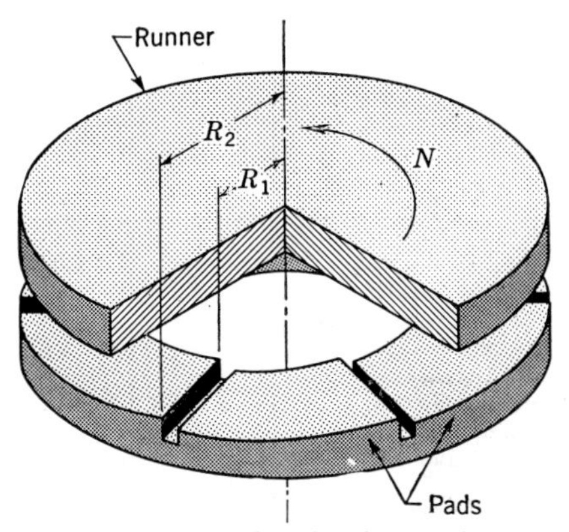

FIG. 9-29. Fixed-pad thrust bearing. (*Courtesy of The Westinghouse Electric Corporation, Research Laboratories.*)

Grooving. Some typical groove patterns are shown in Fig. 9-30. In general, the lubricant may be brought in from the end of the bushing, through the shaft, or through the bushing. The flow may be intermittent or continuous. The preferred practice is to bring the oil in at the center of the bushing so that it will flow out both ends, thus increasing the flow and cooling action.

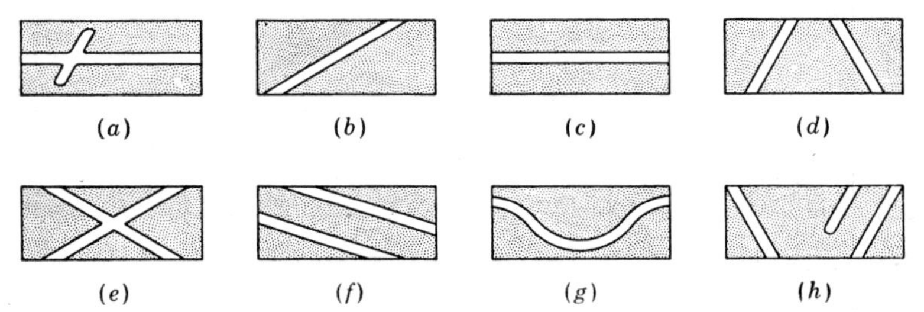

FIG. 9-30. Developed views of typical groove patterns. (*Courtesy of The Cleveland Graphite Bronze Company, Division of Clevite Corporation.*)

9-13. Bearing Materials. The allowable pressure, the life, and the safe temperature rise are all functions of the bearing material. In addition, since some bearings are required to run with thin-film lubrication for a part or all of the time, the resistance to wear and the coefficient of

[1] Space does not permit the inclusion of working curves for thrust bearings. See A. A. Raimondi and John Boyd, Applying Bearing Theory to the Analysis and Design of Pad-type Bearings, *Trans. ASME*, vol. 77, pp. 287–309, 1955.

friction are also important. Some of the commonly used materials are listed in Table 9-7, together with their compositions and characteristics.

TABLE 9-7. COMPOSITION AND CHARACTERISTICS OF BEARING ALLOYS

Alloy name	Thickness, in.	SAE number	% Cu	% Sn	% Pb	% Sb	Relative characteristics	
							Load capacity	Corrosion resistance
Tin-base babbitt	0.022	12	3.25	89	...	7.5	1.0	Excellent
Lead-base babbitt	0.022	15	...	1	83	15	1.2	Very good
Tin-base babbitt	0.004	12	3.25	89	...	7.5	1.5	Excellent
Lead-base babbitt	0.004	15	...	1	83	15	1.5	Very good
Leaded bronze	Solid	792	80	10	10	...	3.3	Very good
Copper-lead	0.022	480	65	...	35	...	1.9	Good
Aluminum alloy	Solid	...	1	6	...	...	3.0	Excellent
Silver plus overlay	0.013	17P	...	...	...	...	4.1	Excellent
Cadmium (1.5% Ni)	0.022	18	...	...	...	...	1.3	Good
Trimetal 88*	...	...	...	...	...	...	4.1	Excellent
Trimetal 77†	...	...	...	...	...	...	4.1	Very good

* This is an 0.008-in. layer of copper-lead on a steel back plus 0.001 in. of tin-base babbitt.
† This is an 0.013-in. layer of copper-lead on a steel back plus 0.001 in. of lead-base babbitt.

The bearing life as a function of the babbitt thickness is presented graphically in Fig. 9-31. This shows a very pronounced change in the fatigue life for variations in the babbitt thickness between 0.001 and 0.014 in. This has led to the manufacture of bearings employing a high-fatigue-strength copper-lead over the backup material, with a layer of babbitt (0.001 to 0.002 in. thick) on top. Thus the babbitt overlay provides excellent surface and corrosion characteristics while the copper-lead provides the strength. If the babbitt should disappear, the copper-lead still makes a good bearing surface.

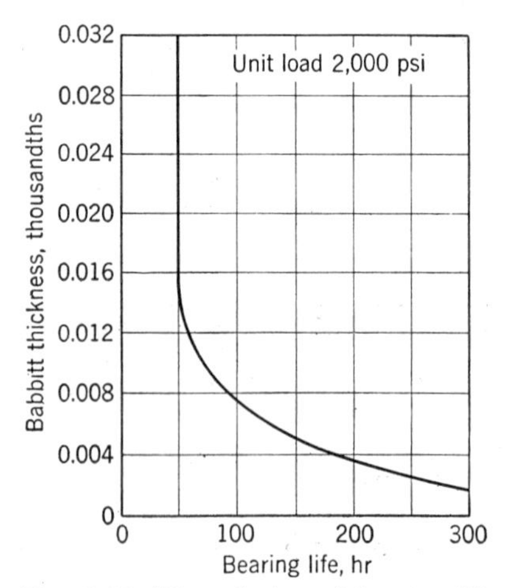

FIG. 9-31. The relation of bearing life to babbitt thickness. (*Courtesy of The Cleveland Graphite Bronze Company, Division of Clevite Corporation.*)

Small bushings and thrust collars are often expected to run with thin-film lubrication. When this is the case, improvements over a solid bearing material can be made to add significantly to the life. A powder-metallurgy bushing is porous and permits the oil to penetrate into the bushing material. Sometimes such a bushing may be enclosed by oil-soaked material to provide additional storage space. Bearings are frequently ball-indented in order to provide small basins for the storage of lubricant while the journal is at rest. This supplies some lubrication during starting. Another method of reducing friction is to indent the bearing wall and to fill these indentations with graphite.

9-14. Journal-bearing Design. There are nearly as many methods of designing journal bearings as there are designers. Bearing design may be as simple as merely finding a standard-size low-cost bushing to fit both the shaft and the housing. The designer specifies this bushing, without making an analysis, because it fits. He writes an instruction sheet in which the user is told to squirt oil into the bearing occasionally, and the designer has acquitted his responsibilities. If the bearing fails, the user did not take care of it.

On the other hand, the design of, say, an aircraft-engine bearing might require a very careful design study. Details concerning the material, construction, assembly, and lubrication would be studied very closely. A whole series of relations between the variables might be obtained in order to plot curves showing the effect of changing each variable. In order to obtain the maximum reliability, the load-life curve would be studied closely and recommendations made for rebuilding after a specified number of engine hours.

In between these extremes there are a great many methods of design from which to choose, and so, on many occasions, the requirements of the problem will dictate a departure from the methods indicated here.

Decisions. As usual, the design is initiated by making a series of tentative decisions. When these have been made, the bearing is analyzed and the decisions altered in accordance with the results of the analysis. The design is then complete. The following information is usually available to assist in making these decisions:

1. The competitive situation.
2. The number of units to be manufactured.
3. The load and its characteristics, that is, whether steady or alternating, predictable or unpredictable.
4. The speed or speed characteristics.
5. Shaft and housing information. The drawings should be available, if possible, together with information concerning the possibility of making changes in these.
6. The method of lubrication, that is, whether force, splash, ring, or wick feed; the lubricant used and its operating temperature; and information concerning whether changes may be made in any of these.

With the preceding information available, the following tentative decisions must be made:

1. The bearing material and construction.
2. The method of analysis, that is, whether to use the hydrodynamic theory, experimental methods, or some other method.
3. The assumptions to be used in the analysis. For example, an assumption as to side leakage or temperature may be necessary.
4. The desired bearing life.
5. The design load. If the load is variable or unpredictable, an analysis may be necessary in order to obtain a load figure on which to base the design.
6. The bearing dimensions, r, l, c, β.
7. The viscosity to be used in the analysis.

These decisions fix, or determine, the bearing. The coefficient of friction, power loss, minimum film thickness, oil flow, and temperature rise are now calculated, using any of the procedures which have been demonstrated or any other procedure selected by the designer as appropriate to the particular problem. Upon completion of the analysis, the tentative decisions are adjusted in accordance with the results. This procedure is then repeated again and again until the independent variables have values which are satisfactory to the designer.

In a relatively simple design a single set of calculations may be sufficient. The designer uses the results of the analysis to alter his preliminary decisions and fixes the design at that point. This procedure is satisfactory for a relatively unimportant bearing application or when the designer has a background of experience upon which to base these alterations. However, in important applications the experienced designer will usually carry the design study to much greater detail than the beginner.

PROBLEMS

9-1. Using SAE 20 oil and Fig. 9-5, construct a viscosity-temperature chart for temperatures from 110 to 210°F. The viscosity should be in reyns and plotted as the ordinate.

9-2. Typical data for an SAE 30 oil are: 489 SUS at 100°F, 65 SUS at 210°F, 28.7 API gravity at 60°F. Plot this oil on ASTM chart paper, and use the resulting information to plot an absolute viscosity-temperature graph. The graph should show the viscosity in reyns for temperatures from 150 to 350°F. (After Slaymaker.)

9-3. Calculate the viscosity in reyns of SAE 40 oil at 180°F from Fig. 9-5.

9-4. What is the absolute viscosity (reyns) of SAE 10 oil at 130°F? Use Fig. 9-5.

9-5. A 360° bearing is 3 in. long and 2 in. in diameter. The bearing load is 1,000 lb, and the journal runs at 1,200 rpm. Using a clearance of 0.001 in. and an average viscosity of $(2)(10)^{-5}$ reyn, find the friction horsepower. Neglect end flow.

Ans.: 0.894 hp.

9-6. A 4-in.-diameter bearing is 8 in. long and has an arc of contact of 360°. The total load is 7,500 lb at 900 rpm. Using a radial clearance of 0.003 in., find the friction horsepower for the following oils: SAE 10, 20, 30, and 40. Use an operating temperature of 160°F. Neglect side leakage.

9-7. (*a*) Repeat Prob. 9-6 except use SAE 40 oil and the following radial clearances: 0.001 in., 0.0015 in., 0.002 in., 0.003 in., 0.004 in. (*b*) Plot a curve showing the relation between the coefficient of friction and the clearance.

9-8. A 3-in.-diameter bearing runs at 400 rpm, is 5½ in. long, and is subjected to a radial load of 1,200 lb. The bearing is lubricated with SAE 30 oil at an average operating temperature of 180°F. The radial clearance is 0.0014 in. Neglecting end flow, calculate the friction torque if (*a*) it is a 360° full bearing, and (*b*) if it is a 180° partial bearing.

9-9. Find the minimum film thickness for the bearings of Prob. 9-8.

9-10. A ¾-in.-diameter × 1¼-in.-long sleeve bearing supports a load of 600 lb at a speed of 3,600 rpm. Using SAE 10 oil at 160°F operating temperature, specify the radial clearance for an h_o/c value of 0.662. Neglect side leakage.

Ans.: 0.000619 in.

9-11. A 1⅛-in.-diameter sleeve bearing 2 in. long has a clearance of 0.001 in. and uses SAE 20 oil at an operating temperature of 140°F. The bearing supports a load of 750 lb. (*a*) Neglecting end flow, calculate the heat generated, in Btu per minute, for speeds of 1,000, 2,000, 3,000, and 4,000 rpm. (*b*) Plot a graph showing the relation between the journal speed and the heat generated.

9-12. Using the data of Prob. 9-11, calculate the temperature rise of the oil corresponding to each speed. Plot a curve showing the relation between temperature rise and speed. *Decisions:* Neglect end flow, assume the oil carries away all the heat generated, and assume the average operating temperature is 140°F for each speed.

9-13. A 180° ring-oiled partial bearing is 4 in. in diameter and 7½ in. long and is lubricated with SAE 30 oil. The radial clearance is 0.003 in., and the oil inlet temperature is 140°F. The journal speed is 480 rpm, and the bearing load is 2,400 lb. Find the oil outlet temperature. *Decisions:* Assume no end flow and a viscosity corresponding to the average of the inlet and outlet temperatures. Assume that the oil carries away all the generated heat. *Ans.:* 148°F.

9-14. A 1½-in.-diameter 120° partial bearing has a length of 3 in. and an r/c ratio of 1,000. The journal speed is 1,200 rpm. The oil is SAE 40 at an inlet temperature of 100°F. If the load is 1,500 lb, find the oil outlet temperature. *Decisions:* Same as for Prob. 9-13.

9-15. An SAE 20 oil at 100°F is used to lubricate a 360° bearing 3 in. long and 2 in. in diameter. The bearing load is 1,400 lb, and the speed is 1,200 rpm. Using an r/c ratio of 1,000, find the friction horsepower. *Ans.:* 0.452 hp.

9-16. A sleeve bearing is 1¼ in. in diameter and 1½ in. long. The shaft rotates at 1,750 rpm and subjects the bearing to a radial load of 250 lb. The clearance is 0.00075 in. Using SAE 30 oil at an initial temperature of 100°F, determine the temperature rise of the bearing and the minimum film thickness.

9-17. Repeat Prob. 9-16 for SAE 10, 20, and 40 oils, and compare the results.

9-18. A 1¾-in.-diameter bearing is 2³⁄₃₂ in. long and has a central annular oil groove which is fed by a pressure system. The oil is SAE 20 at 140°F supply temperature and 30 psi pressure. The radial clearance is 0.003 in. The journal rotates at 3,000 rpm, and the average load is 500 psi of projected bearing area. Find the temperature rise and the minimum oil-film thickness.

9-19. An eight-cylinder diesel engine has a front main bearing 3½ in. in diameter × 1⅝ in. long. The bearing has a central annular groove 0.225 in. wide. It is pressure-lubricated with SAE 30 oil at an inlet temperature of 180°F and at a supply pressure of 50 psi. Using a unit load of 390 psi and a speed of 2,800 rpm, find the temperature rise and the minimum oil-film thickness corresponding to a radial clearance of 0.0025 in.

***9-20.** Using the data of Prob. 9-19, calculate the minimum film thickness and the temperature rise for radial clearances from 0.001 to 0.005 in. in steps of 0.0005 in. Plot curves showing the relation between the maximum temperature ($T + \Delta T$) and the clearance and between the minimum film thickness and the clearance. Recommend a suitable clearance for a clearance range of 0.0014 in.

***9-21 to 9-35.** A manufacturer has decided to go into the business of manufacturing self-aligning general-purpose pillow blocks. He has tentatively selected an l/d ratio of 2 and a ring-oiling system with oil storage in the base of the pillow block. The business is competitive, and he believes that his engineering department has the talent necessary to design a better bearing that will sell at a lower price. The accompanying table lists the shaft sizes for which the pillow blocks are to be made, the price of a competitor's product, and the probable sales for the first year of production. A complete design is required which is to include layout drawings, specifications, and a catalogue page listing the capacity and size of the bearing.

Problem No.	Shaft size, in.	Competitor's list price	Probable sales first year
9-21	$1\frac{7}{16}$	$ 51.75	10,000
9-22	$1\frac{11}{16}$	57.50	4,200
9-23	$1\frac{15}{16}$	62.50	2,000
9-24	$2\frac{3}{16}$	69.00	800
9-25	$2\frac{7}{16}$	80.50	360
9-26	$2\frac{11}{16}$	103.75	170
9-27	$2\frac{15}{16}$	121.00	88
9-28	$3\frac{7}{16}$	138.00	48
9-29	$3\frac{15}{16}$	184.00	28
9-30	$4\frac{7}{16}$	332.50	16
9-31	$4\frac{15}{16}$	400.00	10
9-32	$5\frac{7}{16}$	500.00	8
9-33	6	610.00	6
9-34	7	750.00	4
9-35	8	925.00	2

CHAPTER 10

SPUR GEARS

Whenever rotary motion must be transferred from one shaft to another, gears should be considered as one of the possible means. They have the advantage of a positive and a constant velocity ratio.[1]

Modern demands for greater loads and higher speeds, with the conflicting requirement of weight reduction, require that the machine designer

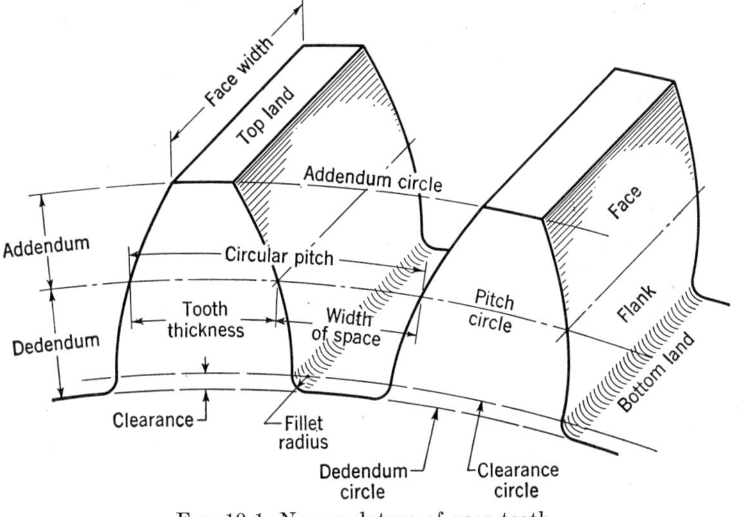

FIG. 10-1. Nomenclature of gear teeth.

be fully informed on current design practices. This must include a knowledge not only of materials, fatigue, and manufacturing methods as applied to gears but also of the accepted methods of analysis and design.

10-1. Introduction. A spur gear is one having teeth parallel to the axis of the gear. The nomenclature is shown in Fig. 10-1.

The design of spur gears to transmit rotary motion at a constant ratio is fundamental to the design of all gears. It is assumed that the reader has had an introduction to the kinematics of gearing, and for this reason only a brief review will be given here.

[1] A geared drive may also be made with a specified variable velocity ratio. See any elementary text on kinematics of machines.

In approaching the problem of designing meshing teeth on wheels to transmit power at a constant ratio, we must remember again that all materials are elastic. Also, masses traveling at high speeds possess inertia and require the application of forces to overcome that inertia. The result of these forces, whether static or dynamic, is to create deflections of these elastic materials. We have already learned that a deflection is the visible evidence of internal stress. The problem of gearing is so complex that it is impossible to reduce all the static and dynamic deflections into simple stress equations. Although a tremendous amount of very difficult investigation has resulted in important contributions, the field is still wide open. The designer should make every effort to visualize the flow of elastic disturbances in the action of gear teeth and the connected masses. With this as a background, he should be in a sound position to take advantage of the peculiarities of each design.

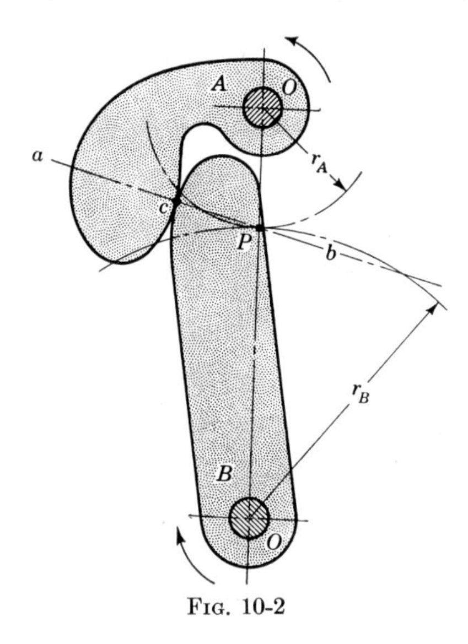

FIG. 10-2

10-2. Conjugate Action. The following discussion assumes the teeth to be perfectly formed, perfectly smooth, and absolutely rigid. Such an assumption is, of course, impossible, because of the limitations of the machinery used to form the teeth and because the application of forces will cause deflections.

Mating gear teeth acting against each other to produce rotary motion are similar to cams. When the tooth profiles, or cams, are designed so as to produce a constant angular-velocity ratio during meshing, they are said to have *conjugate action*. In theory, at least, it is possible arbitrarily to select any profile for one tooth and then to find a profile for the meshing tooth which will give conjugate action. One of these solutions is the *involute* profile, which, with few exceptions, is in universal use for gear teeth and is the only one with which we shall be concerned.

When one curved surface pushes against another (Fig. 10-2), the point of contact occurs where the two surfaces are tangent to each other (point c), and the forces at any instant are directed along the common normal ab to the two curves. The line ab, representing the direction of action of the forces, is called the *line of action*. The line of action will intersect the line of centers O-O at some point P. The angular-velocity ratio between the two arms is inversely proportional to their radii to the point P. Circles drawn through point P from each center are called *pitch circles*, and the radius of each circle is called the *pitch radius*. Point P is called the *pitch point*.

In order to transmit motion at a constant angular velocity the pitch point must remain fixed; that is, all the lines of action for every instantaneous point of contact must pass through the same point P. In the case of the involute profile it will be shown that all points of contact occur on the same straight line ab, that all normals to the tooth profiles at the point of contact coincide with the line ab, and, thus, that these profiles transmit uniform rotary motion.

10-3. Involute Properties. An involute curve may be generated as shown in Fig. 10-3. A partial flange B is attached to the cylinder A,

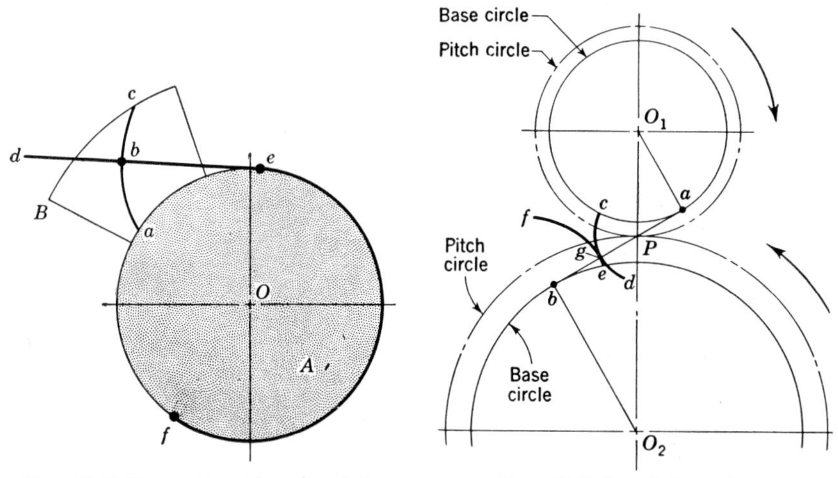

Fig. 10-3. Generation of an involute.

Fig. 10-4. Involute action.

around which is wrapped a cord def which is held tightly. Point b on the cord represents the tracing point, and, as the cord is wrapped and unwrapped about the cylinder, point b will trace out the involute curve ac. The radius of curvature of the involute varies continuously, being zero at point a and a maximum at point c. At point b the radius is equal to the distance be, since point b is instantaneously rotating about point e. Thus the generating line de is normal to the involute at all points of intersection and, at the same time, is always tangent to the cylinder A.

Let us now examine the involute profile to see how it satisfies the requirement for the transmission of uniform motion. In Fig. 10-4 two gear blanks with fixed centers at O_1 and O_2 are shown having base circles whose respective radii are O_1a and O_2b. We now imagine that a cord is wound clockwise around the base circle of gear 1, pulled tightly between points a and b, and wound counterclockwise around the base circle of gear 2. If, now, the base circles are rotated in different directions so as to keep the cord tight, a point g on the cord will trace out the involutes cd on gear 1 and ef on gear 2. The involutes are thus generated simultaneously by the tracing point. The tracing point, therefore, represents the point of contact, while the portion of the cord ab is the generating line. The point of contact moves along the generating line, the generating line does not change position because it is always tangent to the base circles, and, since the generating line is always normal to the involutes at the point of contact, the requirement for uniform motion is satisfied.

10-4. Fundamentals. In laying out a pair of gears, the first step is to locate the centers and draw the pitch circles (Fig. 10-5). The dimen-

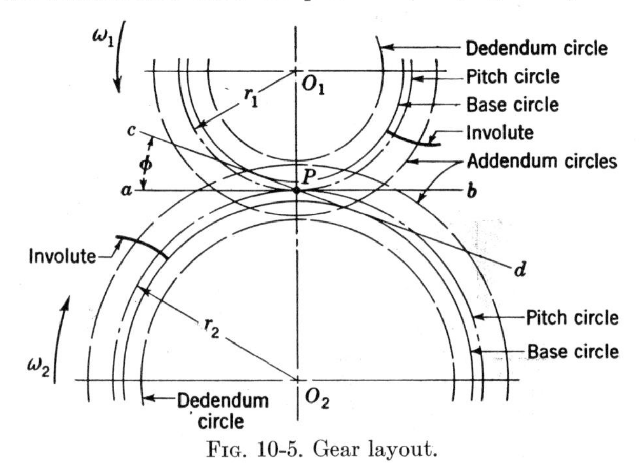

FIG. 10-5. Gear layout.

sions of gears are based on the pitch circle; usually, when a gear is spoken of as so many inches in diameter, this is assumed to be the diameter of the pitch circle. If the radii of the two gears are designated by r_1 and r_2, respectively, and the angular velocities by ω_1 and ω_2, and if we imagine the two pitch circles to roll on one another without slipping, the linear pitch-line velocity is

$$V = r_1\omega_1 = r_2\omega_2$$

This gives the relation between the radii and the angular velocities:

$$\frac{\omega_1}{\omega_2} = \frac{r_2}{r_1} \tag{10-1}$$

This relation may also be written as

$$\frac{n_1}{n_2} = \frac{D_2}{D_1} \tag{10-2}$$

where n designates the rpm and D the pitch diameter.

The next step in laying out the gears (Fig. 10-5) is to draw line ab

through the pitch point P and perpendicular to the line of centers. We now designate gear 1 as the driver, and, since it is rotating counterclockwise, we draw a line cd through point P at an angle ϕ to line ab. The line cd is called the *pressure line*, the generating line, and the line of action. It represents the direction in which the resultant force acts between the gears. The angle ϕ is called the *pressure angle*, and it usually has values of $14\frac{1}{2}$ or 20°.

The next step is to draw the *base circles* in each gear tangent to the pressure line. Since they must be tangent to the pressure line, the pressure angle determines their size. The base circles are used to generate the involute profile and, therefore, conjugate action can be secured only in the space between them. Portions of the tooth extending below them are usually made radial.

An involute is now generated on each base circle, using methods which are described in any kinematics or engineering-drawing text. This involute may be generated in either direction, because a template will be used which can be turned over to obtain the other side of the tooth.

We must now define the term *pitch*. The pitch of a gear tooth is the number of teeth on the gear per inch of pitch diameter. It is defined by the following equation:

$$P = \frac{N}{D} \tag{10-3}$$

where P = pitch
N = number of teeth
D = pitch diameter

Its full name is *diametral pitch* (DP), but it is often abbreviated to "pitch" by the profession.

The *circular pitch*, which is never abbreviated, is the sum of the tooth space and tooth width measured on the pitch circle. In other words, it is the distance from a point on one tooth to the same point on the adjacent tooth when measured on the pitch circle. It can be expressed in equation form by dividing the circumference of the pitch circle by the number of teeth. Thus,

$$p = \frac{\pi D}{N} \tag{10-4}$$

where p is the circular pitch.

We note that the circular pitch is a linear dimension, and so it is measured in inches. These units should always be given when designating the circular pitch. It helps to identify the pitch and to avoid confusion. Note that diametral pitch has units of 1/in. These units are seldom used. The designer prefers to use diametral pitch as a pure number without units. By combining Eqs. (10-3) and (10-4) we obtain the useful relation

$$pP = \pi \tag{10-5}$$

Figure 10-6 is included to give a visual indication of the relative sizes of teeth of different pitches.

The *addendum* is the distance the tooth extends outside the pitch circle (Fig. 10-1). The *dedendum* is the distance from the pitch circle to the

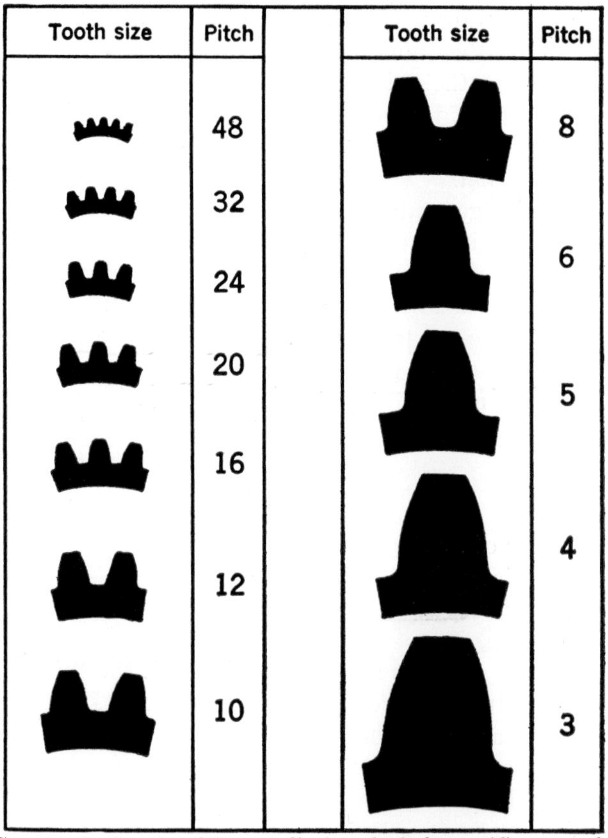

Tooth size	Pitch	Tooth size	Pitch
	48		8
	32		6
	24		5
	20		4
	16		3
	12		
	10		

FIG. 10-6. Gear-teeth sizes for different diametral pitches. (*Courtesy of Boston Gear Works, Inc.*)

bottom land and is equal to the addendum plus an allowance for *clearance*. These distances are usually standard and depend upon the tooth system in use. The addendum and dedendum circles can now be constructed for each gear (Fig. 10-5).

The last step is to mark off the tooth spaces and widths on each pitch circle. These are usually constructed equal to each other, which would be one-half the circular pitch. Using templates cut to fit the involute curves, and with centers at O_1 and O_2, the tooth profiles can now be constructed. The *fillet radius*, at the bottom of the tooth, is usually equal to, or slightly greater than, the clearance.

Angle of Action. Referring now to Fig. 10-7, the gear with its center at O_1 is the driver and turns counterclockwise. Contact will occur along the pressure line. The initial contact will take place when the flank of the driver comes into contact with the tip of the driven tooth. This occurs at point a where the addendum of the driven gear crosses the pressure line. If we now construct tooth profiles through point a and draw

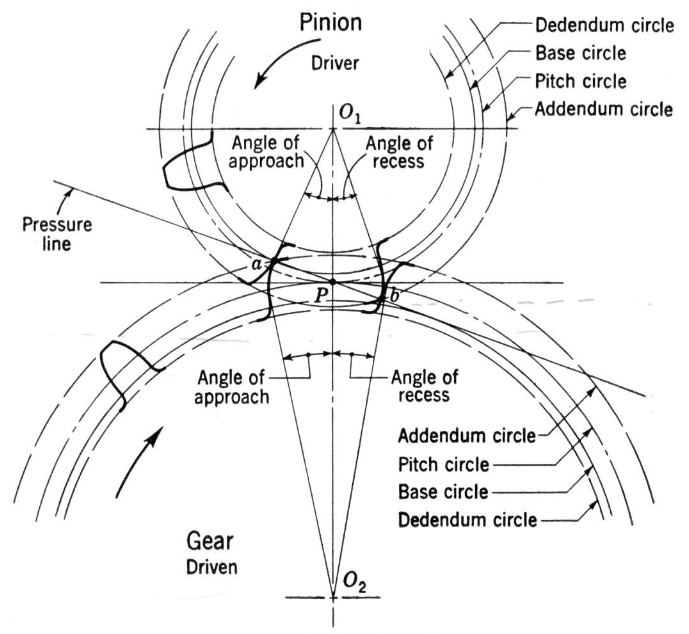

FIG. 10-7. Tooth action.

lines from the intersection of the tooth profiles with the pitch circles to the centers, we obtain the *angles of approach* for each gear.

As the teeth go into mesh, the point of contact will slide up the side of the driving tooth so that the tip of the driver will be in contact just before contact ends. The final point of contact will, therefore, be where the addendum of the driver crosses the line of action. This is point b in Fig. 10-7. Following a similar procedure as before, we obtain the *angles of recess* for each gear. The sum of these two angles is called the *angle of action.*

Interference. In Fig. 10-8 points b and d represent the points of tangency of the base circle with the pressure line. In the case of gear 1, the pinion, the base circle has a relatively large diameter, a considerable portion of the tooth exists below this circle, and contact should not occur on this portion because it is not conjugate. However, the initial point of contact *a* is outside the point of tangency *b*, so that the tip of the driven tooth is forced into contact with the flank of the driver below the base circle. Since this portion of the flank is not of involute shape, conjugate action is not secured. This is called *interference.* Contact ends at point *c*, which is inside the point of tangency *d*, and in this case there is no interference on the tip of the driver.

When the tooth profiles are *generated* by the cutting tools there is no interference, because the flank of the driver is undercut. Since this

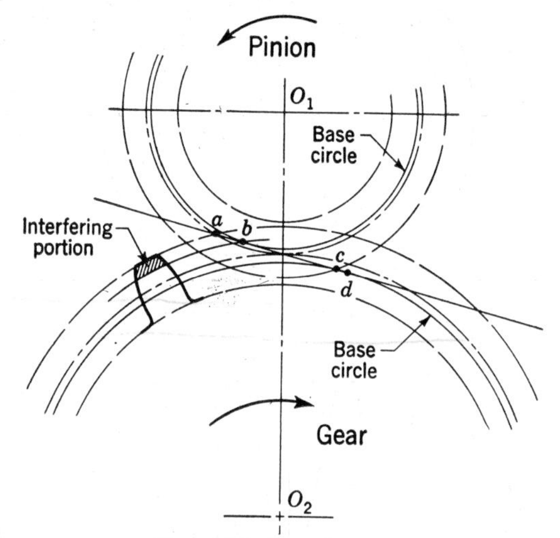

FIG. 10-8. Interference.

weakens the tooth which is already the weakest, a better solution is to cut off the tips of the driven teeth, as shown in Fig. 10-8.

Interference can also be reduced by using a larger pressure angle. This results in a smaller base circle, so that more of the tooth profile becomes involute. The demand for smaller pinions with fewer teeth thus favors the 20° pressure-angle system even though the frictional forces and bearing loads are increased.

Contact Ratio. In order for contact to be continuous, the angle of action must be larger than the angle subtended by the circular pitch. Otherwise there would be an interval of time during which no teeth would be in contact. Calling the angle subtended by the circular pitch the *pitch angle,* then the *contact ratio* is defined as the angle of action divided by the pitch angle.

A contact ratio of unity means that one pair of teeth are engaged at all times, while a contact ratio of 2 would mean that two teeth are engaged at all times. If the ratio is 1.5, it indicates that two teeth are engaged for 50 per cent of the time. For satisfactory performance of spur gears, the contact ratio should be 1.4 or greater, unless the speeds are low.

10-5. Cutting Methods. The cutting of gear teeth is usually performed either by *forming* cutters or by *generating* cutters. In form cutting, the tooth space takes the exact shape of the cutter. In generating, a tool having a shape different from the tooth profile is moved relative to the gear to be generated so that the proper tooth shape is obtained.

Gear teeth may be shaped by milling, shaping, or hobbing. They may be finished by shaving, burnishing, grinding, or lapping.

FIG. 10-9. Generating a spur gear with a pinion cutter. *(Courtesy of Boston Gear Works, Inc.)*

Milling. Gear teeth may be cut with a form milling cutter shaped to conform to the tooth space. With this method it is theoretically necessary to use a different cutter for each gear, because a gear having 25 teeth, for example, will have a different-shaped tooth space than one having, say, 24 teeth. Actually, the change in space is not too great, and it has been found that eight cutters may be used to cut with reasonable accuracy any gear in the range of 12 teeth to a rack. A separate set of cutters is, of course, required for each pitch.

Shaping. Teeth may be generated with either a pinion cutter or a rack cutter. The pinion cutter (Fig. 10-9) reciprocates along the vertical axis and is slowly fed into the gear blank to the required depth. When the pitch circles are tangent, both the cutter and blank rotate slightly after each cutting stroke. Since each tooth of the cutter is a cutting tool, the teeth are all cut after the blank has completed one revolution.

The sides of an involute rack tooth are straight. For this reason, a rack generating tool provides an accurate method of cutting gear teeth. This is also a shaping operation and is illustrated by the drawing of Fig. 10-10. In operation, the cutter reciprocates and is first fed into the gear blank until the pitch circles are tangent. Then, after each cutting stroke, the gear blank and cutter roll slightly on their pitch circles. When the blank and cutter have rolled a distance equal to the circular pitch, the cutter is returned to the starting point, and the process is continued until all the teeth have been cut.

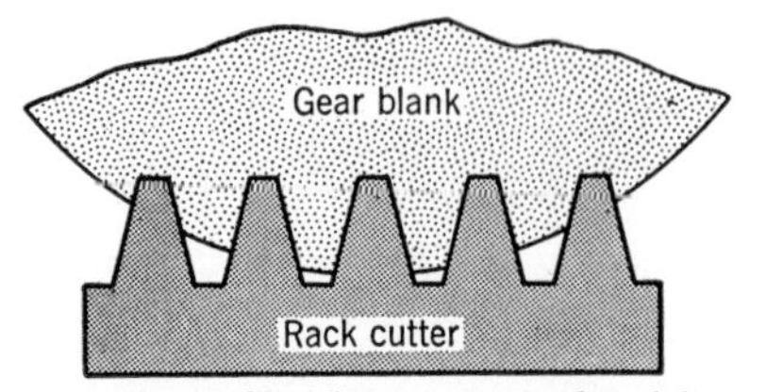

FIG. 10-10. Shaping gear teeth with a rack cutter.

FIG. 10-11. Hobbing a worm gear. (*Courtesy of Boston Gear Works, Inc.*)

Hobbing. The hobbing process is illustrated in Fig. 10-11. The hob is simply a cutting tool which is shaped like a worm. The teeth have straight sides, as in a rack, but the hob axis must be turned through the lead angle in order to cut spur-gear teeth. For this reason, the teeth generated by a hob have a slightly different shape than those generated by a rack cutter. Both the hob and the blank must be rotated at the proper angular-velocity ratio. The hob is then fed slowly across the face of the blank until all the teeth have been cut.

Finishing. Gears which run at high speeds and transmit large forces may be subjected to additional dynamic forces due to errors in tooth profiles. These errors may be diminished somewhat by finishing the tooth profiles. The teeth may be finished, after cutting, either by shaving or burnishing. Several shaving machines are available which cut off a minute amount of metal, bringing the accuracy of the tooth profile within the limits of 0.00025 in.

Burnishing, like shaving, is used with gears which have been cut but not heat-treated. In burnishing, hardened gears with slightly oversize teeth are run in mesh with the gear until the surfaces become smooth.

Grinding and lapping are used for hardened gear teeth after heat-treatment. The grinding operation employs the generating principle and produces very accurate teeth. In lapping, the teeth of the gear and lap slide axially so that the whole surface of the teeth is abraded equally.

10-6. Tooth Systems. A knowledge of the various tooth systems available is a prerequisite to obtaining an economical and long-lasting

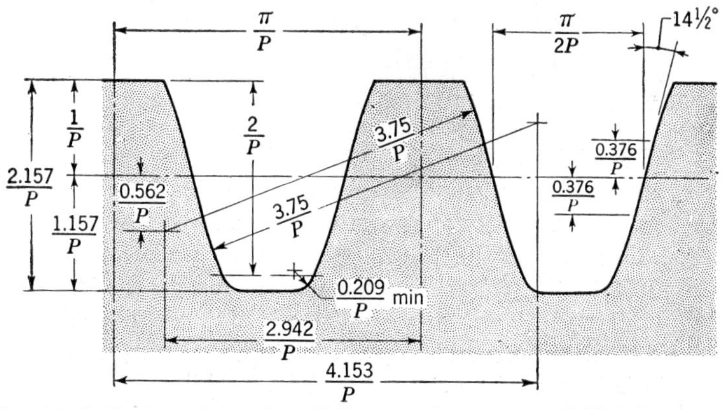

FIG. 10-12. Basic rack for the 14½° composite system. (*ASA Standard.*)

gear. Some of the systems offer the advantages of interchangeability along with low tool cost. When high dynamic strength and wear resistance are important considerations, then interchangeability may have to be sacrificed in order to take advantage of some of the special systems. Special systems may also have to be used when the gears are to be placed in a very small space. All these factors, as well as others to be discussed, must be considered before the designer chooses the tooth system to be used.

The 14½° Composite System. This is a full-depth tooth having the proportions shown in Fig. 10-12. It is a standard system, all gears of a single pitch are interchangeable, and the teeth are produced by form milling cutters. It is called a composite tooth because the profile combines both involute and cycloidal curves in order to minimize interference. Cutters are available to produce gears with as few as 12 teeth. Such gears have no interference because the effect of the cycloidal portion of the tooth profile is to relieve interference. However, the contact ratio is so low that only slow speeds may be used. Even gears having a favorable contact ratio should not be run at high speeds, because of the inherent inaccuracy of this method of cutting. The chief advantage of the 14½° composite system is that it uses tools and machines found even in the smallest shops.

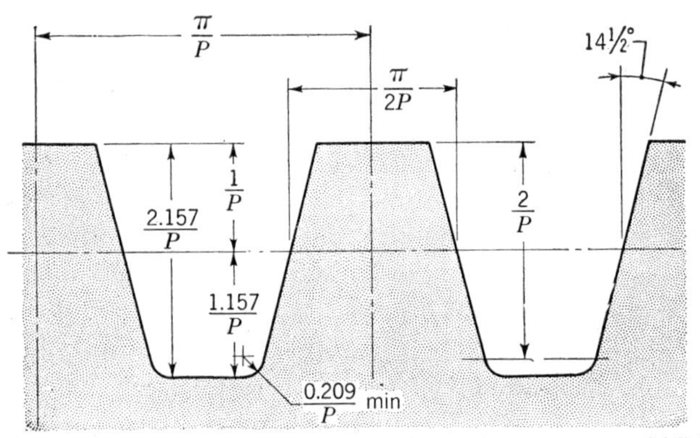

FIG. 10-13. Basic rack for the 14½° full-depth involute system. (*ASA Standard.*)

The 14½° *Full-depth Involute System.* This system provides interchangeable gears having generated teeth. The tooth proportions are shown in Fig. 10-13. Interference is eliminated because the teeth are generated. This causes the pinion teeth to be undercut when there are less than 32 teeth. If the number is less than 22, the teeth become excessively undercut. The contact ratio is 1.4 for two 22-tooth gears in mesh. If the tooth number of either or both gears is increased, then the contact ratio is increased accordingly. The hobbing process is usually used for gears of this system.

The 20° *Full-depth Involute System.* This system also features interchangeability with teeth obtained by generation. Because of the larger pressure angle, the line of action is longer and the base circles are smaller, so that fewer teeth may be used with less undercutting. The tooth proportions for the basic rack are illustrated in Fig. 10-14. With this system, undercutting begins at 18 teeth and becomes excessive if fewer than 14 teeth are used. For two 14-tooth gears in mesh the contact ratio is 1.4.

It is useful to compare the 20° with the 14½° system. Assuming 1P pinions of the smallest size in each system, we should obtain a 22-in.

pinion in the 14½° system and a 14-in. pinion in the 20° system. The latter system, therefore, gives a pinion which is 36 per cent (8/22) smaller if other conditions are equal. Assuming the same shaft rpm, the pitch-line velocity would be correspondingly reduced, which is of considerable

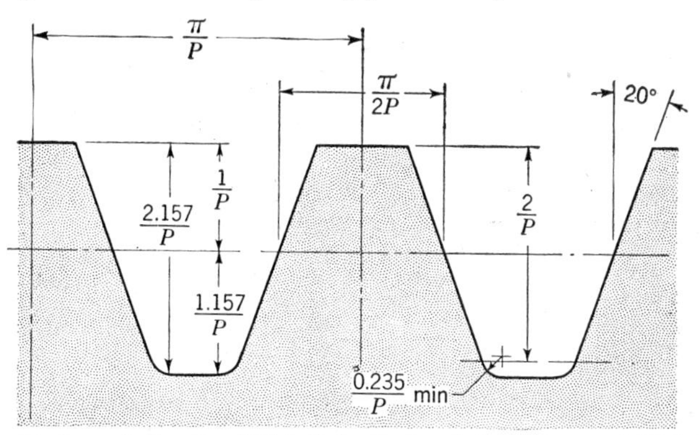

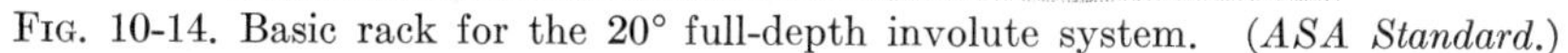

FIG. 10-14. Basic rack for the 20° full-depth involute system. (*ASA Standard.*)

value. On the other hand, the larger pressure angle increases the tooth and bearing loads and also the friction between the teeth. It is also true that 20° gears are noisier than the 14½° gears and should probably be run at slower speeds.

The 20° Full-depth Involute System for Small Pinions. In many cases it is necessary to obtain a pinion with only a few teeth. Ordinarily this

TABLE 10-1. TOOTH PROPORTIONS OF 1-DP SMALL HOBBED PINIONS*

Number of teeth	Pitch diameter	Outside diameter	Root diameter	Base-circle diameter
5	5.00	7.916	4.1012	4.69846
6	6.00	9.018	4.9440	5.63816
7	7.00	10.038	5.7868	6.57784
8	8.00	10.944	6.6294	7.51754
9	9.00	11.786	7.4722	8.45724
10	10.00	12.628	8.3150	9.39692
11	11.00	13.472	9.1578	10.33662
12	12.00	14.314	10.0004	11.27632
13	13.00	15.156	10.8432	12.21600

* Earle Buckingham, "Manual of Gear Design," sec. 2, p. 97, The Industrial Press, New York, 1935.

results in a tooth which is excessively undercut, but this may be minimized by using a larger pinion diameter. This increase in pinion diameter must be compensated for by increasing the center distance. The gears are cut by hobbing, using the 20° full-depth involute system. Table 10-1 gives some of the tooth proportions for 1-DP pinions, and

Table 10-2 gives the increase in center distance. These values must be divided by the actual pitch in order to obtain the correct dimensions in inches.

With the small-pinion system a five-tooth pinion driving a 20-tooth gear gives a contact ratio of 1.04, while a 10- and 15-tooth combination gives a ratio of 1.32.

The 20° Stub Involute System. We have already seen that when full-depth teeth are used with small tooth numbers, undercutting results

TABLE 10-2. INCREASE IN CENTER DISTANCE FOR 1-DP PINIONS*

Number of gear teeth	Number of pinion teeth								
	5	6	7	8	9	10	11	12	13
15	...	...	...	...	...	0.291	0.222	0.151	0.077
20	0.610	0.551	0.490	0.427	0.362	0.294	0.225	0.152	0.077
25	0.622	0.560	0.497	0.432	0.366	0.297	0.226	0.153	0.077
30	0.631	0.568	0.503	0.437	0.369	0.299	0.227	0.153	0.078
40	0.644	0.578	0.511	0.443	0.373	0.301	0.228	0.154	0.078
50	0.653	0.586	0.517	0.447	0.376	0.303	0.230	0.154	0.078
100	0.676	0.604	0.531	0.457	0.383	0.308	0.233	0.155	0.078
200	0.690	0.615	0.540	0.464	0.387	0.311	0.234	0.156	0.079
500	0.700	0.624	0.547	0.469	0.391	0.313	0.234	0.158	0.079

* Earle Buckingham, "Manual of Gear Design," sec. 2, p. 97, The Industrial Press, New York, 1935.

because of interference. Although this can be alleviated somewhat by increasing the pressure angle, there is a limit to how far we can go in this direction. To eliminate the interference we can cut off the top of the interfering tooth. When we do this, we might just as well decrease the dedendum correspondingly in order to maintain the same clearance. This process results in a stub tooth. The basic rack for the ASA Standard stub tooth is shown in Fig. 10-15.

With this system, undercutting is seldom encountered. The greatest problem is the contact ratio. For example, the contact ratio for a pair of 12-tooth gears is 1.18. If a 12-tooth pinion is used with a gear of 20 teeth or more, the contact ratio is 1.24, which is not too unsatisfactory. The stub teeth do have the important advantage of greater strength because of the shorter tooth form. However, this advantage may be lost because of the increase in dynamic load due to the smaller angle of action. The shorter tooth results in less sliding action, and hence less wear will take place.

The Fellows Gear Shaper Company Stub System. This tooth system was widely used before standardization of stub teeth and, hence, is still in considerable use. The pitch is designated as a fraction, as, for example, 5/7, read "five-seven." The numerator is used to obtain the pitch diameter and circular pitch. The denominator is used in the full-depth equations to obtain the tooth height, that is, the addendum, dedendum, and clearance. Standard cutters are available for generating the following pitches: 4/5, 5/7, 6/8, 7/9, 8/10, 9/11, 10/12, and 12/14.

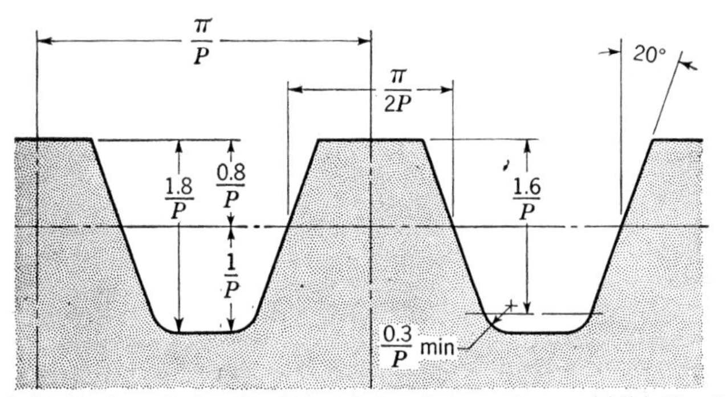

FIG. 10-15. Basic rack for the 20° stub involute system. (*ASA Standard.*)

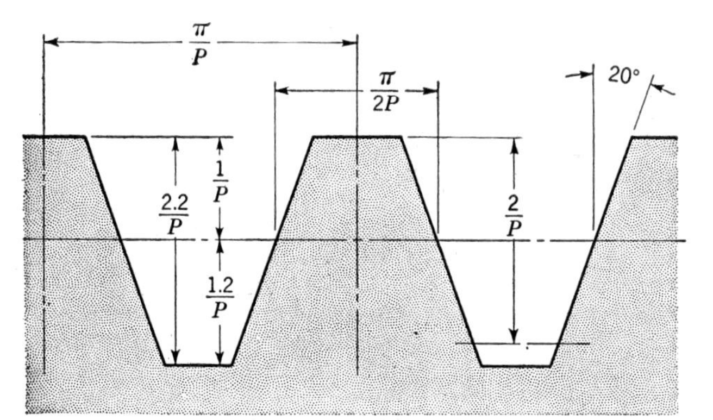

FIG. 10-16. Basic rack for the 20° involute fine-pitch system. (*ASA Standard.*)

The 20° Involute Fine-pitch System. Gears of 20-DP and finer should have a larger clearance. The reasons for this are the additional wear on the point of the generating tool, which causes an increased fillet radius and a reduced clearance, and the foreign matter which may accumulate at the bottom of the teeth. The proportions are shown in Fig. 10-16.

As in the 20° involute full-depth system, pinions with as few as seven teeth may be used by enlarging the blank. The appropriate dimensions are given in the ASA Standard.[1]

[1] 20 Degree Involute Fine-pitch System for Spur and Helical Gears, *AGMA Publ.* 207.03, July, 1950.

Systems for Nonmetallic Gears. Phenolic laminated materials and other relatively soft materials used as driving pinions have a low modulus of elasticity. The result of this is that errors of tooth form and spacing are absorbed by these materials[1] and, therefore, do not affect the value of the dynamic load or the strength of the gears. It is important with these materials to decrease the wear which occurs in the angle of approach.

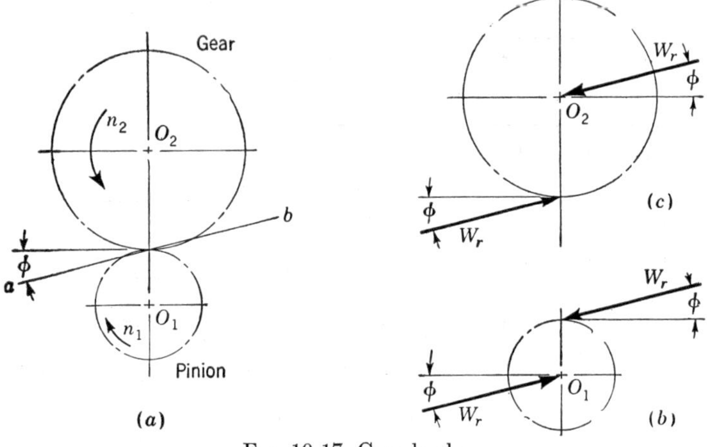

FIG. 10-17. Gear loads.

This is done by making the nonmetallic pinion all addendum, while the driven gear is of conventional form. To do this, the center distance must be changed. It is usual to use the 20° stub-tooth system and to cut the gears by hobbing. Buckingham states that such a drive will carry from 50 to 75 per cent more load.[2]

10-7. Loads. Figure 10-17*a* shows a pinion with center at O_1, rotating clockwise at n_1 rpm, and driving a gear with center at O_2 at a speed of n_2 rpm. The resultant forces take place along the pressure line *ab* with the pinion teeth pushing against the gear teeth. In Fig. 10-17*b* the pinion has been separated from the gear and its action replaced by the resultant load W_r, which is directed along the pressure line. Since the pinion is supported by its shaft, we may replace the action of the shaft

[1] The low modulus of elasticity for these materials (about 1,000,000 psi) means that, for the same load, a nonmetallic material will deform about twenty or thirty times more than cast iron or steel. This not only prevents transmission of vibrations to the shafting but also tends to make the teeth share the load more equally. Although the strength of these materials is only a small fraction of that of steel, in some applications it has been found that they will carry the same load as an unhardened steel gear of the same size, because of the reduction in the dynamic load.

[2] Earle Buckingham, "Manual of Gear Design," sec. 2, p. 150, The Industrial Press, New York, 1935.

by another load W_r, oppositely directed and acting at the center of the shaft. The two loads constitute a couple. By similar reasoning, we obtain the forces and their directions for the gear (Fig. 10-17c).

Considering the pinion alone, let us divide the load W_r into its tangential and radial components. This has been done in Fig. 10-18, which shows the tangential component W and the radial component R. It is thus seen that the radial component serves no useful purpose in the transmission of power but acts only to separate the gears. Designating the pitch-line velocity by V, where $V = \pi D n_1/12$ and is in feet per minute, the tangential force may be obtained from the equation

$$\text{hp} = \frac{WV}{33{,}000} \qquad (10\text{-}6)$$

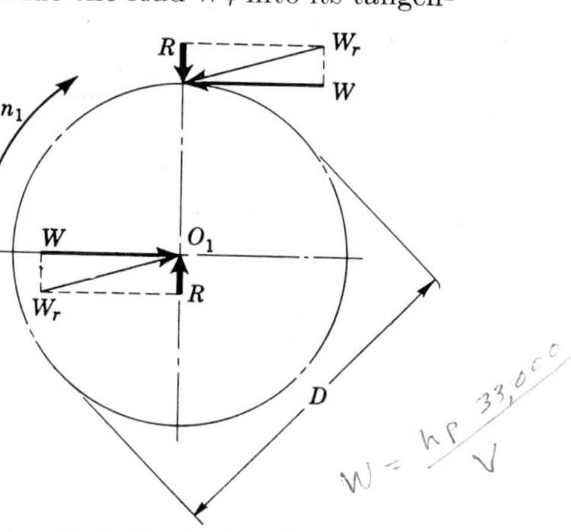

FIG. 10-18. Resolution of gear forces.

The following relations are evident from Fig. 10-18:

$$R = W \tan \phi \qquad \text{and} \qquad W_r = \frac{W}{\cos \phi} \qquad (10\text{-}7)$$

The torque is

$$T = W \frac{D}{2} \qquad (10\text{-}8)$$

where T is in inch-pounds and D is the pitch diameter in inches.

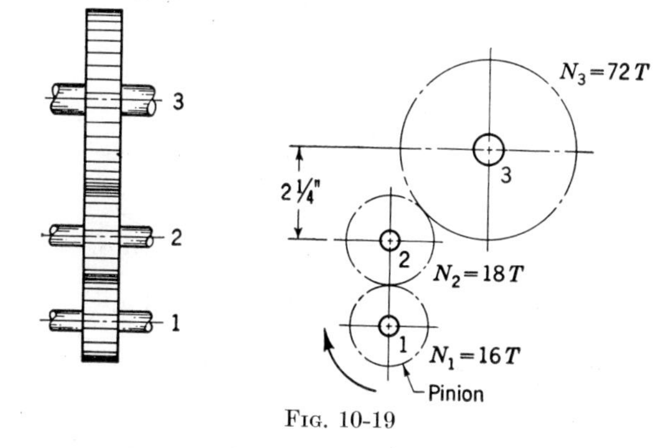

FIG. 10-19

EXAMPLE 10-1. A 16-tooth 8-pitch 20° full-depth pinion rotates clockwise at 1,725 rpm and transmits 4 hp to the gear train shown in Fig. 10-19. (a) Using the tooth numbers shown, find the speed of each shaft. (b) Find the pitch-line velocity. (c) Calculate the tangential tooth load at each pitch point. (d) Determine the resultant reaction at each shaft and its direction. (*e*) How much torque is transmitted by shaft 3?

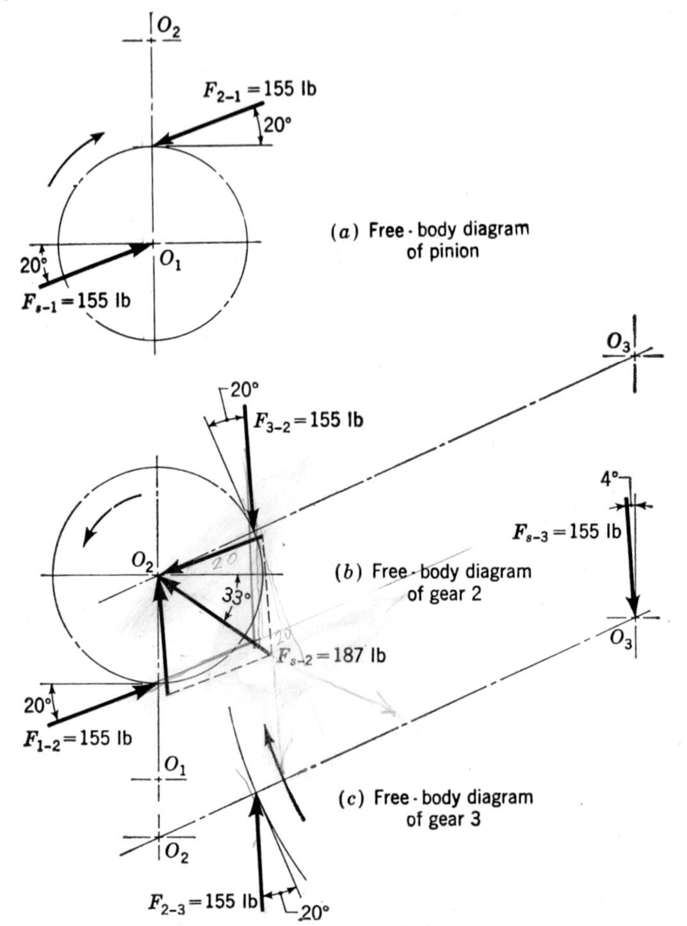

FIG. 10-20. Determination of shaft reactions.

Solution. *a.* The shaft speeds are found as follows:

$$n_2 = n_1 \frac{N_1}{N_2} = 1{,}725 \frac{16}{18} = 1{,}630 \text{ rpm} \qquad \textit{Ans.}$$

$$n_3 = n_2 \frac{N_2}{N_3} = 1{,}630 \frac{18}{72} = 407 \text{ rpm} \qquad \textit{Ans.}$$

b. The diameters of the gears are found from the tooth numbers and the diametral pitch:

$$D_1 = \frac{N_1}{P} = \frac{16}{8} = 2 \text{ in.}$$

$$D_2 = \frac{N_2}{P} = \frac{18}{8} = 2.25 \text{ in.}$$

$$D_3 = \frac{N_3}{P} = \frac{72}{8} = 9 \text{ in.}$$

Using the speed and diameter of the pinion, the pitch-line velocity is

$$V = \frac{\pi D_1 n_1}{12} = \frac{(\pi)(2)(1{,}725)}{12} = 905 \text{ fpm} \qquad \textit{Ans.}$$

c. If we assume that gear 2 is an idler, then all the power is transferred from the pinion to gear 3. The tangential tooth load at each pitch point is, therefore, the same. Rearranging Eq. (10-6), we obtain

$$W = \frac{33{,}000 \text{ hp}}{V} = \frac{(33{,}000)(4)}{905} = 146 \text{ lb} \qquad \textit{Ans.}$$

d. Using Eq. (10-7), the resultant tooth load is

$$W_r = \frac{W}{\cos \phi} = \frac{146}{\cos 20°} = 155 \text{ lb}$$

In order to determine the shaft loads and directions, it is necessary to draw a free-body diagram of each gear. The centers of the adjacent meshing gears should be indicated (Fig. 10-20). Referring to the figure, *a* is the free-body diagram of the pinion, and, since the pinion is rotating clockwise, the gear must push the pinion downward and to the left with a force $F_{2-1} = 155$ lb. The shaft must oppose this force. The shaft reaction F_{S-1} is, therefore, 155 lb and has the direction shown.

The free-body diagram for gear 2 is drawn with center distances and forces to scale in Fig. 10-20*b*. The pinion pushes against this gear with a force $F_{1-2} = 155$ lb, in the direction shown. Gear 3 also pushes with a force $F_{3-2} = 155$ lb. The directions are obtained from the pressure angle and the direction of rotation. The shaft reactions must be placed so as to oppose these forces in both direction and magnitude. This is shown in the figure, and the two reactions are added vectorially to obtain the resultant. By scaling the diagram, the resultant is $F_{S-2} = 187$ lb at 33° from the horizontal. In a similar manner, the shaft reaction for gear 3 is found to be $F_{S-3} = 155$ lb at 4° from the vertical (Fig. 10-20*c*).

e. From Eq. (10-8), the torque at shaft 3 is

$$T = W\frac{D_3}{2} = \frac{(146)(9)}{2} = 657 \text{ lb-in.} \qquad \textit{Ans.}$$

10-8. Discussion of Tooth Loads.[1] The following must be considered as important limiting design factors in specifying the capacity of any gear drive:

1. The heat generated during operation
2. Failure of the teeth by breakage
3. Fatigue failure of the tooth surfaces
4. Abrasive wear of the tooth surfaces
5. Noise as a result of high speeds or heavy loads

All these factors are a function of the tooth loads, and for this reason an accurate determination of these loads becomes very important.

The *transmitted load* is the useful component of force which is trans-

[1] Earle Buckingham, "Analytical Mechanics of Gears," chap. 18, McGraw-Hill Book Company, Inc., New York, 1949.

ferred from one gear to another during action. It is the tangential load W which has been defined in Sec. 10-7.

The *dynamic load* is the maximum instantaneous force acting between gears during action. Knowledge of the exact nature of this load is still incomplete, but by combining theory with the results of a great deal of research it is possible to predict the value of the dynamic load with good accuracy.

Since present design practice employs, in part, the results obtained by investigators nearly a century ago, it will be interesting to trace the development of the subject.

One of the earliest efforts to account for the increase in dynamic load due to velocity employed a number of gears of the same size, material, and strength. Several of these gears were tested to destruction under static loads. The remaining gears were tested to destruction at various pitch-line velocities. Then, for example, if the statically tested gears failed at 5,000 lb and those running at a certain pitch-line velocity failed at 2,500 lb, the velocity factor for this pitch-line velocity was taken as one-half. Another similar pair of gears running at the same velocity were then assumed to have a dynamic load equal to twice the transmitted load.

Wilfred Lewis first presented a formula for the strength of gear teeth in which the tooth form entered into the equation. Although the formula was announced in 1892, it is still widely used. It is called the *Lewis equation* and is

$$W = s_d p f y \tag{10-9}$$

where W = transmitted load
s_d = design stress
p = circular pitch
f = face width
y = form factor which depends upon the shape of the tooth

The development of this equation will be considered in a later section, but the reader can visualize the fundamental character of the equation by noticing that the product pf is proportional to the area of the tooth and that y is both a constant of proportionality and a constant which depends upon the tooth number and the tooth system. It thus takes care of either stubby or undercut teeth.

Lewis also included a table of design stresses (Table 10-3) whose values depended upon the pitch-line velocity. Earle Buckingham states that Lewis obtained these stresses from an English rule published in 1869.

Using the values shown in Table 10-3, Carl G. Barth expressed them in equation form, as follows:

$$s_d = s \frac{600}{600 + V} \tag{10-10}$$

where s is the safe static stress and V is the pitch-line velocity. The static stress s is usually obtained by dividing the strength of the material by a suitable factor of safety.

Equation (10-10) and Table 10-3 are based on tests which took place before 1868 and were made on cast-iron gears with cast teeth.

Equation (10-10), called the *Barth equation*, is modified by some designers to

$$s_d = s \frac{1{,}200}{1{,}200 + V} \tag{10-11}$$

which is then used for cut and generated teeth.

TABLE 10-3. DESIGN STRESSES RECOMMENDED BY WILFRED LEWIS IN 1892

Velocity, fpm	Design stress, psi	
	Cast iron	Steel
100 or less	8,000	20,000
200	6,000	15,000
300	4,800	12,000
600	4,000	10,000
900	3,000	7,500
1,200	2,400	6,000
1,800	2,000	5,000
2,000	1,700	4,300

Between 1911 and 1915 Prof. Guido H. Marx ran a number of tests at Stanford University at various pitch-line velocities. The results of these tests emphasized the importance of the contact ratio and questioned the commonly used velocity factors. In commenting on these tests, Ralph E. Flanders raised the question of whether the strength of a gear running at high speeds was dependent upon the static or the dynamic strength. In other words, could the same velocity factors be used for cast iron as are used, for example, for heat-treated alloy steel? He also raised the question of the effect of cutting accuracy upon the strength at high speeds. In view of these comments, Professor Marx supervised a series of tests in 1924 on cast-iron gears made with varying degrees of accuracy. In these tests it was quite clear that the cutting accuracy had a very pronounced effect upon the strength at high speeds.

Between the years 1900 and 1931 the idea that the total dynamic load could be considered as the sum of the transmitted load and an incremental load gradually gained support. This equation may be expressed as

$$W_d = W + W_i \tag{10-12}$$

where W_i is the incremental load and is due to tooth-form and spacing errors, unbalance, fluctuating loads, and the deformation of the teeth under load.

Oscar Lasche first considered the effects of tooth errors in 1899, using a rigid tooth, and came to the conclusion that the tooth elasticity affected the permissible error. In other words, a greater error is permissible with elastic teeth than with rigid ones, because they can absorb the very short instantaneous forces without disturbing the rotating masses.

In 1908 Ralph E. Flanders discussed the nature of dynamic loads and stated, "After some reflection, the writer has come to the conclusion that a variation in the strength of perfectly formed gearing, due to a variation in the velocity, can be due to but one thing—impact caused by the imperfect meshing of otherwise perfectly shaped teeth, deformed by the load they are transmitting."

A number of investigators then attempted to compare the results of Lasche's analysis with the actual breaking loads of gears running at high speeds. The results were not comparable, and in 1923 Wilfred Lewis proposed to the ASME the construction of a machine to measure these incremental loads without destroying the gears. The result of this proposal was the appointment of the ASME Special Research Committee on the Strength of Gear Teeth, headed by Wilfred Lewis and Ralph E. Flanders.

The research was conducted at the Massachusetts Institute of Technology by Earle Buckingham, who wrote the report.[1] This report gave the following equation for dynamic loads:

$$W_d = W + \sqrt{F_a(2F_2 - F_a)} \qquad (10\text{-}13)$$

where F_a is the acceleration load and is practically independent of the applied load and F_2 is the force required to deform the teeth the amount of the effective tooth error. The report also contains an approximation to Eq. (10-13). It is

$$W_d = W + \frac{0.05VF_2}{0.05V + \sqrt{F_2}} \qquad (10\text{-}14)$$

where V is the pitch-line velocity and the other factors are the same as before. In presenting this equation, Buckingham states that it is only for average mass conditions; in cases where the gear blanks have masses which are either below or above average, Eq. (10-13) should be used. In any case, Eq. (10-13) will give the more accurate results.

In 1949 Buckingham wrote an excellent mathematical analysis of the mechanics of gearing.[2] In discussing dynamic loads, he uses the funda-

[1] Dynamic Loads on Gear Teeth, *ASME Research Publ.*, 1931.

[2] Buckingham, "Analytical Mechanics of Gears."

mental equation [Eq. (10-13)] only.[1] Darle W. Dudley, in his excellent treatise on modern gear design,[2] states that the Buckingham method may give values of the dynamic load which are slightly high, but that it is the best method available and will show clearly the effect of masses, shaft stiffnesses, and tooth errors in producing dynamic overloads.

10-9. Preliminary Design Decisions. The chief difficulty that arises in designing a gearset lies in the fact that it is necessary to know all the dimensions of the gears, as well as the tooth form and size, before the loads and stresses may be accurately determined. This makes it necessary to estimate the size of the gears, using simplified methods, and then to check this estimate, using the various design factors in conjunction with the more exact equations. The estimated size and tooth form are then altered in accordance with the information obtained from the exact equations. Sometimes the information obtained indicates that the estimate is so far off that an entirely new set of dimensions must be specified and the process repeated. The design of gears is thus strictly a trial-and-error process, with each new trial coming closer to the final result.

One of the first problems is the reduction of the given data to a simple set of specifications. These specifications should usually include the following information:

1. The character of the load
2. The power transmitted
3. The pinion and gear speed
4. The operating time

Let us consider some of the variations which may arise in these specifications. For example, suppose that a 1-hp motor drives a gearset. Some of the possibilities are as follows:

1. The motor transmits 1 hp continuously at constant speed.
2. The motor runs at constant speed continuously but transmits power only for very short periods.
3. The motor transmits 1 hp continuously but at a wide range of speeds.
4. The motor is turned on only for very short intervals of time and transmits torques many times the full-load rating.
5. The motor runs continuously but the torque is indeterminate, varying from 30 to 300 per cent of full-load torque.

[1] In correspondence with the author, Buckingham states, "The approximate equation was developed for general use in design where exact blank sizes might be unknown. It is based on an average mass condition and applies primarily to pairs of gears of sizes used in general machine design. The fundamental equation is based on the dynamic operating conditions and is the direct result of our research efforts. It is the one I use myself except when a quick estimate is needed."

[2] Darle W. Dudley, "Practical Gear Design," p. 46, McGraw-Hill Book Company, Inc., New York, 1954.

From these possibilities it is seen that the reduction of the conditions of the problem to a simple set of specifications may not always be easy. Nevertheless, it is necessary to define the problem in rather exact terms, and the care with which this is done will influence the quality of the final result.

Having defined the problem as above, the designer can then reduce the conditions of operation to a set of specifications. The specifications will indicate whether wear, heat, static strength, or dynamic strength is a

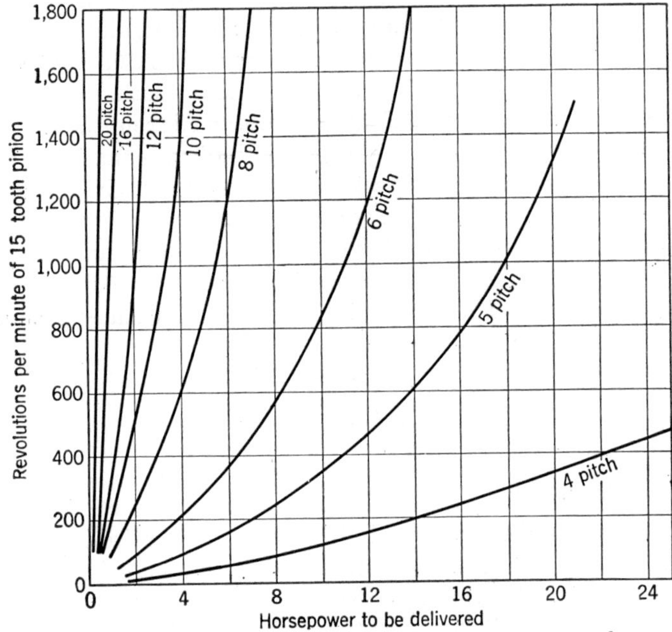

FIG. 10-21. A 20° spur-gear pitch-selection chart. This chart may be employed to obtain a preliminary estimate of the diametral pitch to be used. The gear selected may then be checked by the appropriate equations. Since the chart is only approximate, it should never be used as a final criterion of safety. It is based on a 15-tooth mild-steel pinion. (*Courtesy of Boston Gear Works, Inc.*)

primary consideration. It may be that several of these factors must be considered. In any event, the designer, having made this decision, may select the appropriate formula, or formulas, and proceed with the design. In the next several sections each of these design factors will be considered in detail.

In the solution of many of the equations it is necessary to guess at the pitch in order to obtain a trial solution. Figure 10-21 is included to assist the designer in making the initial guess. This figure should be used only to obtain a trial value and never to obtain a final design unless it is checked with the appropriate equations.

10-10. Beam Strength. The beam strength of a gear tooth is the static strength of an equivalent cantilever beam which has been modified by a suitable velocity factor. This strength is obtained by a variation in the original Lewis equation.

Figure 10-22 shows a cantilever beam of cross-sectional dimensions f and t, having a length l and a load W uniformly distributed across the dimension f. The section modulus is $I/c = ft^2/6$, and therefore the bending stress is

$$s = \frac{M}{I/c} = \frac{6Wl}{ft^2} \qquad (a)$$

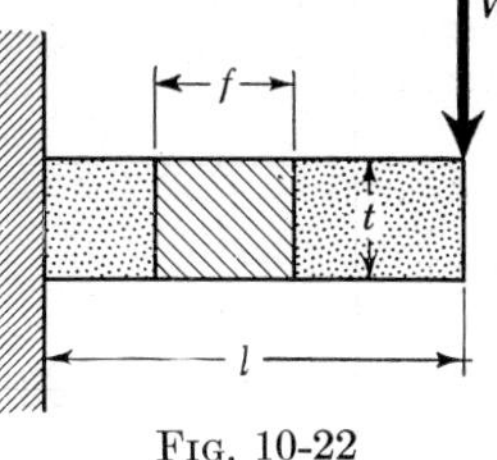

Fig. 10-22

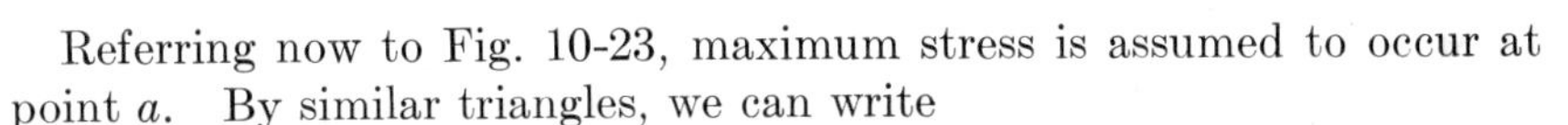

Referring now to Fig. 10-23, maximum stress is assumed to occur at point a. By similar triangles, we can write

$$\frac{t/2}{x} = \frac{l}{t/2} \qquad \text{or} \qquad x = \frac{t^2}{4l} \qquad (b)$$

By rearranging Eq. (a),

$$s = \frac{6Wl}{ft^2} = \frac{W}{f}\frac{1}{t^2/6l} = \frac{W}{f}\frac{1}{t^2/4l}\frac{1}{4/6} \qquad (c)$$

If we now substitute the value of x from Eq. (b) into Eq. (c) and multiply the numerator and denominator by the circular pitch p, we find

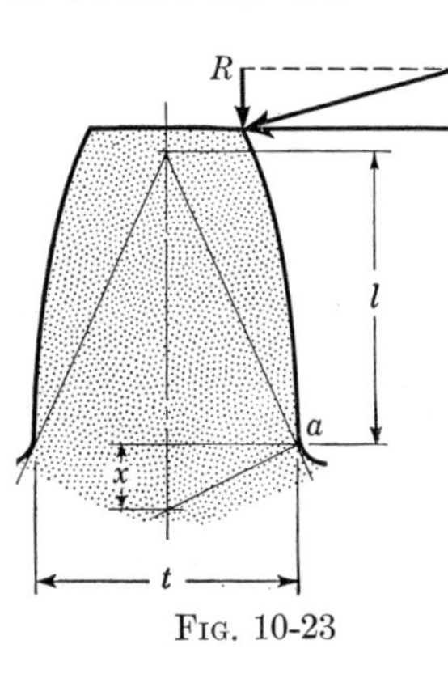

Fig. 10-23

$$s = \frac{Wp}{f(2/3)xp} \qquad (10\text{-}15)$$

Letting $y = 2x/3p$, we have

$$s = \frac{W}{fpy} \qquad (10\text{-}16)$$

This completes the development of the original Lewis equation. The factor y is called the *Lewis form factor*, and it is obtained by a graphical layout of the gear tooth.

In using this equation, most engineers prefer to employ the diametral pitch in determining the stresses. This is done by substituting $P = \pi/p$ and $Y = \pi y$ in Eq. (10-16). This gives

$$s = \frac{WP}{fY} \qquad (10\text{-}17)$$

Values of the form factor Y are given in Table 10-4.

TABLE 10-4. VALUES OF THE FORM FACTOR Y FOR VARIOUS TOOTH SYSTEMS

Number of teeth	14½° composite and involute	20° full-depth	Small pinions 20° full-depth	20° stub	Internal drives, 20° full-depth	
					Pinion	Gear
5	...	...	0.320	...	0.322	
6	...	...	0.301	...	0.322	
7	...	...	0.282	...	0.322	
8	...	...	0.264	...	0.324	
9	...	...	0.264	...	0.324	
10	...	...	0.264	...	0.324	
11	...	...	0.264	...	0.326	
12	0.211	0.245	0.264	0.312	0.326	
13	0.223	0.261	0.270	0.324	0.326	
14	0.236	0.277	0.277	0.340	0.330	
15	0.245	0.290	...	0.350	0.330	
16	0.254	0.296	...	0.362	0.333	
17	0.264	0.303	...	0.368	0.342	
18	0.270	0.309	...	0.378	0.348	
19	0.277	0.314	...	0.388	0.358	
20	0.283	0.322	...	0.394	0.364	
21	0.289	0.328	...	0.400	0.370	
22	0.292	0.331	...	0.406	0.374	
24	0.299	0.337	...	0.416	0.383	
26	0.308	0.346	...	0.425	0.393	
28	0.314	0.353	...	0.432	0.399	0.691
30	0.318	0.359	...	0.438	0.405	0.678
34	0.327	0.371	...	0.447	0.414	0.659
38	0.333	0.384	...	0.457	0.424	0.643
43	0.340	0.397	...	0.463	0.430	0.628
50	0.346	0.409	...	0.476	0.436	0.612
60	0.355	0.422	...	0.485	0.446	0.596
75	0.361	0.435	...	0.497	0.452	0.581
100	0.367	0.447	...	0.507	0.461	0.565
150	0.374	0.460	...	0.520	0.468	0.549
300	0.383	0.472	...	0.535	0.477	0.533
Rack	0.390	0.485	...	0.552		

Assumptions. 1. The Lewis equation is solved using the tangential component of the load. If the radial component is considered, this would produce a uniform compressive stress to which must be added the bending stress. The effect of the radial component, therefore, is to increase the compression and decrease the tension. This is shown clearly by the photograph of Fig. 10-25, in which the stress on the compression side is seen to be significantly larger.

2. The greatest stress is assumed to occur when the load is at the tip of the tooth. If gears are cut with sufficient accuracy, the tip-load condition is not the worst because another pair of teeth will come into contact before this condition is obtained. Examination of run-in teeth will show that the heaviest loads occur near the middle of the tooth. Therefore, the maximum stress probably occurs while a single pair of teeth are carrying the full load, at a point where another pair of teeth are nearly ready to come into contact. If size and weight are important, this condition should be assumed. With this assumption, the stress may be obtained by increasing the form factor Y, 70 per cent for full-depth teeth and 60 per cent for stub teeth.

TABLE 10-5. GEOMETRIC STRESS-CONCENTRATION FACTORS FOR 14½° COMPOSITE PINIONS*

Diametral pitch, P	Tension, k_t	Compression, k_c
4	1.47	1.61
5	1.47	1.61
6	1.42	1.57
7	1.35	1.50
8	1.345	1.500

* From Paul H. Black, An Investigation of Relative Stresses in Solid Spur Gears by the Photoelastic Method, *Univ. Illinois Eng. Expt. Sta. Bull.* 288, 1936.

3. The tangential load W is assumed to be uniformly distributed across the full face of the gear. However, the gears and their supporting shafts are made of elastic materials which deflect under the application of loads. Therefore, we can expect to find deflection of the gear teeth, torsional deflection of the gear blank, and bending deflection of the supporting shaft. The effect of these deformations is to cause a nonuniform distribution of the load. When the ratio of the face width to the circular pitch (f/p) is large, say over 6, these deformations should probably be considered.[1]

4. The effects of stress concentration are neglected. Stress-concentra-

[1] Buckingham, "Analytical Mechanics of Gears," pp. 486–490.

tion factors were not used in Lewis' day, but recent investigations indicate the advisability of doing so.

Black used photoelastic methods to determine the geometric stress-concentration factors. He made tests on 14½° composite pinions with from 12 to 24 teeth. The results of this investigation are shown in Table 10-5.

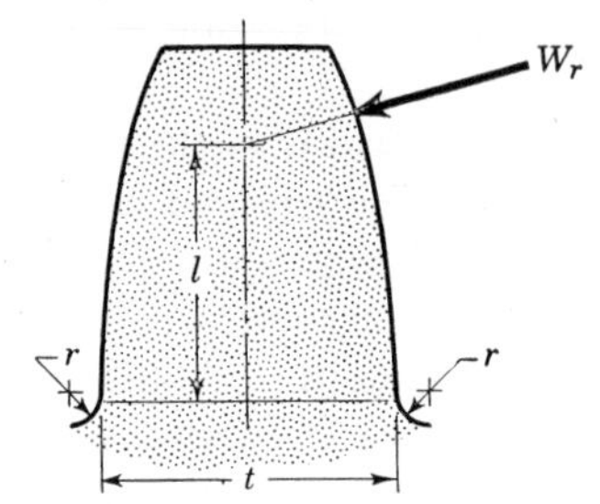

Fig. 10-24. Tooth layout used to calculate the stress-concentration factor k.

A later photoelastic investigation, by Dolan and Broghamer,[1] established the following equations. For 20° involute spur-gear teeth

$$k = 0.18 + \left(\frac{t}{r}\right)^{0.15} \left(\frac{t}{l}\right)^{0.45} \qquad (10\text{-}18)$$

For 14½° involute teeth

$$k = 0.22 + \left(\frac{t}{r}\right)^{0.20} \left(\frac{t}{l}\right)^{0.40} \qquad (10\text{-}19)$$

where the meaning of the quantities t, r, and l is shown in Fig. 10-24. These quantities must be obtained from a layout of the tooth outline which has been generated by a template representing the correct shape of the hob or shaper cutter. Values of the stress-concentration factor k found in this manner rarely exceed 2.5.

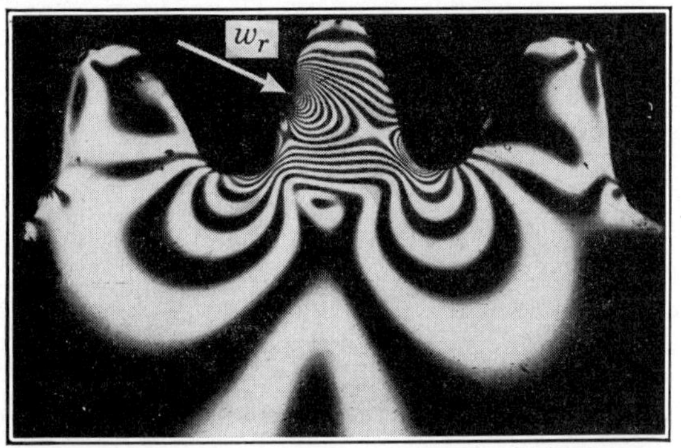

Fig. 10-25. Stress distribution in a gear tooth determined by photoelastic procedures. The photograph shows the Hertz contact stresses at the pitch line, due to the load, and the fillet stresses. The stress at the right-hand fillet is seen to be larger because of the radial compressive component of the load.

It is suggested that the methods of Sec. 4-9 be used to obtain the fatigue stress-concentration factor k_f and that k_f, instead of k, be used in obtaining the beam strength.

Lewis Equation for Dynamic Loads. When the Lewis equation is altered by the methods discussed above, it is quite useful for making a

[1] T. J. Dolan and E. I. Broghamer, A Photoelastic Study of the Stresses in Gear Tooth Fillets, *Univ. Illinois Eng. Expt. Sta. Bull.* 335, March, 1942.

preliminary estimate of the gear sizes. However, it can be made more useful by the introduction of a velocity factor. Figure 10-26 is a graph of velocity factors C_v for gears of both commercial and precision accuracy.[1] These factors should be considered as strength-reduction factors.

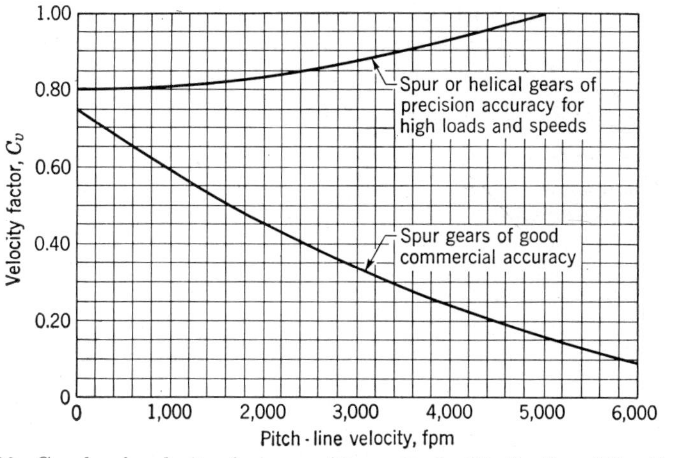

FIG. 10-26. Graph of velocity factors. (*From Darle W. Dudley, "Practical Gear Design," p. 126, McGraw-Hill Book Company, Inc., New York,* 1954.)

The Lewis equation may now be modified by assembling the preceding information. After rearrangement, Eq. (10-17) becomes

$$W_{\max} = \frac{fK_2YC_vs_e}{k_fK_1P} \tag{10-20}$$

where s_e = endurance limit from Table 10-6, psi
C_v = velocity factor from Fig. 10-26
k_f = fatigue stress-concentration factor obtained from Eq. (10-18) or (10-19), or from Table 10-5, and corrected for notch sensitivity, employing Fig. 4-24
K_1 = service factor; suggested values of 1.25 for steady loads, 1.35 for pulsating loads, and 1.50 for shock loads
K_2 = form-factor coefficient used to correct form factor to worst-load condition; 1.70 for full-depth teeth and 1.60 for stub teeth
$W_{\max}$ = maximum tangential load, lb
P = diametral pitch
f = face width, in.
Y = Lewis form factor (based on diametral pitch)

[1] Dudley states, "About the best justification for using a velocity factor is that it is a guess in the right direction and even an inaccurate guess is better than no guess at all!" See Dudley, *op. cit.*, p. 125.

In general the endurance limit used should be for one-way bending unless the gear is an idler. An idler will be subjected to one reversed bending cycle for each revolution. Endurance limit values as recommended by Buckingham are given in Table 10-6.

TABLE 10-6. RECOMMENDED FLEXURAL ENDURANCE LIMITS FOR GEAR MATERIALS*

Gear material	Hardness, Bhn	Reversed bending, psi	One-way bending, psi
Cast iron	180	8,000	12,000
Phosphor bronze	100	16,000	24,000
Steel	150	24,000	36,000
Steel	200	33,000	50,000
Steel	240	40,000	60,000
Steel	280	46,000	70,000
Steel	320	53,000	80,000
Steel	360	60,000	90,000
Steel	400	66,000	100,000

* From Earle Buckingham, "Gear Tooth Loads," p. 63, Massachusetts Gear and Tool Company, Woburn, Mass., 1953.

The modified Lewis equation is frequently used for the design of gears or to obtain a preliminary estimate of gear sizes. When this is done, s_e should be replaced by a design stress obtained from s_e by employing a suitable factor of safety. In addition to the usual unknowns, the factor of safety should account for tooth errors due to shaft misalignment and cutting inaccuracy.

Omitting the velocity factor, Eq. (10-20) becomes

$$W_{max} = \frac{fK_2Ys_e}{k_fK_1P} \tag{10-21}$$

This equation gives the maximum possible value of the tangential load W. When gears are designed using equations for the dynamic load, then the maximum tangential load W_{max} as obtained by Eq. (10-21) should always be greater than the dynamic load W_d.

10-11. The Buckingham Equation for Dynamic Loads.[1] Figure 10-27 is an idealized diagram showing the imagined forces on a pair of teeth during contact. The abscissa represents the length of the line of action, with point a as the initial point of contact and point k as the final point of contact. The forces on the teeth are plotted as ordinates.

In order to visualize the action, we must understand that tooth errors exist because of cutting inaccuracies, shaft misalignment, and the defor-

[1] Buckingham, "Analytical Mechanics of Gears," chap. 20, p. 426.

mation of the teeth under load. In addition, each gear of the pair is a rotating mass possessing inertia and, therefore, requiring the application of force in order to change its velocity. The contact ratio will be such that another pair of teeth will come into contact before the previous pair leave contact.

Referring again to Fig. 10-27, *hj* represents the average force on a pair of teeth which are nearing the end of contact. The sudden reduction in force represented by the line *gh* results from a new pair of teeth coming into contact at *a* and assuming a portion of the load.

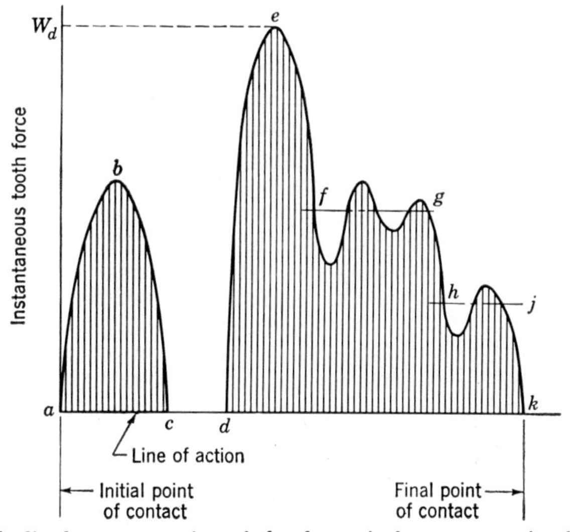

FIG. 10-27. Idealized representation of the dynamic force on a pair of teeth during engagement.

Results of experiments indicate that the effect of tooth errors is greatest when a new pair of teeth are coming into contact. When an error in the form of a high spot comes into engagement, a very rapid increase in force is necessary, as shown by the curve *ab*, in order to accelerate the driven gear. The actual effect is to speed up the driven gear and slow down the driver, with the velocity changes being proportional to the relative masses.

At point *b* the accelerating force has reached a maximum and decreases to point *c*, as the rotating masses take on the changed velocity. At point *c* they have different velocities and, therefore, separate from each other. This separation is opposed by the transmitted load and the elasticity of the shafts. The teeth remain out of engagement for a short period of time, *cd*. However, the load on the driven gear causes it to slow down, while the power applied to the driver causes it to speed up. The result is that the teeth come together again, this time with considerable impact, as shown by curve *de*. Point *e* represents the maximum force and is called the *dynamic load*. This is the load W_d in which we are interested.

When the action passes point *e*, the vibrating motion is assumed to decay and settle down to an average value as represented by *fg*. The secondary effects after point *e* are assumed to be of a minor nature, and no further attention will be given to them.

Oscillograph records have been taken of gear teeth in action, and the presence of two peak loads is clearly indicated, the first being the acceleration load and the second the dynamic, or impact, load.

The Buckingham Equations. In the original work, Buckingham gives two versions of the equation for dynamic load. One of these may be regarded as the exact equation and the other as an approximation. The more accurate method considers the effect of all masses, such as flywheels, pulleys, etc., mounted on the gear shaft. The method to be presented here neglects the shaft-connected masses and considers only the masses of the gears themselves.

The *fundamental Buckingham equation* is

$$W_d = W + \sqrt{F_a(2F_2 - F_a)} \tag{10-22}$$

where W_d = dynamic load, lb
W = tangential load, lb
F_a = acceleration load, lb
F_2 = force required to deform teeth through amount of effective error, lb

The acceleration load is found from the following equation:

$$F_a = \frac{F_1 F_2}{F_1 + F_2} \tag{10-23}$$

where F_1 is the average force in pounds required to accelerate the masses when they are considered as absolutely rigid. This force may be obtained from the equation

$$F_1 = HmV^2 \tag{10-24}$$

where H = coefficient whose value depends upon tooth system and pitch radius
m = effective mass
V = pitch-line velocity

The values of H and m are obtained as follows:

$$H = c_1\left(\frac{1}{R_1} + \frac{1}{R_2}\right) \tag{10-25}$$

where R_1 = pitch radius of pinion, in.
R_2 = pitch radius of gear, in.
c_1 = 0.00086 for 14½° gears and 0.00120 for 20° gears

$$m = \frac{m_1 m_2}{m_1 + m_2} \tag{10-26}$$

where m_1 and m_2 are the effective masses of the pinion and gear, respectively, in slugs, acting at the pitch line. The force required to deform the teeth is

$$F_2 = W\left(\frac{e}{d} + 1\right) \tag{10-27}$$

where e is the measured error in action in inches and d is the deformation of the teeth at the pitch line caused by the tangential load W. This deformation may be obtained from the following equation:

$$d = \frac{c_2 W}{f}\left(\frac{1}{E_1} + \frac{1}{E_2}\right) \tag{10-28}$$

where c_2 = 9.345 for 14½° gears, 9.000 for 20° full-depth gears, and 8.700 for 20° stub gears
E_1 = modulus of elasticity of pinion, psi
E_2 = modulus of elasticity of gear, psi
f = face width, in.

If the value of d from Eq. (10-28) is substituted in Eq. (10-27), we obtain

$$F_2 = f\frac{e}{c_2(1/E_1 + 1/E_2)} + W$$

$$F_2 = fC + W \tag{10-29}$$

where

$$C = \frac{e}{c_2(1/E_1 + 1/E_2)} \tag{10-30}$$

Values of the deformation factor C may now be calculated for the usual combinations of gear materials, using each tooth system and the expected errors in action, and arranged in tabular style (Table 10-7).

Before the value of C can be obtained, the expected error in action must be selected. This depends upon the manner in which the gears are cut. The following classification is used:

Class 1—well-cut commercial gears
Class 2—gears cut with great care
Class 3—carefully ground or precision-cut gears

The maximum expected error in action for these three classes is given in Table 10-8.

TABLE 10-7. VALUES OF C

Material	Tooth form	Error in action, in.					
		0.0005	0.001	0.002	0.003	0.004	0.005
Cast iron and cast iron	14½°	400	800	1,600	2,400	3,200	4,000
Cast iron and steel.....	14½°	550	1,100	2,200	3,300	4,400	5,500
Steel and steel.........	14½°	800	1,600	3,200	4,800	6,400	8,000
Cast iron and cast iron..	20° full-depth	415	830	1,660	2,490	3,320	4,150
Cast iron and steel.....	20° full-depth	570	1,140	2,280	3,420	4,560	5,700
Steel and steel.........	20° full-depth	830	1,660	3,320	4,980	6,640	8,300
Cast iron and cast iron..	20° stub	430	860	1,720	2,580	3,440	4,300
Cast iron and steel.....	20° stub	590	1,180	2,360	3,540	4,720	5,900
Steel and steel.........	20° stub	860	1,720	3,440	5,160	6,880	8,600

TABLE 10-8. MAXIMUM ERROR IN ACTION, e

Diametral pitch	Class 1	Class 2	Class 3
1	0.0048	0.0024	0.0012
2	0.0040	0.0020	0.0010
3	0.0032	0.0016	0.0008
4	0.0026	0.0016	0.0007
5	0.0022	0.0011	0.0006
6 and finer	0.0020	0.0010	0.0005

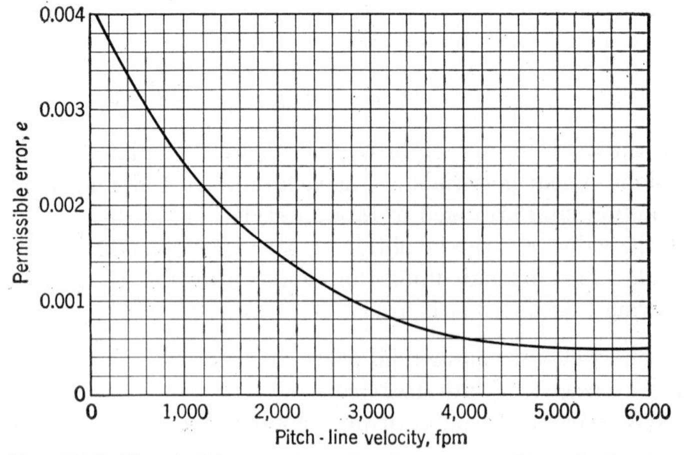

FIG. 10-28. Permissible error in action for a reasonable noise level.

A satisfactory method of selecting the proper class of gear is based upon the desired noise level. It is impossible to obtain a set of gears which will run without some noise. The amount of noise produced is a good indication of the accuracy with which the gears are cut. Figure

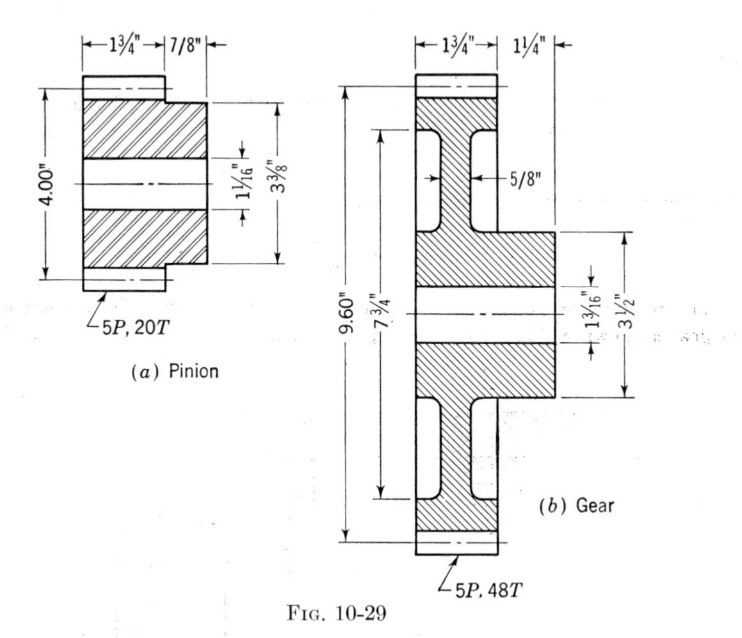

FIG. 10-29

10-28 is a chart which will give the permissible error e for a reasonable noise level. If extreme quietness is necessary, then greater accuracy will be required.

The method of using the fundamental Buckingham equation is illustrated by the following example.

EXAMPLE 10-2. The pinion and gear shown in Fig. 10-29 have been tentatively selected to transmit 10 hp at a pitch-line velocity of 1,200 fpm under steady load conditions. The gears are commercially cut with good accuracy, using the 14½° involute system. The pinion is made of 1020 steel, 149 Bhn, and is not heat-treated. The gear is made of grade 30 cast iron of 170 Bhn hardness. Using the Buckingham equation, determine whether any changes in the design are necessary in order to transmit the load satisfactorily.

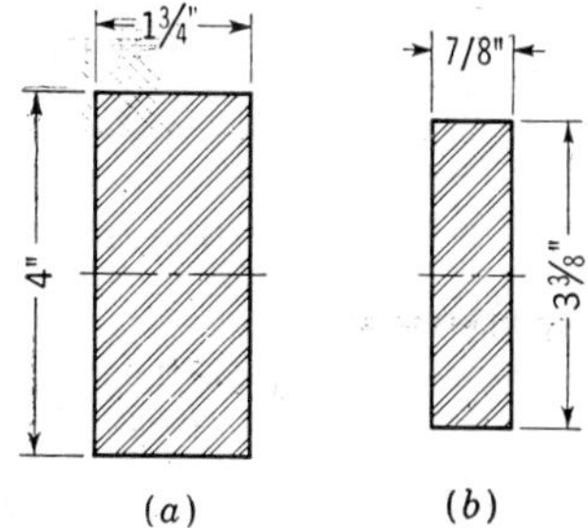

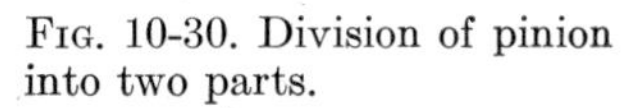

FIG. 10-30. Division of pinion into two parts.

Solution. a. Determination of the dynamic load. The first step in the solution is to obtain the effective masses. The pinion is divided into two parts, as shown in Fig. 10-30, and the mass of each part is computed separately. Thus, where

$$\rho = 0.28 \text{ lb per in.}^3 \text{ for steel}$$

$$m_a = \frac{\rho v_a}{g} = \frac{\rho}{g}\frac{\pi d^2 l}{4} = \frac{(0.28)(\pi)(4)^2(1.75)}{(32.2)(4)} = 0.191 \text{ slug}$$

and

$$m_b = \frac{\rho v_b}{g} = \frac{(0.28)(\pi)(3.375)^2(0.875)}{(32.2)(4)} = 0.0682 \text{ slug}$$

The mass moment of inertia of a cylinder about its own axis is $J = md^2/8$. Therefore, the moment of inertia of the pinion is

$$J = \frac{1}{8}(m_a d_a^2 + m_b d_b^2) = \frac{(0.191)(4)^2 + (0.0682)(3.375)^2}{8}$$
$$= 0.468 \text{ slug - in.}^2$$

The effective mass of the pinion is, then,

$$m_1 = \frac{J}{R_1^2} = \frac{0.468}{(4/2)^2} = 0.117 \text{ slug}$$

The effective mass of the gear is found in a similar manner. The method of dividing the gear is shown in Fig. 10-31. Using the density of cast iron as $\rho = 0.26$ lb per in.^{3},

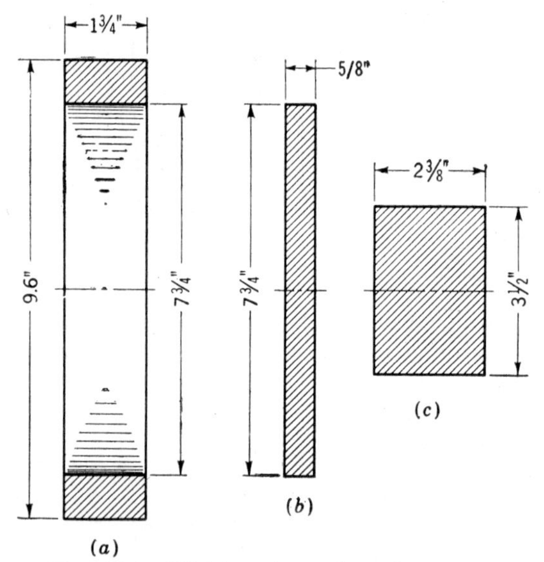

FIG. 10-31. Division of gear into three parts.

the masses are

$$m_a = \frac{\rho}{g}\frac{\pi}{4}(d_o^2 - d_i^2)l = \frac{(0.26)(\pi)[(9.6)^2 - (7.75)^2](1.75)}{(32.2)(4)}$$
$$= 0.357 \text{ slug}$$

$$m_b = \frac{\rho v_b}{g} = \frac{(0.26)(\pi)(7.75)^2(0.625)}{(32.2)(4)} = 0.238 \text{ slug}$$

$$m_c = \frac{\rho v_c}{g} = \frac{(0.26)(\pi)(3.5)^2(2.375)}{(32.2)(4)} = 0.184 \text{ slug}$$

The moment of inertia of a hollow cylinder about its own axis is $J = m(d_o^2 + d_i^2)/8$, where d_o and d_i are the outside and inside diameters, respectively. The moment of inertia of the entire gear is

$$J = \tfrac{1}{8}[m_a(d_{a-o}^2 + d_{a-i}^2) + m_b d_b^2 + m_c d_c^2]$$
$$= \frac{(0.357)[(9.6)^2 + (7.75)^2] + (0.238)(7.75)^2 + (0.184)(3.5)^2}{8}$$
$$= 6.19 \text{ slugs-in.}^2$$

The effective mass of the gear is

$$m_2 = \frac{J}{R_2^2} = \frac{6.19}{(9.6/2)^2} = 0.269 \text{ slug}$$

The tangential load is now computed, assuming that 10 hp is the correct rating and using Eq. (10-6):

$$W = \frac{33{,}000 \text{ hp}}{V} = \frac{(33{,}000)(10)}{1{,}200} = 275 \text{ lb}$$

The effective mass of the gearset is calculated from Eq. (10-26):

$$m = \frac{m_1 m_2}{m_1 + m_2} = \frac{(0.117)(0.269)}{0.117 + 0.269} = 0.0816 \text{ slug}$$

The coefficient H is computed from Eq. (10-25), as follows:

$$H = c_1\left(\frac{1}{R_1} + \frac{1}{R_2}\right) = 0.00086\left(\frac{1}{2.0} + \frac{1}{4.8}\right) = 0.00122$$

Therefore, from Eq. (10-24), the force F_1 is

$$F_1 = HmV^2 = (0.00122)(0.0816)(1{,}200)^2 = 1{,}430 \text{ lb}$$

From Table 10-8 the maximum expected error in action for commercial gears is 0.0022 in. We will use 0.002 in. Using cast iron and steel and a 14½° tooth form, from Table 10-7 the deformation factor C is 2,200. Substitution of this value in Eq. (10-29) obtains

$$F_2 = fC + W = (1.75)(2{,}200) + 275 = 4{,}125 \text{ lb}$$

The acceleration load is, from Eq. (10-23),

$$F_a = \frac{F_1 F_2}{F_1 + F_2} = \frac{(1{,}430)(4{,}125)}{1{,}430 + 4{,}125} = 1{,}060 \text{ lb}$$

Substituting, now, in Eq. (10-22) for the dynamic load, we find

$$W_d = W + \sqrt{F_a(2F_2 - F_a)} = 275 + \sqrt{(1{,}060)[(2)(4{,}125) - 1{,}060]} = 3{,}035 \text{ lb}$$

Ans.

b. Determination of the beam strength. Having now obtained the dynamic load, we must assure ourselves that it is not greater than the maximum tangential load obtained from Eq. (10-21). The values for substitution in this equation, for the pinion, are as follows:

f = 1.75 in. face width, given
K_2 = 1.70 for full-depth teeth
Y = 0.283, from Table 10-4
s_e = 36,000 psi, from Table 10-6
k_f = 1.40, from Table 10-5 and Fig. 4-24, Chap. 4
K_1 = 1.25 for steady loads
P = 5 DP, given

The solution is

$$W_{\max} = \frac{fK_2Ys_e}{k_fK_1P} = \frac{(1.75)(1.70)(0.283)(36{,}000)}{(1.40)(1.25)(5)} = 3{,}460 \text{ lb} \qquad \textit{Ans.}$$

for the pinion. In the case of the gear, $Y = 0.345$ and $s_e = 12{,}000$ psi, with the other values remaining the same. Substituting these values for the gear, we obtain

$$W_{\max} = \frac{fK_2Ys_e}{k_fK_1P} = \frac{(1.75)(1.70)(0.345)(12{,}000)}{(1.40)(1.25)(5)} = 1{,}400 \text{ lb} \qquad \textit{Ans.}$$

It therefore appears that the pinion is satisfactory but the gear is not. If the gear were made of the same material as the pinion, then it would be the stronger of the two. In this example the gear blank should be redesigned for manufacture probably as a steel forging. If this is done, another calculation would not be necessary for the gear.

The Approximate Buckingham Equation. It is frequently desirable to obtain a rapid solution for the dynamic load. Substitution of the value of F_2 from Eq. (10-29) into Eq. (10-14) yields

$$W_d = W + \frac{0.05V(fC + W)}{0.05V + \sqrt{fC + W}} \tag{10-31}$$

which is an approximation to the fundamental equation and may be used for normal mass conditions.

In Dudley's work on gears for gas-turbine applications, he found the dynamic loads to be approximately 135 per cent of the transmitted loads.[1] Calculations of the same load by the Buckingham equations gave values ranging from 135 to 175 per cent, and hence Dudley states that the Buckingham method may give values which are slightly high. Nevertheless, it still seems to be the best method available for predicting the dynamic load.

10-12. Surface Durability. Failure of the surfaces of gear teeth, generally called wear, may occur by *pitting*, which is a surface fatigue failure; by *scoring*, which is a lubrication failure; or by *abrasion* due to foreign material.

In order to assure a satisfactory life, the gears must be designed so that the dynamic surface stresses are within the endurance limit of the material. In many cases the first visible evidence of wear is seen near the pitch line; this seems reasonable, because of the fact that the maximum dynamic load occurs near this area.

In order to obtain an expression for the surface contact stress we shall employ the Hertz theory. In Chap. 2 it was shown that the contact stress between two cylinders may be computed from the equation

$$p_{\max} = \frac{2F}{\pi bl} \tag{2-32}$$

[1] Dudley, *loc. cit.*

where p_{max} = surface stress
F = force pressing two cylinders together
l = length of cylinders
b = obtained from the equation

$$b = \sqrt{\frac{2F}{\pi l} \frac{(1 - \mu^2)(1/E_1 + 1/E_2)}{1/d_1 + 1/d_2}} \tag{2-31}$$

In Eq. (2-31) μ is Poisson's ratio; E_1 and E_2, the modulus of elasticity of each cylinder; and d_1 and d_2, their respective diameters.

In order to apply these equations to gear teeth, we will replace F by W_w, d by $2r$, and l by f. With these changes we may substitute the value of b in Eq. (2-31) into Eq. (2-32). Replacing p_{max} by s and letting $\mu = 0.30$, the surface stress (Hertz stress) is found to be

$$s^2 = \frac{0.35W_w(1/r_1 + 1/r_2)}{f(1/E_1 + 1/E_2)} \tag{10-32}$$

where r = radius
E = modulus of elasticity
W_w = force pressing cylinders together
f = length of cylinders

If the radius of curvature of the gear-tooth profile at the pitch line is used in this equation, it may be employed for calculating the limiting load for wear W_w, provided the surface fatigue strength is known.

Using the subscripts 1 and 2 to designate the pinion and gear, respectively, the radius of curvature is

$$r_1 = \frac{D_1 \sin \phi}{2} \qquad r_2 = \frac{D_2 \sin \phi}{2} \tag{a}$$

where ϕ is the pressure angle. Then

$$\frac{1}{r_1} + \frac{1}{r_2} = \frac{2}{\sin \phi}\left(\frac{1}{D_1} + \frac{1}{D_2}\right) \tag{b}$$

When Eq. (b) is substituted into Eq. (10-32) we obtain

$$s^2 = \frac{0.70W_w(1/D_1 + 1/D_2)}{f \sin \phi(1/E_1 + 1/E_2)} \tag{c}$$

Equation (c) may now be solved for the limiting load for wear, W_w:

$$W_w = \frac{s^2 f \sin \phi(1/E_1 + 1/E_2)}{0.70(1/D_1 + 1/D_2)} \tag{d}$$

Now, since

$$\frac{1}{1/D_1 + 1/D_2} = \frac{D_1 D_2}{D_1 + D_2}$$

TABLE 10-9. VALUES OF THE LOAD-STRESS FACTOR K*

Material		Hardness, Bhn		Surface fatigue strength, psi	Load-stress factor, K	
Pinion	Gear	Pinion	Gear		14½°	20°
Steel....	Steel	150	150	50,000	30	41
Steel....	Steel	200	150	60,000	43	58
Steel....	Steel	250	150	70,000	58	79
Steel....	Steel	200	200	70,000	58	79
Steel....	Steel	250	200	80,000	76	103
Steel....	Steel	300	200	90,000	96	131
Steel....	Steel	250	250	90,000	96	131
Steel....	Steel	300	250	100,000	119	162
Steel....	Steel	350	250	110,000	144	196
Steel....	Steel	300	300	110,000	144	196
Steel....	Steel	350	300	120,000	171	233
Steel....	Steel	400	300	125,000	186	254
Steel....	Steel	350	350	130,000	201	275
Steel....	Steel	400	350	140,000	233	318
Steel....	Steel	400	400	150,000	268	366
Steel....	Cast iron	150	...	50,000	44	60
Steel....	Cast iron	200	...	70,000	87	119
Steel....	Nickel cast iron	150	...	50,000	44	60
Steel....	Nickel cast iron	200	...	70,000	87	119
Steel....	Nickel cast iron	250	...	90,000	144	196
Steel....	Nickel cast iron	300	...	93,000	154	210
Steel....	Phosphor bronze	150	...	50,000	46	62
Steel....	Phosphor bronze	200	...	65,000	73	100
Cast iron	Cast iron	...	...	80,000	152	208
For 10,000,000 Repetitions of Stress						
Steel....	Steel	450	450	188,000	421	575
Steel....	Steel	500	500	210,000	525	718
Steel....	Steel	550	550	233,000	647	884
For 50,000,000 Repetitions of Stress						
Steel....	Steel	450	450	147,000	257	351
Steel....	Steel	500	500	165,000	324	443
Steel....	Steel	550	550	188,000	394	544
For 100,000,000 Repetitions of Stress						
Steel....	Steel	450	450	132,000	208	284
Steel....	Steel	500	500	148,000	261	356
Steel....	Steel	550	550	163,000	316	432

* Earle Buckingham, "Gear Tooth Loads," pp. 53–54, Massachusetts Gear and Tool Company, Woburn, Mass., 1953.

and defining the quantity Q as

$$Q = \frac{2D_2}{D_1 + D_2} \tag{10-33}$$

then

$$\frac{D_1 D_2}{D_1 + D_2} = \frac{D_1 Q}{2} \tag{e}$$

If we now substitute Eq. (e) into Eq. (d), we find that

$$W_w = D_1 f Q \frac{s^2 \sin \phi (1/E_1 + 1/E_2)}{1.40} \tag{f}$$

Equation (f) may be written as

$$W_w = D_1 f Q K \tag{10-34}$$

where

$$K = \frac{s^2 \sin \phi (1/E_1 + 1/E_2)}{1.40} \tag{10-35}$$

Equation (10-34) gives the maximum value of the load for satisfactory wear. When the life of the gears is an important consideration, the limiting load for wear W_w must be equal to the dynamic load, or greater.

The quantity K is called a load-stress factor, and its value depends upon the surface fatigue strength, the pressure angle, and the material of each gear. Values of K may be obtained from experiment or from service data. Table 10-9 shows values of K for various materials as recommended by Buckingham.

In using Table 10-9 it should be noted that the fatigue strength is not the usual flexural endurance limit, but, rather, it is the surface fatigue strength.

Internal Gears. Since the form of the profile on internal-gear teeth is concave instead of convex, the radius of curvature for that profile becomes negative instead of positive. Equation (10-33) for the ratio factor then becomes

$$Q = \frac{2D_2}{D_2 - D_1} \tag{10-36}$$

EXAMPLE 10-3. Using the gearset of Example 10-2, with the gear made of 1020 steel as recommended in the solution, find the limiting load for wear.

Solution. Using Table 10-9, we find the load-stress factor to be $K = 30$. This corresponds to a steel pinion and steel gear with a hardness of 150 Bhn. The ratio factor is

$$Q = \frac{2D_2}{D_1 + D_2} = \frac{(2)(9.6)}{4.0 + 9.6} = 1.41$$

Solving Eq. (10-34), the limiting load for wear is

$$W_w = D_1 f Q K = (4)(1.75)(1.41)(30) = 296 \text{ lb} \qquad \textit{Ans.}$$

These gears are completely unsatisfactory for wear because the dynamic load is 3,035 lb. If we substitute the dynamic load for W_w and solve for K, we find

$$K = \frac{W_d}{D_1 f Q} = \frac{3{,}035}{(4)(1.75)(1.41)} = 308$$

Referring now to Table 10-9, we see that a K of 316 is obtained if the teeth are casehardened to 550 Bhn, and for 100,000,000 cycles of stress. It would be necessary to know the details of the application in order to judge whether or not this would be satisfactory. A better solution might be obtained if, in addition to the casehardening, the face width were increased slightly.

10-13. Friction and Heat. The power loss at each tooth mesh for spur gears is usually less than 1 per cent of the power transmitted. The magnitude of this loss depends upon the gear materials, the tooth system, the lubrication, the character of the tooth surface, and the pitch-line velocity. In addition, there is also a power loss at the bearings which may reach 1 or 2 per cent.

If the gearset is mounted in a gear case, this heat must be dissipated in some manner. If the gears and bearings are lubricated from an oil sump, the lubricant will distribute the heat to the case where it will be dissipated by radiation and conduction. The amount of heat which may be dissipated in this manner can be only a rough guess. It depends upon the character of the surfaces of the case, the temperature and velocity of the surrounding air, and the temperature of the various portions of the case. An average value may be obtained by the equation

$$H = 2.7A(T_2 - T_1) \tag{10-37}$$

where H = amount of heat dissipated by case, Btu per hr
A = surface area of case, ft²
$T_2 - T_1$ = difference in temperature between case and surrounding air, °F

The constant 2.7 may have to be decreased for unfavorable conditions (see Table 9-4).

It is sometimes necessary to direct a stream of cooling oil against the teeth in order to carry away the generated heat. A rule of thumb which is occasionally employed is to use 1 gpm of cooling oil for each 400 hp transmitted.

10-14. Gear Materials. Gears are commonly made of steel, cast iron, bronze, or phenolic resins. Recently nylon, titanium, and sintered iron have been used successfully. The great variety of materials, together with the difficulty of comparing simple tension-test data with complex gear stresses, makes the selection of a satisfactory material very confusing.

In many applications, steel is the only satisfactory material because it combines both high strength and low cost. Gears are made of both plain-carbon and alloy steels, and there is no one best material. In many cases the choice will depend upon the relative success of the heat-treating department with the various steels. When the gear is to be quenched and tempered, a steel with 40 or 50 points of carbon is used. If it is to be casehardened, then one with 20 points or less of carbon is used. The core as well as the surface properties must always be considered.

Cast iron is a very popular gear material. It is easy to cast and machine, has good wearing characteristics, and transmits less noise than steel. The cast irons shown in Table 10-10 are recommended by the American Gear Manufacturers Association (AGMA).

TABLE 10-10. MINIMUM PROPERTIES OF CAST-IRON GEARS*

Class	Minimum tensile strength, psi	Minimum hardness on tooth portion, Bhn
20	20,000	
30	30,000	175
35	35,000	185
40	40,000	200
50	50,000	215
60	60,000	220

* Extracted from AGMA Standard Materials, *AGMA* 242.02, September, 1946, with the permission of the publisher, The American Society of Mechanical Engineers, New York.

Bronzes may be used for gears when corrosion is a problem. They are also very useful where the sliding velocity is high, such as in worm-gear applications. The AGMA lists five tin bronzes containing small percentages of nickel, lead, or zinc which are suitable gear materials. Their hardness varies from 70 to 85 Bhn.

Nonmetallic gears are mated with steel or cast-iron gears in order to obtain the greatest load-carrying capacity. To secure good wear resistance, the metal gear should have a hardness of at least 300 Bhn. A nonmetallic gear will carry almost as much load as a good cast-iron or a mild-steel gear, even though the strength is much lower, because of the low modulus of elasticity. This low modulus permits the nonmetallic gear to absorb the effects of tooth errors so that a dynamic load is not created. A nonmetallic gear also has the important advantage of operating well on marginal lubrication.

Thermosetting laminates are widely used for gears. They are made of sheet materials composed of a fibrous or woven material together with a resin binder. Nylon, as a gear material, has given excellent results in service. The properties of thermosetting laminates are shown in Table 10-11 and those of nylon in Table 10-12.

TABLE 10-11. PROPERTIES OF THERMOSETTING LAMINATES*

NEMA and ASTM grades	C	L
Tensile strength, psi:		
Lengthwise	11,200	14,000
Crosswise	9,500	10,000
Modulus of elasticity in tension, psi:		
Lengthwise	1,000,000	1,200,000
Crosswise	900,000	900,000
Rockwell hardness (M)	103	105
Specific volume, in.^{3} per lb	20.4	20.5

* Darle W. Dudley, "Practical Gear Design," pp. 187–188, McGraw-Hill Book Company, Inc., New York, 1954.

TABLE 10-12. PROPERTIES OF FM-10001 CAST NYLON*

Tensile strength, psi:	
At −70°F	15,700
At 77°F	10,000
At 170°F	7,600
Modulus of elasticity, psi, at 77°F	400,000
Rockwell hardness (R)	118
Specific gravity	1.14
Mold shrinkage, in. per in.	0.015

* Darle W. Dudley, "Practical Gear Design," pp. 187–188, McGraw-Hill Book Company, Inc., New York, 1954.

10-15. Gear-blank Design. Gear blanks are produced by casting, forging, machining from a solid blank, and fabricating. Figure 10-32 illustrates a cast-iron gear in mesh with a pinion which has been made from a steel blank.

Some typical fabrication methods are shown in Fig. 10-33. When the pinion is small it is frequently made integral with the shaft, thus eliminating the key as well as an axial-locating device.

In designing a gear blank, rigidity is almost always a prime consideration. The hub must be thick enough to maintain a proper fit with the shaft and to provide sufficient metal for the key slot. This thickness must also be large enough that the torque may be transmitted through the hub to the web or spokes without serious stress concentrations. The hub must have length in order that the gear will rotate in a single plane without wobble. The arms or web and the rim must also have rigidity but not too much, because of its effect upon the dynamic load.

There are no general rules for the design of hubs. If they are designed with sufficient rigidity, the stresses are usually quite low, especially when compared with the tooth stresses. The length of the hub should be at least equal to the face width, or greater if this does not give sufficient key length. Sometimes two keys are used. If the clearance between the bore and the shaft is large, the hub should have a length which is at least twice the bore diameter, because a slight inaccuracy here is magnified at the rim. Many designers prefer to make a scale drawing of the gear; the

FIG. 10-32. A gearset using a steel pinion and a cast-iron gear. *(Courtesy of Boston Gear Works, Inc.)*

hub dimensions can then be adjusted by eye in order to obtain the necessary rigidity.

Figure 10-34 is a drawing of a portion of a cast-iron gear. The hub bead is used to brace the arms and to reduce the stress concentration caused by the torque transmitted from the hub to the arms. The arms are shown with an elliptical section, but they may also be designed with an H or I section, or any other shape, depending upon the stiffness and strength desired. The rim bead gives additional rigidity and strength to the rim.

If a gear rotates at a high pitch-line velocity, the weight of the rim and teeth may be sufficient to cause large bending stresses in the portion of the rim contained between any two arms. When the gear is made of steel, these stresses are usually not serious, but when cast iron is used this stress should be checked. Although the problem is complicated, an approximation may be obtained by assuming that the rim is a uniformly loaded

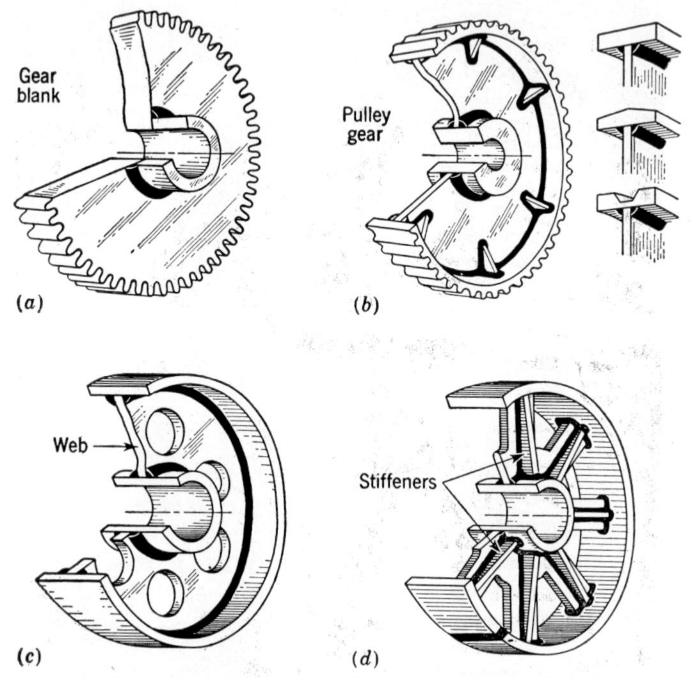

Fig. 10-33. Methods of fabricating gears. In (*a*) is shown a solid gear blank to which the hub is welded. The gear in (*b*) has a solid web with stiffeners giving additional support to the rim. The construction in (*c*) is satisfactory for small-diameter gears with short face widths. A fabricated gear blank with spokes is shown in (*d*). The stiffeners may be carried out to the rim if desired. (*Courtesy of Lincoln Electric Company.*)

beam fixed at the ends by the spokes. The length of the beam would be the length of arc measured at the mean rim diameter between the spoke center lines. Under these assumptions, the total bending load W is

$$W = \frac{wl}{g}\frac{V^2}{r} \qquad (10\text{-}38)$$

where w = unit weight of rim and teeth, lb per in.
V = pitch-line velocity, fps
g = acceleration due to gravity, fps per sec

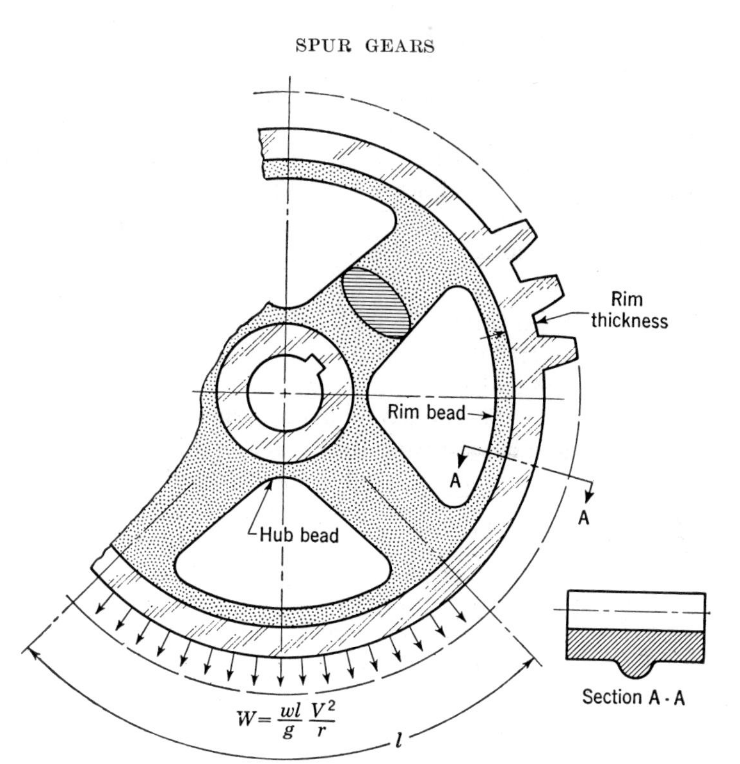

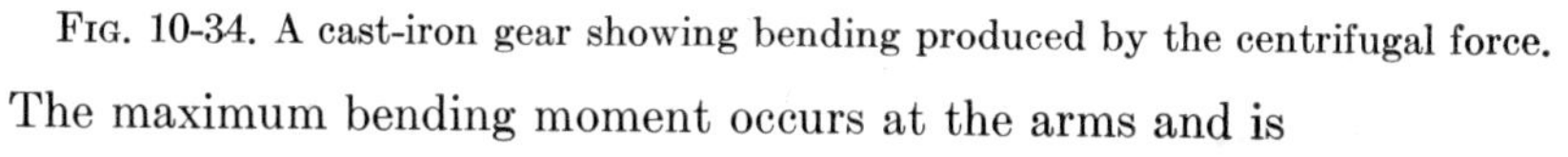
FIG. 10-34. A cast-iron gear showing bending produced by the centrifugal force.

The maximum bending moment occurs at the arms and is

$$M_{\max} = \frac{Wl}{12} \tag{10-39}$$

The stress may then be obtained by substituting the maximum moment and the section modulus into the equation for bending stress, $s = Mc/I$. This solution neglects the curvature of the rim; the tensile, compressive, or bending forces in the rim due to the transfer of torque between the arms and the rim; and the stress-concentration effect where the arm joins the rim. In addition, we cannot be sure of the accuracy of the assumption that the ends are fixed.

FIG. 10-35. Section of rim. The rim must have sufficient rigidity to avoid deflection through the angle α.

The rim must also have rigidity in the direction parallel to the axis of the gear (Fig. 10-35) in order to maintain a uniform load across the face. This means that the arm or web must be thick enough for adequate support.

The loading on the arms of a gear is very complicated. The transmitted torque produces bending, the centrifugal force on the rim produces a combination of bending and tension, and the dynamic load acting between the teeth produces a vibrating bending force. An approximation can be obtained by neglecting all these except the bending produced by the transmitted torque. Then the bending force is (Fig. 10-36)

$$F = \frac{T}{rn} \tag{10-40}$$

where T = transmitted torque, lb-in.
r = length of spoke, in.
n = number of spokes

The stress may then be determined by finding the maximum moment for a cantilever beam and substituting this, together with the section modulus, in the bending-stress equation, $s = Mc/I$. A high factor of safety should be used because this method is only a rough approximation and stress concentration is present.

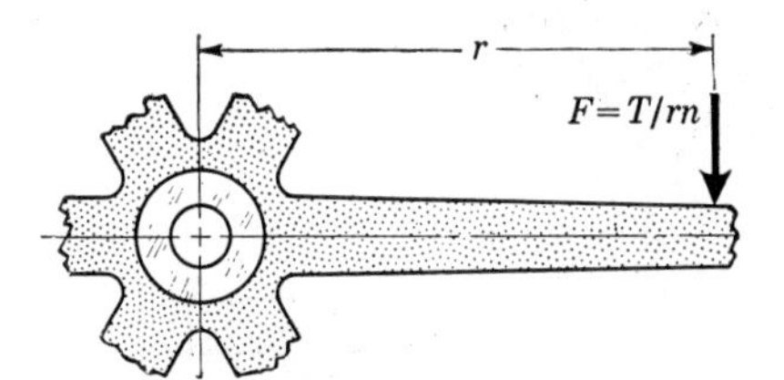

Fig. 10-36. Bending force on a spoke.

The analytical methods investigated above are not used every time a gear is to be designed. Many cases occur in which the loads and velocities are not high, and the gear can be designed on the drawing board by using pleasing proportions. On the other hand, cases sometimes occur where the loads are extremely high, or where the weight of the gear is a very important consideration; in these situations it may be desirable to make a much more thorough investigation than is indicated here.

PROBLEMS

10-1. A 4-DP pinion, having 22 teeth, runs at 1,200 rpm and is to drive a gear at 660 rpm. Find the number of teeth in the gear and the center distance.

10-2. A pair of gears have an angular velocity ratio of 3.2. There are 20 teeth in the driver, and the circular pitch is 3 in. (*a*) Find the number of teeth on the driven gear. (*b*) Find the center distance.

10-3. A 12-DP pinion, having 24 teeth, runs at 1,800 rpm. The driven gear is to run at a speed of 450 rpm. (*a*) Find the number of teeth on the gear. (*b*) Determine the center distance. (*c*) What is the circular pitch?

10-4. The figure illustrates a double-reduction gear train. Shaft 1 is driven by a 1½-hp motor at 1,720 rpm. The reduction between shafts 1 and 2 is 3½:1 and between shafts 2 and 3 is 4:1. The pinion on shaft 1 has 24 teeth, and the gear on shaft 3 has 160 teeth. (*a*) Find the tooth numbers for the gears on shaft 2. (*b*) Find

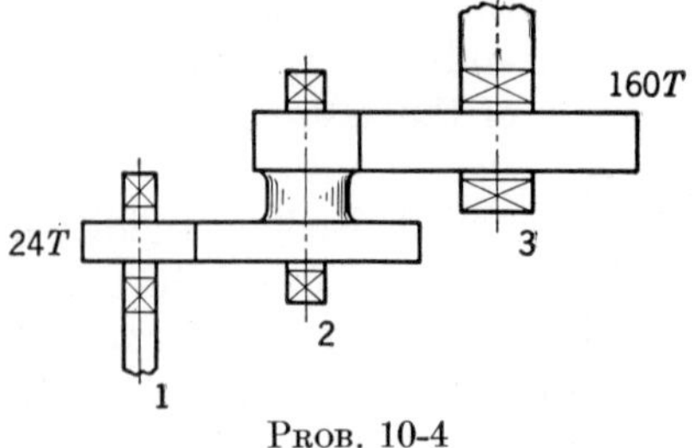

Prob. 10-4

the speed of shafts 2 and 3. (*c*) If the power loss is 4 per cent for each pair of gears and if the motor delivers full power, find the torque at each shaft.

10-5. The pinion driving a set of double-reduction gears, as in Prob. 10-4, is 16-DP, rotates at 3,600 rpm, and has a pitch-line velocity of 942 fpm. The reduction ratio between the first pair of gears is to be 1:12 and between the second pair 1:10. The gears are to transmit ¾ hp. The second set of gears has a pitch-line velocity of 157 fpm and a diametral pitch of 10. (*a*) Find the tooth numbers for each gear. (*b*) Determine the rpm and torque at each shaft. (*c*) Calculate both center distances.

10-6. (*a*) If the gears of Prob. 10-1 are 20° full-depth and 20 hp is transmitted, find the tangential load and the shaft reaction. (*b*) What is the torque at each shaft?

10-7. Find the tangential load and the shaft reaction for the gears of Prob. 10-3 if the teeth are 14½° composite and 1.5 hp is transmitted.

10-8. In the figure the gears connecting shafts 1 and 2 are 10-pitch, 14½° pressure angle, and those connecting shafts 2 and 3 are 8-pitch with the same pressure angle. The pinion transmits 2 hp at 1,120 rpm. Determine the resultant shaft reactions. NOTE: It is necessary to assume that the forces applied to the gears on shaft 2 are both in the same plane.

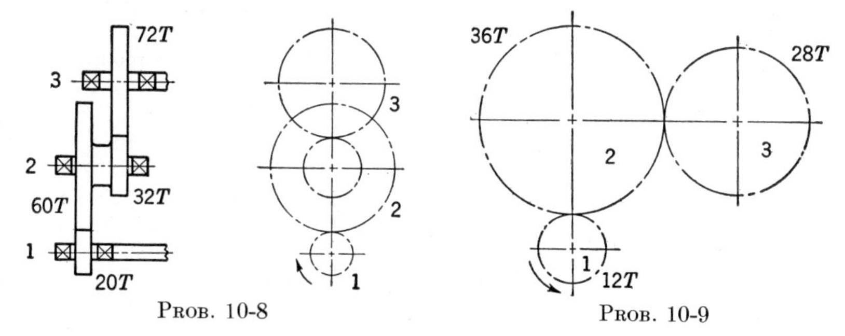

PROB. 10-8

PROB. 10-9

10-9. The gears shown in the figure are 3-DP, 20° stub, and are in the same plane. The pinion rotates counterclockwise at 600 rpm and transmits 25 hp through the idler to the 28-tooth gear on shaft 3. Calculate the resultant shaft reaction on the 36-tooth idler.

10-10. The 16-tooth pinion on shaft 1 rotates at 1,720 rpm and transmits 5 hp to the double-reduction train. Both sets of gears are 20° full-depth. The distances between the centers of the bearings and gears for shaft 2 are shown in the figure. Find the maximum bending moment on shaft 2.

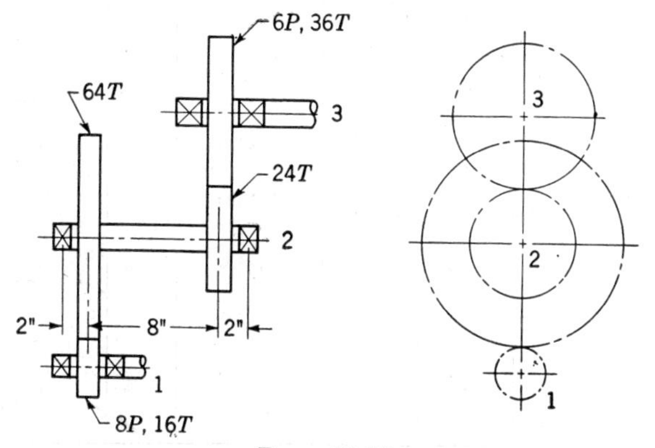

PROB. 10-10

10-11. A 4615 steel pinion, casehardened to 385 Bhn, is 10-DP, has 16 teeth, and is cut by hobbing, using the 20° full-depth system. The pinion has a face width of 1¼ in. and rotates at 1,720 rpm. Using a fatigue stress-concentration factor of 1.4, find the maximum steady tangential load which may be transmitted, as given by the modified Lewis equation. *Ans.:* $W_{max} = 2{,}280$ lb.

10-12. A 5-DP 20° full-depth involute gear has 80 teeth and is made of class 30 cast iron. The gear is to mesh with an 18-tooth pinion which rotates at 1,200 rpm. The load is pulsating. The face width is 2½ in. Using fatigue stress-concentration factors of 1.1 for the gear and 1.3 for the pinion, select a suitable pinion material such that the strengths are approximately equal.

10-13. A gearset is 20-DP, 14½° full-depth involute, with 20 and 96 teeth for the pinion and gear, respectively. The gears have a face width of ⅜ in. and a pitch-line velocity of 900 fpm. The gear is made of class 30 cast iron and the pinion of 1020 steel without heat-treatment. Determine the maximum tangential load which may be transmitted by the set. Use a fatigue stress-concentration factor of 1.3 for the pinion and 1.15 for the year. The load is steady. *Ans.:* $W_{max} = 59.5$ lb.

10-14. The same as Prob. 10-13 except that the teeth are 20° stub.

10-15. A 14-tooth 20° stub pinion is to drive a 21-tooth gear. The pinion is to rotate at 1,150 rpm and transmit 25 hp under steady load conditions. Both gears are to be made of 1040 steel heat-treated to 260 Bhn. Using the modified Lewis equation, determine tentative values for the pitch, face width, and center distance.

***10-16.** An 8-tooth 20° full-depth pinion is to drive a 26-tooth gear at a maximum pitch-line velocity of 2,000 fpm. Both gears are to be made of 3240 steel heat-treated to 400 Bhn. The gears are to transmit 50 hp under heavy shock loading for short intervals of time. Wear and fatigue are not important, but the teeth must be strong enough to resist breakage. Determine a satisfactory pitch and face width.

***10-17 to 10-24.** The table gives sufficient data for a tentative design of a gearset. Using the modified Lewis equation, determine a suitable pitch and face width. The load is continuous with mild shock.

Prob. No.	Tooth system	Tooth numbers		Pinion speed, rpm	Hp	Material	
		Pinion	Gear			Pinion	Gear
10-17	20° full depth	16	64	3,600	1/50	Phosphor bronze	Phosphor bronze
10-18	20° stub	12	32	400	1	Steel, 240 Bhn	Steel, 240 Bhn
10-19	14½° involute	28	34	800–1,400	32	Steel, 320 Bhn	Steel, 320 Bhn
10-20	14½° involute	22	84	300	18	Steel, 200 Bhn	Cast iron, class 40
10-21	20° full depth	30	160	1,200	400	Steel, 360 Bhn	Steel, 360 Bhn
10-22	20° full depth	6	30	1,800	1/10	Steel, 280 Bhn	Steel, 280 Bhn
10-23	20° stub	14	42	100	50	Steel, 200 Bhn	Cast iron, class 30
10-24	20° full depth	14	48	1,720	¼	Steel, 320 Bhn	Cast iron, class 30

10-25. A 10-DP 1-in.-face-width 20° full-depth 20-tooth cast-iron pinion rotates at 1,800 rpm and transmits 1 hp. The gear has 60 teeth and is also made of cast iron. Both gears are of plain disk form, and the error is 0.002 in. Using the Buckingham equation, find the dynamic load. (Courtesy of Massachusetts Gear and Tool Company.) *Ans.:* 268 lb.

10-26. The same as Prob. 10-25 except that the error is 0.004 in.

***10-27.** A pair of gears have 14½° full-depth teeth, a 1/16-in. face width, a diametral pitch of 32, and are made of phosphor bronze in plain disk form. The pinion and gear have 18 and 96 teeth, respectively. They are cut so that the maximum error is 0.0015 in. The pinion runs at 2,400 rpm with a transmitted load which is negligible. Determine the dynamic load.

10-28. The following data apply to a gearset: pinion, 8-DP, 14½°, 1½-in. face, 16 teeth, 2,600 rpm, 1⅝-in.-diameter hub × ⅞-in. projection, 300 Bhn steel; gear, 32 teeth, 2½-in.-diameter hub × 1-in. projection, 300 Bhn steel. Both gears are of disk form with projecting hubs. They have been tentatively designed to transmit 2 hp. Determine the dynamic load if the error is 0.001 in.

10-29. Determine the dynamic load for Prob. 10-28 if the error is 0.002 in.

10-30. The same as Prob. 10-29 except that both gears are of class 30 cast iron.

10-31. The same as Prob. 10-28 except that both gears are of class 30 cast iron.

***10-32.** The pinion and gear shown in the figure have been tentatively designed to transmit 5 hp at 300-fpm pitch-line velocity. The tooth system is 20° full-depth

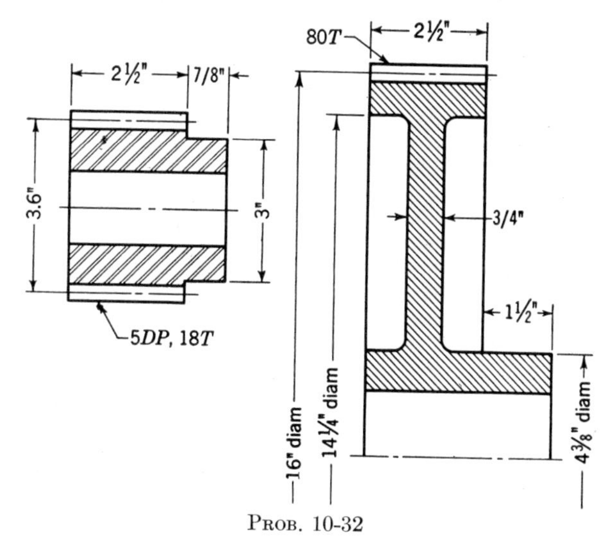

PROB. 10-32

involute. It is believed that a 1020 steel pinion without heat-treatment and a class 30 cast-iron gear will give satisfactory service. The error should not be more than 0.002 in. The load is steady and continuous. Use the Buckingham equation, calculate the dynamic load, and substitute this value into the modified Lewis equation [Eq. (10-21)] to obtain the fatigue stress. Are the gears satisfactory as designed? If not, what changes should be made?

10-33. A 12-DP 20° stub gearset has a face width of 1 in. The pinion and gear have 14 and 18 teeth, respectively, and are both made of 1045 steel heat-treated to 400 Bhn. Calculate the limiting load for wear.

10-34. Repeat Prob. 10-33 if both gears are of cast iron.

10-35. A gearset is made of 3115 steel casehardened to 480 Bhn. The face width is 3 in., the diametral pitch is 3, and the gears are made by the 14½° involute system. If the tooth numbers for the pinion and gear are 28 and 36, respectively, compute the limiting load for wear.

10-36. Repeat Prob. 10-35 if both gears are of cast iron.

10-37. Determine the limiting load for wear for the gears described in Prob. 10-25.

10-38. Determine the limiting load for wear for the gears described in Prob. 10-28.

***10-39.** A spur-gear reduction unit is to transmit 75 hp continuously with moderate shock load. The speeds of the shafts are to be 720 rpm and 144 rpm, respectively. The center distance is not restricted, but it should be small and a satisfactory contact ratio obtained. Thirty-two units are to be constructed. Make a complete design for these two gears, including a sketch showing all dimensions. The cost should be kept low, but it is important that the gears be designed for a long and trouble-free life. Determine the shaft diameter on the basis of pure torsion. The shaft should be made of a 35-point carbon steel, and the key of a 15- or 20-point steel.

***10-40.** Design a pinion for mounting on a ⅜-in. shaft to drive a gear which is to be mounted on a ⅝-in. shaft. The pinion speed is 3,600 rpm, and the power transmitted is negligible. The angular-velocity ratio between the two shafts is to be approximately 5. The space occupied should be a minimum. Wear and cost are important considerations. Five hundred units are to be manufactured.

***10-41.** The figure shows three identical gears connected to parallel shafts with center distances of 1 in. Shaft A receives power from a gear motor and distributes one-third to gear B and one-third to gear C, retaining the remaining one-third for the

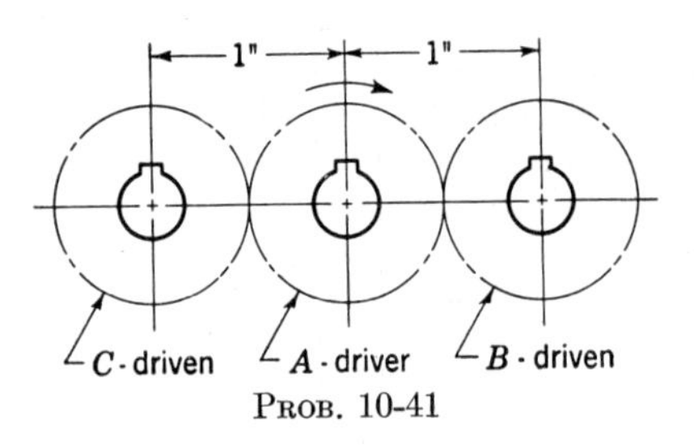

PROB. 10-41

external load connected to shaft A. The speed of the gears is adjustable in 100-rpm steps from 300 to 900 rpm. The motor is rated at 1⁄12 hp intermittent or 1⁄20 hp continuous. The three gears are to be of thin disks without hubs and keyed with 7⁄64-in. square wire. Design the gears for manufacture in quantities of 75,000 units. It is estimated that the units will be used for 3 hr per day as a maximum, but not continuously. The speed which will be most used depends upon the consumer and cannot be determined. The unit should have a very low cost and a life of 5 years.

***10-42 to 10-57.** A pinion and gear are to be designed according to the specifications in the accompanying table. The gears will be exposed and grease-lubricated. The quantity to be manufactured will be 12 at a time, but this will occur frequently over a period of years. Neither center distance nor space requirements are important. Low cost and long life are the desirable characteristics. It is suggested that, where possible, a steel pinion and a cast-iron gear would make a desirable combination. The shafts should be designed for pure torsion, using an ample factor of safety. Design both gears, and make a sketch showing all dimensions.

Prob. No.	Pinion, rpm	Gear, rpm	Hp	Character of load
10-42	1,720	145	20	Steady
10-43	1,720	215	10	Steady
10-44	1,720	285	5	Pulsating
10-45	1,200	86	72	Pulsating
10-46	1,200	120	100	Steady
10-47	1,200	300	200	Steady
10-48	1,120	280	300	Steady
10-49	1,120	224	250	Pulsating
10-50	1,120	185	200	Pulsating
10-51	1,120	140	100	Shock
10-52	900	56	75	Shock
10-53	900	64	60	Pulsating
10-54	900	75	50	Steady
10-55	900	150	40	Steady
10-56	900	180	25	Shock
10-57	900	225	15	Shock

*__10-58.__ Design the gears, shafts, and bearings for a double-reduction unit. The first pinion shaft is to be attached to a standard 50-hp squirrel-cage motor by means of a straight shaft coupling. The motor has a no-load speed of 1,200 rpm. The output shaft of the unit is to rotate at 20 rpm and is to be connected to the driven machine through a straight shaft coupling. The load is steady and continuous. Only one unit is to be built. Size is not important, but the noise level should be as low as possible, using spur gears.

*__10-59.__ The same as Prob. 10-58 except that 500 units are to be manufactured.

*__10-60.__ The same as Prob. 10-58 except that the motor speed is 1,800 rpm.

① $W_{max} = 500$ $W_{max} > W_d > W_w$

② $W_d = 400$ okay

③ $W_w = 200$

CHAPTER 11

HELICAL, WORM, AND BEVEL GEARS

Most engineers prefer to use spur gears when power is to be transferred between parallel shafts, because they are easier to design and manufacture. However, sometimes the design requirements are such that helical gears are a better choice. This may be true when the loads are heavy, the speeds are high, or the noise level must be kept low. While spur gears

FIG. 11-1. A pair of right-hand helical gears. (*Courtesy of Brad Foote Gear Works, Inc.*)

are ordinarily used in slow-speed applications and helical gears are used in high-speed applications, spur gears should not be considered as being limited to slow speeds. If the noise requirement permits, they may be used at very high pitch-line velocities.

When power is to be transmitted between shafts which are not parallel the spur gear cannot be used, and the designer must choose between crossed-helical, worm, bevel, or hypoid gears. Bevel gears are used for high efficiencies. Crossed-helical and worm gears have a lower efficiency because of the rubbing action. Hypoid gears are stronger than bevel gears, but their efficiency is lower. Worm gears are used primarily when very-high-velocity ratios are required.

11-1. Parallel Helical Gears. Helical gears, used to transmit motion between parallel shafts, are shown in Fig. 11-1. The helix angle is the same on each gear, but one gear must have a right-hand helix and the other a left-hand helix. The shape of the tooth is an involute helicoid and is illustrated in Fig. 11-2. If a piece of paper cut into the shape of a parallelogram is wrapped around a cylinder, the angular edge of the paper becomes a helix. If we unwind this paper, each point on the angular edge generates an involute curve. The surface obtained when every point on the edge generates an involute is called an *involute helicoid*.

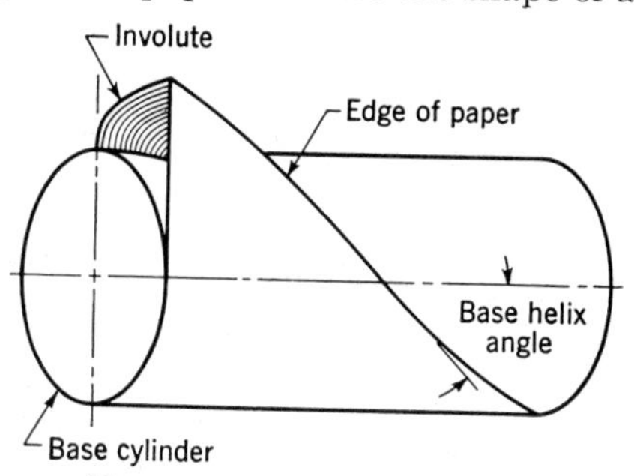

FIG. 11-2. An involute helicoid.

The initial contact of spur-gear teeth is a line extending all the way across the face of the tooth. The initial contact of helical-gear teeth is a point which changes into a line as the teeth come into more engagement. In spur gears the line of contact is parallel to the axis of rotation; in helical gears the line is diagonal across the face of the tooth. It is this gradual engagement of the teeth and the smooth transfer of load from one tooth to another which give helical gears the ability to transmit heavy loads at high speeds. Because of the nature of contact between helical gears, the contact ratio is of only minor importance, and it is the contact area, which is proportional to the face width of the gear, that becomes significant.

Helical gears subject the shaft bearings to both radial and thrust loads. When the thrust loads become high or are objectionable for other reasons, it may be desirable to use double helical gears. A double helical gear (herringbone) is equivalent to two helical gears of opposite hand, mounted side by side on the same shaft. They develop opposite thrust reactions and thus cancel out the thrust load.

When two or more single helical gears are mounted on the same shaft, the hand of the gears should be selected so as to produce the minimum thrust load.

11-2. Tooth Relationships. Figure 11-3 represents a portion of the top view of a helical rack. Lines *ab* and *cd* are the center lines of two adjacent helical teeth taken on the pitch plane. The angle ψ is the *helix angle*. The distance *ac* is the *transverse circular pitch* p in the plane of rotation (usually called the *circular pitch*). The distance *ae* is the *normal circular pitch* p_n and is related to the transverse circular pitch as follows:

$$p_n = p \cos \psi \tag{11-1}$$

The distance *ad* is called the *axial pitch* p_a and is related by the expression

$$p_a = \frac{p}{\tan \psi} \tag{11-2}$$

Since $p_n P_n = \pi$, the *normal diametral pitch* is

$$P_n = \frac{P}{\cos \psi} \tag{11-3}$$

The pressure angle ϕ_n in the normal direction is different from the pressure angle ϕ in the direction of rotation, because of the angularity of the

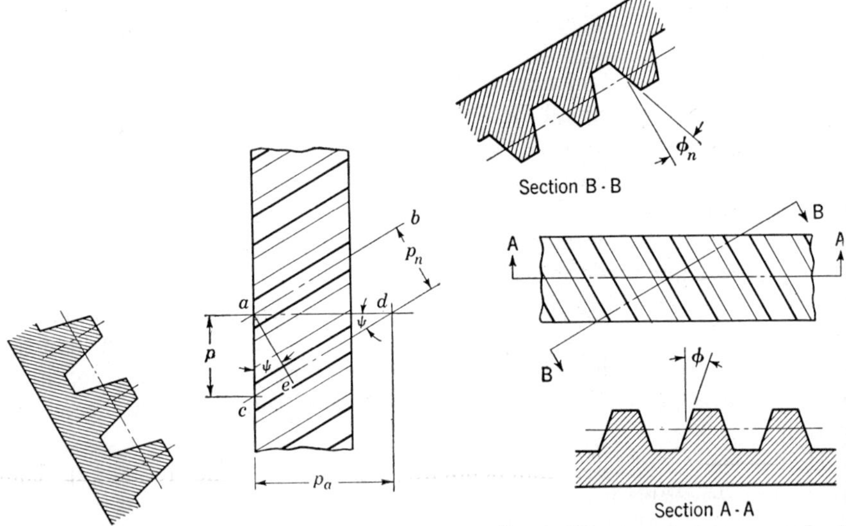

FIG. 11-3. Circular-pitch relations.

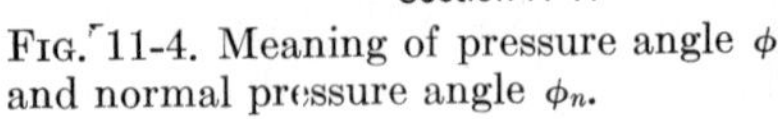

FIG. 11-4. Meaning of pressure angle ϕ and normal pressure angle ϕ_n.

teeth. These angles are related by the equation

$$\cos \psi = \frac{\tan \phi_n}{\tan \phi} \tag{11-4}$$

The distinction between these two pressure angles is illustrated by the rack of Fig. 11-4.

Figure 11-5 illustrates a cylinder cut by an oblique plane *ab* at an angle ψ to a right section. The oblique plane cuts out an arc having a radius of curvature of R. For the condition that $\psi = 0$, the radius of curvature is $R = D/2$. If we imagine the angle ψ to be slowly increased from zero to 90°, we see that R begins at a value of $D/2$ and increases until, when $\psi = 90°$, $R = \infty$. The radius R is the apparent pitch radius of a helical-gear tooth when viewed in the direction of the tooth elements. A gear of the same pitch and with the radius R will have a greater number of teeth, because of the increased radius. In helical-gear design this is called the *virtual number of teeth.* It can be shown by analytical geometry that the virtual number of teeth is related to the actual number by the equation

$$N' = \frac{N}{\cos^3 \psi} \qquad (11\text{-}5)$$

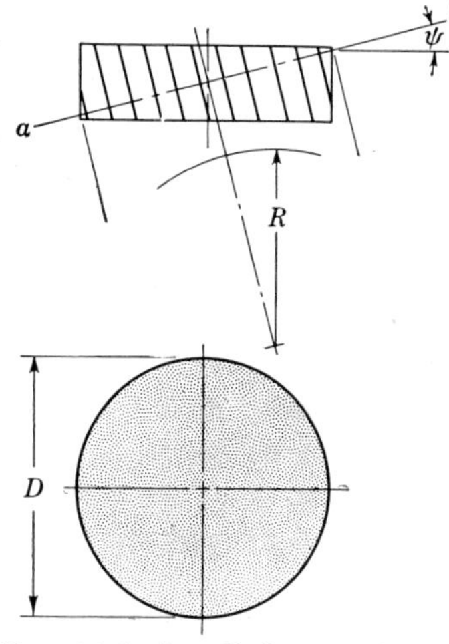

FIG. 11-5. A cylinder cut by an oblique plane.

where N' is the virtual number of teeth and N is the actual number of teeth. It is necessary to know the virtual number of teeth in applying the Lewis equation and also, sometimes, in cutting helical teeth. This apparently larger radius of curvature means that fewer teeth may be used on helical gears, because there will be less undercutting.

11-3. Helical-gear Bearing Loads. The hand of helical gears is illustrated in Fig. 11-6. The reader may avoid confusion by picturing the helix on a right-hand bolt; when the nut is turned clockwise it advances onto the bolt.

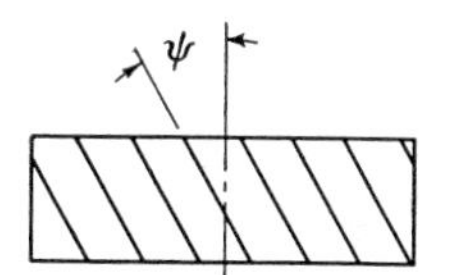

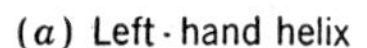
(a) Left-hand helix

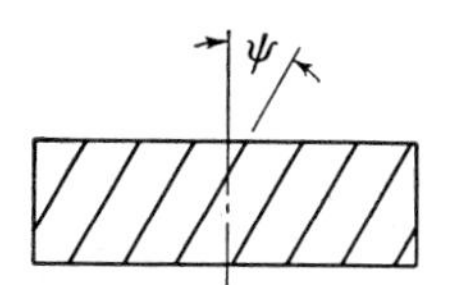

(b) Right-hand helix

FIG. 11-6. The hand of helical gears.

It is convenient, in helical-gear work, to separate out the axial-thrust component of the load, work with it independently, and treat the remaining components as in spur-gear design.

The forces acting upon a portion of a helical rack in the pitch plane are shown in Fig. 11-7. The tooth force is resolved into a tangential component W, parallel to the direction of rotation, and an axial-thrust component W_t. From Fig. 11-7 the axial-thrust component is

$$W_t = W \tan \psi \qquad (11\text{-}6)$$

From Chap. 10, the radial load on the shaft is

$$W_r = \frac{W}{\cos \phi} \qquad (11\text{-}7)$$

EXAMPLE 11-1. A gear train is composed of three helical gears with the shaft centers in line. The driver is a right-hand helical gear with a 20° pressure angle and a 30° helix angle. If the transmitted load is 600 lb, find the radial and thrust forces acting against each shaft.

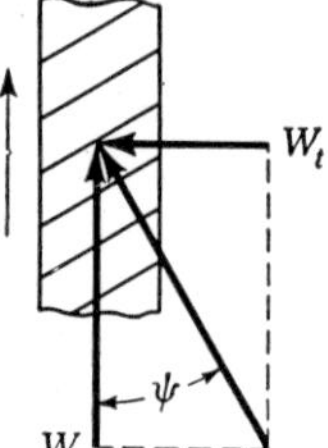

FIG. 11-7. Tooth forces.

Solution. The radial force is

$$W_r = \frac{W}{\cos\phi} = \frac{600}{\cos 20°} = 638 \text{ lb}$$

The thrust force is

$$W_t = W \tan\psi = 600 \tan 30° = 347 \text{ lb}$$

The thrust forces acting against each shaft, and their directions, are shown in Fig. 11-8*a*. The driver subjects the shaft to a thrust of 347 lb and is acting up. The idler has a thrust of 347 lb due to the driver and a thrust of 347 lb due to the driven. These forces act in opposite directions, and so the net thrust on the idler shaft is zero. The driven gear has a thrust force, due to the idler, of 347 lb acting down.

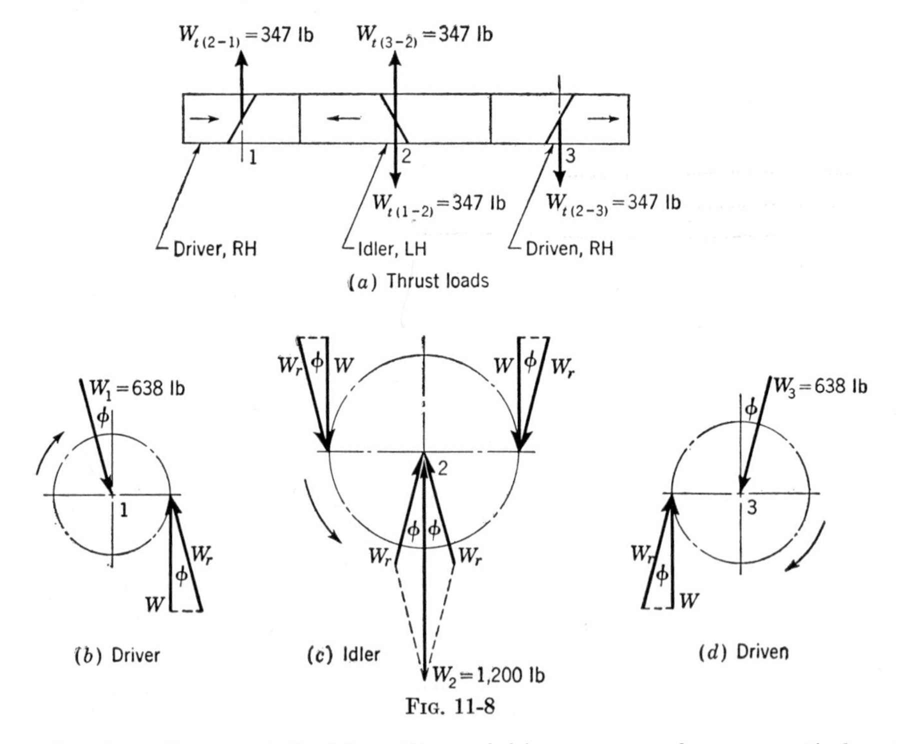

FIG. 11-8

Free-body diagrams of the driver, idler, and driven gears are shown, respectively, in Fig. 11-8*b*, *c*, and *d*. In the three diagrams the forces acting at the centers are the forces and directions with which the shafts push against the gears. The force with which the gear, in each case, pushes against the shaft is, therefore, of the same magnitude but oppositely directed. The radial forces on the shafts are 638 lb for the driver and driven and 1,200 lb for the idler because it is acted upon by two forces.

11-4. Tooth Proportions for Helical Gears. Except for fine-pitch gears (20-DP and finer), there is no standard for the proportions of helical-gear teeth. One reason for this is that it is cheaper to change the design slightly than it is to purchase special tooling. Since helical gears are rarely used interchangeably anyway, and since many different designs

TABLE 11-1. HELICAL-GEAR TOOTH PROPORTIONS FOR $\phi_n = 20°$*
Normal diametral pitch $P_n = 1$
Normal circular pitch $p_n = 3.14159$

Helix angle ψ, deg	Diametral pitch P	Circular pitch p	Axial pitch p_a	Pressure angle ϕ	Working depth	Whole depth
0	1.000	3.14159	. . .	20°	2.000	2.250
5	0.996195	3.15359	36.04560	20°4′ 13.1″	2.000	2.250
8	0.990268	3.17247	22.57327	20°10′50.6″	2.000	2.250
10	0.984808	3.19006	18.09171	20°17′ 0.7″	2.000	2.250
12	0.978148	3.21178	15.11019	20°24′37.1″	2.000	2.250
15	0.965926	3.25242	12.13817	20°38′48.8″	2.000	2.250
18	0.951057	3.30326	10.16640	20°56′30.7″	2.000	2.250
20	0.939693	3.34321	9.18540	21°10′22.0″	2.000	2.250
21	0.933580	3.36510	8.76638	21°17′56.4″	2.000	2.250
22	0.927184	3.38832	8.38636	21°25′57.7″	2.000	2.250
23	0.920505	3.41290	8.04029	21°34′26.3″	2.000	2.250
24	0.913545	3.43890	7.72389	21°43′22.9″	2.000	2.250
25	0.906308	3.46636	7.43364	21°52′58.7″	2.000	2.250
26	0.898794	3.49534	7.16651	22° 2′44.2″	2.000	2.250
27	0.891007	3.52589	6.91994	22°13′10.6″	2.000	2.250
28	0.882948	3.55807	6.69175	22°24′ 9.0″	2.000	2.250
29	0.874620	3.59195	6.48004	22°35′40.0″	2.000	2.250
30	0.866025	3.62760	6.28318	22°47′45.1″	2.000	2.250

* Darle W. Dudley, "Practical Gear Design," pp. 95–97, McGraw-Hill Book Company, Inc., New York, 1954.

will work well together, there is really little advantage in having them interchangeable.

Dudley recommends two sets of basic proportions as a general guide and states that they may usually be modified satisfactorily in order to fit the dimensions of whatever tools may be on hand. The dimensions of the first set are shown in Table 11-1. These are for a normal diametral pitch of 1 and for helix angles between 0 and 30°. For pitch values different from unity, the values given in the table should be divided by the actual value of the normal diametral pitch. These values are for a normal pressure angle of 20°, and so all the various helix angles may be cut with the same hob. Of course, the normal diametral pitch of the hob and the gear to be cut must be equal.

The second set of proportions is based on a transverse diametral pitch of 1 and a pressure angle ϕ of 20°. Values are given for helix angles of 15 to 45°. More than 45° is not recommended. The 30 and 45° angles are usually used for double helical gears. These proportions are shown in Table 11-2 and are especially recommended when the noise level must be kept low.

TABLE 11-2. HELICAL-GEAR TOOTH PROPORTIONS FOR $\phi = 20°$*
Diametral pitch $P = 1$
Circular pitch $p = 3.14159$

Helix angle ψ, deg	Normal diametral pitch P_n	Normal circular pitch p_n	Axial pitch p_a	Normal pressure angle ϕ_n	Working depth	Whole depth
15	1.03528	3.03454	11.72456	19°22′12.2″	2.000	2.350
23	1.0836	2.89185	7.40113	18°31′21.6″	1.840	2.200
30	1.15470	2.72070	5.44140	17°29′42.7″	1.740	2.050
45	1.41421	2.22144	3.14159	14°25′57.9″	1.420	1.700

* Darle W. Dudley, "Practical Gear Design," pp. 95–97, McGraw-Hill Book Company, Inc., New York, 1954.

Many authorities recommend that the face width of helical gears be at least two times the axial pitch ($f = 2p_a$) in order to obtain helical-gear action. Exceptions to this rule are automotive gears which have a face width considerably less, and marine reduction gears which often have a face width much greater.

11-5. Strength of Helical Gears. The beam strength of helical gears is calculated in the same manner as for spur gears. The cross section of the tooth considered must, however, be a normal section. This means that the normal diametral pitch must be used and, also, that the virtual number of teeth must be used to determine the form factor Y. The modified Lewis equation for dynamic loads then becomes

$$W_{\max} = \frac{fYC_v s_e}{k_f K_1 P_n m_p} \tag{11-8}$$

where s_e = endurance limit from Table 10-6, psi
C_v = velocity factor for helical gears, from Fig. 11-9
k_f = fatigue stress-concentration factor obtained from Eq. (10-18) or (10-19), or from Table 10-5, and corrected for notch sensitivity, employing Fig. 4-24
K_1 = service factor = 1.25 for steady loads, 1.35 for pulsating loads, and 1.5 for shock loads

m_p = profile contact ratio determined from layout of gears on transverse plane, or $m_p = 1.4$ may be used for estimating purposes
W_{max} = maximum tangential load, lb
P_n = normal diametral pitch
f = face width, in.
Y = Lewis form factor based on normal diametral pitch and virtual number of teeth

It will be noticed that the modified Lewis equation for helical gears differs from that for spur gears in that the form-factor coefficient K_2 is omitted and the contact ratio m_p is added. In helical-gear action there

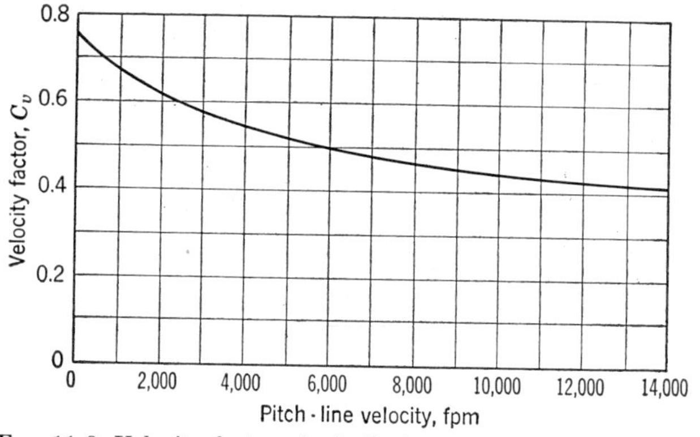

FIG. 11-9. Velocity factors for helical gears of medium quality.

is overlapping tooth contact, the full load is never taken by a single pair of teeth, and so the worst-load condition does not occur. Since the load is distributed among several teeth, the result is divided by the number of teeth in contact.

The velocity factor is higher for helical gears. Dudley[1] recommends the values shown in the graph of Fig. 11-9 for gears of medium quality.

When the velocity factor is omitted from Eq. (11-8) the Lewis equation becomes

$$W_{max} = \frac{fYs_e}{k_f K_1 P_n m_p} \tag{11-9}$$

This gives the static beam strength of helical-gear teeth. The value of W_{max} obtained from Eq. (11-9) must always be equal to, or greater than, the dynamic load.

Dynamic Load. There are a few changes in the fundamental Buckingham equations for the dynamic load when applied to helical gears. The equations are as follows:

$$W_d = W + \sqrt{F_a(2F_2 - F_a)} \tag{11-10}$$

[1] *Ibid.*, p. 126.

where W_d = dynamic load, lb
W = tangential load, lb
F_a = acceleration load, lb
F_2 = force required to deform teeth amount of effective error, lb

$$F_a = \frac{F_1 F_2}{F_1 + F_2} \tag{11-11}$$

where F_1 is the average force, in pounds, required to accelerate the masses when they are considered as rigid bodies.

$$F_1 = HmV^2 \cos^2 \psi \tag{11-12}$$

where m = effective mass, slugs
V = pitch-line velocity, fpm
ψ = helix angle

$$H = c_1 \left(\frac{1}{R_1} + \frac{1}{R_2} \right) \tag{11-13}$$

where R_1 = pitch radius of driver, in.
R_2 = pitch radius of driven, in.
c_1 = 0.00086 for 14½° gears (normal pressure angle)
c_1 = 0.00120 for 20° gears (normal pressure angle)

$$m = \frac{m_1 m_2}{m_1 + m_2} \tag{11-14}$$

where m_1 and m_2 are the masses of the driver and driven, respectively, in slugs.

$$F_2 = fC \cos^2 \psi + W \tag{11-15}$$

The value of C is obtained from Table 10-7 as for spur gears.

As in spur gears, there is an approximation to the Buckingham equation which may be used for rapid computations:

$$W_d = W + \frac{0.05VF_2 \cos \psi}{0.05V + \sqrt{F_2}} \tag{11-16}$$

Limiting Load for Wear. In spur-gear design it is often uncertain whether the dynamic strength or the surface durability is the principal design factor. However, in helical-gear design the wear load is almost always the ruling design factor and hence usually determines the size of the gear. The equation for the limiting load for wear may be adapted for use in helical-gear design as follows:

$$W_w = \frac{D_1 f Q K}{\cos^2 \psi} \tag{11-17}$$

where W_w = limiting load for wear; should be equal to, or greater than, dynamic load
D_1 = pitch diameter of driver
f = face width
Q = ratio factor, with same value as for spur gears
K = load-stress factor, also with same value as for spur gears

11-6. Crossed-helical Gears. Crossed-helical, or spiral, gears are those in which the shaft center lines are neither parallel nor intersecting. They are essentially nonenveloping worm gears, because the gear blanks have a cylindrical form. This class of gears is illustrated in Fig. 11-10.

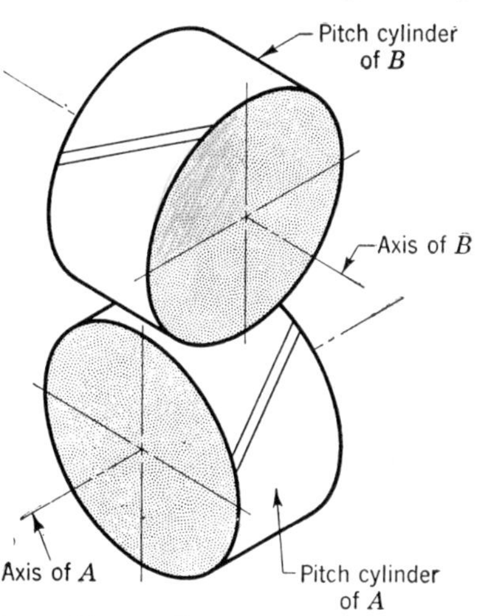

FIG. 11-10. Crossed-helical gears—pitch cylinders.

The teeth of crossed-helical gears have "point contact" with each other, which changes to "line contact" as the gears wear in. For this reason they will carry only very small loads. Crossed-helical gears are for instrumental applications, and they are definitely not recommended for use in the transmission of power.

There is no difference between a crossed-helical gear and a helical gear until they are mounted in mesh with each other. They are manufactured in the same way. A pair of meshed crossed-helical gears usually have the same hand; that is, a right-hand driver goes with a right-hand driven. The relation between thrust, hand, and rotation for crossed-helical gears is shown in Fig. 11-11.

When specifying tooth sizes the normal pitch should always be used. The reason for this is that, when different helix angles are used for the driver and driven, the transverse pitches are not the same. The relation between the shaft and helix angles is as follows:

$$\Sigma = \psi_1 \pm \psi_2 \tag{11-18}$$

where Σ is the shaft angle. The plus sign is used when both helix angles are of the same hand, and the minus sign when they are of opposite hand. Opposite-hand crossed-helical gears are used when the shaft angle is small.

The pitch diameter is obtained from the equation

$$D = \frac{N}{P_n \cos \psi} \tag{11-19}$$

where N = number of teeth
P_n = normal diametral pitch
ψ = helix angle

Since the pitch diameters are not directly related to the tooth numbers, they cannot be used to obtain the angular-velocity ratio. This ratio must be obtained from the ratio of the tooth numbers.

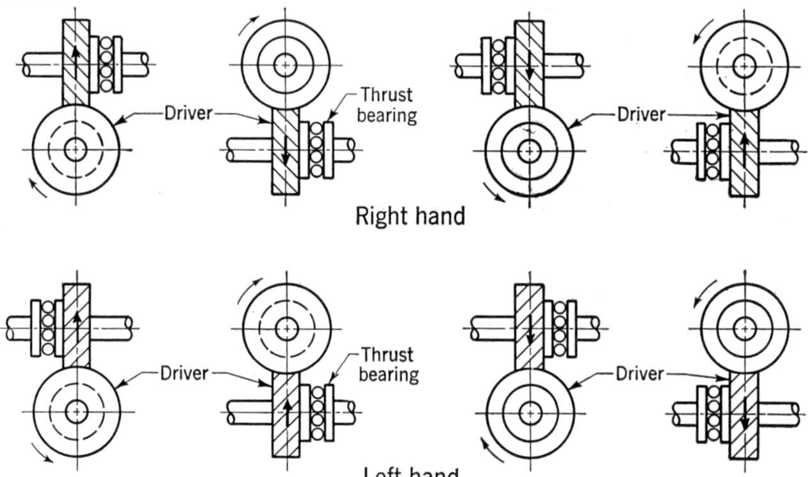

Fig. 11-11. Thrust, rotation, and hand relations in crossed-helical gears. (*Courtesy of Boston Gear Works, Inc.*)

In the design of crossed-helical gears, the minimum sliding velocity is obtained when the helix angles are equal. However, when the helix angles are not equal, the gear with the larger helix angle should be used as the driver if both gears have the same hand.

Table 11-3. Tooth Proportions for Crossed-helical Gears

Normal diametral pitch P_n = 1
Working depth = 2.400
Whole depth = 2.650
Addendum = 1.200

Driver		Driven helix angle ψ_2, deg	Normal pressure angle ϕ_n
Helix angle ψ_1, deg	Minimum tooth number N_1		
45	20	45	14°30′
60	9	30	17°30′
75	4	15	19°30′
86	1	4	20°

There is no standard for crossed-helical gear-tooth proportions. Many different proportions give good tooth action. Since the teeth are in point contact, an effort should be made to obtain a contact ratio of 2 or more. For this reason, crossed-helical teeth are usually cut with a low pressure angle and a deep tooth. Dudley[1] lists the tooth proportions shown in Table 11-3 as representative of good design. The driver tooth numbers shown are the minimum required to avoid undercut. The driven gear should have 20 or more teeth if a contact ratio of 2 is to be obtained.

11-7. Strength of Crossed-helical Gears. The methods available for calculating the strength, or the limiting wear load, of crossed-helical gears can be only a very rough approximation, because of the nature of contact. Initially the two surfaces are in point contact, and after a running-in period either of two conditions may exist. If abrasive wear or galling of the tooth surfaces has been present, this condition is likely to continue, and the teeth will never be able to carry a satisfactory load. If the loads have been light during the running-in period, so that polishing and light cold working can take place, then contact takes place over a greater area, and the final load may be increased to several times the running-in load with very satisfactory results. As yet, the variations which are possible between these extremes have not been expressed in equation form.

Because of the high sliding velocity, the wear load is the principal design factor, and the beam strength and dynamic load are of secondary importance. A method of calculating the limiting load for wear, based on analysis and experiment, is given by Earle Buckingham.[2] The equations are:

$$W_w = A^6 B^3 K Q \qquad (11\text{-}20)$$

In this equation, A and B are factors whose values depend upon the ratio of the radii of curvature of the profiles of the driver and driven teeth. These radii are

$$R_{c1} = \frac{D_1 \sin \phi_n}{2 \cos^2 \psi_1} \qquad R_{c2} = \frac{D_2 \sin \phi_n}{2 \cos^2 \psi_2} \qquad (11\text{-}21)$$

The factors A and B are obtained from Table 11-4. The load-stress factor K is obtained from the equation

$$K = 29.7 s^3 \left(\frac{1}{E_1} + \frac{1}{E_2} \right)^2 \qquad (11\text{-}22)$$

where s is the surface endurance limit and E_1 and E_2 are the moduli of elasticity of the driver and driven, respectively.

[1] *Ibid.*, p. 111.

[2] Earle Buckingham, "Analytical Mechanics of Gears," pp. 533–538, McGraw-Hill Book Company, Inc., New York, 1949.

TABLE 11-4

R_{c2}/R_{c1}	A^6	B^3	A^6B^3
1.000	0.560	1.000	0.560
1.500	1.302	0.449	0.583
2.000	2.411	0.252	0.609
3.000	6.053	0.112	0.678
4.000	11.620	0.064	0.744
6.000	30.437	0.0292	0.889
10.000	106.069	0.0108	1.141

The ratio factor Q is

$$Q = \frac{R_{c1}R_{c2}}{R_{c1} + R_{c2}} \tag{11-23}$$

Values of K recommended by Buckingham are listed in Table 11-5.

TABLE 11-5. LOAD-STRESS FACTORS K FOR CROSSED-HELICAL GEARS*

Driver	Driven	s, psi	K
With Initial Point Contact			
Hardened steel	Hardened steel	150,000	446
Hardened steel	Phosphor bronze	83,000	170
Cast iron	Phosphor bronze	83,000	302
Cast iron	Cast iron	90,000	385
With Short Running-in Period			
Hardened steel	Hardened steel	...	446
Hardened steel	Phosphor bronze	...	330
Cast iron	Phosphor bronze	...	600
Cast iron	Cast iron	...	770
With Extensive Running In			
Hardened steel	Hardened steel	...	446
Hardened steel	Phosphor bronze	...	300
Cast iron	Phosphor bronze	...	1,200
Cast iron	Cast iron	...	1,500

* Earle Buckingham, "Analytical Mechanics of Gears," p. 538, McGraw-Hill Book Company, Inc., New York, 1949.

11-8. Efficiency of Crossed-helical Gears. Since the sliding velocity is high in crossed-helical gears, it is desirable to determine the quantity of heat which must be dissipated. This can be done by finding the efficiency, using the efficiency to find the losses, and then, by applying the methods of Sec. 10-13, designing the drive to dissipate a sufficient quantity of the generated heat.

Figure 11-12 is a view of a driven gear, with the driver shown above in broken lines. The driver pushes the driven tooth at a velocity V_1 which is in the direction of rotation of the driver. We now resolve this velocity vector into two components: One of these, V_2, is the pitch-line velocity

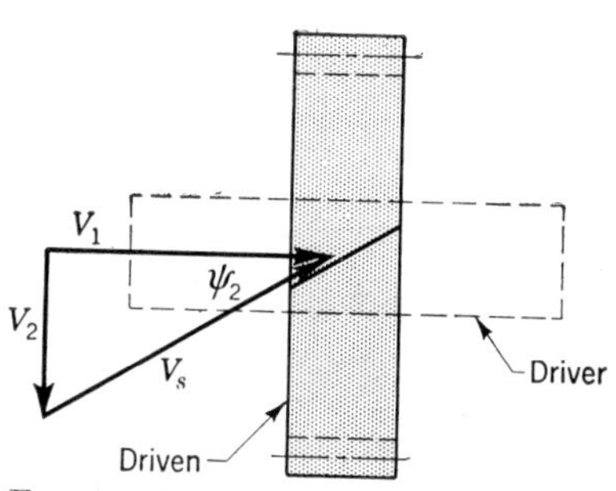

FIG. 11-12. Determination of velocity components in a crossed-helical drive.

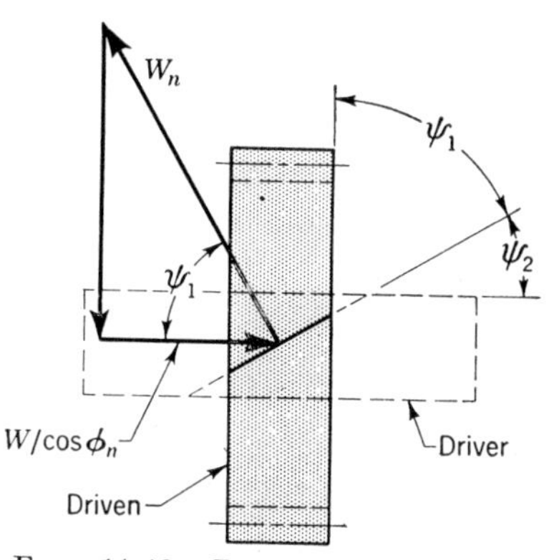

FIG. 11-13. Determination of the normal tooth load.

of the driven gear in the direction of its rotation; the other, V_s, is the sliding velocity. From the trigonometry of the figure, we can write

$$V_s = \frac{V_1}{\cos \psi_2} \tag{11-24}$$

The determination of the normal tooth load on the driven gear is shown in Fig. 11-13. The driver exerts a force of $W/\cos \phi_n$ against the driven tooth. From the trigonometry, we can write

$$W_n = \frac{W}{\cos \phi_n \cos \psi_1} \tag{a}$$

where W is the tangential load on the driver.

Using μ as the coefficient of sliding friction, the work lost in friction in foot-pounds per minute is

$$\text{Work lost in friction} = \mu W_n V_s = \frac{\mu W V_1}{\cos \phi_n \cos \psi_1 \cos \psi_2} \tag{b}$$

The work output is WV_1. The work input is the work output plus the work lost in friction. This gives for the efficiency

$$e = \frac{\text{work output}}{\text{work input}} = \frac{1}{1 + \dfrac{\mu 1}{\cos\phi_n \cos\psi_1 \cos\psi_2}} = \frac{\cos\phi_n \cos\psi_1 \cos\psi_2}{\cos\phi_n \cos\psi_1 \cos\psi_2 + \mu} \tag{c}$$

For shaft angles of 90°, $\sin\psi_1 = \cos\psi_2$, and we can write Eq. (c) in the form

$$e = \frac{\cos\phi_n \sin 2\psi_1}{\cos\phi_n \sin 2\psi_1 + 2\mu} \tag{11-25}$$

Values of the coefficient of friction μ for various values of the sliding velocity, as recommended by Buckingham, are given in Table 11-6. These values were determined for worm-gear drives but are satisfactory for use with crossed-helical gears.

TABLE 11-6. COEFFICIENTS OF FRICTION FOR CROSSED-HELICAL AND WORM GEARS*

V_s, fpm	μ	V_s, fpm	μ
0	0.2000	750	0.0375
10	0.1209	1,000	0.0420
20	0.0993	1,250	0.0465
30	0.0859	1,500	0.0506
40	0.0764	1,750	0.0545
50	0.0693	2,000	0.0582
60	0.0637	2,500	0.0650
70	0.0591	3,000	0.0712
80	0.0553	4,000	0.0822
90	0.0522	5,000	0.0919
100	0.0495	6,000	0.1007
150	0.0408	7,000	0.1088
200	0.0365	8,000	0.1163
300	0.0330	9,000	0.1233
400	0.0327	10,000	0.1300
500	0.0358		

* Earle Buckingham, "Analytical Mechanics of Gears," p. 414, McGraw-Hill Book Company, Inc., 1949.

Having found the efficiency at mesh using Eq. (11-25), the power loss at the bearings may be estimated, and from these results the temperature rise may be obtained, using the method of Sec. 10-13.

11-9. Worm Gears. In Fig. 11-14 is shown a worm and worm-gear application. These gears are used with nonintersecting shafts, and the shaft angle is generally 90°. Worm gears are either single-enveloping or double-enveloping. Single-enveloping worm gears are made so that the worm gear wraps around, or partially encloses, the worm. In double-enveloping worm gearsets, the worm and the gear wrap around each other. Single-enveloping worm gears are characterized by having "line contact," while the double-enveloping type have "area contact."

FIG. 11-14. A single-enveloping worm-gear speed reducer. (*Courtesy of Cleveland Worm and Gear Company.*)

The nomenclature of a worm and worm gear is shown in Fig. 11-15. A worm and worm gear in combination have the same hand of helix, but the helix angles are usually quite different. The helix angle on the worm is generally very large and that on the gear very small. Because of this, it is usual to specify the *lead angle* on the worm and the helix angle on the gear; the two angles are equal for a 90° shaft angle. The worm lead angle is the complement of the worm helix angle.

In specifying the pitch of worm gearsets, it is customary to give the axial pitch of the worm and the circular pitch of the gear. These are equal for a 90° shaft angle. The pitch diameter of the gear is the same as for spur gears; that is,

$$D_2 = \frac{N_2 p}{\pi} \tag{11-26}$$

The pitch diameter of the worm may be any value, but it should be the same as the pitch diameter of the hob used to cut the worm-gear teeth.

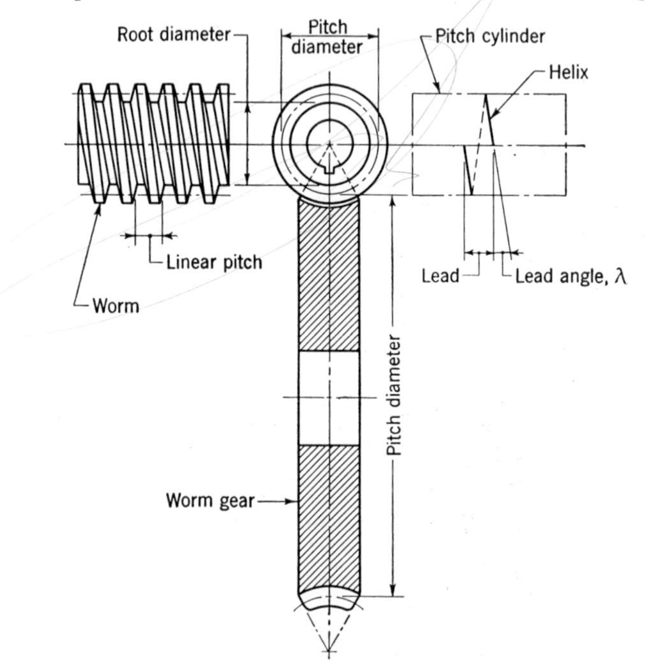

FIG. 11-15. Nomenclature of a single-enveloping worm gearset.

The AGMA[1] recommends the following relation between the pitch diameter of the worm and the center distance:

$$D_1 = \frac{C^{0.875}}{2.2} \tag{11-27}$$

where C is the center distance. This is said to give a set of proportions which will result in a good power capacity. Of course the designer is not required to use this equation; he may find other proportions which will work just as well, or he may not be interested in power capacity. However, there are so many variables in the design of worm gearing that assistance in pinning down some of these variables, or at least in obtaining some trial dimensions, is worthwhile. The AGMA Standard also states that the denominator of Eq. (11-27) may vary from 1.7 to 3 without substantially affecting the capacity.

[1] *AGMA Standard* 213.02, 1952.

The lead of the worm is found from the equation

$$l = p_a N_1 \tag{11-28}$$

and the lead angle of the worm is

$$\lambda = \tan^{-1} \frac{l}{\pi D_1} \tag{11-29}$$

The pressure angles used with worm and worm gears depend upon the lead angles. The pressure angle must be large enough to avoid undercutting of the worm-gear tooth on the side at which contact ends. Buckingham recommends the values shown in Table 11-7.

TABLE 11-7. PRESSURE ANGLES RECOMMENDED FOR WORM-GEAR SETS

Lead angle λ, deg	*Pressure angle φ, deg*
0–16	14½
16–25	20
25–35	25
35–45	30

A satisfactory tooth depth, which remains in about the right proportion to the lead angle, may be obtained by making the depth a proportion of the normal circular pitch. Based on an addendum of $1/P$ for full-depth spur gears, we obtain the following proportions for worm and worm gears:

$$\text{Addendum} = 0.3183p_n$$
$$\text{Whole depth} = 0.6366p_n$$
$$\text{Clearance} = 0.050p_n$$

The face width of the worm gear should be determined as shown in Fig. 11-16.

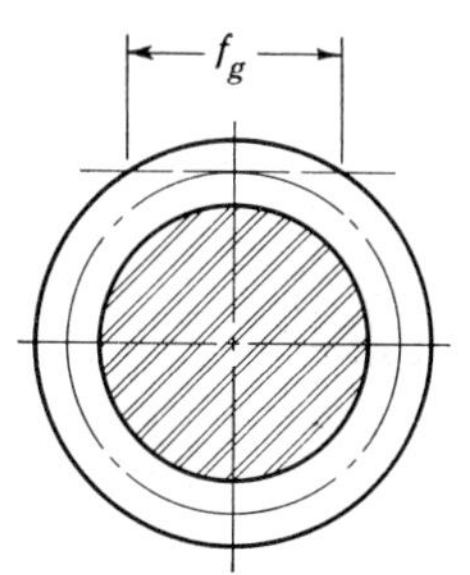

FIG. 11-16. The face width f_g of the worm gear is made equal to the length of a tangent to the worm pitch circle between its points of intersection with the addendum circle.

11-10. Strength of Worm-gear Teeth. A great many variations are possible in the design, manufacture, and contact conditions of worm-gear drives. This makes it very difficult to obtain a satisfactory method of calculating the strength or capacity of such a drive. Worm gearsets usually fail either by overheating, by scoring, or by pitting. For this reason, it is customary to specify the capacity according to the surface durability or according to the amount of heat generated and dissipated.

When worm gearsets are used intermittently, or at slow gear speeds, the beam strength of the gear tooth may become a principal design factor. This is, again, a difficult problem, because worm-gear teeth are thick and short at the two edges of the face and are thin in the central plane. Since the worm teeth are always stronger, they need not be considered.

Buckingham[1] adapts the Lewis equation as follows:

STRENGTH OF WORM GEAR ~~WORM~~ TEETH

$$W_{max} = s_d p_n f_g y \tag{11-30}$$

$$p_n = p_a \cos \lambda \tag{11-31}$$

where W_{max} = maximum tangential load, lb
s_d = design stress, psi
f_g = face width of gear, in.
y = Lewis form factor referred to the circular pitch
p_n = normal circular pitch, in.
p_a = axial circular pitch, in.
λ = lead angle

Since the equation is only a rough approximation, stress concentration is not considered. Also, for this reason, the form factors are not referred to the number of teeth but only to the normal pressure angle. The values of y are listed in Table 11-8.

TABLE 11-8. VALUES OF y FOR WORM GEARS

Normal pressure angle ϕ_n, deg	*Form factor y*
14½	0.100
20	0.125
25	0.150
30	0.175

Materials. The materials which will work well with worm-gear drives are very limited. The reason for this is that the gear is never generated to the degree of finish required, and it is necessary for the worm to perform the finishing by cold working and polishing during the running-in period. Therefore the worm should be made of a hardened steel and the gear of a bearinglike material. Worm gears are usually made of cast iron, phosphor bronze, and a tin-free antimony-copper alloy. Recommended values of the design stress for these materials are listed in Table 11-9.

TABLE 11-9. DESIGN STRESSES FOR WORM GEARS

Worm-gear material	Design stress s_d, psi	
	One-way drive	Reversing drive
Cast iron	12,000	8,000
Phosphor bronze	24,000	16,000
Antimony bronze	15,000	10,000

[1] Buckingham, *op. cit.*, p. 495.

Limiting Load for Wear. The limiting load for wear for worm-gear drives is found from the equation

$$W_w = D_2 f_g K \tag{11-32}$$

where D_2 = pitch diameter of gear
f_g = effective face width of gear
K = load-stress factor

Values of K for various materials and lead angles are listed in Table 11-10.

TABLE 11-10. LOAD-STRESS FACTORS FOR WORM GEARS

Material		Load-stress factor K		
Worm	Gear	λ = 0–10°	λ = 10–25°	λ = 25° and up
Steel, 250 Bhn.....	Phosphor bronze	60	75	90
Hardened steel.....	Phosphor bronze	80	100	120
Hardened steel.....	Chilled phosphor bronze	120	150	180
Hardened steel.....	Antimony bronze	120	150	180
Cast iron..........	Phosphor bronze	150	187	225

Efficiency. We can use Eq. (11-25) to determine the efficiency of worm-gear drives. Since the helix angle of the worm is the complement of the lead angle,

$$\psi_1 = \pi - \lambda \qquad \text{and} \qquad \sin 2\psi_1 = \sin 2\lambda$$

Equation (11-25) then becomes

$$e = \frac{\cos \phi_n \sin 2\lambda}{\cos \phi_n \sin 2\lambda + 2\mu} \tag{11-33}$$

Since the lead angle of the worm is equal to the helix angle of the gear, the sliding velocity, from Eq. (11-24), is

$$V_s = \frac{V}{\cos \lambda} \tag{11-34}$$

Table 11-6 may be used to find the coefficient of friction, and the temperature rise may then be calculated as for crossed-helical gears.

11-11. Straight Bevel Gears. When gears are to be used to transmit motion between intersecting shafts, some form of bevel gear is required. A bevel-gear pinion is shown in Fig. 11-17. Although bevel gears are usually made for a shaft angle of 90°, they may be produced for almost any angle. The teeth may be cast, milled, or generated. Only the generated teeth may be classed as accurate.

The terminology of bevel gears is illustrated in Fig. 11-18. The pitch of bevel gears is measured at the large end of the tooth, and both the circular pitch and the pitch diameter are calculated in the same manner as for spur gears. It should be noted that the clearance is uniform. The pitch angles are defined by the pitch cones meeting at the apex, as shown in the figure. They are related to the tooth numbers as follows:

FIG. 11-17. A straight bevel gear and pinion. (*Courtesy of Gleason Works, Rochester, N. Y.*)

$$\tan \gamma = \frac{N_1}{N_2} \qquad \tan \Gamma = \frac{N_2}{N_1} \tag{11-35}$$

where the subscripts 1 and 2 refer to the pinion and gear, respectively, and where γ and Γ are, respectively, the pitch angles of the pinion and gear.

Figure 11-18 shows that the shape of the teeth, when projected on the back cone, is the same as in a spur gear having a radius equal to the back-cone distance r_b. This is called Tregold's approximation. The number

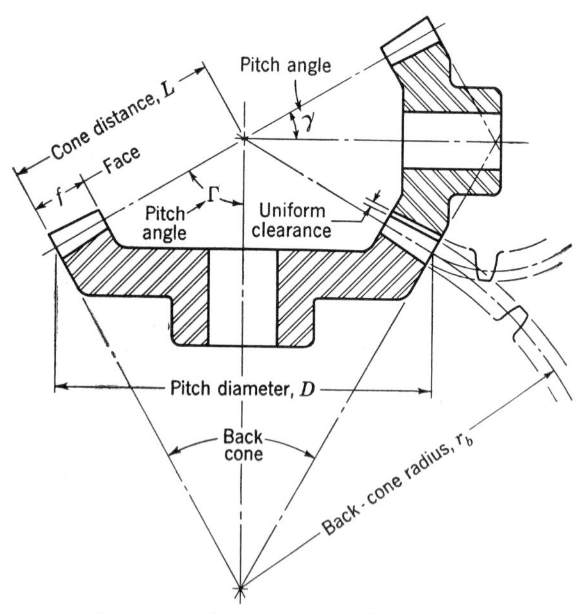

FIG. 11-18. Terminology of bevel gears.

of teeth in this imaginary gear is

$$N' = \frac{2\pi r_b}{p} \tag{11-36}$$

where N' is the *virtual number of teeth* and p is the circular pitch measured at the large end of the teeth.

Practically all straight-tooth bevel gears designed today use the 20° pressure angle. However, since they are not interchangeable, they are well adapted for using the unequal-addendum-dedendum system. The Gleason company has worked out a set of tooth proportions for bevel-gear teeth which is widely used and is based on the velocity ratio.[1] These proportions are given in Table 11-11.

TABLE 11-11. GEAR ADDENDUM FOR 1-DP STRAIGHT BEVEL GEARS*

Ratios		Addendum	Ratios		Addendum	Ratios		Addendum	Ratios		Addendum
From	To		From	To		From	To		From	To	
1.00	1.00	1.000	1.15	1.17	0.880	1.42	1.45	0.760	2.06	2.16	0.640
1.00	1.02	0.990	1.17	1.19	0.870	1.45	1.48	0.750	2.16	2.27	0.630
1.02	1.03	0.980	1.19	1.21	0.860	1.48	1.52	0.740	2.27	2.41	0.620
1.03	1.04	0.970	1.21	1.23	0.850	1.52	1.56	0.730	2.41	2.58	0.610
1.04	1.05	0.960	1.23	1.25	0.840	1.56	1.60	0.720	2.58	2.78	0.600
1.05	1.06	0.950	1.25	1.27	0.830	1.60	1.65	0.710	2.78	3.05	0.590
1.06	1.08	0.940	1.27	1.29	0.820	1.65	1.70	0.700	3.05	3.41	0.580
1.08	1.09	0.930	1.29	1.31	0.810	1.70	1.76	0.690	3.41	3.94	0.570
1.09	1.11	0.920	1.31	1.33	0.800	1.76	1.82	0.680	3.94	4.82	0.560
1.11	1.12	0.910	1.33	1.36	0.790	1.82	1.89	0.670	4.82	6.81	0.550
1.12	1.14	0.900	1.36	1.39	0.780	1.89	1.97	0.660	6.81	∞	0.540
1.14	1.15	0.890	1.39	1.42	0.770	1.97	2.06	0.650			

* Gleason Works, Rochester, N.Y.

11-12. Beam Strength of Straight-tooth Bevel Gears. The determination of the beam strength of bevel-gear teeth is complicated by several factors. Bevel gears are usually mounted on the outboard side of the bearing, which means that the effect of the shaft deflection is much more pronounced, causing the large end of the teeth to take a greater proportion of the load. In addition, it is necessary that the teeth at the large end deflect more under load than those at the small end, so that the line of contact will pass through the cone center. Because of this changing load across the tooth, it is desirable to design a fairly short tooth. Available recommendations limit the face width to about one-fourth or one-third the cone distance; these are maximum values.

We can adapt the Lewis equation to bevel-gear teeth by making some approximations, and the solution so obtained seems to agree fairly well with experiment.

[1] Gleason Works, Rochester, N.Y.

Referring to Fig. 11-19, the circular pitch, and consequently the tooth thickness, vary continuously across the face of the tooth, *ab*. The force across the face varies also, being small at point *a* and larger at point *b*. The problem is to express the strength of the tooth, which varies in thickness, in terms of the varying force.

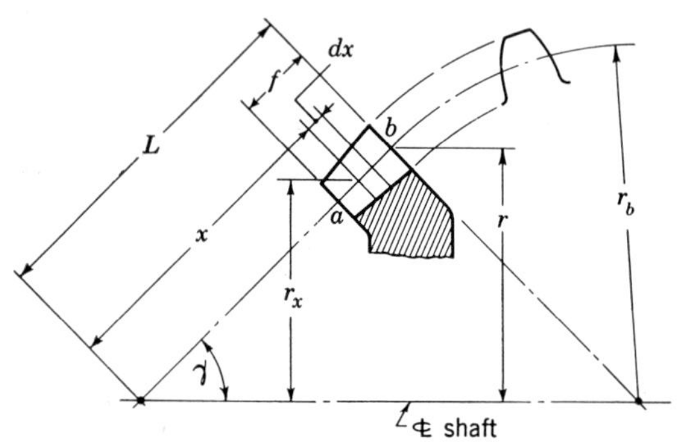

FIG. 11-19. Beam strength of bevel-gear teeth.

We may apply the Lewis equation to an infinitely thin section of the tooth dx, located at a distance x from the cone center. This gives

$$dW_x = \frac{sY\,dx}{P_x} \tag{a}$$

where dW_x is the tangential load on the section dx and P_x is the diametral pitch. We now multiply both sides of Eq. (a) by r_x and integrate:

$$\int r_x\,dW_x = \int \frac{sYr_x\,dx}{P_x} \tag{b}$$

In order to solve this equation, it is necessary to express P_x in terms of P, and r_x in terms of r. From a consideration of similar triangles in Fig. 11-19, the relations are as follows:

$$P_x = \frac{PL}{x} \qquad r_x = \frac{rx}{L}$$

Integration of the left-hand side of Eq. (b) gives the torque T, and substitution of the values for P_x and r_x gives

$$T = \frac{sYr}{PL^2}\int_{L-f}^{L} x^2\,dx \tag{c}$$

where the limits $L - f$ and L include the face width f. Integration of Eq. (c) yields

$$T = \frac{sYrf}{P}\left(1 - \frac{f}{L} + \frac{f^2}{3L^2}\right) \tag{d}$$

If, according to the recommendations, the maximum face width f does not exceed one-third the cone distance L, then the last term $f^2/3L^2$ is never greater than $\frac{1}{27}$ and may, therefore, be neglected. Dividing both sides of Eq. (d) by the radius r, we find

$$W = \frac{T}{r} = \frac{sYf}{P}\left(1 - \frac{f}{L}\right) \tag{11-37}$$

This is the Lewis equation for bevel gears. It should be noted that it is referred to the large end of the tooth. The load W is a fictitious tangential load obtained by dividing the shaft torque by the radius at the large end of the tooth. The diametral pitch P is the pitch at the large end, and Y is the Lewis form factor corresponding to the virtual number of teeth, N'.

Lewis Equation for Dynamic Loads. We may modify Eq. (11-37) for dynamic loads in exactly the same manner as for spur gears. When this is done, we obtain

$$W_{max} = \frac{T_{max}}{r} = \frac{fK_2YC_vs_e}{k_fK_1P}\left(1 - \frac{f}{L}\right) \tag{11-38}$$

where W_{max} = maximum tangential load at radius r, lb
f = face width, in.
K_2 = form-factor coefficient = 1.70 for bevel-gear teeth
Y = Lewis form factor (based upon diametral pitch at large end and virtual number of teeth)
C_v = velocity factor from Fig. 10-26, using velocity at large end
s_e = endurance limit, from Table 10-6, psi
k_f = fatigue stress-concentration factor obtained from Eq. (10-18) or (10-19), or from Table 10-5, and corrected for notch sensitivity, employing Fig. 4-24
K_1 = service factor = 1.25 for steady loads, 1.35 for pulsating loads, and 1.50 for shock loads
P = diametral pitch at large end of teeth
L = cone distance, in.

When using Eq. (11-38) to determine the static beam strength for comparison with the dynamic load as calculated by the Buckingham equations, the velocity factor C_v should be omitted, as in the equation for spur gears.

11-13. Dynamic Load and Wear. The fundamental Buckingham equation for dynamic load may be used for bevel gears by altering the equation for the coefficient H. For bevel gears the value of H is obtained as follows:

$$H = c_1\left(\frac{\cos\gamma}{r_{1,av}} + \frac{\cos\Gamma}{r_{2,av}}\right) \tag{11-39}$$

where $r_{1,\mathrm{av}}$ = average pitch radius of pinion, in.
$r_{2,\mathrm{av}}$ = average pitch radius of gear, in.
c_1 = 0.00120 for 20° bevel gears

The remaining Buckingham equations are repeated here for convenience:

$$W_d = W + \sqrt{F_a(2F_2 - F_a)} \tag{11-40}$$

$$F_a = \frac{F_1 F_2}{F_1 + F_2} \tag{11-41}$$

$$F_1 = HmV^2 \tag{11-42}$$

$$m = \frac{m_1 m_2}{m_1 + m_2} \tag{11-43}$$

$$F_2 = fC + W \tag{11-44}$$

where W_d = dynamic tooth load at mean radius of gear, lb
W = equivalent transmitted tangential tooth load at mean radius of gear, lb
F_a = acceleration load, lb
F_2 = force required to deform teeth amount of effective error, lb
F_1 = average force required to accelerate gear masses when considered as rigid bodies, lb
m_1 = effective mass of pinion, slugs
m_2 = effective mass of gear, slugs
m = effective mass, slugs
V = pitch-line velocity at average pitch radius, fpm
f = face width, in.
C = deformation factor obtained from Table 10-7

The approximate Buckingham equation for bevel gears is

$$W_d = W + \frac{0.05VF_2}{0.05V + \sqrt{F_2}} \tag{11-45}$$

where the quantities have the same meaning as above.

Limiting Load for Wear. By using a virtual spur gear taken at the mean radius of the bevel gear, we can adapt the wear equation for use with bevel gears. The equation is

$$W_w = D'_{1,\mathrm{av}} f_{eq} K Q \tag{11-46}$$

where $D'_{1,\mathrm{av}}$ = diameter of back-cone circle obtained from average bevel-pinion pitch diameter
f_{eq} = equivalent face width, $0.75f$ for outboard pinions and $1.00f$ for inboard pinions, in.
K = load-stress factor, same as for spur gears

$$Q = \frac{2D'_{2,\text{av}}}{D'_{1,\text{av}} + D'_{2,\text{av}}} = \frac{2N'_2}{N'_1 + N'_2} = \text{ratio factor}$$

$D'_{2,\text{av}}$ = diameter of back-cone circle obtained from average bevel-gear pitch diameter

N'_1 = virtual number of pinion teeth

N'_2 = virtual number of gear teeth

It should be noted that for outboard pinions the face width has been reduced. The additional deflection caused by outboard mounting results in contact between a smaller portion of the meshing surfaces. The effective face width, therefore, has been taken at $\frac{3}{4}f$ when this method of mounting is used.

EXAMPLE 11-2.[1] The pair of bevel gears whose dimensions are shown in Fig. 11-20 are to transmit 1 hp at 1,800-rpm pinion speed. The material is steel with a 350 Bhn

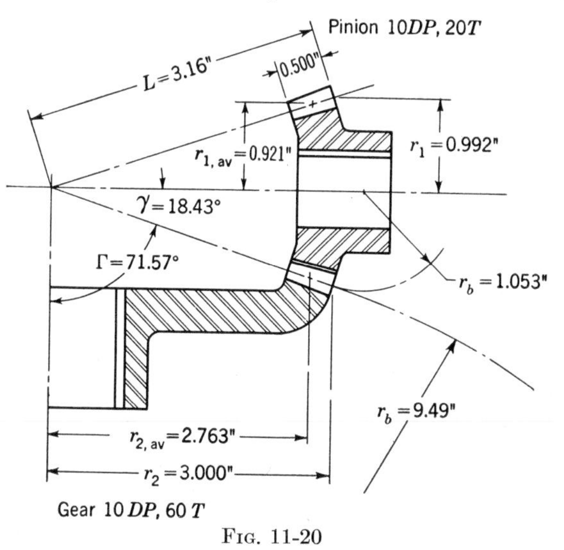

FIG. 11-20

pinion and a 300 Bhn gear. It is required to determine the dynamic load and to check this against the strength and the limiting load for wear. The moments of inertia are $J_1 = 0.015$ slug-in.² for the pinion and $J_2 = 0.347$ slug-in.² for the gear.

Solution. a. Determination of the dynamic load. The pitch-line velocity at the average pitch radius is

$$V = \frac{2\pi r_{1,\text{av}}\, n}{12} = \frac{(2\pi)(0.921)(1{,}800)}{12} = 868 \text{ fpm}$$

The average transmitted load is

$$W = \frac{33{,}000 \text{ hp}}{V} = \frac{(33{,}000)(1)}{868} = 38 \text{ lb}$$

[1] Courtesy of Massachusetts Gear and Tool Company.

The effective masses of each gear are

$$m_1 = \frac{J_1}{r_{1,\text{av}}^2} = \frac{0.015}{(0.921)^2} = 0.0177 \text{ slug}$$

$$m_2 = \frac{J_2}{r_{2,\text{av}}^2} = \frac{0.347}{(2.763)^2} = 0.0455 \text{ slug}$$

Therefore, the effective mass m is

$$m = \frac{m_1 m_2}{m_1 + m_2} = \frac{(0.0177)(0.0455)}{0.0177 + 0.0455} = 0.0127 \text{ slug}$$

The coefficient H is

$$H = c_1\left(\frac{\cos\gamma}{r_{1,\text{av}}} + \frac{\cos\Gamma}{r_{2,\text{av}}}\right) = 0.00120\left(\frac{\cos 18.43°}{0.921} + \frac{\cos 71.57°}{2.763}\right)$$
$$= 0.00137$$

from which

$$F_1 = HmV^2 = (0.00137)(0.0127)(868)^2 = 13.1 \text{ lb}$$

Since the pinion is mounted outboard, the error in action will be taken as 0.003 in. Using Table 10-7, the deformation factor C is 4,980. Therefore,

$$F_2 = fC + W = (0.5)(4{,}980) + 38 = 2{,}528 \text{ lb}$$

The acceleration load is

$$F_a = \frac{F_1 F_2}{F_1 + F_2} = \frac{(13.1)(2{,}528)}{13.1 + 2{,}528} = 13.0 \text{ lb}$$

The dynamic load is now obtained from Eq. (11-40):

$$W_d = W + \sqrt{F_a(2F_2 - F_a)} = 38 + \sqrt{13[(2)(2{,}528) - 13]} = 294 \text{ lb} \qquad \textit{Ans.}$$

b. Determination of the beam strength. The circular pitch at the large end of the tooth is $p = \pi/10 = 0.314$ in. From Eq. (11-36), the virtual number of teeth in the pinion is

$$N_1' = \frac{2\pi r_b}{p} = \frac{2\pi(1.053)}{0.314} = 21.1$$

We will use the Lewis equation [Eq. (11-38)] and omit the velocity factor since we wish to find the maximum static load for comparison with the dynamic load. The quantities are as follows:

$f = 0.50$ in.
$K_2 = 1.70$
$Y = 0.328$ for 21.1 teeth and a 20° pressure angle (Table 10-4)
$s_e = 58{,}000$ psi for the pinion (Table 10-6)
$k_f = 1.8$ (assumed value)
$K_1 = 1.25$ (a steady load is assumed)
$P = 10$
$L = 3.16$ in.

Substitution of these values yields

$$W_{\max} = \frac{fK_2Ys_e}{k_fK_1P}\left(1 - \frac{f}{L}\right) = \frac{(0.50)(1.70)(0.328)(58{,}000)}{(1.8)(1.25)(10)}\left(1 - \frac{0.50}{3.16}\right)$$
$$= 605 \text{ lb}$$

This is the load which would be concentrated at the radius r at the large end of the teeth. In order to compare it with the dynamic load, we must find the equivalent value at the average radius. The two torques must be equal; therefore,

$$\text{Av } W_{\max} = W_{\max} \frac{r}{r_{\text{av}}} = 605 \frac{0.992}{0.921} = 652 \text{ lb} \qquad \textit{Ans.}$$

Since this load is considerably higher than the dynamic load, the teeth have satisfactory beam strength.

c. Limiting load for wear. The virtual number of teeth on the gear is

$$N'_2 = \frac{2\pi r_b}{p} = \frac{(2\pi)(9.49)}{0.314} = 190$$

The diameter of the pinion back-cone circle, corresponding to the average pitch diameter, is

$$D'_{1,\text{av}} = \frac{2r_{1,\text{av}}}{\cos \gamma} = \frac{(2)(0.921)}{\cos 18.43°} = 1.94 \text{ in.}$$

The remaining quantities for use in Eq. (11-46) are as follows:

$$f_{eq} = 0.75f = (0.75)(0.5) = 0.375 \text{ in.}$$

$$Q = \frac{2N'_2}{N'_1 + N'_2} = \frac{(2)(190)}{21.1 + 190} = 1.8$$

$$K = 233 \qquad \text{(Table 10-9)}$$

Substituting in Eq. (11-46),

$$W_w = D'_{1,\text{av}} f_{eq} K Q = (1.94)(0.375)(233)(1.8) = 305 \text{ lb} \qquad \textit{Ans.}$$

Since the dynamic load is less than the wear load, the gears are satisfactory as designed.

11-14. Shaft Loads. The shaft loads for bevel gears are found in much the same manner as for spur gears. The bevel gear, however, introduces a thrust component.

In determining the tangential tooth load, the load which would occur at the mid-point of the tooth is used. While the resultant tangential load actually occurs somewhere between the mid-point and the large end, there is only a small error in making this assumption. For the tangential or transmitted load, this gives

$$W = \frac{T}{r_{\text{av}}} \tag{11-47}$$

where T is the torque and r_{av} is the pitch radius of the gear at the mid-point of the tooth.

The forces acting at the mid-point of the tooth are illustrated in Fig. 11-21. The resultant force is W_r and it has three components, the tangential component W, the radial component W_R, and the thrust component W_T. From the trigonometry of the figure, the radial and thrust components are

$$W_R = W \tan \phi \cos \gamma \tag{11-48}$$

$$W_T = W \tan \phi \sin \gamma \tag{11-49}$$

These forces, W, W_R, and W_T, are used to find the bearing reactions.

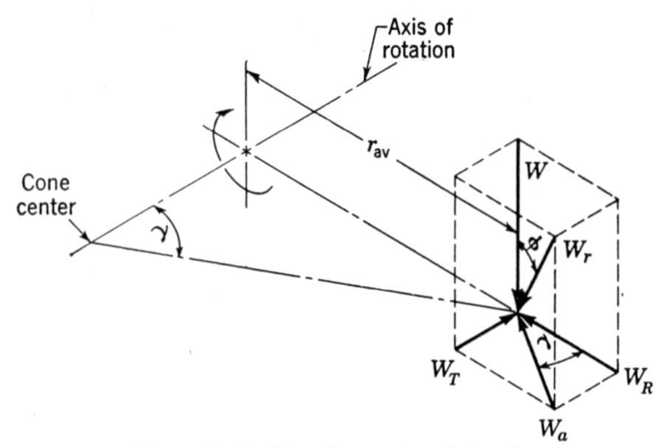

FIG. 11-21. Bevel-gear tooth loads.

The total radial shaft load F_R may be found as follows:

$$F_R = W \sqrt{1 + \tan^2 \phi \cos^2 \gamma} \tag{11-50}$$

When the tooth load has been resolved into these components, the method of statics, as previously illustrated, may be used to obtain the corresponding bearing loads.

11-15. Spiral Bevel Gears. In Fig. 11-22 is shown a cluster gear with spiral-bevel-gear teeth cut at one end. The use of spiral-shaped teeth results in more teeth in contact at the same time and secures a smoother meshing action.

The *Zerol bevel gear* is a patented gear having curved teeth with a zero-degree spiral angle. The curved teeth give somewhat better tooth action than may be obtained with straight-tooth bevel gears. In general, the procedure is to design a straight-tooth gear and then to substitute a Zerol bevel gear.

Hypoid gears are much like spiral bevel gears. They are used on nonintersecting, crossed-axis shafts, and for this reason they have a taper which is like that of bevel gears. The distance between the two shaft centers is called the *offset*. If this offset becomes equal to zero, then the gears become spiral bevel gears. Fig. 11-23 shows a typical hypoid gearset.

Tooth Proportions. Spiral-bevel-gear teeth are usually made with a 20° pressure angle and with a stub height. The addenda for 1-DP

FIG. 11-22. Cluster gears with spiral-bevel teeth at one end. (*Courtesy of Fairfield Manufacturing Company.*)

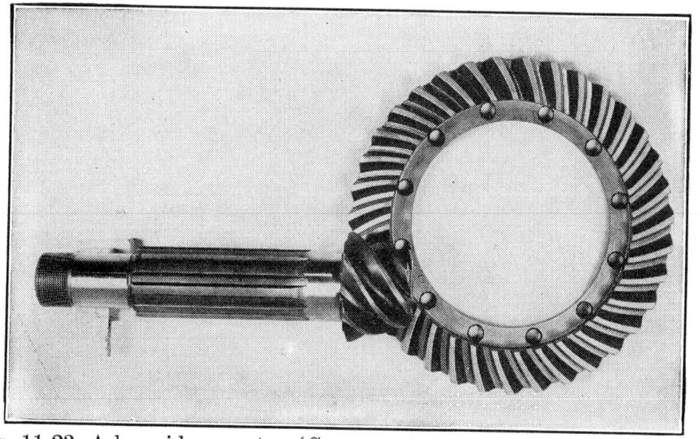

FIG. 11-23. A hypoid gearset. (*Courtesy of Automotive Gear Works, Inc.*)

gears and for various velocity ratios are given in Table 11-12. The working depth is $1.700/P$, and the clearance is $0.188/P$.

Strength. The relation between bevel gears with straight teeth and those with spiral teeth is the same as for spur gears and helical gears. Therefore we can use the Lewis equation for bevel-gear teeth and adapt it for spiral teeth, as in the case of helical gears. The same equations can also be used for hypoid gears. We then have

$$W_{\max} = \frac{fK_2YC_v s_c}{k_f K_1 P_n}\left(1 - \frac{f}{L}\right) \tag{11-51}$$

where

$$P_n = \frac{P}{\cos \psi} \tag{11-52}$$

The other quantities are the same as for bevel gears, and ψ is the spiral angle at the mid-point of the gear face.

The limiting load for wear is set up on the same basis as the Lewis equation. Thus, we have

$$W_w = \frac{D'_{1,\text{av}} f_{eq} KQ}{\cos^2 \psi} \tag{11-53}$$

where the quantities have the same meaning as before. Equation (11-53) may be used also for hypoid gears, although it should be pointed out that more wear may take place because of the increased sliding action.

TABLE 11-12. GEAR ADDENDUM FOR 1-DP SPIRAL BEVEL GEARS*

Ratios		Addendum	Ratios		Addendum	Ratios		Addendum
From	To		From	To		From	To	
1.00	1.00	0.850	1.23	1.26	0.710	1.82	1.90	0.570
1.00	1.02	0.840	1.26	1.28	0.700	1.90	1.99	0.560
1.02	1.03	0.830	1.28	1.31	0.690	1.99	2.10	0.550
1.03	1.05	0.820	1.31	1.34	0.680	2.10	2.23	0.540
1.05	1.06	0.810	1.34	1.37	0.670	2.23	2.38	0.530
1.06	1.08	0.800	1.37	1.41	0.660	2.38	2.58	0.520
1.08	1.09	0.790	1.41	1.44	0.650	2.58	2.82	0.510
1.09	1.11	0.780	1.44	1.48	0.640	2.82	3.17	0.500
1.11	1.13	0.770	1.48	1.52	0.630	3.17	3.67	0.490
1.13	1.15	0.760	1.52	1.57	0.620	3.67	4.56	0.480
1.15	1.17	1.750	1.57	1.63	0.610	4.56	7.00	0.470
1.17	1.19	0.740	1.63	1.68	0.600	7.00	∞	0.460
1.19	1.21	0.730	1.68	1.75	0.590			
1.21	1.23	0.720	1.75	1.82	0.580			

* Gleason Works.

Dynamic Load. Buckingham states that a considerable amount of experiment is needed on spiral gears in order to determine the true dynamic loads.[1] The following equations will give an approximate value of the dynamic load. In using these equations, however, the engineer should realize that he is working close to the border of existing knowledge and that where more accurate designs are necessary, or where the margin

[1] Buckingham, *op. cit.*, p. 460.

TABLE 11-13. SHAFT-LOAD FORMULAS FOR SPIRAL BEVEL GEARS

Pinion: Hand of spiral	Pinion: Rotation	Thrust component W_T	Radial component W_R
Pinion			
Right	Clockwise	$W_T = \frac{W}{\cos \psi} (\tan \phi_n \sin \gamma - \sin \psi \cos \gamma)$	$W_R = \frac{W}{\cos \psi} (\tan \phi_n \cos \gamma + \sin \psi \sin \gamma)$
Right	Counterclockwise	$W_T = \frac{W}{\cos \psi} (\tan \phi_n \sin \gamma + \sin \psi \cos \gamma)$	$W_R = \frac{W}{\cos \psi} (\tan \phi_n \cos \gamma - \sin \psi \sin \gamma)$
Gear			
Left	Counterclockwise	$W_T = \frac{W}{\cos \psi} (\tan \phi_n \sin \Gamma + \sin \psi \cos \Gamma)$	$W_R = \frac{W}{\cos \psi} (\tan \phi_n \cos \Gamma - \sin \psi \sin \Gamma)$
Left	Clockwise	$W_T = \frac{W}{\cos \psi} (\tan \phi_n \sin \Gamma - \sin \psi \cos \Gamma)$	$W_R = \frac{W}{\cos \psi} (\tan \phi_n \cos \Gamma + \sin \psi \sin \Gamma)$

W = tangential load at mid-point of tooth, lb
W_T = thrust component at mid-point of tooth, lb
W_R = radial component at mid-point of tooth, lb
ψ = spiral angle
ϕ_n = normal pressure angle
γ = pitch angle of pinion
Γ = pitch angle of gear

of safety must be accurately known, he should use experimental means of investigation. The equations are as follows:[1]

$$V = \frac{2\pi r_{1,\text{av}} n}{12} \tag{11-54}$$

$$m = \frac{m_1 m_2}{m_1 + m_2} \tag{11-55}$$

$$H = 0.00120 \left(\frac{\cos \gamma}{r_{1,\text{av}}} + \frac{\cos \Gamma}{r_{2,\text{av}}} \right) \tag{11-56}$$

$$F_2 = fC \cos^2 \psi + W \tag{11-57}$$

$$F_a = \frac{F_1 F_2}{F_1 + F_2} \tag{11-58}$$

$$W_d = W + \sqrt{F_a(2F_2 - F_a)} \tag{11-59}$$

where V = pitch-line velocity at mid-tooth, fpm
$r_{1,\text{av}}$ = pitch radius of pinion at mid-tooth, in.
$r_{2,\text{av}}$ = pitch radius of gear at mid-tooth, in.
n = pinion speed, rpm
m = effective mass at pitch line, slugs
m_1 = effective mass of pinion at mid-point radius, slugs
m_2 = effective mass of gear at mid-point radius, slugs
γ = pitch angle of pinion
Γ = pitch angle of gear
f = face width, in.
C = deformation factor (same as for spur gears)
W = tangential load at mid-point of tooth, lb
W_d = dynamic load at mid-point of tooth, lb

Shaft Loads. Formulas for the shaft loads for spiral gears are given in Table 11-13.

PROBLEMS

11-1. A gear train is composed of four helical gears with the shaft centers in line, as shown in the figure. The gears have a 20° pressure angle and a 30° helix angle.

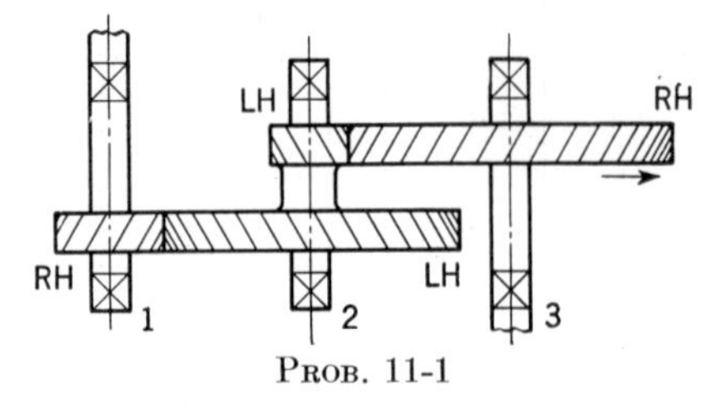

PROB. 11-1

[1] Earle Buckingham, "Gear Tooth Loads," p. 49, Massachusetts Gear and Tool Company, Woburn, Mass., 1953.

The gears on shafts 1 and 3 are both right-hand. If the transmitted load is 500 lb, find the radial and thrust forces acting on each shaft, and their directions. The gears on shaft 2 have 56 and 14 teeth and are each 7-DP.

11-2. Repeat Prob. 11-1 if the hand of the second pair of gears is reversed.

11-3. Repeat Prob. 11-1 if the gear on shaft 1 has a 15° helix angle and the one on shaft 3 a 30° helix angle.

11-4. In the figure, gear 1, the driver, is a 16-tooth 8-DP 20°-pressure-angle 15°-helix-angle right-hand gear. It drives the idler on shaft 2, which has 36 teeth. The

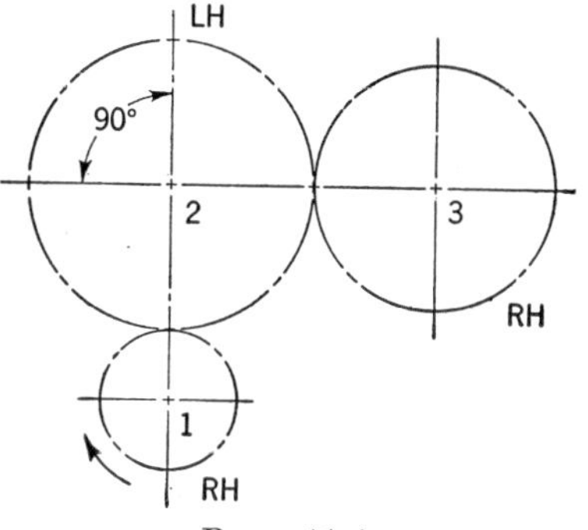

PROB. 11-4

driven gear on shaft 3 has 28 teeth. The driver rotates at 1,720 rpm and transmits 7½ hp. Find the radial and thrust loads on each shaft.

11-5. A parallel-shaft gearset is a 20-DP 15°-helix-angle 20° stub-tooth system, with 20 teeth on the driver and 96 teeth on the driven gear. The face width is ¾ in., and the gears run at a pitch-line velocity of 1,600 fpm. The driver is made of 1020 steel without heat-treatment and the driven gear of class 30 cast iron. Using a fatigue stress-concentration factor of 1.20 for the driver and 1.10 for the driven and a contact ratio of 1.39, find the maximum tangential load which may be transmitted. The load is steady.

11-6. The same as Prob. 11-5 except that the normal diametral pitch is 20, the normal pressure angle is 20°, and the helix angle is 30°.

11-7. A pair of meshed helical gears are made of 2315 steel, casehardened to 380 Bhn. The driver has 12 teeth and the driven 20 teeth. The teeth are cut by hobbing, with a transverse pressure angle of 20° and a helix angle of 45°, and are full depth in the normal section. The face width is 1½ in., and the driver rotates at 1,720 rpm. Using a contact ratio of 1.24 and a fatigue stress-concentration factor of 1.3, find the maximum steady tangential load which may be transmitted, as given by the modified Lewis equation. The gears are 8-DP.

11-8. The following data apply to a parallel-shaft gearset: driver, right-hand helical. 0° helix angle, 20° transverse pressure angle, stub teeth in a transverse section, 16 teeth, 2,800 rpm, 1⅝-in.-diameter hub × ⅞-in. projection, 2-in. face, 8-DP, 320 Bhn steel; driven, 32 teeth, 2½-in.-diameter hub × 1-in. projection, 320 Bhn steel. Both gears are of disk form with projecting hubs. Determine the dynamic load for an error of 0.001 in. if the gears have been tentatively designed to transmit a load of hp.

11-9. The same as Prob. 11-8 except that the helix angle is 15°.

11-10. Determine the limiting load for wear for the gears of Prob. 11-8.

***11-11 to 11-24.** A helical gearset for parallel shafts is to be designed according to the data in the accompanying table. The gears will be enclosed and lubricated from a central supply. The shafts will be connected to a source of power through a straight coupling and will also deliver power through a straight coupling. The shafts should be designed to resist torsion, bending, and thrust. The application is such that the load is steady and continuous. Life is an important factor. One hundred units are to be manufactured, and cost is important but secondary to strength and life. Design the gears and shafts, and make a sketch showing all dimensions and pertinent details.

Prob. No.	Horsepower	Driver rpm	Driven rpm
11-11	5,000	1,200	120
11-12	4,000	1,200	150
11-13	3,000	1,200	200
11-14	2,000	1,200	400
11-15	1,500	1,200	500
11-16	1,000	1,200	600
11-17	500	1,800	200
11-18	400	1,800	300
11-19	250	1,800	450
11-20	100	1,800	600
11-21	50	3,600	300
11-22	25	3,600	400
11-23	10	3,600	600
11-24	5	3,600	100

11-25. A pair of right-hand crossed-helical gears is to transmit power at an angular-velocity ratio of 1 between shafts at an angle of 90° to each other. The gears are 45°-helix-angle, 8-DP (normal), 1-inch-face, 14½°-normal-pressure-angle and have 24 teeth. Both gears are of steel, hardened to 320 Bhn. (*a*) Considering wear as the limiting design factor, find the maximum horsepower that can be transmitted if the speed is 1,120 rpm. (*b*) Find the efficiency of the gearset. (*c*) Find the thrust and radial shaft loads, corresponding to the maximum horsepower, caused by each gear.

11-26. The same as Prob. 11-25 except that one of the gears is made of phosphor bronze.

11-27. A 10-DP 14½°-pressure-angle two-tooth hardened-steel worm has a lead angle of 9°5′, a pitch diameter of 1.25 in., and a face of 2 in., and the teeth are ground and polished. It is to drive a bronze worm gear having a ⅝-in. face, 40 teeth, and a pitch diameter of 4.00 in. The speed of the worm is 1,720 rpm. (*a*) Using the Lewis equation for worm gears, find the maximum tangential load. (*b*) Find the limiting load for wear. (*c*) Calculate the efficiency of the gearset.

11-28. A 5-DP three-tooth steel worm with ground and polished teeth has a 20° pressure angle, a 14°37′ lead angle, a 2.30-in. pitch diameter, and a 3-in. face. The worm rotates at 1,740 rpm and drives a 50-tooth 1⅜-in.-face bronze worm gear. Determine the maximum horsepower that may be transmitted by this gearset.

11-29. A 16-DP four-tooth hardened-steel worm has a lead angle of 21°48′ and a ⅝-in. pitch diameter. It drives a bronze worm gear having a 5⁄16-in. face, 40 teeth, and a 20° pressure angle. The worm is right-hand and rotates at 600 rpm. (*a*) Determine the maximum horsepower of this gearset. (*b*) Calculate the efficiency.

***11-30.** Design a worm and worm gear for a drive according to the following specifications: input, 1½ hp at 1,800 rpm; output, 300 rpm; shaft center distance to be held to a minimum; worm-shaft diameter, ¾ in.; gear-shaft diameter, 1⅜ in.; load, steady and continuous. These drives are to be manufactured in quantities of 5,000 units. Cost is a primary consideration. The life is to be approximately 4 years at 1½ hr per day.

11-31. A 6-DP 15-tooth 1020 steel straight-tooth bevel pinion drives a 60-tooth cast-iron gear. The shaft angle is 90°, and the face width of the gears is 1¼ in. The pitch diameters are 2½ in. for the pinion and 10 in. for the gear, measured at the large end of the teeth. The teeth are cut with a 20° pressure angle. The pinion is to rotate at 900 rpm and transmit a pulsating load. (*a*) Find the maximum horsepower that may be transmitted, using the modified Lewis equation for dynamic loads. (*b*) Find the maximum horsepower if wear is considered as the principal design factor. (*c*) Find the shaft loads caused by transmitting the horsepower found in (*a*).

7.0 hp
.26 hp
=1137
958

***11-32.** A 4-pitch 16-tooth straight-tooth 20°-pressure-angle steel bevel pinion drives a 32-tooth cast-iron gear. The gears have a face width of 1½ in. and a shaft angle of 90°. The mass moments of inertia are $J = 0.498$ slug-in.^{2} for the pinion and $J = 2.30$ slugs-in.^{2} for the gear. If the pinion is hardened to 300 Bhn, how much horsepower, at a steady and continuous load, will these gears transmit at a pitch-line velocity (large end) of 1,500 fpm?

11-33. A pair of straight-tooth miter gears are 8-DP, 3.50-in. pitch diameter, and of 360 Bhn steel. The gears have 28 teeth cut with a 20° pressure angle and a face width of ⅞ in. The mass moment of inertia of each gear is 0.125 slug-in.^{2} The gears have been tentatively selected to transmit 25 hp at 1,200 rpm. Check this selection by finding the dynamic load, using the fundamental Buckingham equation and comparing it with the wear load and the static beam strength.

11-34. Determine the shaft loads for the gears of Prob. 11-33.

$W_w = 738$ lbf
$W_{max} = 2070$ lbf
$W_d = 1959$ lbf

1) Cal. of pitch line velocity V

$V = \frac{\pi D N}{12} = \frac{2\pi(1.495)1200}{12} = 908$ fpm

2) Cal. of transmitted load, W

from Eq. 10-6 $W = \frac{33000 \text{ hp}}{V} = 909$ lbf

3) Cal. of radial load W_R

Eq. 11-43 $W_R = W \tan\phi \cos\gamma = 909 \tan 20° \cos 45° = 234$ lbf

4) Cal of the radial shaft load, F_r

Eq. 11-50 $F_r = \sqrt{W^2 + W_r^2} = \sqrt{909^2 + 234^2} = 940$ lbf

5) Cal. of the thrust shaft load, W_T

$W_T = W \tan\phi \sin\gamma = 909 \tan 20° \sin 45$
$= 2341$ lbs

CHAPTER 12

CLUTCHES, BRAKES, AND COUPLINGS

Clutches, brakes, and couplings, a group of devices used to control the flow of mechanical power, have very similar functions. The trend toward higher speeds, heavier loads, and compactness, together with the cyclic requirements in automatic machinery, imposes severe restrictions on the designer and requires that he analyze very carefully the problem of selecting or designing these elements.

There are two ways in which a designer may specify a clutch or brake. One of these is to design it as a part of the machine. The other is to specify a commercial unit. Since these devices are available in endless variety from many manufacturers, the designer should usually give considerable thought to the possibility of using a commercial unit, unless considerations of economy or simplicity make it necessary for him to design the clutch or brake as a part of the machine. He is thus faced with either the problem of selection or the problem of design. We shall, therefore, study this problem from both these viewpoints.

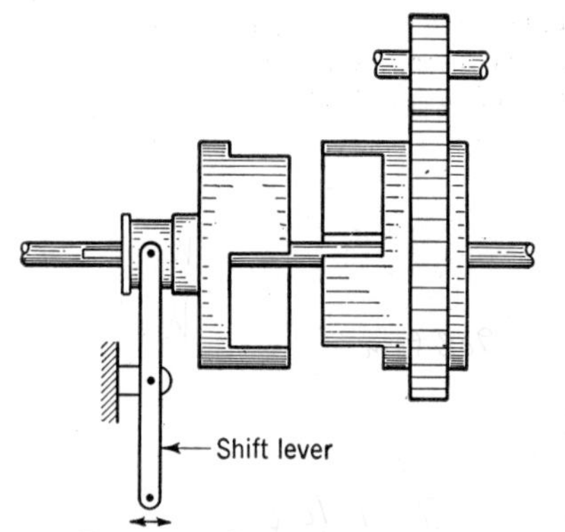

FIG. 12-1. Square-jaw clutch.

12-1. Positive-contact Clutches. The square-jaw clutch shown in Fig. 12-1 is one form of positive-contact clutch. This group of clutches have the following characteristics:

1. They do not slip.
2. No heat is generated.
3. They cannot be engaged at high speeds.
4. Sometimes they cannot be engaged when both shafts are at rest.
5. Engagement at any speed is accompanied by shock.

The greatest differences between the various types of positive clutches are concerned with the design of the jaws. In order to provide a longer period of time for shift action during engagement, the jaws may be ratchet-shaped, spiral-shaped, or gear-tooth-shaped. Sometimes a great many teeth or jaws are used, and they may be cut either circumferentially, so that they engage by cylindrical mating, or on the faces of the mating elements.

Although positive clutches are not used to the extent of the frictional-contact types, they do have important applications where synchronous operation is required, as, for example, in power presses or rolling-mill screw-downs.

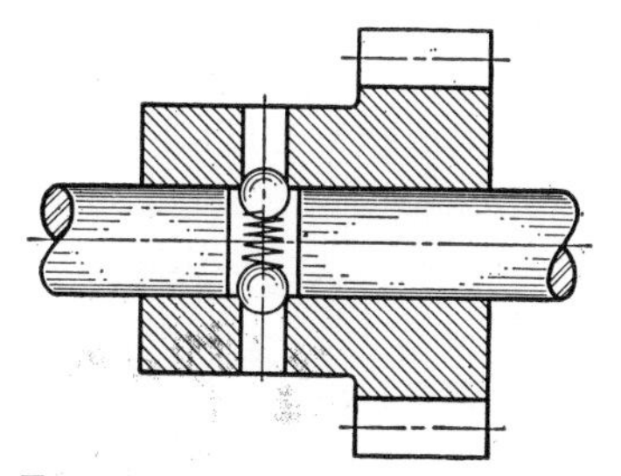

FIG. 12-2. Overload-release clutch.

Devices such as linear drives or motor-operated screw drivers must run to a definite limit and then come to a stop. An overload-release type of clutch is required for these applications. Figure 12-2 is a schematic drawing illustrating the principle of operation of such a clutch. These clutches are usually spring-loaded so as to release at a predetermined torque. The clicking sound which is heard when the overload point is reached is considered to be a desirable signal.

FIG. 12-3. An internal-expanding centrifugal-acting rim clutch. (*Courtesy of The Hilliard Corporation.*)

Both fatigue and shock loads must be considered in obtaining the stresses and deflections of the various portions of positive clutches. In addition, wear must generally be considered. The application of the fundamentals discussed in Part 1 is usually sufficient for the complete design of these devices.

12-2. Frictional-contact Rim Clutches and Brakes. When two mating frictional surfaces, one attached to the driving member and the other attached to the driven member, are brought into contact with each other, frictional forces are created because of the normal pressure between the elements. These frictional forces allow torque to be transmitted from one member to the other and enable a load on the driven shaft to be accelerated smoothly up to the speed of the driving member.

Fig. 12-4. An external-contracting clutch-brake which is engaged by expanding the flexible tube with compressed air. (*Courtesy of Fawick Corporation.*)

A great many clutch and brake designs have the frictional surfaces arranged either on the inside or the outside of a rim, and hence these are frequently called rim clutches. Figure 12-3 shows an internal-expanding rim clutch. It is seen that the clutch consists essentially of three elements: the mating friction surfaces, the means of transmitting the torque to and from the surfaces, and the actuating mechanism. The clutch-brake of Fig. 12-4 has external-contracting friction elements, and the actuating mechanism is pneumatic.

Theoretical Considerations. In designing a friction block or shoe we are particularly interested in the torque transmitted, the normal forces and the maximum pressure between the friction materials, and the amount of energy absorbed or heat generated. A characteristic of hinged friction elements is that, for a certain direction of rotation, the normal force between the two elements is a function of the frictional force, and under certain conditions this normal force may increase without limit and result in self-locking.

The analysis of all types of friction clutches and brakes uses the same general procedure. The following steps are necessary:

1. Assume or determine the distribution of pressure on the frictional surfaces.

2. Find a relation between the maximum pressure and the pressure at any point.

3. Apply the conditions of statical equilibrium to find (*a*) the actuating force, (*b*) the torque, and (*c*) the support reactions.

Let us now apply these steps to the theoretical problem shown in Fig. 12-5. The figure shows a short shoe hinged at A, having an actuating force F, a normal force N pushing the surfaces together, and a frictional force fN, f being the coefficient of friction. The body is moving to the right, and the shoe is stationary. We designate the pressure at any point by p and the maximum pressure by p_a. The area of the shoe is designated by A.

Step 1. Since the shoe is short, we assume the pressure is uniformly distributed over the frictional area.

Step 2. From step 1 it follows that

$$p = p_a \qquad (a)$$

Step 3. Since the pressure is uniformly distributed, we may replace the unit normal forces by an equivalent normal force. Thus

$$N = p_a A \qquad (b)$$

We now apply the conditions of statical equilibrium by taking a summation of moments about the hinge pin. This gives

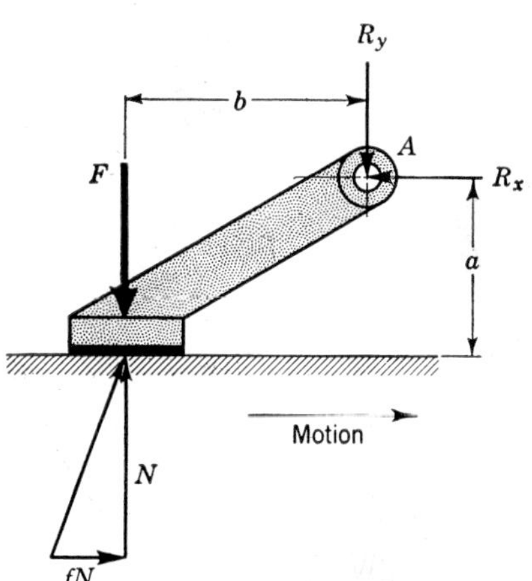

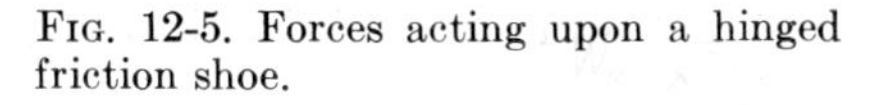
FIG. 12-5. Forces acting upon a hinged friction shoe.

$$Fb - Nb + fNa = 0 \qquad (c)$$

Substituting $p_a A$ for N and solving Eq. (*c*) for the actuating force,

$$F = \frac{p_a A(b - fa)}{b} \qquad (d)$$

Taking a summation of forces in the horizontal and vertical directions gives the hinge-pin reactions:

$$\Sigma F_x = 0 \qquad R_x = fp_a A \qquad (e)$$

$$\Sigma F_y = 0 \qquad R_y = p_a A - F \qquad (f)$$

This completes the analysis of the problem.

The preceding analysis is very useful when the dimensions of the clutch or brake are known and when the characteristics of the friction material are specified. In machine design, however, we are interested more in synthesis than in analysis; that is, our purpose is to select a set of dimensions to obtain the best brake or clutch within the limitations of the frictional material we have specified.

In the previous problem (Fig. 12-5) we are making good use of the frictional material because the pressure is a maximum at all points of contact. Let us examine the dimensions. In Eq. (*d*), if we make $b = fa$, the numerator becomes zero, and no actuating force is required. This is the condition for self-locking. We are usually not interested in designing a brake to be self-locking, but on the other hand we should take full advantage of the self-energizing effect. This can be done by selecting for the frictional material a value of f which will never be exceeded, even under the most adverse conditions. One way to do this is to increase the manufacturer's specification for the coefficient of friction by, say, 25 to 50 per cent. Thus, if we let $f' = 1.25f$ to $1.50f$, the equation

$$b = f'a$$

may be used to obtain the dimensions of a and b to give the degree of self-energization desired.

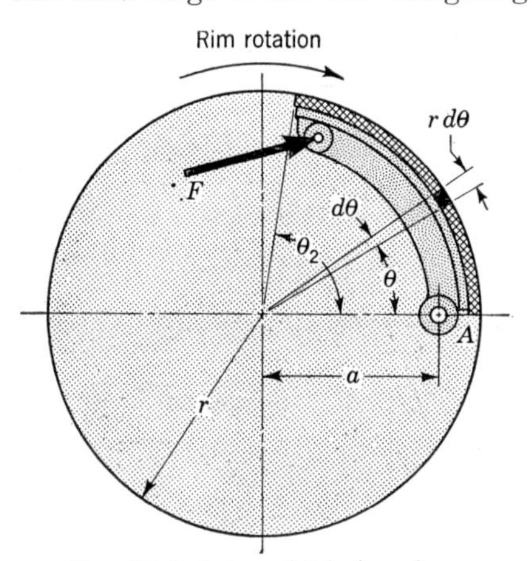

FIG. 12-6. Internal friction shoe.

Design of Internal-expansion Elements. Let us now apply this analysis to an internal friction shoe. Figure 12-6 shows such a shoe pivoted at point A, with the actuating force acting at the other end of the shoe. Since the shoe is long, we cannot make the assumption that the distribution of normal forces is uniform. The mechanical arrangement permits no pressure to be applied at the heel, and we will therefore assume the pressure at this point to be zero.

It is the usual practice to omit the friction material for a short distance away from the heel. This eliminates interference, and it would have contributed little to the performance anyway. In some designs the hinge pin is made movable in order to provide additional heel pressure. This gives the effect of a floating shoe. (Floating shoes will not be treated in this book although their design follows the same general principles.)

Let us consider the unit pressure p acting upon an element of area of the frictional material located at an angle θ from the hinge pin (Fig. 12-6). We designate the maximum pressure by p_a located at the angle θ_a from the hinge pin. We now make the assumption (step 1) that the pressure at any point is proportional to the vertical distance from the hinge pin. This vertical distance is proportional to $\sin\theta$, and (step 2) the relation between the pressures is

$$\frac{p}{\sin \theta} = \frac{p_a}{\sin \theta_a} \tag{g}$$

Rearranging,

$$p = p_a \frac{\sin \theta}{\sin \theta_a} \tag{12-1}$$

From Eq. (12-1) we see that p will be a maximum when $\theta = 90°$, or, if the toe angle θ_2 is less than 90°, then p will be a maximum at the toe.

When $\theta = 0$, Eq. (12-1) shows that the pressure is zero. The frictional material located at the heel, therefore, contributes very little to the braking action and might as well be omitted. A good design would concen-

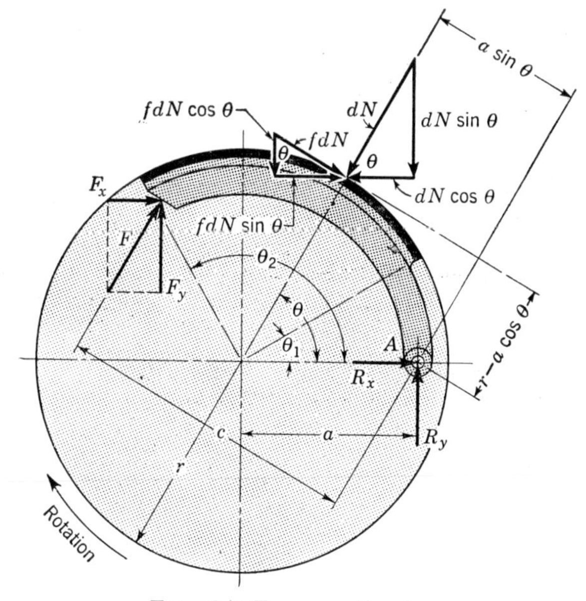

Fig. 12-7. Forces on the shoe.

trate as much frictional material as possible in the neighborhood of the point of maximum pressure. Such a design is shown in Fig. 12-7. In this figure the frictional material begins at an angle θ_1, measured from the hinge pin A, and ends at an angle θ_2. Any arrangement such as this will give a good distribution of the frictional material. In general, there is not much advantage in making θ_2 more than 120°.

Proceeding now to step 3 (Fig. 12-7), the hinge-pin reactions are R_x and R_y. The actuating force F has components F_x and F_y and operates at distance c from the hinge pin. At any angle θ from the hinge pin there acts a differential normal force dN whose magnitude is

$$dN = pbr\,d\theta \tag{h}$$

where b is the face width (perpendicular to the paper) of the friction material. Substituting the value of the pressure from Eq. (12-1), the normal force is

$$dN = \frac{p_a br \sin \theta \, d\theta}{\sin \theta_a} \tag{i}$$

The normal force dN has horizontal and vertical components $dN \cos \theta$ and $dN \sin \theta$, as shown in the figure. The frictional force $f\,dN$ has horizontal and vertical components whose magnitudes are $f\,dN \sin \theta$ and $f\,dN \cos \theta$, respectively. By applying the conditions of statical equilibrium, we may find the actuating force F, the torque T, and the pin reactions R_x and R_y.

We shall find the actuating force F, using the condition that the summation of the moments about the hinge pin is zero. The frictional forces have a moment arm about the pin of $r - a \cos \theta$. The moment M_f of these frictional forces is

$$M_f = \int f\,dN(r - a \cos \theta) = \frac{fp_a br}{\sin \theta_a} \int_{\theta_1}^{\theta_2} \sin \theta (r - a \cos \theta) \, d\theta \tag{12-2}$$

which is obtained by substituting the value for dN from Eq. (i). It is convenient to integrate Eq. (12-2) for each problem, and we shall therefore retain it in this form. The moment arm of the normal force dN about the pin is $a \sin \theta$. Designating the moment of the normal forces by M_N and summing these about the hinge pin give

$$M_N = \int dN(a \sin \theta) = \frac{p_a bra}{\sin \theta_a} \int_{\theta_1}^{\theta_2} \sin^2 \theta \, d\theta \tag{12-3}$$

The actuating force F must balance these moments. Thus

$$F = \frac{M_N - M_f}{c} \tag{12-4}$$

As in the previous problem, we see that a condition for zero actuating force exists. In other words, if we make $M_N = M_f$, self-locking is obtained, and no actuating force is required. This furnishes us with a method for obtaining the dimensions for some self-energizing action. Thus, by using f' instead of f in Eq. (12-2), we may solve for a from the relation

$$M_N = M_{f'} \tag{12-5}$$

where, as before, f' is made about 1.25 to $1.50f$.

The torque T, applied to the drum by the brake shoe, is the sum of the frictional forces $f\,dN$ times the radius of the drum:

$$T = \int f\,dN\,r = \frac{fp_abr^2}{\sin\theta_a}\int_{\theta_1}^{\theta_2}\sin\theta\,d\theta$$
$$= \frac{fp_abr^2(\cos\theta_1 - \cos\theta_2)}{\sin\theta_a} \tag{12-6}$$

The hinge-pin reactions are found by taking a summation of the horizontal and vertical forces. Thus, for R_x, we have

$$R_x = \int dN\cos\theta - \int f\,dN\sin\theta - F_x$$
$$= \frac{p_abr}{\sin\theta_a}\left(\int_{\theta_1}^{\theta_2}\sin\theta\cos\theta\,d\theta - f\int_{\theta_1}^{\theta_2}\sin^2\theta\,d\theta\right) - F_x \tag{12-7}$$

The vertical reaction is found in the same way:

$$R_y = \int dN\sin\theta + \int f\,dN\cos\theta - F_y$$
$$= \frac{p_abr}{\sin\theta_a}\left(\int_{\theta_1}^{\theta_2}\sin^2\theta\,d\theta + f\int_{\theta_1}^{\theta_2}\sin\theta\cos\theta\,d\theta\right) - F_y \tag{12-8}$$

The direction of the frictional forces is reversed if the rotation is reversed. Thus, for counterclockwise rotation the actuating force is

$$F = \frac{M_N + M_f}{c} \tag{12-9}$$

and, since both moments have the same sense, the self-energizing effect is lost. Also, for counterclockwise rotation the signs of the frictional terms in the equations for the pin reactions change, and Eqs. (12-7) and (12-8) become

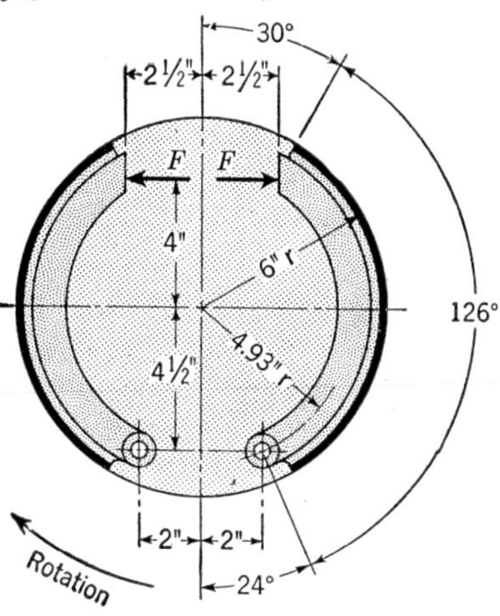

Fig. 12-8. Brake with internal-expanding shoes.

$$R_x = \frac{p_abr}{\sin\theta_a}\left(\int_{\theta_1}^{\theta_2}\sin\theta\cos\theta\,d\theta + f\int_{\theta_1}^{\theta_2}\sin^2\theta\,d\theta\right) - F_x \tag{12-10}$$
$$R_y = \frac{p_abr}{\sin\theta_a}\left(\int_{\theta_1}^{\theta_2}\sin^2\theta\,d\theta - f\int_{\theta_1}^{\theta_2}\sin\theta\cos\theta\,d\theta\right) - F_y \tag{12-11}$$

Example 12-1. The brake shown in Fig. 12-8 is 12 in. in diameter and is actuated by a mechanism which exerts the same force F on each shoe. The shoes are identical and have a face width of 1¼ in. The lining is molded asbestos having a coefficient of friction of 0.32 and a maximum pressure of 150 psi. (*a*) Determine the actuating force F. (*b*) Find the braking capacity. (*c*) Calculate the hinge-pin reactions.

Solution. a. Determination of the actuating force. The right-hand shoe is self-energizing. For the same actuating force this shoe will have the higher pressure of the two. Therefore, the force F is determined on the basis of $p_a = 150$ psi for this shoe. Both shoes are symmetrical, with the frictional surfaces assumed to extend through an angle of 126°. Therefore, $\theta_1 = 0°$, $\theta_2 = 126°$, $\theta_a = 90°$, and $\sin \theta_a = 1$. Integration of Eq. (12-2) between zero and θ_2 yields

$$M_f = \frac{fp_abr}{\sin \theta_a}\left\{\left[-r \cos \theta\right]_0^{\theta_2} - a\left[\tfrac{1}{2} \sin^2 \theta\right]_0^{\theta_2}\right\}$$

$$= \frac{fp_abr}{\sin \theta_a}\left(r - r \cos \theta_2 - \frac{a}{2} \sin^2 \theta_2\right)$$

$$= (0.32)(150)(1.25)(6)\left(6 - 6 \cos 126° - \frac{4.93}{2} \sin^2 126°\right)$$

$$= 2{,}850 \text{ lb-in.}$$

The moment of the normal forces is obtained from Eq. (12-3). Integrating from 0 to θ_2 gives

$$M_N = \frac{p_abra}{\sin \theta_a}\left[\frac{\theta}{2} - \frac{1}{4} \sin 2\theta\right]_0^{\theta_2} = \frac{p_abra}{\sin \theta_a}\left(\frac{\theta_2}{2} - \frac{1}{4} \sin 2\theta_2\right)$$

$$= (150)(1.25)(6)(4.93)\left[\frac{\pi}{2}\frac{126}{180} - \frac{1}{4} \sin (2)(126°)\right] = 6{,}530 \text{ lb-in.}$$

From Eq. (12-4), the actuating force is

$$F = \frac{M_N - M_f}{c} = \frac{6{,}530 - 2{,}850}{8.5} = 433 \text{ lb} \qquad \textit{Ans.}$$

b. Calculation of the braking capacity. From Eq. (12-6), the torque applied by the right-hand shoe is

$$T_R = \frac{fp_abr^2(\cos \theta_1 - \cos \theta_2)}{\sin \theta_a} = \frac{(0.32)(150)(1.25)(6)^2(\cos 0 - \cos 126°)}{1}$$

$$= 3{,}430 \text{ lb-in.}$$

The torque contributed by the left-hand shoe cannot be obtained until the maximum pressure is determined. Proceeding to this problem, Eqs. (12-2) and (12-3) indicate that the frictional and normal moments are proportional to the maximum pressure. Thus, for the left-hand shoe,

$$M_N = \frac{6{,}530p_a}{150} \qquad M_f = \frac{2{,}850p_a}{150}$$

Then, from Eq. (12-9),

$$F = \frac{M_N + M_f}{c} \qquad 433 = \frac{(6{,}530/150)p_a + (2{,}850/150)p_a}{8.5}$$

Solving for p_a,

$$p_a = \frac{(433)(150)(8.5)}{6{,}530 + 2{,}850} = 59.0 \text{ psi}$$

Then, from Eq. (12-6), the torque on the left-hand shoe is

$$T_L = \frac{fp_abr^2(\cos \theta_1 - \cos \theta_2)}{\sin \theta_a}$$

$$= (0.32)(59.0)(1.25)(6)^2(\cos 0 - \cos 126°) = 1{,}350 \text{ lb-in.}$$

The braking capacity is the total torque:

$$T = T_R + T_L = 3{,}430 + 1{,}350 = 4{,}780 \text{ lb-in.} \qquad Ans.$$

c. The hinge-pin reactions. For the right-hand shoe these are found from Eqs. (12-7) and (12-8). Substituting $\sin \theta_a = 1$ and $\theta_1 = 0$ and integrating, we have

$$\begin{aligned} R_x &= p_a br \left\{ \left[\tfrac{1}{2} \sin^2 \theta \right]_0^{\theta_2} - f \left[\frac{\theta}{2} - \frac{1}{4} \sin 2\theta \right]_0^{\theta_2} \right\} - F_x \\ &= p_a br \left(\tfrac{1}{2} \sin^2 \theta_2 - \frac{f\theta_2}{2} + \frac{f}{4} \sin 2\theta_2 \right) - F_x \\ &= (150)(1.25)(6) \left[\tfrac{1}{2} \sin^2 126° - \frac{(0.32)(\pi)(126)}{(2)(180)} + \frac{0.32}{4} \sin (2)(126°) \right] \\ &\qquad - 433 \sin 24° \\ &= -290 \text{ lb} \end{aligned}$$

In the same way

$$R_y = 734 \text{ lb}$$

The resultant on this hinge pin is

$$\text{Res} = \sqrt{(734)^2 + (290)^2} = 788 \text{ lb} \qquad Ans.$$

The reactions at the hinge pin of the left-hand shoe are found using Eqs. (12-10) and (12-11) for a pressure of 59.0 psi. They are found to be

$$R_x = 156 \text{ lb} \qquad R_y = 46 \text{ lb}$$
$$\text{Res} = \sqrt{(156)^2 + (46)^2} = 170 \text{ lb} \qquad Ans.$$

The reactions for both hinge pins, together with their directions, are shown in Fig. 12-9.

This example dramatically shows the benefit to be gained by arranging the shoes to be self-energizing. If the left-hand shoe were turned over so as to place the hinge pin at the top, then it could apply the same torque as the right-hand shoe. This would make the capacity of the brake (2)(3,430) = 6,860 lb-in. instead of the present torque capacity of 4,780 lb-in. In addition, some of the friction material at the heel could be eliminated without seriously affecting the capacity, because of the low pressures in this area. This change might actually improve the over-all design because the additional rim exposure would improve the heat-dissipation capacity.

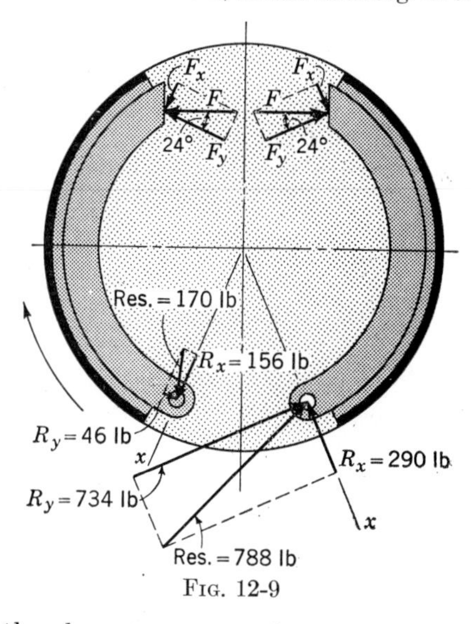

Fig. 12-9

Assumptions. The following assumptions are implied by the preceding analysis:

1. The pressure at any point on the shoe was assumed to be proportional to the distance from the hinge pin, being zero at the heel. This should be considered from the standpoint that pressures specified by manufacturers are averages rather than maximums.

2. The effect of centrifugal force has been neglected. In the case of brakes, the shoes are not rotating, and no centrifugal force would exist. In clutch design, the effect of this force must be considered in writing the equations of statical equilibrium.

3. The shoe was assumed to be rigid. Since this cannot be true, some deflection will occur, depending upon the load, pressure, and stiffness of the shoe. The resulting pressure distribution may be different from that which has been assumed.

4. The entire analysis has been based upon a coefficient of friction which does not vary with pressure. Actually, the coefficient may vary with a number of conditions, including temperature, wear, and environment. Because of this variation, the design of a clutch or brake can never be exact.

Design of External-contracting Elements. The notation for external-contracting shoes is shown in Fig. 12-10. The moments of the frictional forces and normal forces about the hinge pin are the same as for the internal-expanding shoes. Equations (12-2) and (12-3) apply and are repeated here for convenience:

$$M_f = \frac{fp_a br}{\sin \theta_a} \int_{\theta_1}^{\theta_2} \sin \theta \, (r - a \cos \theta) \, d\theta \qquad (12\text{-}2)$$

$$M_N = \frac{p_a bra}{\sin \theta_a} \int_{\theta_1}^{\theta_2} \sin^2 \theta \, d\theta \qquad (12\text{-}3)$$

Both these equations give positive values for clockwise moments (Fig. 12-10) when used for external-contracting shoes. The actuating force must be large enough to balance both moments:

$$F = \frac{M_N + M_f}{c} \qquad (12\text{-}12)$$

The horizontal and vertical reactions at the hinge pin are found in the same manner as for internal-expanding shoes. They are

$$\begin{aligned} R_x &= \int dN \cos \theta + \int f \, dN \sin \theta - F_x \\ &= \frac{p_a br}{\sin \theta_a} \left(\int_{\theta_1}^{\theta_2} \sin \theta \cos \theta \, d\theta + f \int_{\theta_1}^{\theta_2} \sin^2 \theta \, d\theta \right) - F_x \qquad (12\text{-}13) \\ R_y &= \int f \, dN \cos \theta - \int dN \sin \theta + F_y \\ &= \frac{p_a br}{\sin \theta_a} \left(f \int_{\theta_1}^{\theta_2} \sin \theta \cos \theta \, d\theta - \int_{\theta_1}^{\theta_2} \sin^2 \theta \, d\theta \right) - F_y \qquad (12\text{-}14) \end{aligned}$$

If the rotation is counterclockwise, the sign of the frictional term in each equation is reversed. Thus Eq. (12-12) for the actuating force becomes

$$F = \frac{M_N - M_f}{c} \tag{12-15}$$

and self-energization exists for counterclockwise rotation. The horizontal and vertical reactions are

$$R_x = \frac{p_a br}{\sin \theta_a}\left(\int_{\theta_1}^{\theta_2} \sin \theta \cos \theta \, d\theta - f \int_{\theta_1}^{\theta_2} \sin^2 \theta \, d\theta\right) - F_x \tag{12-16}$$

$$R_y = \frac{p_a br}{\sin \theta_a}\left(-f \int_{\theta_1}^{\theta_2} \sin \theta \cos \theta \, d\theta - \int_{\theta_1}^{\theta_2} \sin^2 \theta \, d\theta\right) + F_y \tag{12-17}$$

It should be noted that, when external-contracting designs are used as clutches, the effect of centrifugal force is to decrease the normal force.

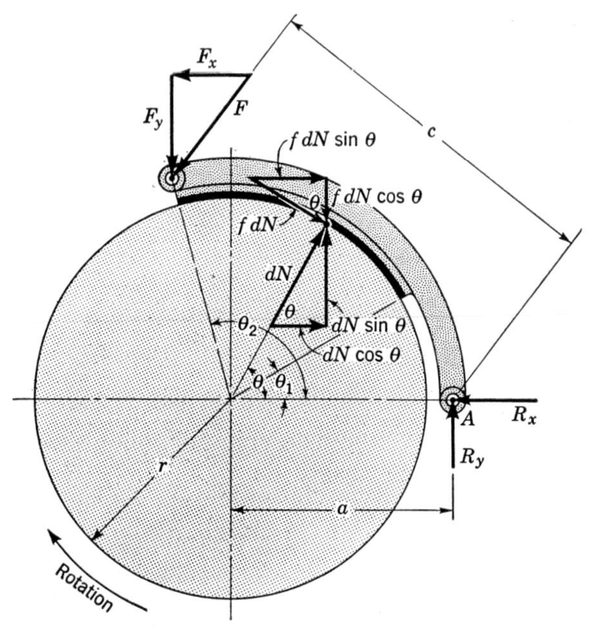

FIG. 12-10. Notation for external-contracting shoe.

Thus, as the speed increases, a larger value of the actuating force F is required.

Band-type Clutches and Brakes. Flexible clutch and brake bands are used in power excavators and in hoisting and other machinery. The analysis follows the notation of Fig. 12-11.

Because of friction and the rotation of the drum, the actuating force P_2 is less than the pin reaction P_1. Any element of the band, of angular length $d\theta$, will be in equilibrium under the action of the forces shown in

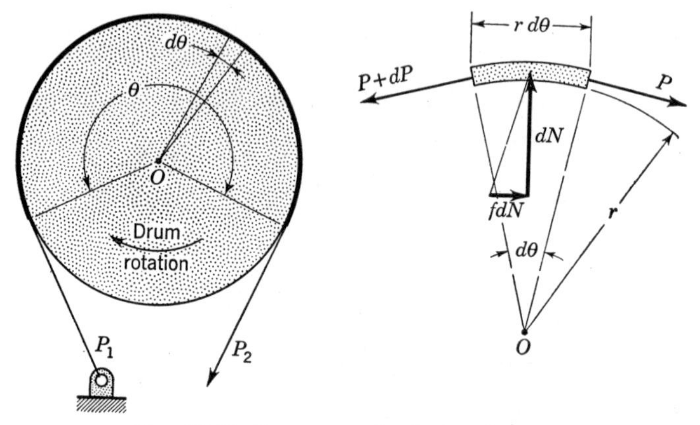

FIG. 12-11. Forces on a brake band.

the figure. Summing these forces in the vertical direction, we have

$$(P + dP) \sin \frac{d\theta}{2} + P \sin \frac{d\theta}{2} - dN = 0 \tag{j}$$

$$dN = P\, d\theta \tag{k}$$

since for small angles $\sin d\theta/2 = d\theta/2$. Summing the forces in the horizontal direction gives

$$(P + dP) \cos \frac{d\theta}{2} - P \cos \frac{d\theta}{2} - f\, dN = 0 \tag{l}$$

$$dP - f\, dN = 0 \tag{m}$$

Substituting the value of dN from Eq. (k) into Eq. (m) and integrating,

$$\int_{P_2}^{P_1} \frac{dP}{P} = f \int_0^\theta d\theta \qquad \ln \frac{P_1}{P_2} = f\theta$$

and

$$\frac{P_1}{P_2} = e^{f\theta} \tag{12-18}$$

The torque may be obtained from the equation

$$T = (P_1 - P_2) \frac{D}{2} \tag{12-19}$$

The normal force dN acting on an element of area of width b and length $r\, d\theta$ is

$$dN = pbr\, d\theta \tag{n}$$

where p is the pressure. Substitution of the value of dN from Eq. (k)

gives

$$P\,d\theta = pbr\,d\theta$$

Therefore,

$$p = \frac{P}{br} = \frac{2P}{bD} \tag{12-20}$$

The pressure is, therefore, proportional to the tension in the band. The maximum pressure p_a will occur at the toe and has the value

$$p_a = \frac{2P_1}{bD} \tag{12-21}$$

12-3. Frictional-contact Axial Clutches. An axial clutch is one in which the mating frictional members are moved in a direction parallel

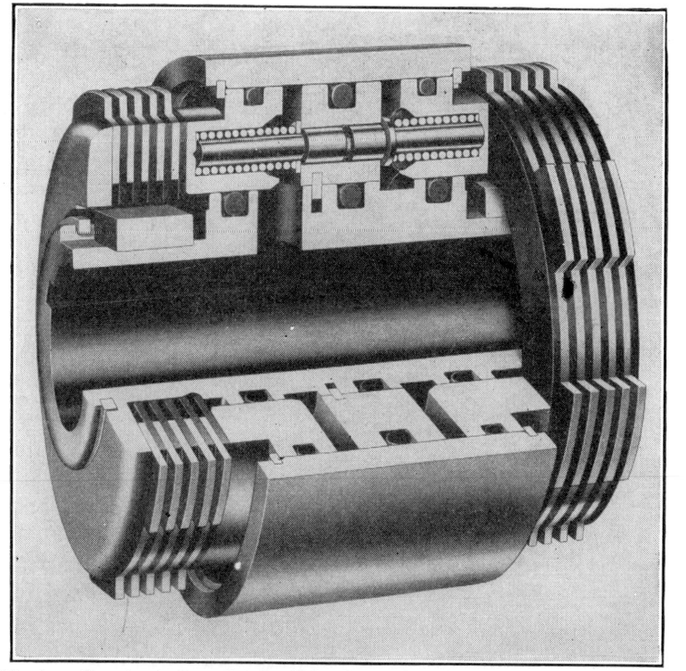

FIG. 12-12. An oil-actuated multiple-disk clutch-brake or clutch-clutch for enclosed operation in an oil bath or spray. It is especially useful for rapid cycling. (*Courtesy of Twin Disc Clutch Company.*)

to the shaft. One of the earliest of these is the cone clutch which is simple in construction and quite powerful. However, except for relatively simple installations, it has been largely displaced by the disk clutch employing one or more disks as the operating members. Advantages of the disk clutch include the freedom from centrifugal effects, the large frictional area which can be installed in a small space, the more effective heat-dissipation surfaces, and the favorable pressure distribution. One very successful disk-clutch design is shown in Fig. 12-12. Let us now determine the capacity of such a clutch or brake in terms of the material and dimensions.

Figure 12-13 shows a friction disk having an outside diameter D and an inside diameter d. We are interested in obtaining the axial force F necessary to produce a certain torque T and pressure p. Two methods of solving the problem, depending upon the construction of the clutch, are in general use. If the disks are rigid, then, at first, the greatest amount of wear will occur in the outer areas, since the work of friction is greater in those areas. After a certain amount of wear has taken place, the pressure distribution will change so as to permit the wear to be uniform. This is the basis of the first method of solution.

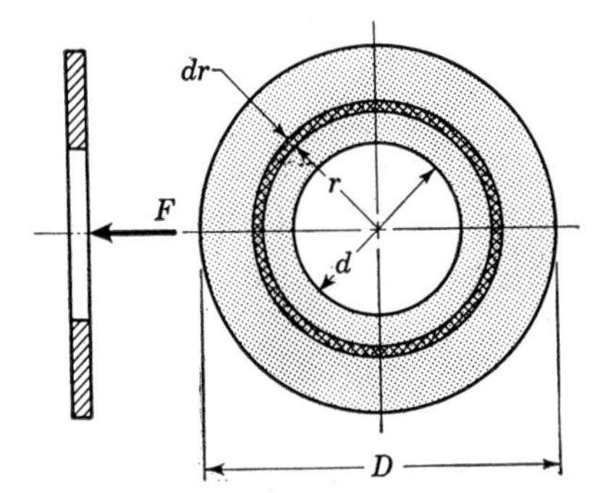

FIG. 12-13. Disk friction member.

Another method of construction employs springs to obtain a uniform pressure over the area. It is this assumption of uniform pressure that is used in the second method of solution.

Uniform Wear. After initial wear has taken place and the disks have worn down to the point where uniform wear becomes possible, the greatest pressure must occur at $r = d/2$ in order for the wear to be uniform. Denoting the maximum pressure by p_a, we can then write

$$pr = p_a \frac{d}{2} \qquad \text{or} \qquad p = p_a \frac{d}{2r} \tag{a}$$

which is the condition for having the same amount of work done at radius r as is done at radius $d/2$. Referring to Fig. 12-13, we have an element of area of radius r and thickness dr. The area of this element is $2\pi r\, dr$, so that the normal force acting upon this element is $dF = 2\pi pr\, dr$. We can find the total normal force by letting r vary from $d/2$ to $D/2$ and integrating. Thus,

$$F = \int_{d/2}^{D/2} 2\pi pr\, dr = \pi p_a d \int_{d/2}^{D/2} dr = \frac{\pi p_a d}{2} (D - d) \tag{12-22}$$

The torque is found by integrating the product of the frictional force and the radius:

$$T = \int_{d/2}^{D/2} 2\pi f p r^2\, dr = \pi f p_a d \int_{d/2}^{D/2} r\, dr = \frac{\pi f p_a d}{8} (D^2 - d^2) \tag{12-23}$$

By substituting the value of F from Eq. (12-22) we may obtain a more convenient expression for the torque. Thus

$$T = \frac{Ff}{4}(D + d) \tag{12-24}$$

In use, Eq. (12-22) gives the actuating force per friction surface for the selected maximum pressure p_a. Equation (12-24) is then used to obtain the torque capacity per friction surface.

Uniform Pressure. When uniform pressure can be assumed over the area of the disk, the actuating force F is simply the product of the pressure and the area. This gives

$$F = \frac{\pi p_a}{4}(D^2 - d^2) \tag{12-25}$$

As before, the torque is found by integrating the product of the frictional force and the radius:

$$T = 2\pi f p \int_{d/2}^{D/2} r^2\, dr = \frac{2\pi f p}{24}(D^3 - d^3) \tag{12-26}$$

Since $p = p_a$, we can rewrite Eq. (12-26) as

$$T = \frac{Ff}{3}\frac{D^3 - d^3}{D^2 - d^2} \tag{12-27}$$

It should be noted for both equations that the torque is for a single pair of mating surfaces. This value must therefore be multiplied by the number of pairs of surfaces in contact.

12-4. Friction Materials. A brake or clutch friction material should have the following characteristics to a degree which is dependent upon the severity of the service:

1. A high and uniform coefficient of friction
2. Properties which are not affected by environmental conditions such as moisture
3. The ability to withstand high temperatures, together with good heat conductivity
4. Good resiliency
5. High resistance to wear, scoring, and galling

Table 12-1 lists some of the commonly employed friction materials, together with their characteristics. In selecting a coefficient of friction for design purposes, only one-half to three-quarters of the value listed should be used. This will provide some margin of safety against wear, dirt, and other unfavorable conditions.

TABLE 12-1. FRICTION MATERIALS FOR CLUTCHES*

Contact surfaces		Friction coefficient†		Maximum tempera-ture, F	Maximum pressure, psi	Relative cost	Comment
Wearing	Opposing‡	Wet	Dry				
Cast bronze	Cast iron or steel	0.05	...	300	80–120	Low	Subject to seizing
Cast iron	Cast iron	0.05	0.15–0.2	600	150–250	Very low	Good at low speeds
Cast iron	Steel	0.06	...	500	120–200	Very low	Fair at low speeds
Hard steel	Hard steel	0.05	...	500	100	Moderate	Subject to galling
Hard steel	Hard steel, chromium-plated	0.03	...	500	200	High	Durable combination
Hard-drawn phosphor bronze	Hard steel, chromium-plated	0.03	...	500	150	High	Good wearing qualities
Powder metal¶	Cast iron or steel	0.05–0.1	0.1–0.4	1,000	150	High	Good wearing qualities
Powder metal¶	Hard steel, chromium-plated	0.05–0.1	0.1–0.3	1,000	300	Very high	High energy absorption
Wood	Cast iron or steel	0.16	0.2–0.35	300	60–90	Lowest	Unsuitable at high speed
Leather	Cast iron or steel	0.12–0.15	0.3–0.5	200	10–40	Very low	Subject to glazing
Cork	Cast iron or steel	0.15–0.25	0.3–0.5	200	8–14	Very low	Cork-insert type preferred
Felt	Cast iron or steel	0.18	0.22	280	5–10	Low	Resilient engagement
Vulcanized fiber or paper	Cast iron or steel	...	0.3–0.5	200	10–40	Very low	Low speeds, light duty
Woven asbestos¶	Cast iron or steel	0.1–0.2	0.3–0.6	350–500	50–100	Low	Prolonged slip service ratings given
Woven asbestos	Cast iron or steel	0.1–0.2	...	500	100–200	Low	This rating for short infrequent engagements
Woven asbestos	Hard steel, chromium-plated	0.1	...	...	1,200	Moderate	Used in Napier Sabre engine
Molded asbestos¶	Cast iron or steel	0.08–0.12	0.2–0.5	500	50–150	Very low	Wide field of applications
Impregnated asbestos	Cast iron or steel	0.12	0.32	500–750	150	Moderate	For demanding applications
Carbon graphite	Steel	0.05–0.1	0.25	700–1,000	300	High	For critical requirements
Molded phenolic plastic, macerated cloth base	Cast iron or steel	0.1–0.15	0.25	300	100	Low	For light special service

* A. F. Gagne, Jr., Clutches, *Machine Design*, vol. 24, no. 8, p. 136, August, 1952. Reproduced with the permission of *Machine Design*.

† Conservative values should be used to allow for possible glazing of clutch surfaces in service and for adverse operating conditions.

‡ Steel, where specified, should have a carbon content of approximately 0.70 per cent. Surfaces should be ground true and smooth.

¶ For a specific material within this group, the coefficient usually is maintained within plus or minus 5 per cent.

Some of the materials may be run wet by allowing them to dip in oil or to be sprayed by oil. This reduces the coefficient of friction somewhat but carries away more heat and permits higher pressures to be used.

12-5. Energy Considerations. When the rotating members of a machine are caused to stop by means of a brake, the kinetic energy of rotation must be absorbed by the brake. This energy appears in the brake in the form of heat. In the same way, when the members of a machine which are initially at rest are brought up to speed, slipping must occur in the clutch until the driven members have the same speed as the driver. Kinetic energy is absorbed during slippage of either a clutch or brake, and this energy appears as heat.

We have seen how the torque capacity of a clutch or brake depends upon the coefficient of friction of the material and upon a safe normal pressure. However, the character of the load may be such that, if this torque value is permitted, the clutch or brake may be destroyed by its own generated heat. The capacity of a clutch is therefore limited by two factors, the characteristics of the material and the ability of the clutch to dissipate heat. The following discussion is aimed at establishing the capacity of a clutch or brake according to its ability to dissipate heat.

Newton's law for angular motion states that the torque required to accelerate a rotating mass is

$$T = J\alpha \tag{a}$$

where J is the polar moment of inertia of the mass and α is the angular acceleration. In the case of a brake, the shaft-connected masses have an initial speed of n rpm and a final speed of zero rpm. In the case of a clutch, the initial speed is zero and the final speed is n rpm. Therefore, for both cases, the change in speed is n rpm; the acceleration is, therefore, $2\pi n/60t$ radians per sec per sec, where t is the time of clutching or braking, in seconds. Equation (a) becomes

$$T = 12J\frac{2\pi n}{60t} \qquad \text{or} \qquad t = \frac{2\pi nJ}{5T} \tag{b}$$

where J is in slugs-feet squared. The energy required for a single braking or clutching operation is

$$E_k = \left(\frac{2\pi T}{12}\right)\left(\frac{1}{2}\frac{n}{60}t\right) = \frac{2\pi Tnt}{1{,}440} \tag{c}$$

where $2\pi T/12$ is the work done per revolution and $nt/(2)(60)$ is the number of revolutions for the speed to change from zero to n rpm. Substituting the value of t from Eq. (b) into Eq. (c), we obtain

$$E_k = \frac{\pi^2 n^2 J}{1{,}800} \tag{12-28}$$

Therefore, the heat generated in Btu during each operation is

$$H = \frac{E_k}{778} \tag{12-29}$$

The temperature of the clutch plates at the end of a single clutching or braking operation is approximated by the equation

$$t_2 = \frac{H}{cW} + t_1 \tag{12-30}$$

where t_1 is the initial temperature of the plates and t_2 is the final temperature, both being in degrees Fahrenheit. The coefficient c is the specific heat of the clutch-plate material; an average value of 0.12 may be used for cast iron or steel. In Eq. (12-30) W is the weight of the clutch plates.

It may be that the operating frequency is rapid enough that the elements do not cool off completely after each cycle is completed. When this condition exists, some of the heat will be retained after each cycle, and the temperature will climb in a saw-tooth fashion until an equilibrium condition is obtained. The temperature corresponding to this equilibrium condition is difficult to estimate. The heat is dissipated by both radiation and conduction, and so it depends upon the character of the surroundings, the ventilation, the nature and shape of the radiating and conducting surfaces, and the temperature distribution throughout the clutch. For this reason, any calculation which is made can be only a rough one and, at best, will indicate whether or not the temperature rise is likely to be a major consideration. Gagne suggests the following approximation:

$$C(t_{av} - t_1)\left[\frac{Nt}{3{,}600} + 1.5\left(1 - \frac{Nt}{3{,}600}\right)\right] = \frac{HN}{A} \tag{12-31}$$

where C = heat-transfer coefficient, Btu per hr per ft² per °F
t_{av} = average equilibrium temperature, °F
t_1 = initial or ambient temperature, °F
N = number of clutching or braking cycles per hr
t = time of single clutching or braking operation, sec
H = heat generated during single operation, Btu
A = exterior area, ft²

The heat-transfer coefficient C depends upon the exterior speed, the character of the materials, and the environment. The values of C listed in Table 12-2 are suggested for average conditions. Gagne[1] states that the average temperature t_{av} obtained by Eq. (12-31) should generally be from 100 to 150° less than that recommended by the manufacturer of the lining material, in order to allow for operating peaks.

[1] A. F. Gagne, Jr., Torque Capacity and Design of Cone and Disk Clutches, *Machine Design*, vol. 24, no. 12, pp. 182–187, December, 1953.

TABLE 12-2. VALUES OF THE HEAT-TRANSFER COEFFICIENT C FOR ROUGH BLACK SURFACES

Velocity V, fps	0	20	40	60	80	100
Heat-transfer coefficient C	1.5	2.49	3.32	3.95	4.50	5.10

EXAMPLE 12-2. A solid steel flywheel 10 in. in diameter and 2 in. thick rotates at 1,750 rpm. Determine the kinetic energy of the flywheel and the braking torque necessary to bring it to a stop in 2 sec.

Solution. The weight of the flywheel is

$$W = \frac{\pi d^2 t \rho}{4} = \frac{(\pi)(10)^2(2)(0.285)}{4} = 44.8 \text{ lb}$$

where the density of steel is $\rho = 0.285$ lb per in.^{3} The moment of inertia is

$$J = \frac{1}{2} Mr^2 = \frac{(44.8)(5)^2}{(2)(32.2)(144)} = 0.121 \text{ slug-ft}^2$$

From Eq. (12-23), the kinetic energy of the flywheel is

$$E_k = \frac{\pi^2 n^2 J}{1{,}800} = \frac{(\pi^2)(1{,}750)^2(0.121)}{1{,}800} = 2{,}030 \text{ ft-lb} \qquad \textit{Ans.}$$

Applying Newton's law, the torque is

$$T = J\alpha = J\frac{\omega}{t} = 12J\frac{2\pi n}{60t} = \frac{(12)(0.121)(2\pi)(1{,}750)}{(60)(2)} = 133 \text{ lb-in.} \qquad \textit{Ans.}$$

12-6. Miscellaneous Clutches and Brakes. *Overrunning Clutches.* An overrunning clutch or coupling permits the driven member of a machine to "freewheel" or "overrun" because the driver is stopped or because another source of power increases the speed of the driven mechanism. The construction shown in Fig. 12-14 uses rollers or balls mounted between an outer sleeve and an inner member having cam flats machined around the periphery. Driving action is obtained by wedging the rollers between the sleeve and the cam flats. The clutch shown is therefore equivalent to a pawl and ratchet with an infinite number of teeth.

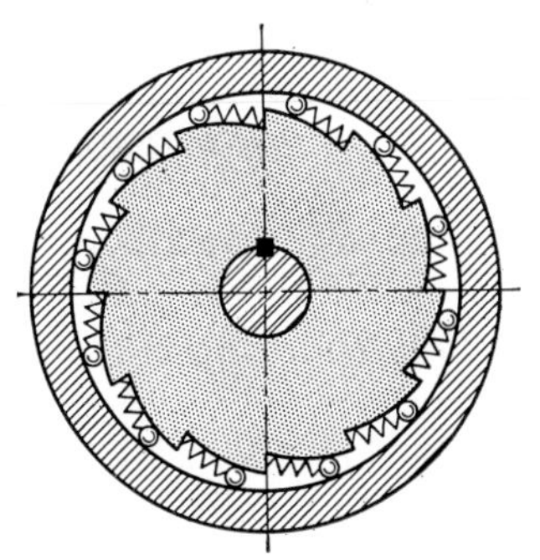

FIG. 12-14. An overrunning clutch.

There are many varieties of overrunning clutches available, and they are built in capacities up to hundreds of horsepower. The example shown is probably typical. Since no slippage is involved, the only power loss is that due to bearing friction and windage.

Eddy-current Couplings. An eddy-current brake or clutch consists essentially of two rotors, one operating inside the other but without physical contact. One of the rotors has d-c field coils. When these coils are excited, the resulting magnetic field produces eddy currents in the other rotor. These eddy currents induce between the two rotors a pull which is proportional to the slippage and the excitation. It is seen from Fig. 12-15 that some slippage must exist in order that the torque may be developed.

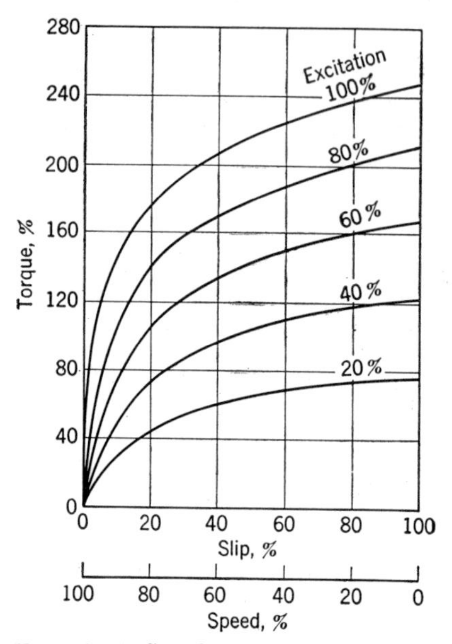

FIG. 12-15. Speed-torque curves for an eddy-current clutch. (*From A. F. Gagne, Jr., Clutches, Machine Design, vol.* 24, *no.* 8, *p.* 153, 1952.)

These couplings are made in capacities up to 18,000 hp. They must be cooled, using either water or air, since there is a considerable power loss in slipping.

Magnetic Fluid Clutches. The magnetic fluid clutch or brake is a relatively new development which has two parallel magnetic plates. Between these plates is a lubricated magnetic powder mixture. An electromagnetic coil is inserted somewhere in the magnetic circuit. By varying the excitation to this coil, the shearing strength of the magnetic fluid mixture may be accurately controlled. Thus any condition from a full slip to a frozen lockup may be obtained.

12-7. Hydraulic Couplings. A *fluid coupling* is a device for connecting a driving shaft to a driven shaft; the torque on each shaft is the same, but the speed of the driven shaft is slower by the amount of slippage. A *torque converter* is somewhat more than a clutch in that it is capable of multiplying the input torque. The discussion in this section is concerned only with fluid couplings.

The fluid coupling (Fig. 12-16) consists of an impeller, which is the driving member, and a runner, which is the driven member. They are enclosed by a housing, which may be a part of the impeller, and are filled with a hydraulic fluid. A series of radial blades, usually straight, is mounted in both the impeller and runner. When the impeller is rotated, centrifugal force directs the fluid outward. At the same time, it is carried across the space and its momentum delivered to the blades of the runner, causing the runner to rotate.

An important application of the fluid coupling occurs when it is used with a squirrel-cage motor as the driving source. In starting high-inertia loads, the motor starting current may be so high as to require an oversize motor. On the other hand, if the application of the load can be delayed long enough to allow the motor to build up to a speed at which it can deliver maximum torque, then the starting current will be considerably reduced and a smaller motor can be used. One solution to this problem involves the use of a fluid coupling. Referring to Fig. 12-17, it is seen that, in a typical example, the motor torque during starting is about 230 per cent of full-load torque and the current is approximately 600 per cent of full load. If the motor is permitted to build up to a speed of about 1,500 rpm before the major portion of the load is applied, then the motor current is only about 350 per cent of full load. Thus the selection of a fluid coupling, such that the drag-torque curve (torque at 100 per cent slip) crosses the motor-torque curve at or near its peak, permits the motor to accelerate rapidly out of the low-speed region and to pick up the load as the motor speed nears the maximum-torque condition.

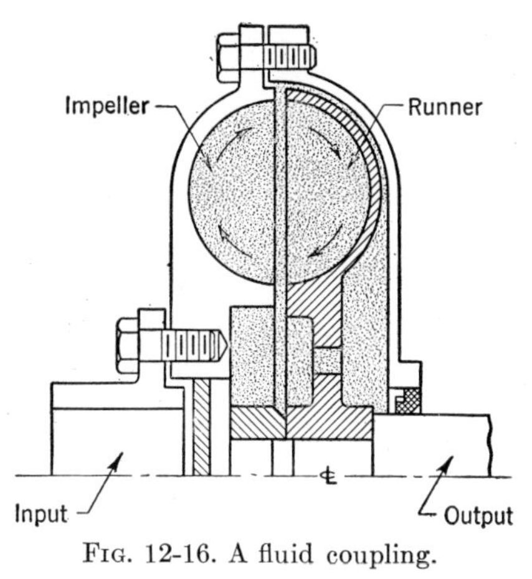

Fig. 12-16. A fluid coupling.

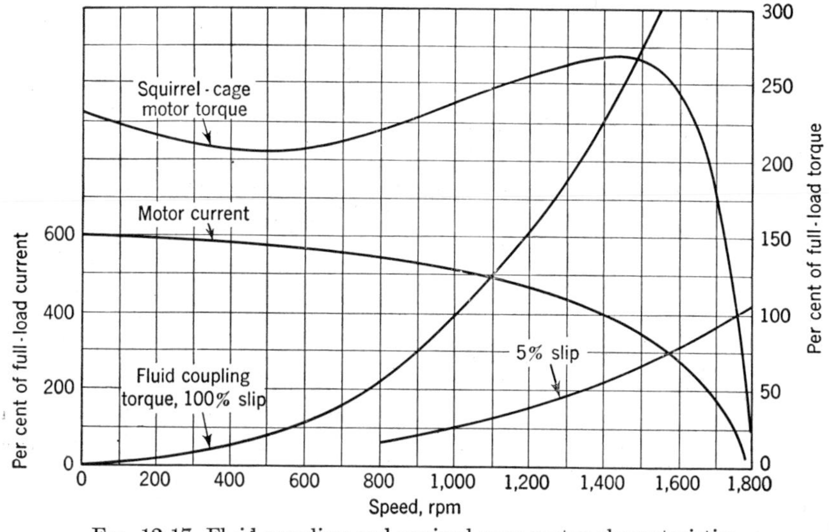

Fig. 12-17. Fluid-coupling and squirrel-cage-motor characteristics

The heat generated in a fluid coupling depends upon the slip. Normally a coupling is selected to have a slip of 3 to 5 per cent when operating at full load. If the slip is greater than this, or if a heavy heat load is imposed by, say, a rapid start-stop cycle, then additional means for dissipating the heat must be provided.

A *variable-fill* fluid coupling is one which is designed with an external circuit. This circuit customarily has two purposes. First, it provides storage for excess fluid and a method of cooling it; and second, a coupling in which the amount of fluid may be varied makes it possible to control the slip and consequently the output speed of the unit. The methods to

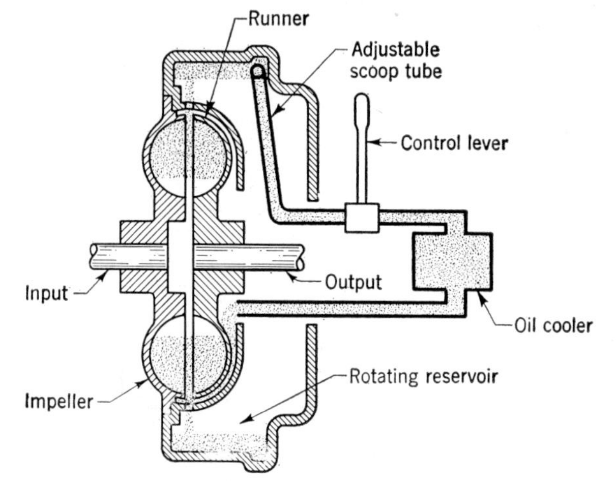

Fig. 12-18. Fluid coupling with scoop control.

vary the amount of fluid in the unit sometimes use a pump to increase or decrease it and to circulate it through a cooler. Another method which is frequently employed has a rotating reservoir around the unit and a scoop tube, whose position can be adjusted according to the output speed desired. The scoop tube picks up oil from the reservoir and circulates it through a cooler. Its position determines the percentage of oil in the working circuit and in this way controls the speed of the driven member (Fig. 12-18).

12-8. Decisions. Whether to design and manufacture the clutch or brake or to purchase a commercial unit is the first decision to be made. In many cases the lack of manufacturing facilities or the small number of units to be built will require the selection of a commercial unit. Sometimes the operating conditions are so specialized, or the installation requirements are so unusual, that a commercial unit satisfying these requirements cannot be found, and so the design and manufacture of a unit become necessary. Decisions like these, however, are easy to make; it is the case in between these extremes which is difficult.

The amount of study which can be given to this problem depends upon the number of units to be manufactured or purchased and the probable savings which would result. If these savings appear to justify the design and manufacture of a unit, a tentative design should be drawn up in order that detailed cost estimates may be made. These cost estimates will then indicate the direction in which to proceed. If they show only a slight margin in favor of designing and manufacturing a clutch, it is probably best to select a commercial unit, because there are many hidden problems in clutch design which are likely to be rather costly. The large amount of experience in back of commercial units should receive very careful consideration.

Commercial Units. The torque and the horsepower at 100 rpm are usually listed together as the capacity of a clutch or brake. The designer must choose one of two methods of altering the actual load in order to obtain a figure to use in the selection.

In the first method the actual horsepower or torque is multiplied by a rating factor whose value depends upon the source of power and the type of load. Typical rating factors are listed in Table 12-3. This gives the required capacity. In using Table 12-3, the rating factors for the load and power source should be multiplied together.

Most catalogue ratings are based on a very few operations per hour. If the operating cycles are frequent, or if a single cycle is long, then the clutch or brake must be selected according to its ability to dissipate heat. If the characteristic curve for the cycle of operation is known or can be determined, it is a simple matter to calculate the heat dissipation required for a given period of time. A commercial unit is then selected according to its ability to withstand the heat load.

TABLE 12-3. CLUTCH AND BRAKE RATING FACTORS*

Service condition	*Rating factor*
Power source:	
Electric motor or steam turbine	1.00
Steam engine or four-cylinder gas engine	1.50
Single-cylinder gas engine	2.00
Type of load:	
Blowers, belt conveyors, generators	1.00
Hoists, heavy-duty line shafts, rotary kilns	1.50
Crushers, rolling mills, reciprocating conveyors	2.00
Low-inertia loads	0.75–1.00
Average inertia	1.00–1.25
High inertia, ball mills, centrifuges	1.50–2.00

* A. F. Gagne, Jr., Clutches, *Machine Design*, vol. 24, no. 8, p. 157, August, 1952.

Although this discussion has been limited to friction units, the designer should not lose sight of the advantages to be obtained in the use of either electric or hydraulic units.

Design. When a clutch or brake is to be designed, the following items are typical of the decisions which must be made:

1. The type of clutch, whether radial or axial, internal-expanding or external-contracting, disk or plate, band or block. This decision includes the design or selection of the operating mechanism, and so it is dependent upon the characteristics of the machine into which it is to be installed.

2. The friction material, the design coefficient of friction, and the maximum pressure to be used. These three decisions are interdependent and also depend upon the environment and the characteristics of the load.

3. The method of solving the problem. This includes the assumptions made in the analysis and whether the solution is to be very exact or only approximate. It also includes the decision on whether to design for maximum horsepower and torque transmitted or to size the unit on the basis of the heat to be dissipated.

In addition to these major decisions, the designer will find it necessary to make other decisions as the design progresses. These include the type of bearings, seals, shaft and housing materials and the manufacturing processes, as well as decisions on the factors of safety to be employed. These have all been discussed in the appropriate chapters.

BIBLIOGRAPHY

Gagne, A. F., Jr.: Clutches, *Machine Design,* vol. 24, no. 8, pp. 121–158, August, 1952.

Gibson, W. B.: Selecting the Right Fluid Coupling for a Prime Mover, *Product Eng.,* vol. 21, no. 10, pp. 136–140, 1950.

Morrison, James A.: Fluid Clutches for Electric Drives, *Product Eng.,* vol. 25, no. 8, pp. 174–178, 1954.

Nanfeldt, W. J.: Friction Materials for Brakes, *Product Eng.,* vol. 21, no. 10, pp. 136–140, 1950.

Rasmussen, A. C.: Friction Blocks and Shoes, Analysis and Design, *Product Eng.,* vol. 18, no. 3, pp. 133–138; no. 5, pp. 152–155; no. 7, pp. 106–110; no. 10, pp. 119–121; no. 12, pp. 134–136, 1947.

Trickey, P. H.: Applying Magnetic-particle Clutches and Brakes, *Machine Design,* vol. 26, no. 11, pp. 189–194, 1954.

Von Mehren, O.: Internal-shoe Clutches and Brakes, *Trans. ASME,* vol. 69, pp. 913–924, 1947.

PROBLEMS

12-1. A two-jaw clutch has the dimensions shown in the figure and is made of ductile steel. The clutch has been designed to transmit 2½ hp at 500 rpm. Find the bearing and shear stress in the key and in the jaws.

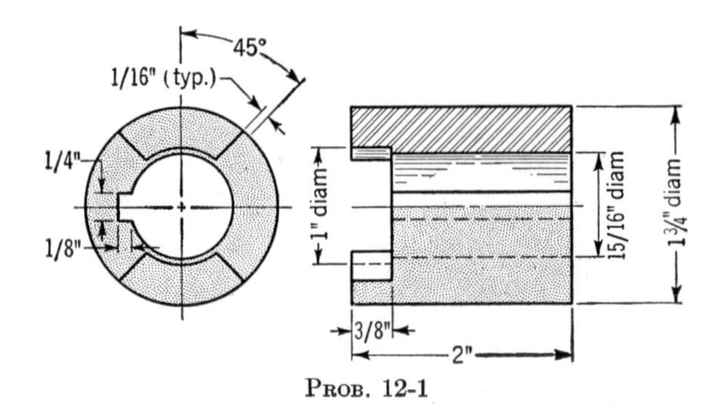

PROB. 12-1

12-2. The figure shows one end of a shaft coupling which has been tentatively selected to transmit 180 hp at 300 rpm. The coupling is made of cast carbon steel having a yield strength of 58,000 psi and a tensile strength of 92,000 psi. The bolts

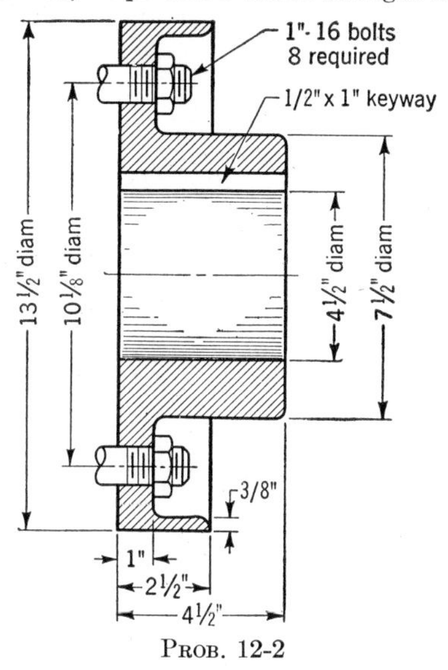

PROB. 12-2

are of 1035 steel drawn at 800°F. The key is cold-drawn 1020 steel. (*a*) Find the bearing and shear stress in the key and the factor of safety. (*b*) Find the bearing and shear stress in the bolts and the factor of safety. (*c*) Is there a possibility of the flange shearing off at the hub? (Assume perfect shaft alignment.)

12-3. If a factor of safety of 4 is employed, what horsepower may be transmitted by the coupling of Prob. 12-2? Use a speed of 300 rpm.

12-4. An internal-expanding rim-type brake is shown in the figure. The brake

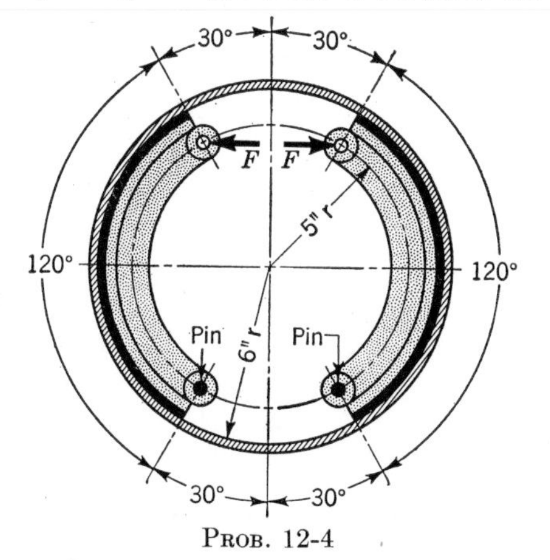

PROB. 12-4

drum is 12 in. in diameter and has shoes with a face width of 1½ in., both of which are actuated by the same force F. The design coefficient of friction is to be 0.28 with a maximum pressure of 120 psi. (*a*) Find the actuating force F. (*b*) Calculate the torque capacity. (*c*) Find the hinge-pin reactions.

12-5. If the brake-shoe actuating forces may differ from each other in Prob. 12-4, what values should they have in order to obtain a maximum pressure of 120 psi on each shoe?

12-6. The figure shows a 16-in.-diameter brake drum with four internally expanding shoes. Each of the hinge pins A and B supports a pair of shoes. The actuating

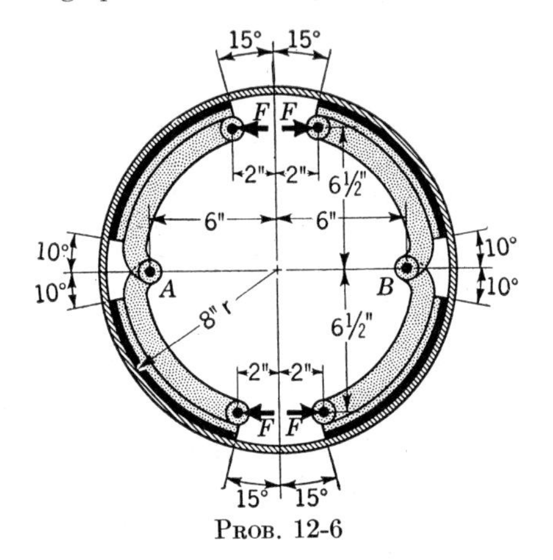

PROB. 12-6

mechanism is to be arranged to produce the same force F on each shoe. The face width of the shoes is 3 in. The material used permits a coefficient of friction of 0.24 and a maximum pressure of 150 psi. (*a*) Determine the actuating force. (*b*) Calculate the braking capacity. (*c*) What are the hinge-pin reactions? (Note that the rotation may be in either direction.)

12-7. Determine the actuating force for Prob. 12-6 if the hinge pins are moved 1 in. closer to the drum rim.

***12-8.** Determine the cross-sectional dimensions of a T-section shoe for the brake of Prob. 12-6. The shoe should be made of forged carbon steel and should have less than 0.003-in. deflection.

***12-9.** Specify suitable dimensions, material, and heat-treatment, if any, for the hinge pin of Prob. 12-6. The pin is to be cantilevered so that the load center is located at a distance of one-half the face width of the shoe from the support.

12-10. The block-type hand brake shown in the figure has a face width of 1¾ in. The frictional material permits a maximum pressure of 80 psi and a coefficient of friction of 0.24. (*a*) Determine the force F. (*b*) What is the maximum torque

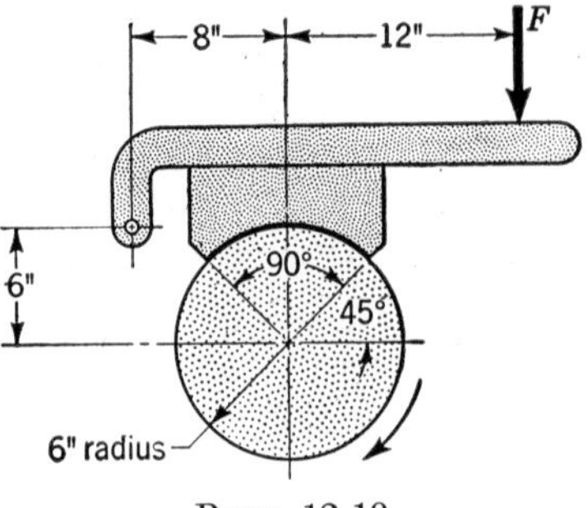

PROB. 12-10

capacity? (*c*) If the speed is 100 rpm and the brake is applied for 5 sec at full capacity to bring the shaft to a stop, how much heat is generated?

12-11. The brake whose dimensions are shown in the figure has a coefficient of friction of 0.30 and is to have a maximum pressure of 150 psi against the friction material. (*a*) Using an actuating force F of 400 lb, determine the width of face of the shoes. (Both shoes are to have the same width.) (*b*) What torque will the brake absorb?

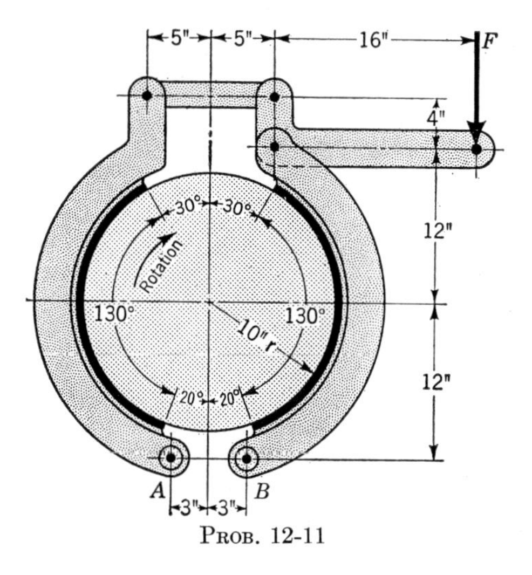

PROB. 12-11

12-12. The same as Prob. 12-11 except that rotation is counterclockwise.

12-13. The brake of Prob. 12-11 is to be used to stop a machine which rotates at 600 rpm. If full brake torque must be applied for 3 sec in order to bring the machine to a stop, how much heat in Btu is generated in this braking operation?

***12-14 to 12-25.** A line of industrial brakes is to be designed according to the figure and the data in the accompanying table. The brakes are to be manufactured in

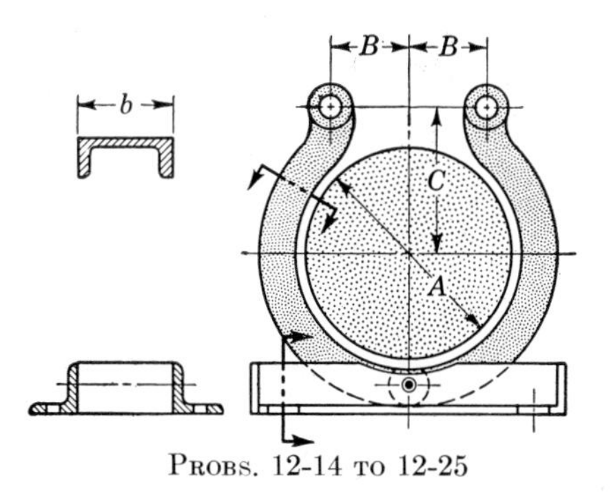

PROBS. 12-14 TO 12-25

quantities of 500. The price situation is competitive, and the company has a reputation for producing conservative and well-designed machines. Design the brake shoes, specifying all materials, treatment, and dimensions. They are to be actuated by hydraulic means which is not considered a part of this problem. Make a sketch showing all dimensions. Specify a rated capacity for the catalogue and the maximum recommended frequency of operation corresponding to this capacity.

Prob. No.	Diameter A, in.	Face width b, in.	Dimension B, in.	Dimension C, in.
12-14	8	$1\frac{3}{4}$	3	$5\frac{1}{2}$
12-15	8	$2\frac{1}{4}$	3	$5\frac{1}{2}$
12-16	8	3	3	$5\frac{1}{2}$
12-17	10	2	4	$6\frac{3}{4}$
12-18	10	3	4	$6\frac{3}{4}$
12-19	10	4	4	$6\frac{3}{4}$
12-20	14	3	$5\frac{1}{4}$	$9\frac{1}{2}$
12-21	14	4	$5\frac{1}{4}$	$9\frac{1}{2}$
12-22	14	6	$5\frac{1}{4}$	$9\frac{1}{2}$
12-23	18	4	7	$12\frac{1}{2}$
12-24	18	6	7	$12\frac{1}{2}$
12-25	18	8	7	$12\frac{1}{2}$

12-26. A 20-in. externally contracting brake has heat-dissipating surfaces whose combined weight is 40 lb. The brake has a rated torque capacity of 25,000 lb-in. A load has a speed of 1,800 rpm and can be stopped in 8 sec at full torque capacity. Determine the temperature rise for a single operation if the specific heat of the materials is 0.12.

12-27. A cast-iron flywheel is 60 in. in diameter and has a rim 6 in. thick × 14 in. wide, as shown in the figure. The flywheel rotates at 240 rpm and is to be brought to rest in 20 sec by a brake. (*a*) Calculate the total amount of energy to be absorbed. (*b*) What torque capacity must the brake have? *Decisions:* Assume the arms and hub contribute one-tenth as much as the rim to the flywheel capacity.

Ans.: (*a*) 204,000 ft-lb, (*b*) 9,740 lb-in.

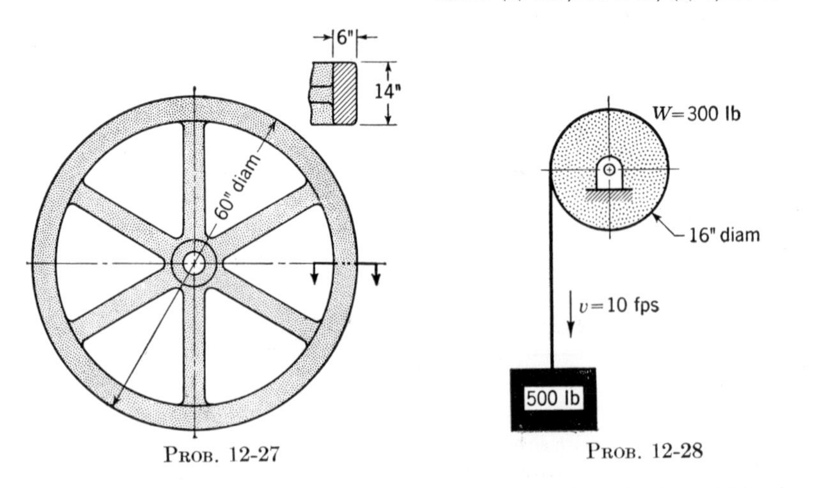

PROB. 12-27 PROB. 12-28

12-28. A brake permits a load of 500 lb to be lowered at a velocity of 10 fps from a drum, as shown in the figure. The drum is 16 in. in diameter, weighs 300 lb, and has a radius of gyration of $7\frac{1}{4}$ in. (*a*) Calculate the kinetic energy of the system. (*b*) How much additional braking torque must be applied if the load is to be stopped in 0.5 sec?

12-29. If the load of Prob. 12-28 is at rest, what torque capacity must a clutch have in order to accelerate it upward to a velocity of 5 fps in 0.30 sec?

12-30. The band brake shown in the figure is to have a maximum lining pressure of 90 psi. The drum is 14 in. in diameter, and the band width is 4 in. The coefficient of friction is 0.25 and the angle of wrap 270°. (*a*) Find the band tensions. (*b*) Calculate the torque capacity. *Ans.:* (*a*) 2,520 lb, 773 lb, (*b*) 12,230 lb-in.

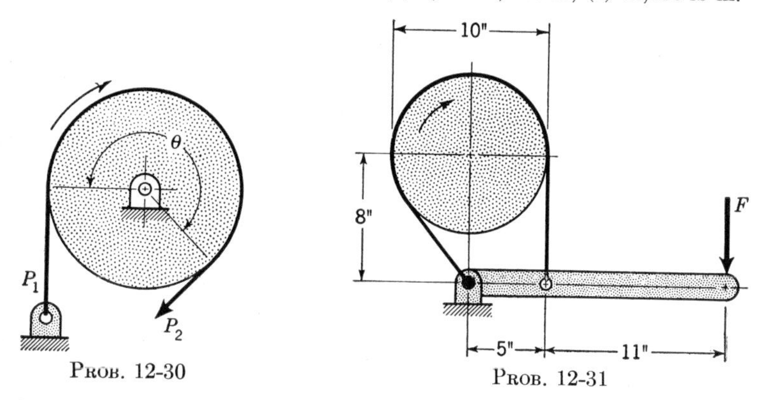

PROB. 12-30 PROB. 12-31

12-31. The brake shown in the figure has a coefficient of friction of 0.30 and is to operate at a maximum pressure of 150 psi. The width of the band is 2 in. (*a*) What is the limiting value of the force *F*? (*b*) Determine the torque capacity of the brake.

12-32. Repeat Prob. 12-31 except that the drum rotates counterclockwise.

12-33. The figure shows a 16-in. differential band brake. The maximum pressure is to be 60 psi with a coefficient of friction of 0.26 and a band width of 4 in. Determine the band tensions and the actuating force for clockwise rotation.

Ans.: $F = 35.4$ lb.

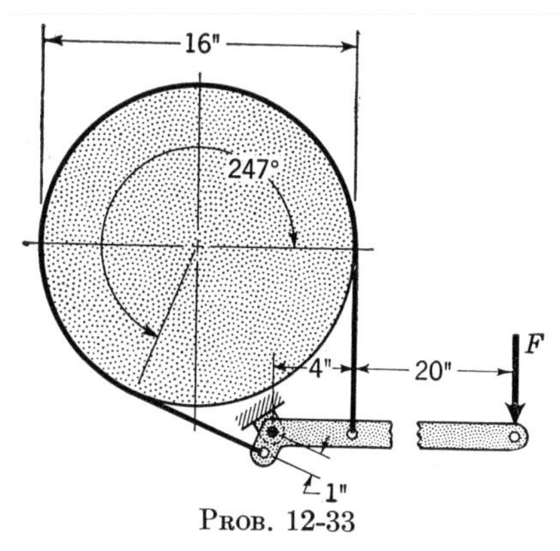

PROB. 12-33

12-34. Solve Prob. 12-33 for counterclockwise rotation. *Ans.:* $F = 291$ lb.

12-35. A plate clutch has a single pair of mating friction surfaces 12 in. OD × 9 in. ID. The coefficient of friction is 0.25, and the maximum pressure is 120 psi. Find the torque capacity, using the uniform-wear assumption. *Ans.:* 6,675 lb-in.

12-36. Use the data of Prob. 12-35 to find the torque capacity of a similar clutch, employing the uniform-pressure assumption.

12-37. A plate clutch has a single pair of mating friction surfaces, is 8 in. in diameter and 4 in. ID, and has a coefficient of friction of 0.30. What is the maximum pressure corresponding to an actuating force of 3,750 lb? Use the uniform-wear method.

12-38. Repeat Prob. 12-37 using the uniform-pressure method.

12-39. A disk clutch has four pairs of mating friction surfaces, is 5 in. OD × 3 in. ID, and has a coefficient of friction of 0.10. (*a*) What actuating force is required for a pressure of 120 psi? (*b*) What is the torque rating? (Use the uniform-pressure method.)

12-40. A plate clutch has two pairs of mating friction surfaces 14 in. OD × 6 in. ID. The coefficient of friction is 0.24, and the pressure is not to exceed 80 psi. (*a*) Determine the actuating force. (*b*) Calculate the torque capacity. (Use the uniform-wear method.)

***12-41 to 12-50.** The data in the accompanying table is to be used either in the design of a disk clutch or in the selection of a commercial clutch. The application is such that 100 machines employing the clutch will be manufactured at a time. Long and trouble-free service life is important. Moderate shock as well as occasional overloads may be present. The table lists the space available in terms of the maximum diameter and length. The load is determined as a function of the operating time for each cycle and the summation of the Wr^2 values (product of the weights of the masses to be accelerated and the square of their radii of gyration referred to the clutch speed). The cycle frequency may require external cooling. (The instructor should specify whether the clutch is to be designed or a commercial unit is to be selected.)

Prob. No.	Space available, in.		Speed, rpm	Operating time, sec	Frequency, cycles per hr	ΣWr^2, lb-ft²
	Diameter	Length				
12-41	4½	4	1,800	0.01	10	0.85
12-42	5	4¾	1,200	0.02	20	0.43
12-43	5¾	5½	900	0.04	30	1.35
12-44	6½	5½	1,800	0.08	10	2.00
12-45	7¼	5¾	1,200	0.16	20	9.50
12-46	7¾	5¾	900	0.32	30	33.0
12-47	8½	6	1,800	0.64	10	41.0
12-48	9¾	7	1,200	1.25	20	170
12-49	11	7¾	900	2.50	30	685
12-50	12	8	1,800	5.00	10	850

CHAPTER 13

FLEXIBLE MACHINE ELEMENTS

Flexible machine elements, such as belts, ropes, or chains, are used for the transmission of power over comparatively long distances. When these elements are employed, they usually replace a group of gears, shafts, and bearings or similar power-transmission devices. They thus greatly simplify a machine and consequently are a major cost-reducing element.

In addition, since these elements are elastic and usually long, they play an important part in absorbing shock loads and in damping out the effects of vibrating forces. Although this advantage is important as concerns the life of the driving machine, the cost-reduction element is generally the major factor in the selection of this means of power transmission.

13-1. Belts. Ordinarily, belts are used to transmit power between two parallel shafts. The shafts must be separated a certain minimum distance, which is dependent upon the type of belt used, in order to work most efficiently. Belts have the following characteristics:

1. They may be used for long center distances.
2. Because of the slip and creep of belts, the angular-velocity ratio between the two shafts is neither constant nor exactly equal to the ratio of the pulley diameters.
3. When using flat belts, clutch action may be obtained by shifting the belt from a loose to a tight pulley.
4. When V belts are used, some variation in the angular-velocity ratio may be obtained by employing a small pulley with spring-loaded sides. The diameter of the pulley is then a function of the belt tension and may be varied by changing the center distance.
5. Some adjustment of the center distance is usually necessary when belts are used.
6. By employing step pulleys, an economical means of changing the velocity ratio may be obtained.

Flat Belts. Flat belts are usually made of either oak-tanned leather or a fabric, such as cotton or rayon, which has been impregnated with rubber. They find their greatest use where the center distances are fairly long. Because of the clutching action which can be obtained and because of their adaptability to fairly long distances, flat belts are very useful in group-drive installations. Because of the convenience and appearance of unit drives, most machines manufactured today have a built-in drive; hence the use of flat belts has greatly decreased in recent years. There remain, however, many applications for which flat belting is a very satisfactory solution.

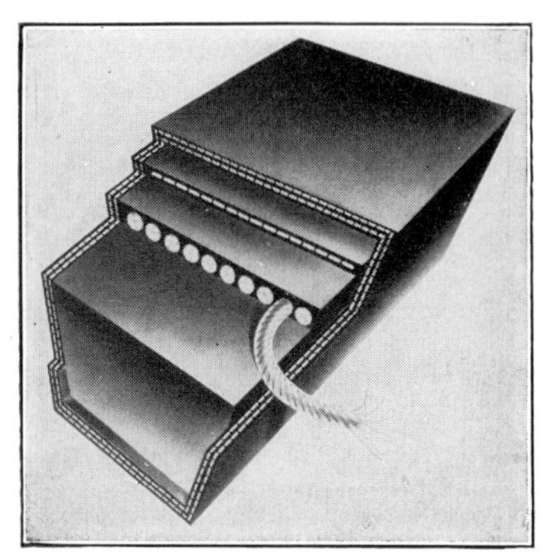

Fig. 13-1. Pictorial section showing the construction of a V belt. (*Courtesy of Durkee-Atwood Company.*)

V Belts. **A V** belt is made of fabric and cord, usually cotton or rayon, impregnated with rubber, as shown in Fig. 13-1. In contrast to flat belts, V belts may be operated with smaller pulleys or sheaves and at shorter center distances. In addition, a number of them may be used on a single sheave, thus making

Fig. 13-2. Link V belts successfully applied to a press. The use of endless belts would necessitate dismantling of the press in order to replace belts. (*Courtesy of Manheim Manufacturing and Belting Company.*)

a multiple drive. They are endless, thus eliminating the joint which must be made in flat belts.

A *link V belt* is composed of a large number of rubberized-fabric links joined by suitable metal fasteners. This type of belt may be disassembled at any point, and adjusted to any length by removing some of the links. This eliminates the necessity for adjustable centers and simplifies the installation. It makes it possible to change the tension for maximum efficiency and also reduces the inventory of belt sizes which would usually be stocked. A typical application of the link V belt is shown in Fig. 13-2.

Timing Belt. This is a patented belt, made of rubberized fabric and steel wire, having teeth which fit into grooves cut on the periphery of the pulleys (Fig. 13-3). The Timing belt does not stretch or slip and consequently transmits power at a constant angular-velocity ratio. The fact that the belt is toothed provides several advantages over ordinary belting. One of these is that no initial tension is necessary, so that fixed center drives may be used. Another is the elimination of the restriction on speeds; the teeth make it possible to run the belts at nearly any speed, slow or fast. Disadvantages are the first cost of the belt and the necessity of grooving the pulleys.

FIG. 13-3. A Timing belt drive for textile machinery. (*Courtesy of U.S. Rubber Company.*)

13-2. Flat Belts. To design a belt drive, the following information should be available:

1. The horsepower and speed of the drive unit
2. The speed of the driven unit
3. The center distance desired
4. The operating conditions

Selection of Pulley Size. The minimum pulley size is limited by the elongation of the outer fibers of the belt as it bends or wraps around the pulley circumference. Small pulley sizes cause this elongation to be larger and hence materially shorten the life of the belt. Minimum pulley sizes, depending upon the width and thickness of the belt, as recommended by the American Leather Belting Association are listed in Table 13-1.

It will be shown that the horsepower transmitted by a belt is proportional to its linear velocity. It would therefore seem that the most economical use of a belt would be obtained by running it at a high velocity, since more horsepower could be transmitted. However, as the belt speed increases, centrifugal force begins to pull the belt away from the pulley, thus reducing its effectiveness. In addition, high speeds require large pulleys which use up space.

TABLE 13-1. MINIMUM PULLEY DIAMETERS FOR FLAT LEATHER BELTS*

Number of plies:	Single		Double			Triple	
Thickness, in.:	11/64	13/64	18/64	20/64	23/64	30/64	34/64
Up to 8 in. wide	3	5	6	8	12	20	24
Over 8 in. wide	...	...	8	10	14	24	30

* Recommended by the American Leather Belting Association.

A satisfactory compromise between these two conflicting requirements is obtained, in general, when a belt speed between 2,500 and 4,500 fpm is selected. When space requirements make it possible, the higher velocity is recommended.

Center Distance and Belt Length. Figure 13-4 illustrates open and crossed belts and gives equations for the angle of contact θ and the total belt length L for each case. When a horizontal open-belt arrangement is used, the driver should rotate so that the slack side is on top. This makes for a larger angle of contact on both pulleys. When the drive is vertical or the center distance is short, a larger angle of contact may be obtained by using an idler tension pulley.

Selection of Flat Belts. Flat belts are usually employed as an economical substitute for some other means of power transmission. When a belt fails, it may break or tear or the joint may fail. This places the driven machine out of production, and the down time may be more expensive than the belt. For this reason, unless the machine is used only occasionally, it is considered good practice to design very conservatively.

Belts probably fail by fatigue. The fatigue failure of a flexible material should not, however, be compared with that of metals. A belt will eventually fail in fatigue when a combination of the following causes is present:

1. A high belt tension caused by overloads
2. Excessive slippage
3. An accumulation of the weakening effects of momentary overloads due to vibration, shock, and belt slapping
4. Adverse environmental conditions such as the presence of oil or moisture or failure to apply suitable dressings, any of which may result in a rapid deterioration of the belt material

Let us now investigate the relation between the belt tensions and the horsepower which is transmitted. When a belt is running and transmitting power, there exist a tension P_1 on the tight side and a lesser tension P_2 on the slack side. If the centrifugal force on the belt is neglected, the relation between these tensions is the same as for a band brake. From

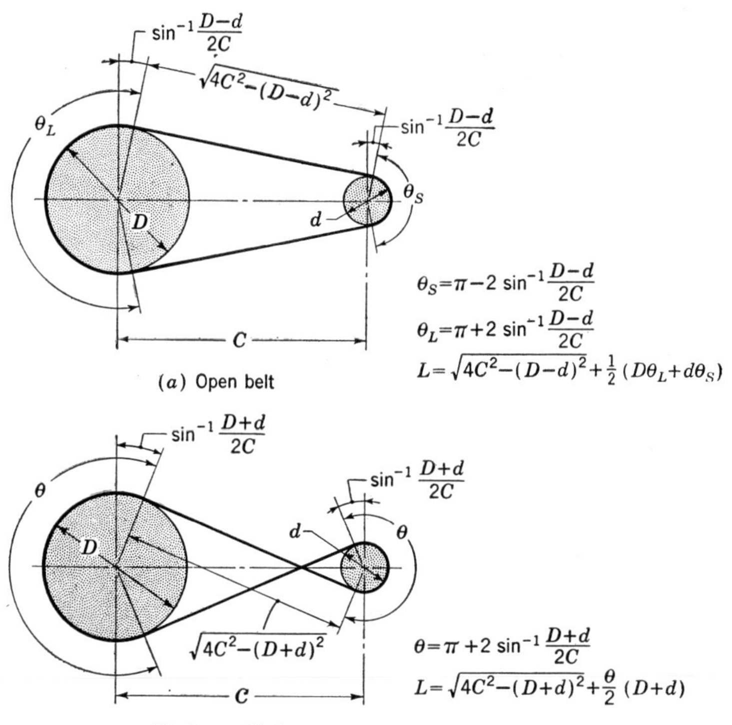

FIG. 13-4. Belt lengths and contact angles for open and crossed belts.

Eq. (12-18), Sec. 12-2, we have

$$\frac{P_1}{P_2} = e^{f\theta} \tag{13-1}$$

where f is the coefficient of friction between the belt and the pulley and θ is the angle of contact. The horsepower transmitted is

$$\text{hp} = \frac{(P_1 - P_2)V}{33{,}000} \tag{13-2}$$

where V is the belt velocity in feet per minute.

The effect of centrifugal force is not shown in Eq. (13-1). By including the centrifugal force F_c in the development of the equation, it can be shown that

$$\frac{P_1 - F_c}{P_2 - F_c} = e^{f\theta} \tag{13-3}$$

where

$$F_c = \frac{wv^2}{g} \tag{13-4}$$

and where w = weight of belt, lb per ft
v = belt velocity, fps
g = acceleration due to gravity, fps per sec
The weight of leather belting is 0.035 lb per in.[3]

TABLE 13-2. HORSEPOWER PER INCH OF WIDTH—OAK-TANNED LEATHER BELTS*

Belt speed, fpm	Single ply		Double ply			Triple ply	
	11/64	13/64	18/64	20/64	23/64	30/64	34/64
600	1.1	1.2	1.5	1.8	2.2	2.5	2.8
800	1.4	1.7	2.0	2.4	2.9	3.3	3.6
1,000	1.8	2.1	2.6	3.1	3.6	4.1	4.5
1,200	2.1	2.5	3.1	3.7	4.3	4.9	5.4
1,400	2.5	2.9	3.5	4.3	4.9	5.7	6.3
1,600	2.8	3.3	4.0	4.9	5.6	6.5	7.1
1,800	3.2	3.7	4.5	5.4	6.2	7.3	8.0
2,000	3.5	4.1	4.9	6.0	6.9	8.1	8.9
2,400	4.2	4.9	5.9	7.1	8.2	9.5	10.4
2,800	4.9	5.6	6.8	8.2	9.5	11.0	12.1
3,200	5.4	6.3	7.6	9.2	10.6	12.3	13.5
3,600	5.9	6.9	8.3	10.1	11.7	13.4	14.8
4,000	6.4	7.4	9.0	10.9	12.6	14.5	16.0
4,400	6.9	7.9	9.6	11.7	13.4	15.4	16.9
4,800	7.2	8.3	10.1	12.3	14.1	16.2	17.8
5,200	7.5	8.6	10.5	12.8	14.6	16.8	18.5
5,600	7.7	8.8	10.8	13.1	15.0	17.3	19.0
6,000	7.8	8.9	10.9	13.2	15.2	17.6	19.3

* Reproduced from Lionel S. Marks (ed.), "Mechanical Engineers' Handbook," 5th ed., p. 919, McGraw-Hill Book Company, Inc., New York, 1951, by permission of the publisher.

Equations (13-1) to (13-4) are frequently used for the design of belting. When this is done, the maximum tension P_1 is limited by the material used. For leather a conservative figure is 250 psi of cross-sectional area. The coefficient of friction is quite variable, depending not only on the belt and pulley material and their condition but also on the belt velocity.

TABLE 13-3. CORRECTION FACTOR FOR CENTER DISTANCE AND SMALL PULLEY DIAMETER*

Small pulley diameter, in.	Center distance, ft															
	Up to 4		4 to 6		6 to 8		8 to 10		10 to 12		12 to 15		15 to 20		25 and up	
	Tight side		Tight side		Tight side		Tight side		Tight side		Tight side		Tight side		Tight side	
	Above	Below	Above	Below	Above	Below	Above	Below	Above	Below	Above	Below	Above	Below	Above	Below
3	0.45	0.45	0.46	0.47	0.47	0.48	0.47	0.49	0.48	0.50	0.49	0.52	0.48	0.54	0.48	0.55
4	0.53	0.53	0.54	0.55	0.55	0.57	0.56	0.59	0.57	0.61	0.58	0.63	0.59	0.65	0.59	0.56
5	0.59	0.59	0.60	0.62	0.62	0.64	0.63	0.66	0.63	0.68	0.65	0.70	0.66	0.72	0.66	0.74
6	0.62	0.62	0.63	0.65	0.65	0.68	0.66	0.70	0.67	0.72	0.68	0.74	0.69	0.76	0.70	0.78
8	0.66	0.66	0.67	0.69	0.69	0.72	0.70	0.74	0.71	0.76	0.72	0.78	0.73	0.80	0.74	0.82
10	0.68	0.68	0.70	0.71	0.71	0.74	0.73	0.77	0.73	0.79	0.75	0.81	0.76	0.83	0.77	0.85
12	0.70	0.70	0.72	0.74	0.73	0.77	0.75	0.79	0.76	0.81	0.77	0.83	0.78	0.86	0.79	0.88
15	0.73	0.73	0.74	0.76	0.76	0.79	0.77	0.82	0.78	0.84	0.80	0.86	0.81	0.89	0.82	0.91
18	0.75	0.75	0.76	0.78	0.78	0.81	0.79	0.84	0.80	0.86	0.82	0.89	0.83	0.91	0.84	0.93
24	0.77	0.77	0.79	0.81	0.81	0.84	0.82	0.87	0.83	0.89	0.85	0.92	0.86	0.94	0.87	0.96
30	0.79	0.79	0.81	0.82	0.82	0.86	0.84	0.89	0.85	0.91	0.87	0.94	0.88	0.96	0.89	0.98
36	0.80	0.80	0.82	0.84	0.83	0.87	0.85	0.90	0.86	0.92	0.88	0.95	0.89	0.98	0.90	1.00

* Reproduced from Lionel S. Marks (ed.), "Mechanical Engineers' Handbook," 5th ed., p. 920, McGraw-Hill Book Company, Inc., New York, 1951, by permission of the publisher.

Marks[1] lists average design values as follows: leather on cast iron, 0.30; on wooden pulleys, 0.45; on paper pulleys, 0.55.

Another method of design, which eliminates the uncertainty in choosing the coefficient of friction, has the sanction of the American Leather Belting Association. Although this method is completely empirical, it recognizes those causes which tend to reduce belt life. The horsepower per inch of width for various belt sizes and speeds is listed in Table 13-2. This horsepower is then multiplied by a series of correction factors obtained from Tables 13-3 and 13-4.

TABLE 13-4. SERVICE CORRECTION FACTORS*

Atmospheric condition...	Clean, scheduled maintenance	1.2
	Normal	1.0
	Oily, wet, or dusty	0.7
Angle of center line......	Horizontal to 60° from horizontal	1.0
	60–75° from horizontal	0.9
	75–90° from horizontal	0.8
Pulley material.........	Fiber on motor and small pulleys	1.2
	Cast iron or steel	1.0
Service.................	Temporary or intermittent	1.2
	Normal	1.0
	Important or continuous	0.8
Peak loads.............	Light, steady load, such as steam engines, steam turbines, diesel engines, and multicylinder gasoline engines	1.0
	Jerky loads, reciprocating machines such as normal-starting-torque squirrel-cage motors, shunt-wound d-c motors, and single-cylinder engines	0.8
	Shock and reversing loads; full-voltage start such as squirrel-cage and synchronous motors	0.6

* Reproduced from Lionel S. Marks (ed.), "Mechanical Engineers' Handbook," 5th ed., p. 920, McGraw-Hill Book Company, Inc., New York, 1951, by permission of the publisher.

EXAMPLE 13-1. Determine the horsepower capacity of a $4 \times {}^{13}\!/_{64}$-in. single-ply leather belt. The belt runs horizontally on pulleys 6×16 in. in diameter, both made of cast iron. The belt is used to connect a squirrel-cage motor to an industrial washing machine which is started under full load. The belt runs at 3,200 fpm over 8-ft centers. The tight side is below.

Solution. From Table 13-2, the horsepower per inch of width is 6.3. The correction factor for 8-ft center distance and a 6-in. pulley, from Table 13-3, is 0.68. We obtain five correction factors from Table 13-4. They are: 0.7, 1.0, 1.0, 1.0, and 0.6.

[1] Lionel S. Marks (ed.), "Mechanical Engineers' Handbook," 5th ed., p. 918, McGraw-Hill Book Company, Inc., New York, 1951.

Therefore, the capacity of the drive is

$$\text{hp} = (4)(6.3)(0.68)(0.7)(1.0)(1.0)(1.0)(0.6) = 7.2 \qquad \textit{Ans.}$$

13-3. V Belts. The cross-sectional dimensions of V belts have been standardized by manufacturers, with each section designated by a letter of the alphabet. The dimensions, minimum sheave diameters, and the horsepower range for each section are listed in Table 13-5.

To specify a V belt, give the belt-section letter, followed by the inside circumference in inches. For example, B75 is a B-section belt having an inside circumference of 75 in.

Calculations involving the belt length usually are based on the pitch length. For any given belt section the pitch length is obtained by adding a quantity to the inside circumference (Table 13-6). For example, a B75 belt has a pitch length of 76.8 in. Similarly, calculations of the velocity ratios are made using the pitch diameters of the sheaves, and for this reason the stated diameters are usually understood to be the pitch diameters even though they are not always so specified.

a b 40°

TABLE 13-5. STANDARD V-BELT SECTIONS

Belt section	Width a, in.	Thickness b, in.	Minimum sheave diameter, in.	Hp range one or more belts
A	½	11/32	3.0	¼–10
B	21/32	7/16	5.4	1–25
C	⅞	17/32	9.0	15–100
D	1¼	¾	13.0	50–250
E	1½	1	21.6	100 and up

TABLE 13-6. CONVERSION QUANTITIES—INSIDE CIRCUMFERENCE TO PITCH LENGTH

Belt section:	A	B	C	D	E
Quantity to be added to inside circumference, in.	1.3	1.8	2.9	3.3	4.5

The groove angle of a sheave is made somewhat less than the belt-section angle. This causes the belt to wedge itself into the groove, thus increasing the friction. The exact value of this angle depends upon the belt section, the sheave diameter, and the angle of contact. If it is made too much smaller than the belt, the force required to pull the belt out of the groove as the belt leaves the pulley will be excessive. Optimum values are given in the commercial literature.

The design of a V-belt drive is similar to that of a flat-belt drive, both of them requiring the same initial information.

Selection of the Sheave Diameter. The minimum sheave diameters have been listed in Table 13-5. For best results a V belt should run quite fast; 4,000 fpm is a good speed. Trouble may be encountered if the belt runs much faster than 5,000 fpm or much slower than 1,000 fpm. Therefore, when possible, the pulleys should be sized for a belt speed in the neighborhood of 4,000 fpm.

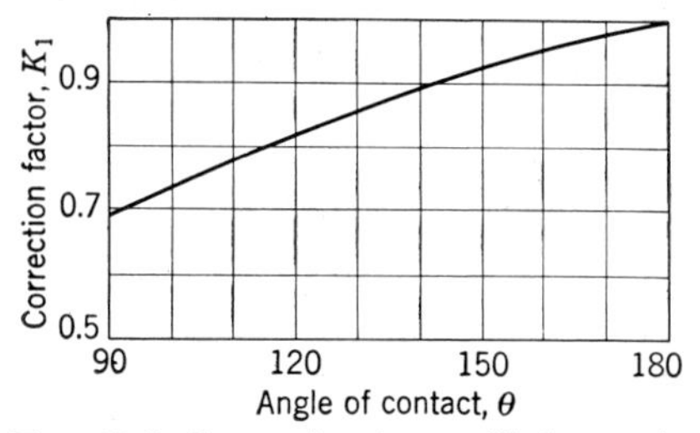

FIG. 13-5. Correction factor K_1 for angle of contact. Multiply the rated horsepower per belt by this factor to obtain the corrected horsepower.

Center Distance and Belt Length. The length of a V belt is obtained in the same way as for a flat belt. In the case of flat belts there is virtually no limit to the center distance. Long center distances, however, are not recommended for V belts because the excessive vibration of the slack side will shorten the belt life materially. In general, the center distance should not be greater than three times the sum of the sheave diameters nor less than the diameter of the larger sheave. Link-type V belts have less vibration, because of better balance, and hence may be used with longer center distances.

Selection of V Belts. The selection of V belts is based on obtaining a long and trouble-free life. Table 13-7 gives the horsepower capacity of standard single V belts for various sheave diameters and belt speeds corresponding to a satisfactory life. These ratings are based on a 180° contact angle. For smaller angles this rating must be reduced. Figure 13-5 gives the values of the correction factor K_1 which is used to reduce the rated horsepower when the angle of contact is less than 180°.

For a given sheave speed, the hours of life of a short belt are less than those of a long belt, because the short belt is subjected to the action of the load a greater number of times. For this reason it is necessary to apply a second factor K_2, which is called a belt-length correction factor. These factors are itemized in Table 13-8 for various belt sections and lengths. The rated belt horsepower must be multiplied by this factor in order to obtain the corrected horsepower.

The characteristics of both the driving and driven machinery must be considered in selecting the belt. If, for example, the load is started frequently by a source of power which develops 200 per cent of full-load

TABLE 13-7. HORSEPOWER RATINGS OF STANDARD V BELTS*

Belt section	Sheave pitch diameter, in.	Belt speed, fpm				
		1,000	2,000	3,000	4,000	5,000
A	2.6	0.47	0.62	0.53	0.15	
	3.0	0.66	1.01	1.12	0.93	0.38
	3.4	0.81	1.31	1.57	1.53	1.12
	3.8	0.93	1.55	1.92	2.00	1.71
	4.2	1.03	1.74	2.20	2.38	2.19
	4.6	1.11	1.89	2.44	2.69	2.58
	5.0 up	1.17	2.03	2.64	2.96	2.89
B	4.2	1.07	1.58	1.68	1.26	0.22
	4.6	1.27	1.99	2.29	2.08	1.24
	5.0	1.44	2.33	2.80	2.76	2.10
	5.4	1.59	2.62	3.24	3.34	2.82
	5.8	1.72	2.87	3.61	3.85	3.45
	6.2	1.82	3.09	3.94	4.28	4.00
	6.6	1.92	3.29	4.23	4.67	4.48
	7.0 up	2.01	3.46	4.49	5.01	4.90
C	6.0	1.84	2.66	2.72	1.87	
	7.0	2.48	3.94	4.64	4.44	3.12
	8.0	2.96	4.90	6.09	6.36	5.52
	9.0	3.34	5.65	7.21	7.86	7.39
	10.0	3.64	6.25	8.11	9.06	8.89
	11.0	3.88	6.74	8.84	10.0	10.1
	12.0 up	4.09	7.15	9.46	10.9	11.1
D	10.0	4.14	6.13	6.55	5.09	1.35
	11.0	5.00	7.83	9.11	8.50	5.62
	12.0	5.71	9.26	11.2	11.4	9.18
	13.0	6.31	10.5	13.0	13.8	12.2
	14.0	6.82	11.5	14.6	15.8	14.8
	15.0	7.27	12.4	15.9	17.6	17.0
	16.0	7.66	13.2	17.1	19.2	19.0
	17.0 up	8.01	13.9	18.1	20.6	20.7
E	16.0	8.68	14.2	17.5	18.1	15.3
	18.0	9.92	16.7	21.2	23.0	21.5
	20.0	10.9	18.7	24.2	26.9	26.4
	22.0	11.7	20.3	26.6	30.2	30.5
	24.0	12.4	21.6	28.6	32.9	33.8
	26.0	13.0	22.8	30.3	35.1	36.7
	28.0 up	13.4	23.7	31.8	37.1	39.1

* Courtesy of Browning Manufacturing Company. These ratings are for single belts having an angle of contact of 180°.

torque in starting (such as a squirrel-cage motor), then the full-load horsepower must be multiplied by an overload service factor. The characteristics of the driven machinery are considered in a similar manner. Manufacturers of V belts list these overload service factors in considerable detail. Space does not permit their inclusion here. Table 13-9 may be used to obtain this factor if the percentage overload is known.

TABLE 13-8. BELT-LENGTH CORRECTION FACTOR K_2*

Length factor	Nominal belt length, in.				
	A belts	B belts	C belts	D belts	E belts
0.85	Up to 35	Up to 46	Up to 75	Up to 128	
0.90	38–46	48–60	81–96	144–162	Up to 195
0.95	48–55	62–75	105–120	173–210	210–240
1.00	60–75	78–97	128–158	240	270–300
1.05	78–90	105–120	162–195	270–330	330–390
1.10	96–112	128–144	210–240	360–420	420–480
1.15	120 up	158–180	270–300	480	540–600
1.20	....	195 up	330 up	540 up	660

* Multiply the rated horsepower per belt by this factor to obtain the corrected horsepower.

TABLE 13-9. OVERLOAD SERVICE FACTORS*

Per cent overload..	100	125	150	175	200	250
Service factor......	1.0	1.1	1.2	1.3	1.4	1.5

* Multiply the given horsepower by these factors in order to obtain the design horsepower. For 16 to 24-hr operation add 0.1 to these values.

EXAMPLE 13-2. A 10-hp split-phase motor running at 1,750 rpm is to be used to drive a rotary pump which operates 24 hr per day. The pump should run at approximately 1,175 rpm. The center distance should not exceed 44 in. Space limits the diameter of the driven sheave to 11.5 in. Determine the sheave diameters, the belt size, and the number of belts.

Decisions. 1. An overload service factor of 1.2 corresponding to a 150 per cent overload is selected from Table 13-9.

2. From Table 13-5, a B-section belt is selected.

3. Since the driven sheave should not exceed 11.5 in., the next smaller standard size of 11 in. will be tentatively selected.

4. A center distance of 42 in. is tentatively selected.

Solution. The pump is to operate 24 hr per day, and so 0.1 is to be added to the service factor, making it 1.3. The design horsepower of the belt is therefore

$$\text{Design hp} = (10)(1.3) = 13$$

The diameter of the small sheave is

$$d = D\frac{n_1}{n_2} = 11\,\frac{1,175}{1,750} = 7.40 \text{ in.} \qquad \textit{Ans.}$$

This is a standard pitch diameter for B-section belts and is also over the minimum diameter listed in Table 13-5. It will therefore be used.

From Fig. 13-4a, the angles of contact for a center distance of 42 in. are

$$\theta_s = \pi - 2\sin^{-1}\frac{D-d}{2C} = \pi - 2\sin^{-1}\frac{11-7.4}{(2)(42)} = 3.056 \text{ radians}$$

$$\theta_L = \pi + 2\sin^{-1}\frac{D-d}{2C} = \pi + 2\sin^{-1}\frac{11-7.4}{(2)(42)} = 3.227 \text{ radians}$$

The belt length is

$$\begin{aligned} L &= \sqrt{4C^2 - (D-d)^2} + (\tfrac{1}{2})(D\theta_L + d\theta_s) \\ &= \sqrt{(4)(42)^2 - (11-7.4)^2} + (\tfrac{1}{2})[(11)(3.227) + (7.4)(3.056)] \\ &= 112.97 \text{ in.} \end{aligned}$$

The nearest standard size, a B112, is selected. From Table 13-6, a B112 belt has a pitch length of 113.8 in.

The belt speed is

$$V = \frac{\pi d n}{12} = \frac{(\pi)(7.4)(1{,}750)}{12} = 3{,}390 \text{ fpm}$$

Using Table 13-7 and interpolating, the rated horsepower per belt is 4.66. This must be corrected for the contact angle and the belt length. The contact angle for the small sheave is 3.056 radians, or 175°. From Fig. 13-5, the correction factor is 0.99. The belt-length correction factor is 1.05, from Table 13-8. Therefore the corrected horsepower per belt is

$$\text{hp per belt} = (4.66)(0.99)(1.05) = 4.85$$

and so the number of belts required is

$$N = \frac{13}{4.85} = 2.68$$

Three B-section belts must therefore be used.

13-4. General Considerations. The methods of selecting flat- and V-belt drives which have been demonstrated are typical of the current practice in this field. Many types of flat and V belts having properties different from those illustrated here are manufactured. The selection of any belt drive, however, follows the same general principles. In order to obtain a satisfactory and economical drive with a long life, the designer should be familiar with the various belts and pulleys which are commercially available. This requires an up-to-date and carefully kept file of commercial literature and catalogues.

Assumptions. The reader has by now observed that the design of belt drives deviates considerably from the usual method of design. In many methods the members are sized by selecting an area large enough that the stress is somewhat less than the strength of the material, or, if elongation happens to be an important consideration, the area is proportioned and arranged so as to create a reasonable elongation.

Either of these methods could be applied to the design of belt drives. The difficulty, however, is that there is not sufficient correlation between the simple stresses and strains and the life of a belt, so that very large factors of safety must be employed. Stresses and strains are usually determined with a static-testing machine. But the load on a belt is dynamic; it is continually being flexed and straightened as it passes around the pulley; the slack portion is usually vibrating; local irregularities or bumps which cause vibration and stress concentration often exist; the portion in contact with the pulley is acted upon by complicated shearing forces due to slipping and creeping; and torsional vibration may exist

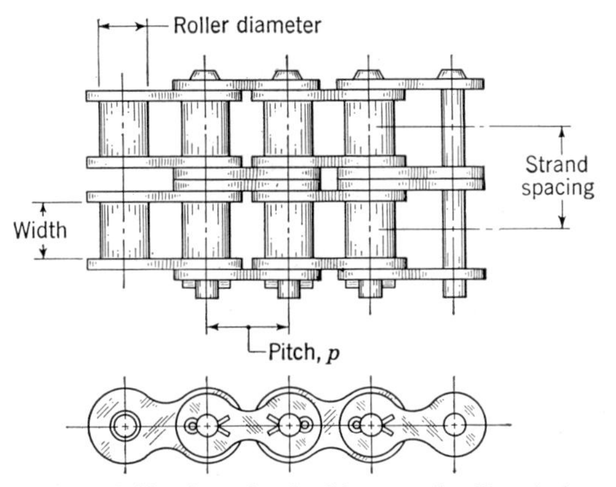

Fig. 13-6. Portion of a double-strand roller chain.

in the shafts of both the driving and driven machinery, much of which is absorbed by the belt. The difficulty of translating these forces into equation form as a function of belt life is apparent.

This means that we do not fully understand the effect of those factors which lengthen or shorten belt life. It then becomes necessary to resort to experimental methods. For this reason the horsepower capacity of belts is tabulated for certain standard conditions. When actual conditions deviate, then correction factors, which have also been determined experimentally, are applied. Actual drives may sometimes vary considerably from laboratory drives, and, although the belt manufacturer's factor of safety will accommodate some variation, it will occasionally be found that the belt life of a particular drive is too short. It is probably for this reason that manufacturers encourage the practice of "overbelting."

There are several lessons to be learned. First, no existing method of design is perfect; improvement may be expected as knowledge of the materials and forces of nature advances. Second, when rational methods of analysis fail, the designer must resort to experiment, approximating actual conditions as closely as possible. Third, the most satisfactory method of design for a given problem may not be that method which is most academic or most rational, nor is it always the easiest method. Rather, it is that method which most closely approximates the actual conditions and results, considering the economics of the entire problem.

13-5. Roller Chain. Basic features of chain drives include a constant ratio, since no slippage or creep is involved; long life; and the ability to drive a number of shafts from a single source of power.

Roller chains have been standardized as to sizes by the ASA. Figure 13-6 shows the nomenclature. The pitch is the linear distance between the centers of the rollers. The width is the space between the inner link plates. These chains are manufactured in single, double, triple, and quadruple strands. The dimensions of standard sizes are listed in Table 13-10.

TABLE 13-10. DIMENSIONS OF AMERICAN STANDARD ROLLER CHAIN (SINGLE STRAND)

American Standard chain no.	Pitch, in.	Width, in.	Average tensile strength, lb	Average weight, lb per ft	Roller diameter, in.	Multiple strand spacing, in.
25	1/4	1/8	875	0.09	0.130	0.252
35	3/8	3/16	2,100	0.21	0.200	0.399
41	1/2	1/4	2,000	0.25	0.306	
40	1/2	5/16	3,700	0.42	5/16	0.566
50	5/8	3/8	6,100	0.69	0.400	0.713
60	3/4	1/2	8,500	1.00	15/32	0.897
80	1	5/8	14,500	1.71	5/8	1.153
100	1 1/4	3/4	24,000	2.58	3/4	1.408
120	1 1/2	1	34,000	3.87	7/8	1.789
140	1 3/4	1	46,000	4.95	1	1.924
160	2	1 1/4	58,000	6.61	1 1/8	2.305
200	2 1/2	1 1/2	95,000	10.96	1 9/16	2.817

Fundamental Relations. In Fig. 13-7 is shown a sprocket driving a chain in a counterclockwise direction. Denoting the chain pitch by p, the pitch angle by γ, and the pitch diameter of the sprocket by D, from the trigonometry of the figure we see

$$\sin \frac{\gamma}{2} = \frac{p/2}{D/2} \quad \text{or} \quad D = \frac{p}{\sin (\gamma/2)} \tag{a}$$

Since $\gamma = 360°/N$, where N is the number of sprocket teeth, Eq. (a) can be written

$$D = \frac{p}{\sin (180/N)} \tag{13-5}$$

The angle $\gamma/2$, through which the link swings as it enters contact, is called the *angle of articulation.* It can be seen that the magnitude of this angle is a function of the number of teeth. Rotation of the link through this angle causes impact between the rollers and the sprocket teeth and also causes wear in the chain joint. Since the life of a properly selected drive is a function of the wear and the surface fatigue strength of the rollers, it is important to reduce the angle of articulation as much as possible. The values of this angle have been plotted as a function of the number of teeth in Fig. 13-8.

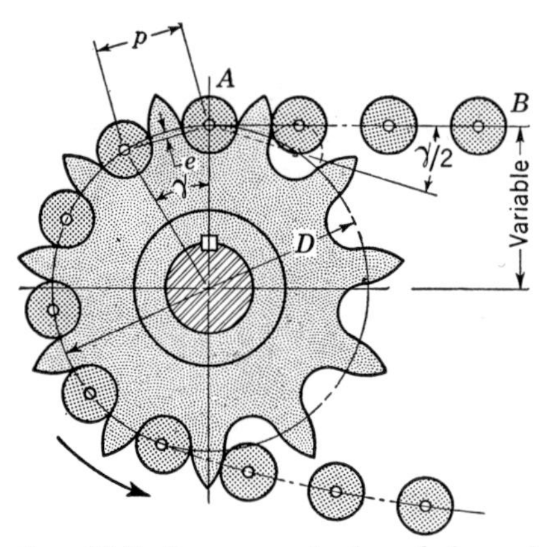

FIG. 13-7. Engagement of a chain and sprocket.

The number of sprocket teeth also affects the velocity ratio during the period in which the sprocket is rotating through a pitch angle. At the position shown (Fig. 13-7) the portion of the chain AB is being pulled onto the sprocket, and the pitch line of the straight portion of the chain is tangent to the pitch circle of the sprocket. However, when the sprocket has turned an angle $\gamma/2$, the pitch line AB has moved closer to the sprocket center line by an amount e. This means not only that the straight portion AB is moving up and down as the sprocket turns but also that the lever arm varies and hence the velocity ratio is not constant

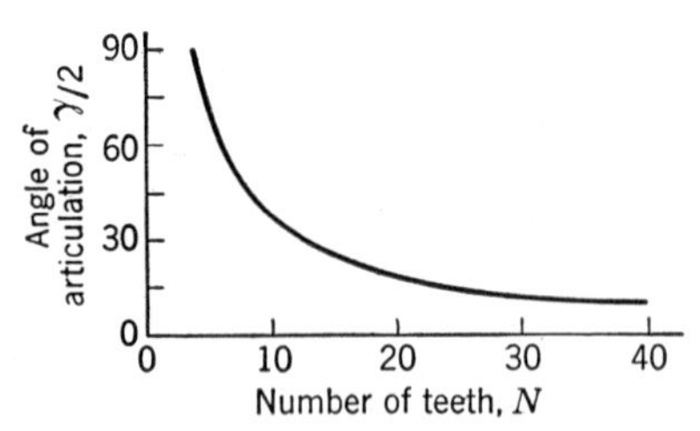

FIG. 13-8. Relation between the angle of articulation and the number of sprocket teeth.

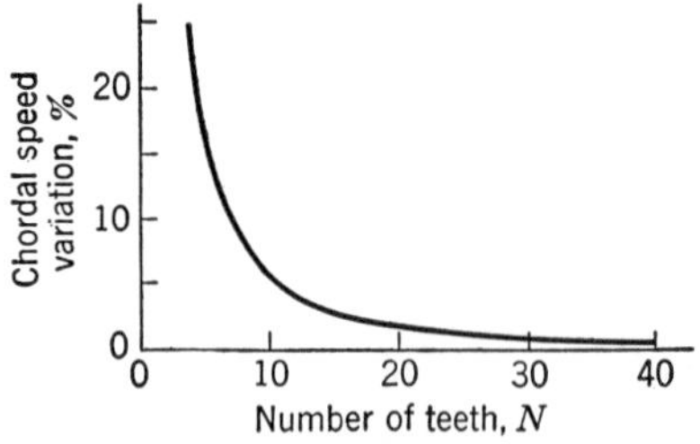

FIG. 13-9. Relation between the number of sprocket teeth and the chordal speed variation.

for rotation of the sprocket through the pitch angle. This is called the *chordal speed variation*, and it is also a function of the number of teeth on the sprocket. In Fig. 13-9 this variation has been plotted as a function of the number of teeth.

The chain velocity is usually defined as the number of feet coming off the sprocket in unit time. Thus, the velocity V in feet per minute is

$$V = \frac{\pi D n}{12} = \frac{Npn}{12} \tag{13-6}$$

where N = number of teeth on sprocket
p = chain pitch
n = speed of sprocket, rpm

Although a large number of teeth is considered desirable for the driving sprocket, in the usual case it is advantageous to obtain as small a sprocket as possible, and this requires one with a small number of teeth. For smooth operation at moderate and high speeds it is considered good

TABLE 13-11. RATED HORSEPOWER CAPACITY OF ROLLER CHAINS*

Sprocket speed, rpm	American Standard chain number											
	25	35	41	40	50	60	80	100	120	140	160	200
50	0.08	0.139	0.193	0.322	0.620	1.05	2.44	4.67	7.91	12.3	18.0	34.2
100	0.10	0.264	0.367	0.611	1.16	1.97	4.52	8.56	14.4	22.2	32.4	60.2
150	0.12	0.379	0.523	0.870	1.65	2.82	6.39	12.0	19.9	30.6	44.2	81.3
200	0.14	0.494	0.678	1.13	2.14	3.59	8.09	15.1	24.9	38.0	54.5	98.8
300	0.21	0.705	0.954	1.59	2.99	4.98	11.1	20.3	33.2	49.9	70.5	
400	0.28	0.90	1.21	2.02	3.77	6.22	13.6	25.0	39.7	58.8		
500	0.34	1.08	1.44	2.41	4.46	7.32	15.8	28.2	44.6			
600	0.40	1.25	1.66	2.77	5.09	8.29	17.6	30.9				
800	0.51	1.56	2.04	3.41	6.17	9.91	20.5					
1,000	0.61	1.83	2.37	3.95	7.05	11.1						
1,200	0.70	2.08	2.65	4.41	7.75	12.1						
1,400	0.79	2.29	2.88	4.80	8.31	12.7						
1,600	0.87	2.48	3.06	5.10	8.70							
1,800	0.94	2.65	...	5.38	8.98							
2,000	1.00	2.79	...	5.57	9.13							

* The capacities shown are for a 17-tooth sprocket. For other sprocket sizes use the correction factors in Table 13-12.

practice to use a driving sprocket with at least 17 teeth; 19 or 21 will, of course, give a better life expectancy with less chain noise. Where space limitations are severe or for very slow speeds, smaller tooth numbers may be used by sacrificing the life expectancy of the chain.

Driven sprockets are not made in standard sizes over 120 teeth because the pitch elongation will eventually cause the chain to "ride" high long before the chain is worn out. The most successful drives have velocity ratios up to 6:1, but higher ratios may be used at the sacrifice of chain life.

Selection of Chains. Roller chains seldom fail because they lack tensile strength but rather because they have been subjected to a great many hours of service. Actual failure may be due either to wear of the rollers on the pins or to fatigue of the surfaces of the rollers. Roller-chain manufacturers have compiled tables which give the horsepower capacity corresponding to a life expectancy of 15,000 hr for various sprocket speeds. These capacities are tabulated in Table 13-11 for 17-tooth sprockets. In order to obtain the capacity for a sprocket with a different number of teeth, the capacity listed in the table should be multiplied by a tooth correction factor as listed in Table 13-12.

TABLE 13-12. TOOTH CORRECTION FACTORS*

Number of teeth on driving sprocket	*Tooth correction factor,* K_t	*Number of teeth on driving sprocket*	*Tooth correctioa factor,* K_t
11	0.53	22	1.29
12	0.62	23	1.35
13	0.70	24	1.41
14	0.78	25	1.46
15	0.85	30	1.73
16	0.92	35	1.95
17	1.00	40	2.15
18	1.05	45	2.37
19	1.11	50	2.51
20	1.18	55	2.66
21	1.26	60	2.80

* Multiply the rated horsepower from Table 13-11 by the tooth correction factor K_t.

The characteristics of the load are important considerations in the selection of roller chain. In general, extra chain capacity is required for any of the following conditions:

1. The small sprocket has less than nine teeth for slow-speed drives or less than 16 teeth for high-speed drives.
2. The sprockets are unusually large.
3. Shock loading occurs, or there are frequent load reversals.
4. There are three or more sprockets in the drive.
5. The lubrication is poor.
6. The chain must operate under dirty or dusty conditions.

In order to account for these and other conditions of operation the horsepower of the load must be multiplied by a service factor. Suggested values for these factors are listed in Table 13-13.

Chain Length. The length of a chain should be determined in pitches. It is preferable to have an even number of pitches; otherwise an offset link is required. The approximate length may be obtained from the following equation:

$$\frac{L}{p} = \frac{2C}{p} + \frac{N_1 + N_2}{2} + \frac{(N_2 - N_1)^2}{4\pi^2(C/p)} \tag{13-7}$$

where L = chain length, in.
p = chain pitch, in.
C = center distance, in.
N_1 = number of teeth on small sprocket
N_2 = number of teeth on large sprocket

The length of chain for a multiple-sprocket drive is most easily obtained by making an accurate scale layout and determining the length by measurement.

Lubrication. Lubrication of roller chains is essential in order to obtain a long and trouble-free life. Either a drip feed or a shallow bath in the lubricant is satisfactory. A medium or light mineral oil, without additives, should be used. Except for unusual conditions, heavy oils and greases are not recommended because they are too viscous to enter the small clearances in the chain parts.

TABLE 13-13. LOAD SERVICE FACTORS K_S FOR ROLLER CHAIN*

Type of load	Service conditions	10-hr day	24-hr day
Uniform load	Average	1.0	1.2
Moderate shock	Abnormal	1.2	1.4
Heavy shock	Abnormal	1.4	1.7
Load reversals	Abnormal	1.5	1.9

* Courtesy of Morse Chain Company. Multiply the horsepower of the load by K_S to find the required capacity of the chain.

EXAMPLE 13-3. A 7½-hp speed reducer which runs at 300 rpm is to drive a conveyor at 200 rpm. The center distance is to be approximately 28 in. Select a suitable chain drive.

Decisions. 1. Although an odd number of sprocket teeth is to be preferred, sprockets of 20 and 30 teeth are tentatively chosen in order to obtain the proper velocity ratio. A 20-tooth sprocket will have a longer life and generate less noise than a 16- or an 18-tooth sprocket. It is chosen because space does not seem to be at a premium.

2. From Table 13-13 a service factor of 1.4 is chosen for 24-hr operation with moderate shock.

Solution. The required rating is

$$\text{Required hp} = (7.5)(1.4) = 10.5$$

Examination of Table 13-11 indicates that either a No. 50 or No. 60 chain may be satisfactory. From Table 13-12 the tooth correction factor corresponding to a 20-tooth sprocket is 1.18. Therefore, from Table 13-11 the corrected capacity of a No. 50 single-strand chain at 300 rpm is

$$\text{Rated hp per strand} = (2.99)(1.18) = 3.53 \qquad \text{No. 50 chain}$$

Similarly, the capacity of a No. 60 chain is

$$\text{Rated hp per strand} = (4.98)(1.18) = 5.88 \qquad \text{No. 60 chain}$$

The number of strands required for No. 50 is

$$\text{Number of strands} = \frac{10.5}{3.53} = 2.97 \qquad \text{or 3 strands of No. 50}$$

The number required for No. 60 chain is

$$\text{Number of strands} = \frac{10.5}{5.88} = 1.79 \qquad \text{or 2 strands of No. 60}$$

The No. 60 chain would require larger sprockets and hence it would run at a higher velocity, generate more noise, and have a shorter life. The No. 50 seems to be the better choice and is selected for this example. A comparison of the prices of the sprockets and chain for both cases might, however, make the No. 60 a better solution.

From Table 13-10, the pitch of No. 50 chain is ⅝ in. Using a center distance of 28 in. in Eq. (13-7), the required length of triple-strand chain in pitches is

$$\begin{aligned} \frac{L}{p} &= \frac{2C}{p} + \frac{N_1 + N_2}{2} + \frac{(N_2 - N_1)^2}{4\pi^2(C/p)} \\ &= \frac{(2)(28)}{0.625} + \frac{20 + 30}{2} + \frac{(30 - 20)^2}{4\pi^2(28/0.625)} \\ &= 114.7 \text{ pitches} \end{aligned}$$

The nearest even number of pitches is 114, and this will be used. A slight adjustment in the center distance is required. Substitution of $L/p = 114$ into Eq. (13-7) and solving for C give approximately 27¾ in. as the new center distance.

In general, the center distance should not exceed 80 pitches; 30 to 50 pitches is a better value. In this problem the center distance is $27.75/0.625 = 44.4$ pitches, which is satisfactory.

13-6. Rope Drives. Rope drives consisting of manila or cotton rope on multiple-grooved pulleys may often be a most economical form of drive

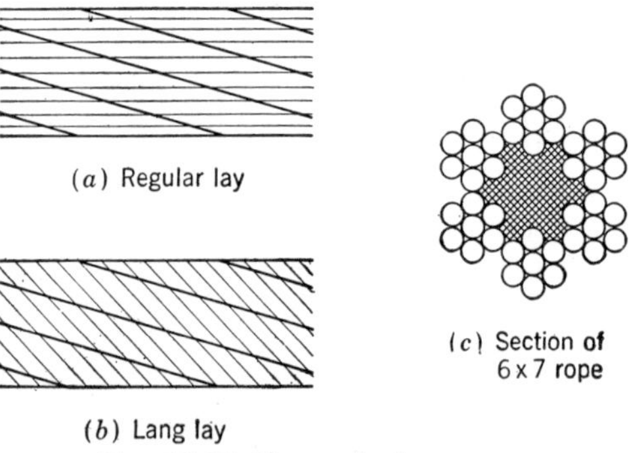

FIG. 13-10. Types of wire rope.

over long distances and for large amounts of power. Accurate alignment of the pulleys is not necessary because they are grooved. The velocity of the rope should be quite high; 5,000 fpm is a good speed for greatest economy.

13-7. Wire Rope. Wire rope is made with two types of winding, as shown in Fig. 13-10. The *regular lay*, which is the accepted standard, has the wire twisted in one direction to form the strands and the strands twisted in the opposite direction to form the rope. In the completed rope the visible wires are approximately parallel to the axis of the rope. Regular-lay ropes do not kink or untwist and are easy to handle.

Lang-lay ropes have the wires in the strand and the strands in the rope twisted in the same direction, and hence the outer wires run diagonally across the axis of the rope. Lang-lay ropes are more resistant to abrasive wear and failure due to fatigue than are regular-lay ropes, but they are more likely to kink and untwist.

Standard ropes are made with a hemp core which supports and lubricates the strands. When the rope is subjected to heat, either a steel center or a wire-strand center must be used.

Wire rope is designated as, for example, a $1\frac{1}{8}$-in. 6×7 haulage rope. The first figure is the diameter of the rope (Fig. 13-10*c*). The second and third figures are the number of strands and the number of wires in each strand, respectively. Table 13-14 lists some of the various ropes which are available, together with their characteristics and properties.

When a wire rope passes around a sheave there is a certain amount of readjustment of the elements. Each of the wires and strands must slide on one another, and presumably some individual bending takes place. It is probable that in this complex action there exists some stress concentration. The stress in one of the wires of a rope passing around a sheave may be calculated as follows: From strength of materials we have

$$M = \frac{EI}{r} \qquad \text{and} \qquad M = \frac{sI}{c} \tag{a}$$

where the quantities have their usual meaning. Eliminating M and solving for the stress give

$$s = \frac{Ec}{r} \tag{b}$$

For the radius of curvature r we can substitute the radius of the sheave $D/2$. Also $c = d_w/2$, where d_w is the diameter of the wire. This substitution gives

$$s = E\frac{d_w}{D} \tag{13-8}$$

In Eq. (13-8) s is the bending stress in the individual wires and E is the modulus of elasticity of the rope (not of the wires). The sheave diameter is represented by D. Equation (13-8) illustrates the importance of using a large-diameter sheave. The suggested minimum sheave diameters in Table 13-14 are based on a D/d_w ratio of 400. If possible, the sheaves should be designed for a larger ratio. For elevators and mine hoists, D/d_w is usually taken from 800 to 1,000. If the ratio is less than 200, heavy loads will often cause a permanent set in the rope.

A wire rope may fail because the static load exceeds the ultimate strength of the rope. Failure of this nature is generally not the fault of the designer but rather that of the operator in permitting the rope to be subjected to loads for which it was not designed. On the other hand, ropes

TABLE 13-14. WIRE-ROPE DATA*

Rope	Weight per ft, lb	Minimum sheave diameter, in.	Standard sizes, d, in.	Material	Size of outer wires, in.	Modulus of elasticity,† psi	Strength,‡ psi
6 × 7 haulage.....	$1.50d^2$	$42d$	¼–1½	Monitor steel	$d/9$	14,000,000	100,000
				Plow steel	$d/9$	14,000,000	88,000
				Mild plow steel	$d/9$	14,000,000	76,000
6 × 19 standard hoisting	$1.60d^2$	$26d$–$34d$	¼–2¾	Monitor steel	$d/13$–$d/16$	12,000,000	106,000
				Plow steel	$d/13$–$d/16$	12,000,000	93,000
				Mild plow steel	$d/13$–$d/16$	12,000,000	80,000
6 × 37 special flexible	$1.55d^2$	$18d$	¼–3½	Monitor steel	$d/22$	11,000,000	100,000
				Plow steel	$d/22$	11,000,000	88,000
8 × 19 extra flexible	$1.45d^2$	$21d$–$26d$	¼–1½	Monitor steel	$d/15$–$d/19$	10,000,000	92,000
				Plow steel	$d/15$–$d/19$	10,000,000	80,000
7 × 7 aircraft......	$1.70d^2$	...	1/16–3/8	Corrosion-resistant steel	...	...	124,000
				Carbon steel	...	...	124,000
7 × 19 aircraft.....	$1.75d^2$	...	⅛–⅜	Corrosion-resistant steel	...	...	135,000
				Carbon steel	...	...	143,000
19-wire aircraft....	$2.15d^2$	...	1/32–5/16	Corrosion-resistant steel	...	...	165,000
				Carbon steel	...	...	165,000

* Compiled from American Steel and Wire Company Handbook.

† The modulus of elasticity is only approximate; it is affected by the loads on the rope and, in general, increases with the life of the rope.

‡ The strength is based upon the nominal area of the rope. The figures given are only approximate and are based on 1-in. rope sizes and ¼-in. aircraft-cable sizes.

do fail because of abrasive wear and because of fatigue. A fatigue failure first appears as a few broken wires on the surface of the rope. Examination of the wires indicates no apparent contraction of the cross section. The failure is thus of a brittle nature and traceable to fatigue.

Spotts[1] shows that this failure is a function of the pressure of the rope on the sheave. This pressure is given by the equation

$$p = \frac{2F}{dD} \qquad (13\text{-}9)$$

where F = tensile force on rope
d = rope diameter
D = sheave diameter

Figure 13-11 is a graph showing the relation between the ratio of the pressure to the ultimate strength of the wire and the life of the rope. Examination of the graph shows that a rope is not likely to fail by fatigue if the

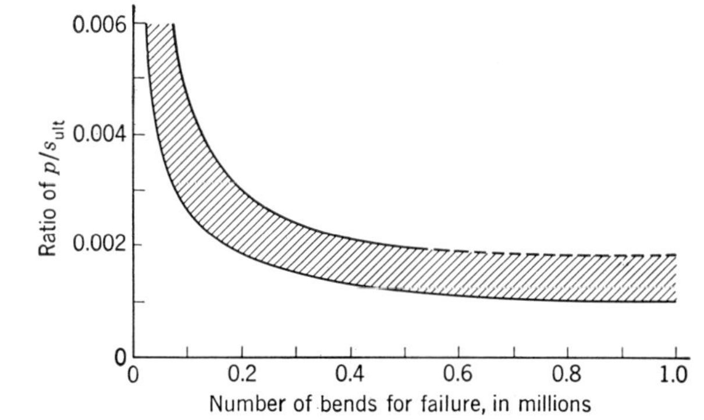

FIG. 13-11. Experimentally determined relation between the fatigue life of wire rope and the sheave pressure.

ratio p/s_{ult} is less than 0.001. Substitution of this ratio in Eq. (13-9) gives

$$s_{ult} = \frac{2{,}000F}{dD} \qquad (13\text{-}10)$$

where s_{ult} is the ultimate strength of the wire in pounds per square inch. This strength varies considerably, because it depends upon the wire diameter as well as the material. Spotts lists the following values:

Improved plow steel	200,000 psi
Plow steel	175,000 psi
Extra-strong cast steel	160,000 psi
Cast steel	140,000 psi
Iron	65,000 psi

Equation (13-10) is very useful for the design of ropes and sheaves and is unique in that it contains all four variables, strength, load, rope

[1] M. F. Spotts, "Design of Machine Elements," 2d ed., p. 393, Prentice-Hall, Inc., New York, 1953. Also see D. C. Drucker and H. Tachau, A New Design Criterion for Wire Rope, *Trans. ASME*, vol. 67, p. A-33, 1945.

diameter, and sheave diameter. When it is used in design, the engineer should assure himself that an ample static factor of safety exists. Factors of safety listed in Table 13-15 should be applied to the tensile strength of the rope as a check on Eq. (13-10) and to ensure safety. For abnormal load conditions these values should be increased, since they are set up for the most favorable conditions of load, environment, and lubrication.

TABLE 13-15. MINIMUM FACTORS OF SAFETY FOR WIRE ROPE

Track cables	3.2
Guys	3.5
Mine shafts:	
Up to 500 ft	8
1,000–2,000 ft	7
2,000–3,000 ft	6
Over 3,000 ft	5
Passenger elevators:	
50 fpm	7.50
300 fpm	9.17
800 fpm	11.25
Hoisting	5
Haulage	6
Cranes and derricks	6
Electric hoists	7

13-8. Flexible Shafts. One of the greatest limitations of the solid shaft is that it cannot transmit motion or power around corners. It is therefore necessary to resort to belts, chains, or gears, together with bearings and the supporting framework associated with them. The flexible shaft may often be an economical solution to the problem of transmitting motion around corners. In addition to the elimination of costly parts, its use may reduce noise very considerably.

There are two main types of flexible shafts: the power-drive shaft for the transmission of power in a single direction, and the remote-control or manual-control shaft for the transmission of motion in either direction.

The construction of a flexible shaft is shown in Fig. 13-12. The cable is made by winding several layers of wire around a central core. For the power-drive shaft, rotation should be in a direction such that the outer layer is wound up. Remote-control cables have a different lay of the wires forming the cable, with more wires in each layer, so that the torsional deflection is approximately the same for either direction of rotation.

Flexible shafts are rated by specifying the torque corresponding to various radii of curvature of the casing. A 15-in. radius of curvature, for example, will give from two to five times more torque capacity than a 7-in. radius. When flexible shafts are used in a drive in which gears are also used, the gears should be placed so that the flexible shaft runs at as

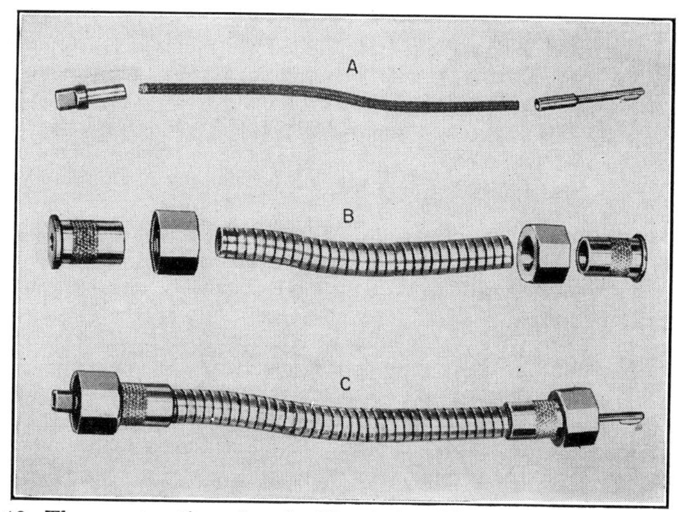

Fig. 13-12. The construction of a flexible shaft. The wire-wound cable and end fittings are shown at *A*. These must be enclosed by a flexible casing and end fittings which are shown at *B*. At *C* is shown the assembled flexible shaft. (*Courtesy of F. W. Stewart Corporation.*)

high a speed as possible. This permits the transmission of the maximum amount of horsepower.

PROBLEMS

13-1. A double-ply 18⁄64-in. flat leather belt is 6 in. wide and transmits 15 hp. The pulley arrangement is shown in the figure. (*a*) Determine the tension in the tight

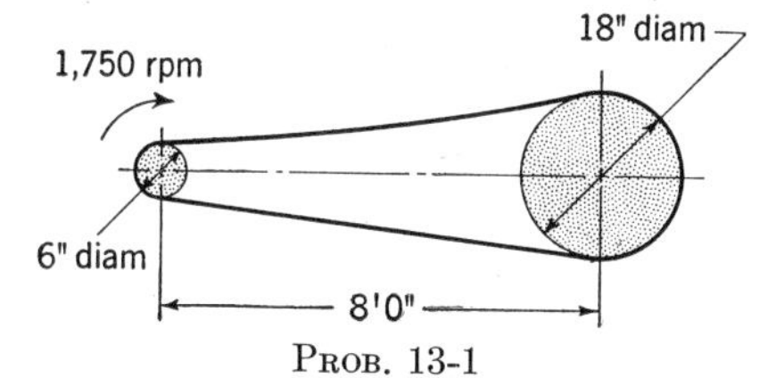

Prob. 13-1

and slack sides of the belt if the coefficient of friction is 0.30. (*b*) If adverse conditions cause the coefficient of friction to decrease to 0.20, what would be the belt tensions?

Ans.: (*b*) 264 lb, 445 lb.

13-2. Calculate the length of the belt in Prob. 13-1.

13-3. A belt drive is to have two 4-ft cast-iron pulleys spaced 16 ft apart. The tensile stress in the belt should not exceed 250 psi. Use $f = 0.30$ and $w = 0.035$ lb per in.^{3} Determine the width of 23⁄64-in. leather belt required if 75 hp is to be transmitted at 350 rpm.

13-4. A 10-in. leather belt 20⁄64 in. thick runs on a 16-in. pulley, which is the driver, and a 36-in. pulley. Both pulleys are of cast iron, and the coefficient of friction of the drive is 0.28. (*a*) Using a center distance of 16 ft, a maximum tensile stress of 200 psi in the belt, and a belt velocity of 4,000 fpm, calculate the maximum horsepower that can be transmitted. (*b*) What are the shaft loads?

***13-5.** An air compressor requiring a 15-hp motor is to run at approximately 300 rpm for 8 hr per day. A squirrel-cage motor is selected which runs at 1,150 rpm and has a frame diameter of 16 in. Design a flat-belt drive occupying the minimum practical center distance, and specify appropriate pulley sizes.

***13-6.** A refrigeration compressor requires 50 hp at 900 rpm. It is to be driven by a flat belt from a 1,750-rpm squirrel-cage motor. The driving pulley should not exceed a diameter of 18 in. The center distance is 8 ft. Specify a satisfactory belt and suitable pulley sizes for the installation.

***13-7.** A flat belt is to be used out of doors to drive a centrifugal irrigation pump. The motor is 10 hp, 1,720 rpm; the pump should be driven at approximately 1,200 rpm. The motor pulley should be 10 in. or less in diameter. Specify a suitable belt and pulleys.

***13-8.** A 5-hp 260-rpm fan is driven by a 1,720-rpm motor. The center distance should not exceed 24 in. The duty is continuous. Select suitable V belts and sheaves.

***13-9.** A 3,600-rpm 7½-hp motor drives a ripsaw at 2,400 rpm. The saw-shaft pulley should not exceed 7 in. in diameter. Select suitable V belts and sheaves for intermittent operation 8 hr per day.

***13-10.** An air-conditioning compressor requires 50 hp at 275 rpm. The center distance should not exceed 41 in.; the motor pulley must have a diameter less than 16 in. Select suitable belts and pulleys.

***13-11.** The figure shows the shaft extension and bearing spacing of a 40-hp 720-rpm squirrel-cage motor. Five C96 belts are used to connect this motor to the load.

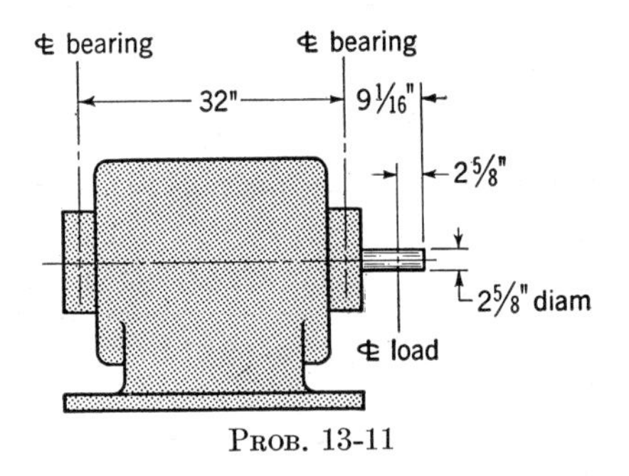

PROB. 13-11

The driving sheave is 8.0 in. pitch diameter × 5¼ in. face width. The driven sheave is 20 in. pitch diameter. (*a*) Find the center distance. (*b*) Calculate the additional radial load on the motor bearings as a result of the use of belts.

13-12. A double-strand No. 60 roller chain is used to transmit power between a 13-tooth driving sprocket rotating at 300 rpm and a 52-tooth driven sprocket. (*a*) What is the rated horsepower of this drive? (*b*) Determine the approximate center distance if the chain length is 82 pitches. *Ans.:* (*a*) 6.98 hp, (*b*) 18 in.

13-13. Calculate the torque and the bending force on the shaft produced by the chain of Prob. 13-12.

13-14. A quadruple-strand No. 40 roller chain transmits power from a 21-tooth driving sprocket which turns at 1,200 rpm. The velocity ratio between the two sprockets is 4:1. (*a*) Calculate the rated horsepower of this drive. (*b*) Find the tension in the chain. (*c*) What is the factor of safety for the chain, based upon the average tensile strength? (*d*) What should be the chain length for a center distance of approximately 20 in.?

13-15. A 15-tooth No. 35 sprocket rotates at 500 rpm and transmits ¾ hp to another 15-tooth sprocket through a single-strand roller chain. (*a*) Calculate the shaft torque. (*b*) Find the tension in the chain. (*c*) What is the pitch diameter of the sprockets?

13-16. The roller chain shown in the figure is No. 120 double-strand. The center distances shown are expressed in terms of the pitch. The 11-tooth driver rotates at

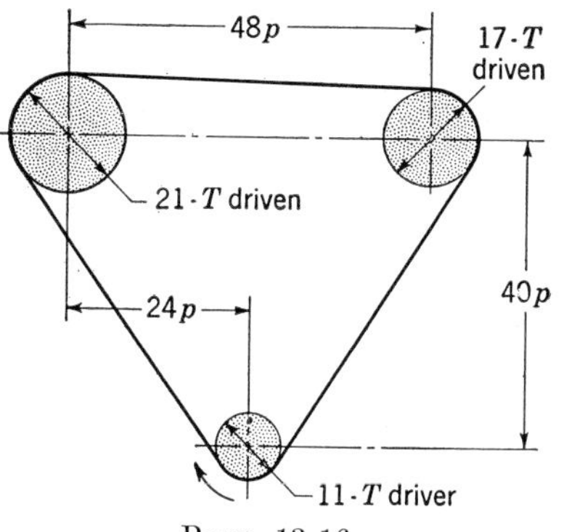

PROB. 13-16

100 rpm and transmits 5 hp to the 21-tooth sprocket and 5 hp to the 17-tooth sprocket. (*a*) Calculate the tension in the various portions of the chain. (*b*) Find all the shaft reactions.

13-17. The roller chain in Prob. 13-16 is single-strand No. 80. The 11-tooth sprocket is the driver and rotates at 50 rpm. (*a*) Find the rated horsepower of the drive. (*b*) The 17- and 21-tooth sprockets are to transfer equal torques to their shafts. For counterclockwise rotation of the 11-tooth sprocket and for transmission of the rated horsepower, what is the tension in the various portions of the chain? (*c*) Determine the shaft reaction of each sprocket.

***13-18.** A roller chain is to transmit 90 hp from a 17-tooth sprocket to a 34-tooth sprocket. The load characteristics are moderate shock with abnormal service conditions. The equipment is to run for 18 hr per day. Specify the length and size of chain required for a center distance of about 25 pitches.

***13-19.** A 720-rpm 25-hp squirrel-cage motor is to drive a two-cylinder reciprocating pump which is to be located out of doors under a shed. The pump is to run at full load for 24 hr per day, and freedom from breakdowns is especially desired. The pump speed is 144 rpm. Select suitable chain and sprocket sizes for a roller-chain drive.

***13-20.** A 5-hp 300-rpm speed reducer is to drive a bucket elevator at 200 rpm on approximately 20-in. centers. Specify a satisfactory chain size and length and the sprocket sizes. (Data courtesy of Browning Manufacturing Company.)

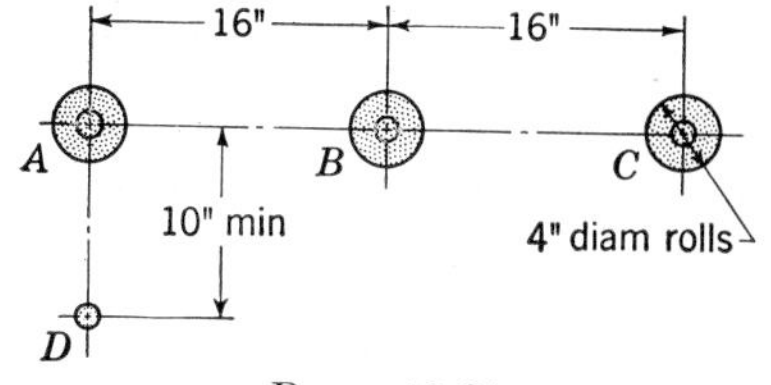

PROB. 13-21

***13-21.** The figure shows three rolls, at centers *A*, *B*, and *C*, having 4-in. diameters and $1\frac{5}{16}$-in. shaft diameters. The rolls are to be driven at 12-fpm surface velocity by a shaft with center at *D* which is also $1\frac{5}{16}$ in. in diameter. Shaft *D* may not be located closer than 10 in. to the roll centers. A torque of 1,200 lb-in. is required to operate each roll. The load is smooth. Operation will be for 8 hr per day. Make a complete design for a roller-chain drive, specifying in detail each item which is required. Idler sprockets may be located where necessary.

***13-22 to 13-41.** The data in the accompanying table are to be used to design a flexible power-transmission drive. Make a sketch of the completed design, indicating all details of the flexible element, the correct center distance, and the sizes of the driving and driven elements.

Problem No.	Power source			Load			Center distance, in.	Remarks
	Type	Hp	Speed, rpm	Operation, hr per day	Service	Speed, rpm		
13-22	Motor	50	1,800	8	Shock	600	72 minimum	Vertical drive
13-23	Motor	50	1,200	8	Shock	400	72 minimum	Vertical drive
13-24	Motor	50	900	8	Shock	300	72 minimum	Vertical drive
13-25	Motor	50	720	8	Shock	240	72 minimum	Vertical drive
13-26	Motor	50	600	8	Shock	200	72 minimum	Vertical drive
13-27	Countershaft	20	800	18	Smooth	400	36 minimum	60° inclined drive
13-28	Countershaft	20	600	18	Smooth	300	36 minimum	60° inclined drive
13-29	Countershaft	20	400	18	Smooth	200	36 minimum	60° inclined drive
13-30	Countershaft	20	200	18	Smooth	100	36 minimum	60° inclined drive
13-31	Countershaft	20	100	18	Smooth	50	36 minimum	60° inclined drive
13-32	Motor	½	1,800	2	Average	1,200	20 maximum	Horizontal drive
13-33	Motor	½	1,800	2	Average	600	20 maximum	Horizontal drive
13-34	Motor	½	1,800	2	Average	300	20 maximum	Horizontal drive
13-35	Motor	½	1,800	2	Average	150	20 maximum	Horizontal drive
13-36	Countershaft	100	500	24	Average	100	Very short	Horizontal to 30°
13-37	Countershaft	50	500	24	Average	100	Very short	Horizontal to 30°
13-38	Countershaft	25	500	24	Average	100	Very short	Horizontal to 30°
13-39	Countershaft	10	500	24	Average	100	Very short	Horizontal to 30°
13-40	Countershaft	1	500	24	Average	100	Very short	Horizontal to 30°
13-41	Countershaft	0.1	500	24	Average	100	Very short	Horizontal to 30°

13-42. A mine hoist uses a 2-in. 6 × 19 monitor steel wire rope. The rope is used to haul loads up to 10 tons from a shaft 480 ft deep. The drum has a diameter of 6 ft. (*a*) Using a maximum hoisting speed of 1,200 fpm and a maximum acceleration of 2 fps per sec, determine the stress in the rope. (*b*) What is the factor of safety? *Ans.:* (*a*) 6,830 psi, (*b*) 15.5.

13-43. (*a*) Determine the bending stress in the wires of the rope of Prob. 13-42. (*b*) Considering fatigue, what maximum force can be applied to this rope? (Use $d/15$ for the diameter of the wires.) *Ans.:* (*a*) 5,650 psi, (*b*) 14,400 lb.

13-44. The assumption is frequently made that the area of the metal in a wire rope is 40 per cent of the area of the rope. (*a*) With this assumption, determine the stress in the wires of the rope in Prob. 13-43 due to both the direct and bending loads. (*b*) What is the factor of safety for this assumption?

Ans.: (*a*) 39,300 psi, (*b*) 5.09.

***13-45.** A 1-in. 6 × 37 monitor steel wire rope is used on a mine shaft 220 ft deep. The velocity of the cage is 250 fpm. The drum is 4 ft in diameter. The time required to accelerate the cage to full velocity is 14 sec. (*a*) Determine the maximum hoisting load, considering fatigue as the design factor. (*b*) Using a factor of safety of 8, determine the maximum hoisting load based on the tensile strength of the rope. (*c*) If the area of the metal in the rope is 40 per cent of the area of the rope, what is the maximum hoisting load based upon the strength of the wires? Use a factor of safety of 8.

***13-46.** A mine shaft 1,200 ft deep employs a cage weighing 3,200 lb. The cars and ore to be lifted weigh 2,800 lb. The drum is to be 72 in. in diameter. The load is to be lifted at a speed of 1,400 fpm, using an acceleration of 4 fps per sec. Select a suitable wire rope.

CHAPTER 14

MISCELLANEOUS MACHINE ELEMENTS

14-1. Stresses in Thin-walled Cylinders. A thin-walled cylinder is one in which the stresses may be assumed to be uniformly distributed over the wall thickness. Pressure vessels, tanks, pipe, and hoops may usually be treated in this manner.

Two types of stresses, with directions which are perpendicular to each other, may exist in such cylinders. The first is a hoop stress, or *tangential stress,* due to the internal pressure on the walls of the cylinder. The second is a transverse stress, or *longitudinal stress,* which exists because of the internal pressure on the ends of the cylinder.

Referring to Fig. 14-1, the internal pressure p is exerted on the sides of a cylinder of thickness t and internal diameter D. Using a unit length of the cylinder, the load tending to separate two halves of the cylinder is pD. This load is resisted by the tangential stress acting uniformly over the stressed area. We then have $pD = 2ts_t$, or

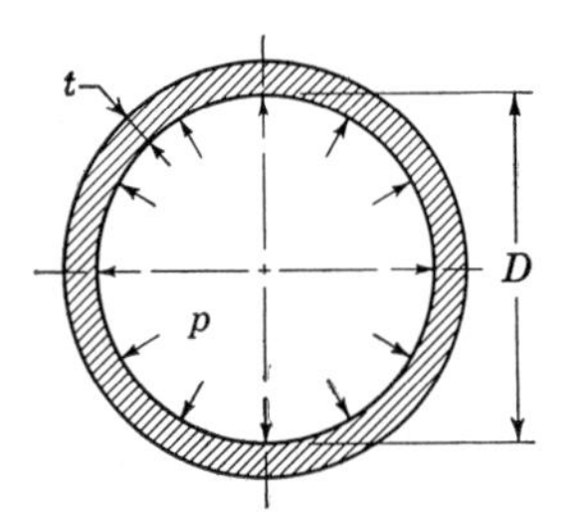

FIG. 14-1. Tangential, or hoop, stress is caused by internal pressure.

$$s_t = \frac{pD}{2t} \tag{14-1}$$

where s_t is the tangential stress.

The longitudinal stress is found from a consideration of the forces which would act upon the ends of a closed cylinder. This force is $p(\pi D^2/4)$ and must be equated to the longitudinal stress times the area over which it acts. We then have

$$p\frac{\pi D^2}{4} = s_l(\pi Dt)$$

so that the longitudinal stress is

$$s_l = \frac{pD}{4t} \tag{14-2}$$

Assumptions. The assumptions made in deriving both of the above equations are:

1. The cylinder is thin. This means that the ratio of the thickness to the diameter of the cylinder is small. For practical purposes, if the cylinder has a ratio of t/D of $\frac{1}{10}$ or less, it is said to be a thin cylinder.
2. The stress is uniformly distributed across the wall thickness.
3. Bending stresses at the juncture between the head and the shell are assumed to be negligible.
4. The material obeys Hooke's law.

Pressure Vessels. Pressure vessels are designed according to safety codes. Recent use of higher pressures and temperatures, together with the availability of newer materials, makes it necessary that these elements be very carefully designed. The following items must usually be considered:

1. Tangential stress
2. Longitudinal stress
3. Juncture stresses between the head and the shell
4. Residual stresses induced by welding or riveting
5. The possibility of low-temperature brittle-type failure
6. High-temperature creep
7. Thermal stresses
8. Fatigue stresses
9. Corrosion effects
10. Accidental application of external pressure
11. Stress concentrations
12. Failure at openings for manholes, nozzles, and connections

14-2. Stresses in Thick-walled Cylinders. A thick-walled cylinder subjected to external or internal pressure, or both, has radial stress and tangential stress with values which are dependent upon the radius of the element under consideration. A thick-walled cylinder may also be stressed longitudinally, but this is seldom of significant magnitude. In design, gun barrels, high-pressure hydraulic cylinders, and pipe carrying fluids at high pressures all must be considered as thick-walled cylinders.

In determining the radial stress s_r and the tangential stress s_t we make use of the assumption that the longitudinal elongation is constant around the circumference of the cylinder. In other words, a right section of the cylinder remains plane after stressing.

Referring to Fig. 14-2, we designate the inside radius of the cylinder by a, the outside radius by b, the internal pressure by p_i, and the external pressure by p_o. Let us consider the equilibrium of an infinitely thin semicircular ring cut from the cylinder at radius r and having unit length. Taking a summation of forces in the vertical direction equal to zero, we have

$$2s_t\,dr - 2rs_r + 2(s_r + ds_r)(r + dr) = 0 \qquad (a)$$

Simplifying and neglecting higher-order quantities give

$$s_t + s_r + r\frac{ds_r}{dr} = 0 \tag{b}$$

Equation (*b*) relates the two unknowns s_t and s_r, but we must obtain a second relation in order to evaluate them. The second equation is obtained from the assumption that the longitudinal deformation is constant. The tensile stress s_t causes a contraction in the longitudinal direction, while the compressive stress s_r causes an expansion. Using the

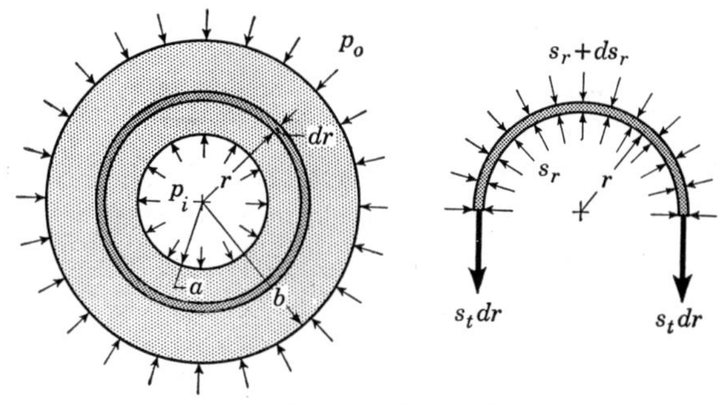

FIG. 14-2. A thick cylinder.

method of Sec. 3-4, the resultant longitudinal unit deformation ϵ_l is

$$\epsilon_l = \frac{\mu s_r}{E} - \frac{\mu s_t}{E} \tag{c}$$

where μ is Poisson's ratio and E is the modulus of elasticity. For a given material, both of these are constants. We can therefore rearrange Eq. (*c*) to read

$$s_r - s_t = -2C_1 \tag{d}$$

We now have two relations between the stresses. Solving Eqs. (*b*) and (*d*) simultaneously to eliminate the tangential stress, we obtain

$$r\frac{ds_r}{dr} + 2s_r = -2C_1 \tag{e}$$

Multiplying Eq. (*e*) by r gives

$$r^2\frac{ds_r}{dr} + 2rs_r = -2rC_1 \tag{f}$$

We note that

$$\frac{d(r^2 s_r)}{dr} = r^2\frac{ds_r}{dr} + 2rs_r \tag{g}$$

which is the same as the left side of Eq. (f). Therefore,

$$\frac{d(r^2 s_r)}{dr} = -2rC_1 \tag{h}$$

which, when integrated, gives

$$r^2 s_r = -r^2 C_1 + C_2 \tag{i}$$

where C_2 is a constant of integration. Solving for s_r, we obtain

$$s_r = -C_1 + \frac{C_2}{r^2} \tag{j}$$

Substituting this value of s_r in Eq. (d), we find

$$s_t = C_1 + \frac{C_2}{r^2} \tag{k}$$

We may evaluate the constants C_1 and C_2 using the pressures p_i and p_o at the boundaries of the cylinder. Thus,

$$s_r = p_i \text{ when } r = a \qquad \text{and} \qquad s_r = p_o \text{ when } r = b$$

Substituting these values in Eq. (j), we obtain

$$p_i = -C_1 + \frac{C_2}{a^2} \qquad \text{and} \qquad p_o = -C_1 + \frac{C_2}{b^2} \tag{l}$$

The constants are found by solving these two equations simultaneously. This gives

$$C_1 = \frac{p_i a^2 - p_o b^2}{b^2 - a^2} \qquad C_2 = \frac{a^2 b^2 (p_i - p_o)}{b^2 - a^2} \tag{m}$$

Substituting these values into Eqs. (j) and (k) yields

$$s_t = \frac{p_i a^2 - p_o b^2 + a^2 b^2 (p_i - p_o)/r^2}{b^2 - a^2} \tag{14-3}$$

$$s_r = \frac{p_o b^2 - p_i a^2 + a^2 b^2 (p_i - p_o)/r^2}{b^2 - a^2} \tag{14-4}$$

It should be noted in the above equations that when s_t is positive the tangential stress is tension and when s_r is positive the radial stress is compression.

Let us now determine the stresses when the external pressure is zero. Substitution of $p_o = 0$ in Eqs. (14-3) and (14-4) gives

$$s_t = \frac{p_i a^2}{b^2 - a^2}\left(\frac{b^2}{r^2} + 1\right) \tag{14-5}$$

$$s_r = \frac{p_i a^2}{b^2 - a^2}\left(\frac{b^2}{r^2} - 1\right) \tag{14-6}$$

These equations are plotted in Fig. 14-3 to show the distribution of stresses over the wall thickness. The maximum stresses occur at the inner surface where $r = a$. Their magnitudes are

$$s_t = p_i \frac{b^2 + a^2}{b^2 - a^2} \tag{14-7}$$

$$s_r = p_i \tag{14-8}$$

We can also determine the stresses in the outer surface of a cylinder subjected to external pressure. In this case $p_i = 0$ and $r = b$. Substituting these values in Eqs. (14-3) and (14-4), we find that

$$s_t = -p_o \frac{b^2 + a^2}{b^2 - a^2} \tag{14-9}$$

$$s_r = p_o \tag{14-10}$$

where the minus sign in Eq. (14-9) indicates that the tangential stress is compression.

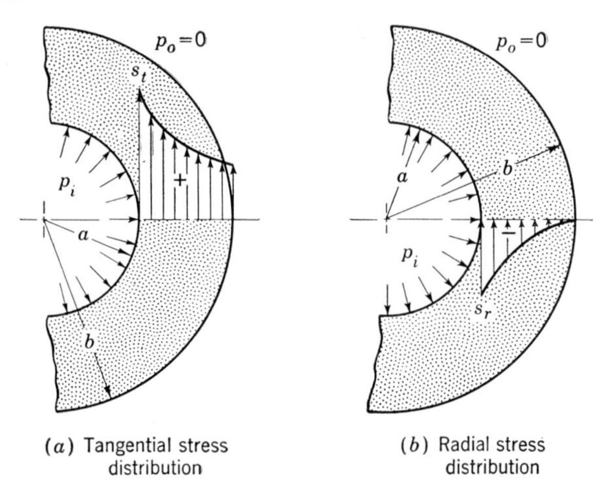

FIG. 14-3. Distribution of stresses in a thick-walled cylinder subjected to internal pressure.

Assumptions. These equations have been developed using the following assumptions:

1. The material is homogeneous and obeys Hooke's law.
2. The longitudinal stress is uniformly distributed over the entire cross-sectional area of the cylinder.

14-3. Press and Shrink Fits. When two cylindrical parts are assembled by shrinking or press-fitting one part upon another, a contact pressure is created between the two parts. The stresses resulting from this pressure may easily be determined with the equations of the preceding section.

Figure 14-4 shows two cylindrical members which have been assembled with a shrink fit. A contact pressure p exists between the members at radius b, causing radial stresses $s_r = p$ in each member at the contacting surfaces. From Eq. (14-9), the tangential stress at the outer surface of the inner member is

$$s_{it} = -p \frac{b^2 + a^2}{b^2 - a^2} \tag{14-11}$$

In the same manner, from Eq. (14-7), the tangential stress at the inner surface of the outer member is

$$s_{ot} = p \frac{c^2 + b^2}{c^2 - b^2} \tag{14-12}$$

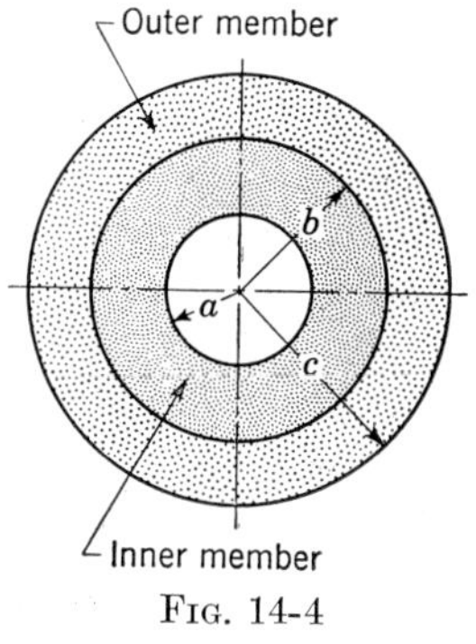

FIG. 14-4

These equations cannot be solved until the contact pressure is known. In obtaining a shrink fit the diameter of the male member is made larger than the diameter of the female member. The difference in these dimensions is called the interference and is the deformation which the two members must experience. Since these dimensions are usually known, the deformation should be introduced in order to evaluate the stresses.

Considering the inner surface of the outer member, the stress s_{ot} causes a unit deformation ϵ_{ot}. The total increase in circumference is $2\pi b\epsilon_{ot}$, which, when divided by 2π, gives the increase in radius. That is,

$$\delta_o = \frac{2\pi b\epsilon_{ot}}{2\pi} = b\epsilon_{ot} \tag{a}$$

where δ_o is the radial deformation of the inner surface of the outer member. Using the method of Sec. 3-4 and Eq. (14-12), the deformation is found to be

$$\delta_o = b\epsilon_{ot} = b\left(\frac{s_{ot}}{E} + \frac{\mu s_r}{E}\right) = \frac{bp}{E}\left(\frac{c^2 + b^2}{c^2 - b^2} + \mu\right) \tag{b}$$

Using the same method, we find the radial deformation of the inner member to be

$$\delta_i = b\epsilon_{it} = b\left(\frac{s_{it}}{E} + \frac{\mu s_r}{E}\right) = -\frac{bp}{E}\left(\frac{b^2 + a^2}{b^2 - a^2} - \mu\right) \tag{c}$$

where the minus sign indicates that the deformation is directed toward the center.

Taking δ as the original difference in the radii of the two cylinders, then δ must equal the increase in diameter of the outer cylinder plus the decrease in diameter of the inner cylinder. This gives

$$\frac{bp}{E}\left(\frac{c^2 + b^2}{c^2 - b^2} + \mu\right) + \frac{bp}{E}\left(\frac{b^2 + a^2}{b^2 - a^2} - \mu\right) = \delta \qquad (d)$$

so that

$$p = \frac{E\delta}{b}\,\frac{(b^2 - a^2)(c^2 - b^2)}{2b^2(c^2 - a^2)} \qquad (14\text{-}13)$$

Substitution of this value of p in Eqs. (14-11) and (14-12) will then give the tangential stresses at the inner surface of the outer cylinder and at the outer surface of the inner cylinder. In addition, Eq. (14-13) can be used to obtain the value of p for use in the general equations [Eqs. (14-3) and (14-4)] in order to obtain the stress at any point in either cylinder.

Assumptions. In addition to the assumptions of Sec. 14-2, it is necessary to assume that both members have the same length. In the case of a hub which has been press-fitted to a shaft this assumption would not be true, and there would be an increased pressure at each end of the hub. It is customary to allow for this condition by the employment of a stress-concentration factor. The value of this factor is a function of the contact pressure, the stress, and the design of the female member. It is seldom greater than 2.

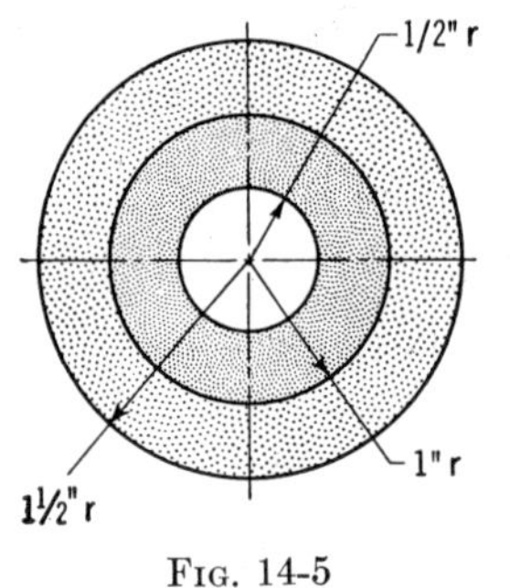

Fig. 14-5

Example 14-1. Figure 14-5 shows a tube, such as a gun barrel, having nominal dimensions of 1 in. ID × 2 in. OD, over which a second tube having nominal dimensions of 2 in. ID × 3 in. OD is to be shrink-fitted. The material is steel. It is desired to fit these two members together to cause a stress of $s_t = 10{,}000$ psi at the inner surface of the outer member. (*a*) Find the required original dimensions of the members. (*b*) Determine the resulting stress distribution.

Decisions. The outside diameter of the inner member will be made equal to the nominal dimensions. The interference will be subtracted from the nominal inside diameter of the outer member. The effect upon the stresses is considered to be negligible.

Solution. *a.* Using Eq. (14-12), we solve for the contact pressure. Thus

$$p = s_{ot}\frac{c^2 - b^2}{c^2 + b^2} = (10{,}000)\frac{(1.5)^2 - (1)^2}{(1.5)^2 + (1)^2} = 3{,}850 \text{ psi}$$

Solving Eq. (14-13) for the deformation, we obtain

$$\delta = \frac{bp}{E}\,\frac{2b^2(c^2 - a^2)}{(b^2 - a^2)(c^2 - b^2)} = \frac{(1)(3{,}850)}{(30)(10)^6}\,\frac{(2)(1)^2[(1.5)^2 - (0.5)^2]}{[(1)^2 - (0.5)^2][(1.5)^2 - (1)^2]}$$
$$= 0.000548 \text{ in.}$$

The dimensions selected are as follows:

Outside diameter of inner member = 2.00000 in. *Ans.*
Inside diameter of outer member = 2.00000 − (2)(0.000548)
= 1.998904 in. *Ans.*

b. We will determine the stress distribution in the outer member first. This is a cylinder subjected to an internal pressure of $p_i = 3{,}850$ psi and an external pressure $p_o = 0$. Equations (14-5) and (14-6) apply. In these equations $a = 1$ in. and $b = 1.5$ in., and they are to be solved for various values of r between 1 and 1.5 in. Using $r = 1.1$ in., a sample calculation is as follows:

$$s_t = \frac{p_i a^2}{b^2 - a^2}\left(\frac{b^2}{r^2} + 1\right) = \frac{(3{,}850)(1)^2}{(1.5)^2 - (1)^2}\left[\frac{(1.5)^2}{(1.1)^2} + 1\right]$$
$$= 8{,}810 \text{ psi}$$
$$s_r = \frac{p_i a^2}{b^2 - a^2}\left(\frac{b^2}{r^2} - 1\right) = \frac{(3{,}850)(1)^2}{(1.5)^2 - (1)^2}\left[\frac{(1.5)^2}{(1.1)^2} - 1\right]$$
$$= 2{,}650 \text{ psi}$$

These, and other results obtained in the same manner, are shown in Table 14-1.

TABLE 14-1. TANGENTIAL AND RADIAL STRESSES IN THE OUTER MEMBER

Radius r, in.	Tangential stress s_t, psi	Radial stress s_r, psi
1.0	10,000	3,850
1.1	8,810	2,650
1.2	7,900	1,740
1.3	7,180	950
1.4	6,630	460
1.5	6,160	0

Equations (14-3) and (14-4) are used for the inner member. When $p_i = 0$ and $p_o = p$, these equations reduce to

$$s_t = -\frac{pb^2}{b^2 - a^2}\left(1 + \frac{a^2}{r^2}\right) \tag{14-14}$$
$$s_r = \frac{pb^2}{b^2 - a^2}\left(1 - \frac{a^2}{r^2}\right) \tag{14-15}$$

Applying these equations to this example, $a = 0.5$ in., $b = 1$ in., and r varies from 0.5 to 1 in. The contact pressure p is 3,850 psi. The results are shown in Table 14-2.

TABLE 14-2. TANGENTIAL AND RADIAL STRESSES IN THE INNER MEMBER

Radius r, in.	Tangential stress s_t, psi	Radial stress s_r, psi
0.50	10,300	0
0.60	8,720	1,570
0.70	7,750	2,520
0.80	7,160	3,130
0.90	6,730	3,560
1.00	6,420	3,850

These stresses are plotted in Fig. 14-6. It is noted that the radial stresses are compressive in both members, while the tangential stress is compressive in the inner member and tensile in the outer member.

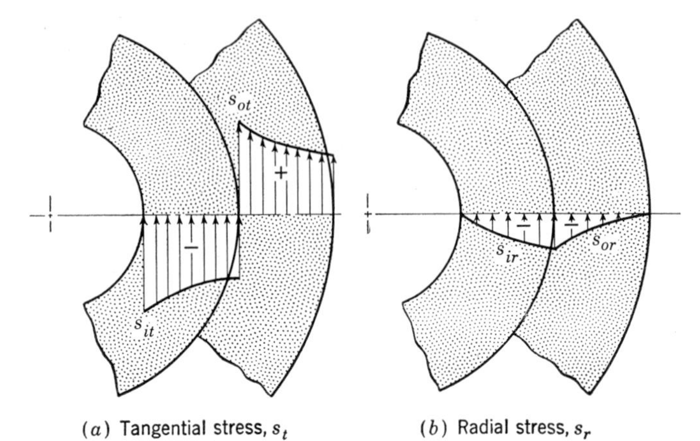

Fig. 14-6. Distribution of radial and tangential stresses in shrink-fitted members.

14-4. Flat Plates. The determination of the stresses and strains in flat plates subjected to various loading conditions is frequently necessary in machine design. For example, in the design of a cylinder head or the bottom or side of a tank such information might be required. It will not be possible to present the equations for the deflections of such members in this book, but one of the methods of analyzing the stresses will be presented.[1]

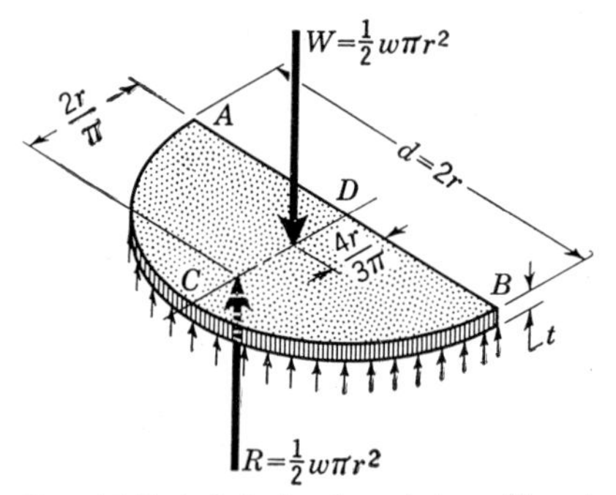

Fig. 14-7. A flat circular plate uniformly loaded and simply supported.

Let us consider a flat circular plate of uniform thickness t, subjected to a uniform load of w lb per in.[2] and simply supported around the edge. If we consider one-half of the plate (Fig. 14-7), the load acting upon it will be $w\pi r^2/2$, and this must be supported by the resultant reaction which will therefore be of the same magnitude. We may replace the action of the distributed load by the concentrated load W acting at the centroid of the semicircular area. This centroid is located at a distance of $4r/3\pi$ from the center, as shown in the figure. In the same way, we replace the reaction at the rim by a resultant reaction R_1 acting at the centroid of half the circumference. This distance is $2r/\pi$ from center, as shown in the figure.

[1] Fred B. Seely, "Advanced Mechanics of Materials," pp. 133–159, John Wiley & Sons, Inc., New York, 1947.

The bending moment, about the diametral plane AB, is

$$M = R_1 \frac{2r}{\pi} - W \frac{4r}{3\pi} = \frac{w\pi r^2}{2} \frac{2r}{\pi} - \frac{w\pi r^2}{2} \frac{4r}{3\pi} = \frac{wr^3}{3} \tag{a}$$

The section modulus of the plate, at the diametral plane, is $I/c = (2r)t^2/6$. Substituting the moment and the section modulus in the fundamental bending-stress equation gives

$$s = \frac{M}{I/c} = \frac{wr^3/3}{2rt^2/6} = \frac{wr^2}{t^2} \tag{14-16}$$

Assumptions. The use of the fundamental equation for bending stress means, of course, that we have used all the assumptions which were originally used in deriving it. There is, however, a more important source of error. Equation (a) implies that the moment varies from C to D (Fig. 14-7), becoming a maximum at D. But when this moment was substituted in the bending-stress formula to obtain Eq. (14-16), the assumption implied by its use is that the stress from A to B is uniform. Yet the value of that stress 1 in. from A, for example, should be no different than the value 1 in. from C. Seely[1] states that the maximum stress in the plate is higher than indicated by the above equation, but, probably because of local yielding, the equation will give reliable values of the stress when the plate is made of a ductile material; and, he states, this has been verified by experiment.

Concentrated Loads. We can use the same procedure if the load is concentrated instead of distributed. If a concentrated load F acts at the center of the plate the resultant reaction is $F/2$. This causes a moment $M = (F/2)(2r/\pi) = Fr/\pi$. Substitution of this moment into the bending-stress equation gives

$$s = \frac{M}{I/c} = \frac{Fr/\pi}{2rt^2/6} = \frac{3F}{\pi t^2} \tag{b}$$

Concentrated loads always result in stress concentrations. We shall, therefore, multiply Eq. (b) by a stress-concentration factor k, as follows:

$$s = k \frac{3F}{\pi t^2} \tag{14-17}$$

Seely states that values of k from 1 to 1.5 may be used, depending upon the degree of concentration of the load.

Fixed Edges. In case the edges of the plate are fixed we actually have less bending moment, because of the negative action near the edge of the plate. In addition, in design, it would be difficult to obtain complete

[1] *Ibid.*, p. 136.

fixity at the edges. We can conclude that only a small amount of fixity will ever be present and that, therefore, Eq. (14-16) or (14-17) can usually be used. The results would then be even more conservative than the conditions for which they were developed.

14-5. Rectangular Plates. A similar argument will lead to the stress equation for the bending of a rectangular plate with the edges simply supported.

In such a plate, experiments show that the corners may turn up, so that the critical section is a diagonal. We are interested in obtaining the maximum bending moment about the diagonal AC in Fig. 14-8. Again we let w be the load per unit area and t be the thickness of the plate. Then the total load on the plate is wab, where a and b are the dimensions of the sides. Therefore, the load on the triangular section is $wab/2$, and it must act through the centroid at a distance $h/3$ from the diagonal AC. It is noted that the reactions R_1 and R_2 have the same moment arm; we need not, therefore, determine their separate values. The sum of R_1 and R_2 is also equal to $wab/2$. Taking moments about the diagonal, we have

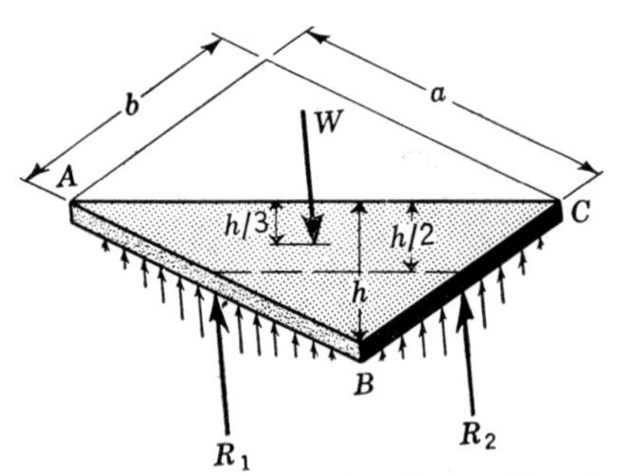

FIG. 14-8. A rectangular plate uniformly loaded and simply supported.

$$M = (R_1 + R_2)\frac{h}{2} - W\frac{h}{3} = \frac{wab}{2}\frac{h}{2} - \frac{wab}{2}\frac{h}{3} = \frac{wabh}{12} \qquad (a)$$

We now make the assumption that the stress is uniformly distributed along the diagonal. However, it is usual, at this point in the development, to determine the moment per unit length of the diagonal. This moment is

$$M' = \frac{wabh}{12}\frac{1}{\sqrt{a^2 + b^2}} \qquad (b)$$

where $\sqrt{a^2 + b^2}$ is the length of the diagonal. Referring to Fig. 14-8, by similar triangles, we can write

$$\frac{b}{\sqrt{a^2 + b^2}} = \frac{h}{a} \quad \text{or} \quad h = \frac{ab}{\sqrt{a^2 + b^2}} \qquad (c)$$

Substitution of this value of h in Eq. (b) gives

$$M' = \frac{wa^2b^2}{12(a^2 + b^2)} \qquad (d)$$

For a unit length of diagonal the section modulus is $I/c = t^2/6$, and so the bending stress is

$$s = \frac{M}{I/c} = \frac{wa^2b^2}{12(a^2 + b^2)} \frac{6}{t^2} = \frac{wa^2b^2}{2t^2(a^2 + b^2)} \tag{14-18}$$

For a square plate, $a = b$, and this equation reduces to

$$s = \frac{wb^2}{4t^2} \tag{14-19}$$

Assumptions. In this development we have made the assumption that the stress is uniformly distributed along the diagonal. A complete mathematical analysis shows that the stresses are higher at the corners and lower at the center.[1] There seems little doubt that the high corner stresses are local in nature and that when yielding occurs they are redistributed and become more nearly equal to the values indicated by Eq. (14-18). If dangerous conditions are present, such as fatigue, low or high temperatures, or the possibility of corrosion, the designer should certainly investigate the problem more thoroughly than has been indicated here.

14-6. Rotating Disks. Flywheels, steam and gas-turbine elements, fans, and blowers may frequently be simplified to a rotating disk and the stresses determined according to the following analysis. In such a disk the inertia forces set up stresses like those in thick cylinders, and so the same method of analysis may be used.

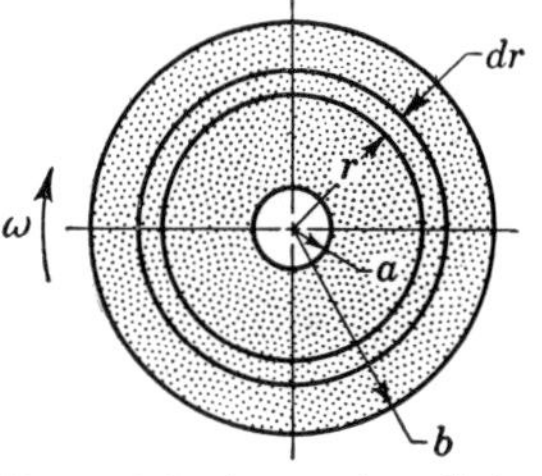

FIG. 14-9. A rotating disk.

We shall use a disk of unit thickness rotating at a velocity of ω radians per sec (Fig. 14-9). The disk has a radius b and a hole whose radius is a. Because of the inertia force, tangential and radial stresses will exist on any element of the disk. Adding the inertia force to Eq. (b), Sec. 14-2, we have

$$s_t - s_r - r\frac{ds_r}{dr} - \frac{\rho\omega^2r^2}{g} = 0 \tag{a}$$

where both the radial and tangential stresses are positive for tension and where ρ is the weight of the material per unit volume.

We must now relate these stresses to the elongation. The circumference of the circle at radius r is $2\pi r$, and so the total elongation of the circle is $2\pi r\epsilon_t$, where ϵ_t is the unit tangential elongation. The circle has expe-

[1] "ASME Handbook, Metals Engineering–Design," pp. 361–383, McGraw-Hill Book Company, Inc., New York, 1953.

rienced a total increase in radius Δr of

$$\Delta r = \frac{2\pi r \epsilon_t}{2\pi} = r\epsilon_t \tag{b}$$

The unit elongation in radius is $\epsilon_r = d(\Delta r)/dr$. To obtain ϵ_t in terms of ϵ_r, we differentiate Eq. (*b*). This gives

$$\epsilon_r = \frac{d(r\epsilon_t)}{dr} = r\frac{d\epsilon_t}{dr} + \epsilon_t$$

or

$$\epsilon_t - \epsilon_r + r\frac{d\epsilon_t}{dr} = 0 \tag{c}$$

The relations between the stresses and strains for two-dimensional strain are given by Eqs. (3-10) and (3-11) as

$$\epsilon_t = \frac{1}{E}(s_t - \mu s_r) \qquad \epsilon_r = \frac{1}{E}(s_r - \mu s_t) \tag{d}$$

where μ is Poisson's ratio. Substituting these values of the strains in Eq. (*c*) gives

$$\frac{1}{E}(s_t - \mu s_r) - \frac{1}{E}(s_r - \mu s_t) + \frac{r}{E}\frac{d}{dr}(s_t - \mu s_r) = 0 \tag{e}$$

A rearrangement of Eq. (*a*) gives

$$r\frac{ds_r}{dr} + s_r = s_t - \frac{\rho\omega^2 r^2}{g} \tag{f}$$

Also, we note that

$$\frac{d(rs_r)}{dr} = r\frac{ds_r}{dr} + s_r \tag{g}$$

so that, from Eq. (*f*),

$$\frac{d(rs_r)}{dr} = s_t - \frac{\rho\omega^2 r^2}{g}$$

or

$$s_t = \frac{d(rs_r)}{dr} + \frac{\rho\omega^2 r^2}{g} \tag{h}$$

We will now substitute the value of s_t in Eq. (*h*) into Eq. (*e*). This gives

$$\frac{1}{E}\frac{d(rs_r)}{dr} + \frac{\rho\omega^2 r^2}{gE} - \frac{\mu s_r}{E} - \frac{s_r}{E} + \frac{\mu}{E}\frac{d(rs_r)}{dr} + \frac{\mu}{E}\frac{\rho\omega^2 r^2}{g} + \frac{r}{E}\frac{d}{dr}\left[\frac{d}{dr}(rs_r) + \frac{\rho\omega^2 r^2}{g}\right] - \frac{r}{E}\frac{d(\mu s_r)}{dr} = 0 \tag{i}$$

When the indicated operations are performed and the resulting equation simplified, after multiplying through by r, we have

$$r^2\frac{d^2(rs_r)}{dr^2} + r\frac{d(rs_r)}{dr} - rs_r + (3 + \mu)\frac{\rho\omega^2 r^3}{g} = 0 \tag{j}$$

This is a second-order differential equation. The solution is

$$s_r = C_1 + \frac{C_2}{r^2} - \frac{3+\mu}{8}\frac{\rho\omega^2 r^2}{g} \tag{k}$$

which may be verified by substitution into Eq. (j). We can obtain the tangential stress by substituting the value of s_r from Eq. (k) into Eq. (f). This gives

$$s_t = C_1 - \frac{C_2}{r^2} - \frac{1+3\mu}{8}\frac{\rho\omega^2 r^2}{g} \tag{l}$$

The constants of integration, C_1 and C_2, may be evaluated from a consideration of the boundary conditions. At the two boundaries, $r = a$ and $r = b$, the radial stresses must be zero. Substituting both of these conditions in Eq. (k) and solving the two resulting equations for C_1 and C_2 give

$$C_1 = \frac{3+\mu}{8}\frac{\rho\omega^2}{g}(a^2+b^2) \tag{m}$$

$$C_2 = -\frac{3+\mu}{8}\frac{\rho\omega^2}{g}a^2b^2 \tag{n}$$

Substitution of these values into Eqs. (k) and (l) gives the general equations. They are

$$s_r = \frac{3+\mu}{8}\frac{\rho\omega^2}{g}\left(a^2+b^2-\frac{a^2b^2}{r^2}-r^2\right) \tag{14-20}$$

$$s_t = \frac{3+\mu}{8}\frac{\rho\omega^2}{g}\left(a^2+b^2+\frac{a^2b^2}{r^2}-\frac{1+3\mu}{3+\mu}r^2\right) \tag{14-21}$$

The maximum radial stress occurs at $r = \sqrt{ab}$. Its value is

$$s_{r,\max} = \frac{3+\mu}{8}\frac{\rho\omega^2(b-a)^2}{g} \tag{14-22}$$

The maximum tangential stress occurs at the inner boundary where $r = a$. Its value is

$$s_{t,\max} = \frac{3+\mu}{4}\frac{\rho\omega^2}{g}\left(b^2+\frac{1-\mu}{3+\mu}a^2\right) \tag{14-23}$$

Solid Disk. By expressing a new set of boundary conditions we can obtain the stresses in a solid disk. The second term of Eqs. (k) and (l) is C_2/r^2. This term must be zero; otherwise the stresses at the center of such a disk, where $r = 0$, would be infinite. Therefore $C_2 = 0$. The radial stress at the outer boundary, where $r = b$, must also be zero. Substitution of these conditions in Eq. (k) gives for C_1

$$C_1 = \frac{3+\mu}{8}\frac{\rho\omega^2 b^2}{g} \tag{o}$$

When this value of C_1 is substituted into Eqs. (k) and (l), the stresses are found to be

$$s_r = \frac{3 + \mu}{8} \frac{\rho \omega^2}{g} (b^2 - r^2) \tag{14-24}$$

$$s_t = \frac{3 + \mu}{8} \frac{\rho \omega^2}{g} \left(b^2 - \frac{1 + 3\mu}{3 + \mu} r^2 \right) \tag{14-25}$$

The maximum values are at the center, where $r = 0$, and are equal to each other. Thus

$$s_{r,\max} = s_{t,\max} = \frac{3 + \mu}{8} \frac{\rho \omega^2 b^2}{g} \tag{14-26}$$

Problems are frequently encountered in which additional forces operate on the disks. For example, a centrifugal pull might exist at the outer boundary, because of a heavy rim or gear teeth. The disk might be stressed at the inner boundary because of the method of joining it to the hub. In such cases these stresses may be calculated using the thick-walled cylinder theory (Sec. 14-2) and the results superposed upon the stresses given by the formulas above. When this is done, care must be taken with the signs of the quantities.

Assumptions. The assumptions used in the above derivations are:

1. There is no stress concentration.
2. The radius of the disk is large compared with the thickness.
3. The thickness of the disk is constant.
4. The stresses are constant over the thickness of the disk.

14-7. Flywheels. A flywheel is the mechanical filtering element in a circuit through which power is flowing. It serves to smooth, or equalize, the back-and-forth flow of energy through the mechanical circuit. It must, therefore, be able both to absorb and to deliver energy. In any power-transmission circuit two elements must exist. These two elements are the source of power and the "user" of power. The source may be an electric motor, internal-combustion engine, gas turbine, etc. The "user" is a machine for converting the power into something useful. The flywheel is a third element which is placed between the source and the machine and serves the important purpose of preventing the transmission of serious short-time energy disturbances, in either direction, between the two principal elements of the circuit.

One of three situations may exist. They are:

1. The source delivers power in irregular quantities.
2. The machine requires power in irregular quantities.
3. Both the power delivered by the source and that required by the machine are in irregular quantities.

An example of (1) would be an internal-combustion engine. An example of (2) would be a punch press. An internal-combustion engine driving a reciprocating pump or compressor would be a good example of (3).

A flywheel rotating at a certain angular velocity contains a definite amount of kinetic energy. From elementary kinetics, we know that this energy is given by the equation

$$U = \frac{W}{2g} v^2 \tag{a}$$

where U = kinetic energy, ft-lb
W = weight of rim, lb
v = mean linear velocity of rim, ft per sec
g = acceleration due to gravity, ft per sec per sec

Equation (a) shows that the only way we can change the energy content of the flywheel is by changing its velocity. In other words, if we want to store more energy we must make it speed up; if we want it to deliver some of its energy it must slow down. For this reason, a flywheel is not a device which runs at a constant speed, for if this were so there would be no interchange of energy. Accepting the fact that for a flywheel to store or deliver energy it must change its speed, we can set up a relation between the change in energy and the change in speed:

$$U_2 - U_1 = \frac{W}{2g} (v_2^2 - v_1^2) \tag{14-27}$$

which is obtained from Eq. (a) and where the subscripts 1 and 2 refer to the initial and final conditions, respectively.

It is customary in flywheel design to define a *coefficient of speed fluctuation* as follows:

$$C_s = \frac{v_2 - v_1}{v} \tag{14-28}$$

where

$$v = \frac{v_1 + v_2}{2} \tag{14-29}$$

so that v is the average velocity of the rim. Equation (14-27) may be factored to give

$$U_2 - U_1 = \frac{W}{2g} (v_2 - v_1)(v_2 + v_1) \tag{b}$$

Since $v_2 - v_1 = C_s v$ and $v_2 + v_1 = 2v$, we have

$$U_2 - U_1 = \frac{C_s W}{g} v^2 \tag{14-30}$$

Equation (14-30) permits us to select an appropriate value of C_s and then to solve for the weight W when the speed and the energy variation are known. Typical values of C_s are listed in Table 14-3.

TABLE 14-3. TYPICAL VALUES OF THE COEFFICIENT OF SPEED FLUCTUATION C_s

Driven machinery	C_s
Stamp mills, crushers, hammers	0.10 –0.20
Punch presses	0.05 –0.10
Pumps	0.03 –0.05
Weaving machinery, machine tools, paper mills	0.02 –0.03
Speed reducers, textile mills, flour mills	0.015–0.025
Spinning frames, twisters	0.010–0.020
Electrical machinery	0.002–0.010

The next step is to determine the maximum energy fluctuation to be handled by the flywheel. This value must be determined from the characteristics of the power source, from the driven machinery, or both.

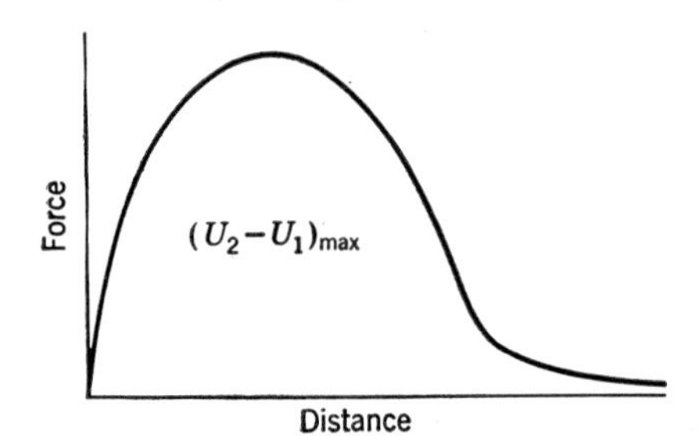

FIG. 14-10. The energy requirement of a punch press.

It is often necessary to plot a force-distance diagram for the power source or for the driven machine. Such a diagram for a punch press is illustrated in Fig. 14-10. Once such a diagram has been obtained, it may be integrated to obtain the maximum energy fluctuation. This integration may be performed graphically, using the method of Chap. 3; arithmetically; or with a planimeter. Such a diagram for a gas-engine power source is shown in Fig.

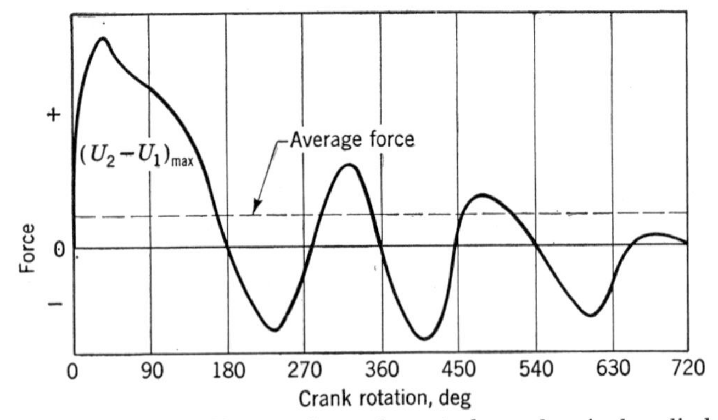

FIG. 14-11. Rotative-force diagram for a four-stroke-cycle, single-cylinder, single-acting, slow-speed engine. (*From Lester C. Lichty, "Internal Combustion Engines," 6th ed., p. 488, McGraw-Hill Book Company, Inc., New York,* 1951.)

14-11. This diagram was obtained from the design indicator card and a consideration of the inertia forces. If the engine has more than one cylinder, then curves for each cylinder are arranged in the proper position along the crank-rotation axis and added together. The maximum energy fluctuation would then be obtained from the composite curve.

In the case of a gas engine, the energy delivered by the shaft per revolution is

$$U = \frac{33{,}000 \text{ hp}}{n} \tag{14-31}$$

The equation

$$C_u = \frac{(U_2 - U_1)_{\max}}{U} \tag{14-32}$$

defines a *coefficient of energy fluctuation* which permits a tabulation of typical values without reference to the horsepower output or the speed. Lichty has determined the values of this coefficient for various engine types, making the determination of the maximum energy fluctuation possible without the tedious work which would be necessary in composing and integrating a force-distance diagram. These values are listed in Table 14-4.

TABLE 14-4. APPROXIMATE VALUES OF THE COEFFICIENT OF ENERGY FLUCTUATION C_u*

Type of engine (four-stroke cycle)	C_u
Single-cylinder	2.40
Two-cylinder, opposed 180° cranks	1.00
Three-cylinder, 120° cranks	0.70
Four-cylinder, 180° cranks	0.20
Six-cylinder, 120° cranks	0.05
Eight-cylinder, 90° cranks	0.06
12-cylinder V, 120° cranks	0.02
16-cylinder V, 90° cranks	0.01

* Lester C. Lichty, "Internal Combustion Engines," 6th ed,. p. 488, McGraw-Hill Book Company, Inc., New York, 1951.

Equation (14-32) may now be solved to give $(U_2 - U_1)_{\max} = C_u U$. Substituting this for $U_2 - U_1$ in Eq. (14-30) and solving for the weight, we obtain

$$W = \frac{C_u}{C_s} \frac{gU}{v^2} \tag{14-33}$$

Decisions. Some of the decisions which must usually be made in the design of a flywheel are as follows:

1. The material to be used. If cast iron is selected, some authorities say that the mean rim velocity should not exceed 6,000 fpm; otherwise the stresses due to centrifugal force may cause failure. This would also rule out cast iron if the occurrence of runaway speeds is a possibility.

2. The diameter. The diameter of the flywheel is usually governed by the amount of space it can occupy. The diameter can be reduced if some means of speeding up the flywheel can be found. Obviously, the largest possible diameter should generally be used because this reduces the weight.

3. Whether the weight of the hub and that of the arms or web are to be used in determining the total flywheel effect. Quite often they are neglected in order to simplify the calculation. The arms and hub, of course, do contribute something, but frequently the given data are less accurate than the effect of not making this assumption, and for this reason it is usually made.

4. The selection of the coefficient of speed fluctuation. Even though values of this factor are given in Table 14-3, the designer must decide whether these values are proper for his application. He may, for example, find it necessary to express the maximum and minimum limiting speeds and use Eq. (14-27) instead.

5. Determination of the energy fluctuation. Ordinarily a number of assumptions must be made in order to obtain this result and they must be based upon the particular machine or application which is involved. The preceding discussion indicated that a choice of two methods is available in the design of a gas-engine flywheel. If the method chosen employs the coefficient of energy fluctuation, then the designer must decide whether to use the values listed in the table or some other value. For example, would the same coefficient be used for a single-cylinder lawn-mower engine as would be used for a single-cylinder marine engine?

6. The method of calculating the strength of the rim, the arms or web, and the hub of the flywheel. If the stresses are known to be low, these calculations need not be made. When they are made, it is necessary to decide upon a method of solution. Sections 14-2 and 14-6 suggest methods which could be used for designing the hub and web. However, these are not the only methods of solution. In designing the arms and the rim, the methods of Sec. 10-15 or Castigliano's theorem (Chap. 3), for example, could be used. In each case it is necessary for the designer to choose a method of attack which is appropriate to the conditions of the problem.

A flywheel, of course, is an extra element in a machine and adds to the final cost of the assembly. It should not always be taken for granted that a flywheel is needed; if some means can be found to reduce the energy fluctuation, then the need for the flywheel is also reduced. In other cases it is often possible that the function of the flywheel may be replaced by other rotating elements of the machine.

14-8. Hydraulic Machines. One of the first decisions which the designer is required to make in the design of a new machine is the method of transmitting power. Sometimes the use of hydraulic machines offers many advantages over other means of power transmission. The following list of characteristics of hydraulic power should assist the designer in making this decision:

1. Hydraulic power may be transmitted over long or short distances, around corners and curves, and into difficult or confined spaces.
2. Large forces may be applied at variable velocities with either long or short strokes.
3. Almost any force-time relationship may be obtained, and this may be repeated automatically for any period of time.
4. The velocity and position of a reciprocating member may be accurately controlled.
5. When several motions are involved they may be accurately synchronized.
6. Both light and heavy forces may be applied at very high velocities.
7. Completely automatic reversing drives may be obtained which will operate at either a constant speed or over a wide range of speeds.
8. The speed, direction of rotation, and acceleration may be accurately controlled at remote distances.
9. Several rotating elements may be closely synchronized.
10. Either constant-speed output or constant-horsepower output may be obtained.

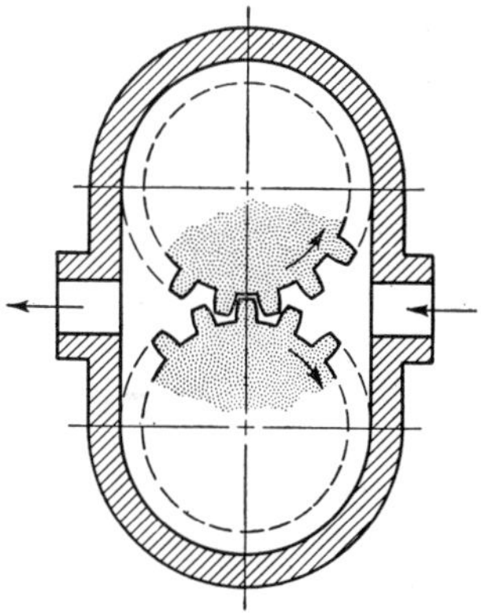

FIG. 14-12. Schematic drawing of a gear pump.

If hydraulic power is selected as the means of transmission, the designer's job is usually to design the circuit to be used and then to select from manufacturers' catalogues the various elements making up this circuit.[1] We shall briefly discuss the various hydraulic elements first and then show how these elements are assembled in order to accomplish various purposes.

Pumps. Three types of rotary pumps are used for the generation of hydraulic power. They are *gear pumps*, *vane pumps*, and *plunger pumps*.

Figure 14-12 shows the operating principle of a gear pump. Two gears, closely fitted to each other and to the housing, carry the oil around the periphery of the gears to the discharge side of the pump. The teeth occupy most of the space between the gears, and so the oil is prevented from returning.

[1] The design of the individual hydraulic elements will not be considered in this book. The principles already studied are basic to their design, and the engineer should have no difficulty in applying them to hydraulic machine parts.

Typical performance curves for a gear pump are illustrated in Fig. 14-13. These curves were obtained for a discharge pressure of 1,000 psi. The volumetric efficiency is defined as

$$e = \frac{Q_o}{Q_g} \tag{14-34}$$

where Q_o is the net output in gallons per minute and Q_g is the theoretical or geometrical output. The efficiency should be 100 per cent at zero pressure. Gear pumps are, of course, constant-displacement pumps. The mechanical efficiency ranges from about 80 to 90 per cent, depending upon the pressure used.

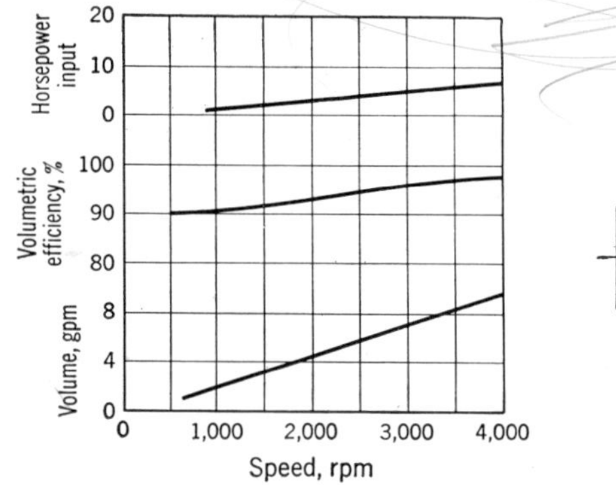

FIG. 14-13. Typical performance curves for a gear pump. *(Courtesy of Pesco Products Division, Borg-Warner Corporation.)*

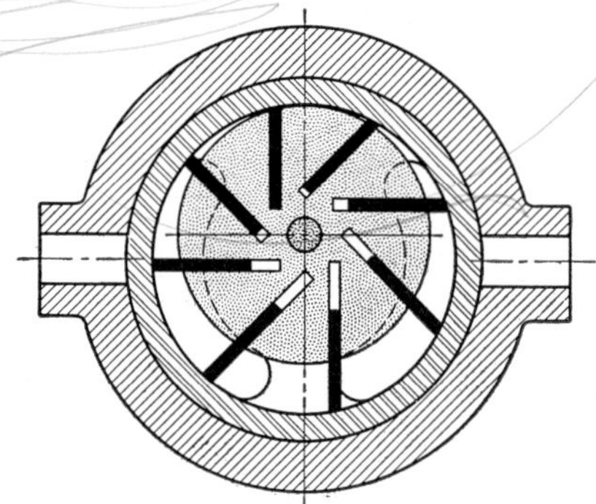

FIG. 14-14. Schematic drawing of a vane pump.

The vane pump is shown in Fig. 14-14. The pump has a rotor, mounted eccentrically with respect to the housing, which is fitted closely between the end plates. Vanes, which are mounted in rotor slots, slide against a hardened steel track on the periphery of the housing when the rotor turns. Because of the eccentrically mounted rotor, a large space for conveying oil exists on one side, while only a clearance exists on the other. The oil is thus forced to travel in a single direction.

Vane pumps are probably more versatile than gear pumps because they can be made in either the constant- or variable-delivery type. They also handle large volumes of oil in a small space. Typical performance curves at 1,200 rpm are illustrated in Fig. 14-15.

Vane pumps are made in sizes ranging up to about 60-gpm output. The speeds usually employed vary from about 1,000 to 1,800 rpm, depending upon the size. The maximum pressure used is customarily about 1,000 psi, although high-pressure models that will function well at pressures of up to 2,000 psi are available.

Vane pumps are frequently used in combinations of two units to secure certain effects. For example, it may be desirable to advance a hydraulic ram rapidly at a moderate pressure and then to follow up this action with a slow-speed force at very high pressure. This can be done by using two units in parallel, each having different capacities. The large-volume pump is used first, at a moderate pressure, and this action is followed by the use of the small-volume pump which brings the pressure up to a maximum value. Pump units may also be operated in a series-parallel combination. With this combination both pumps would operate in parallel to, say, 1,000 psi and would thus handle a large volume. At 1,000 psi a

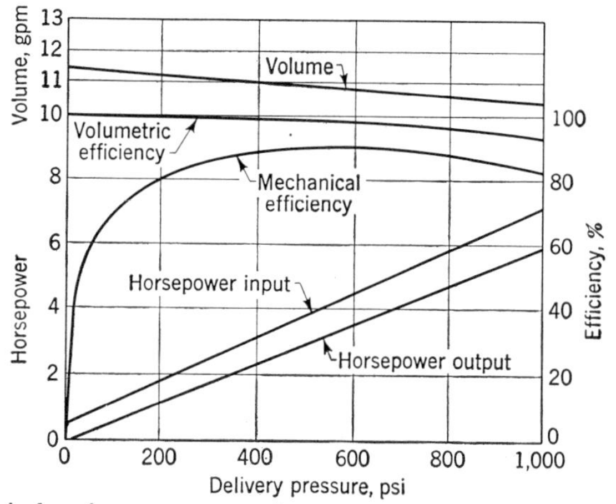

FIG. 14-15. Typical performance curves for a vane pump. (*Courtesy of Vickers, Inc.*)

valve would automatically shift them over to a series operation where they would operate at reduced volume but at pressures up to 2,000 psi.

Figure 14-16 is a schematic drawing which illustrates the principle of operation of a radial plunger pump. The pump shown has eight cylinders arranged radially in a cylindrical rotor A. The rotor turns on a central valve spindle which contains the inlet and discharge passages. The rotor is in an eccentric relation with respect to the reaction piece B so that the rotation forces the plungers to reciprocate in their cylinders. In the drawing, for clockwise rotation, the plungers in the upper half are moving away from the center, thus pulling oil up into the cylinders. The plungers in the lower half of the rotor are moving inwardly and discharging the oil into the exhaust side.

The reaction piece B is arranged in the frame C so that it can be shifted, by means of a projecting lever, either to the right or to the left. The rotor A is fixed in position with respect to the frame C. The drawing shows the reaction piece shifted to the extreme right. If now, the reaction piece is shifted to the left, the eccentricity is reduced, which reduces the flow. If it is shifted farther to the left, the centers coincide and the eccentricity and consequently the flow become zero. By shifting the reaction piece still farther to the left, the eccentricity is increased in the opposite direction, causing the flow to be reversed.

We see, then, that not only can the delivery of this pump be accurately controlled, and even reversed, but that it can be done without reversing the direction of rotation and while the rotor continues to turn. In addition to these advantages, the pumps can handle very high pressures. A

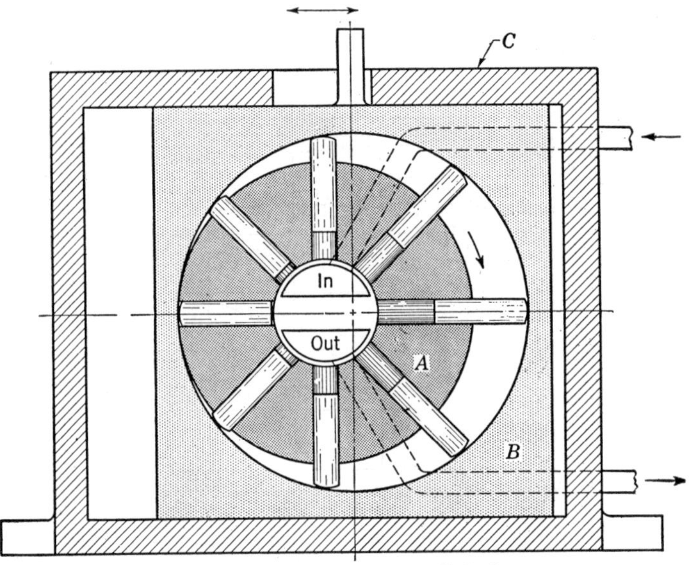

FIG. 14-16. Schematic drawing of a radial plunger pump.

pressure of 3,000 psi is not unusual. They are commonly used in heavy-duty equipment, such as steel-mill machinery, and also where accurate control is required, such as in machine-tool equipment.

The volumetric efficiency of plunger pumps usually ranges from about 85 to 95 per cent. The mechanical efficiency is quite good, varying from 90 to 95 per cent.

Rotary Motors. Theoretically, at least, a hydraulic pump may be used as a motor, but, practically, some design modifications are necessary in order to make it operate efficiently. Rotary hydraulic motors are not used to a great extent, because of the convenience and economy of electric motors. The principal advantages of a rotary hydraulic motor are, first, that it will pack the greatest amount of horsepower into the smallest space with the least weight and, second, that, when a motor and a pump are combined as a single package to form a hydraulic transmission unit, it becomes an extremely versatile combination useful over a wide range of speeds and providing very fine adjustments of the speeds.

Hydraulic Cylinders. The most frequently used application of hydraulic power is the hydraulic cylinder, sometimes called a *reciprocating motor.* A typical cylinder is shown in Fig. 14-17. Hydraulic cylinders are made either single-acting or double-acting in diameters from a fraction of an inch up. For cylinder bores 8 in. and smaller it is customary to manufacture standardized ends and then to cut the piston rods and cylinder sleeves to match the stroke. There is no limit to the length of stroke except column action of the piston rod. The cylinders may be obtained with cushions to permit deceleration at the ends of the stroke.

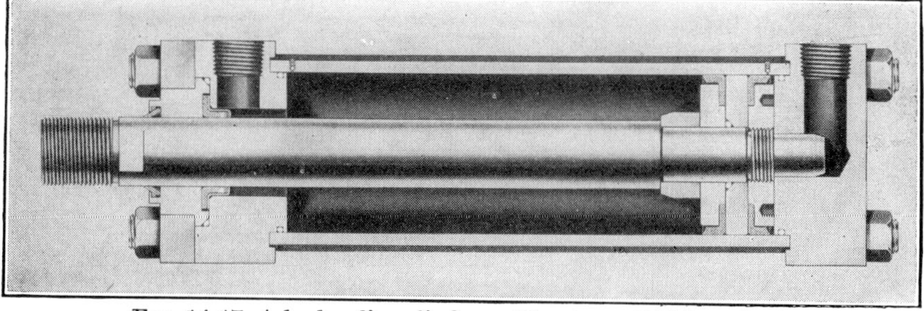

FIG. 14-17. A hydraulic cylinder. (*Courtesy of Vickers, Inc.*)

Hydraulic Piping. It is customary to use steel pipe or seamless steel tubing for interconnecting hydraulic components. The piping should be firmly anchored in order to prevent deflection due to the inertia of the moving oil. Table 14-5 gives the internal diameters, areas, and safe working pressures (factor of safety of 6) for pipe and tubing.

The pipe size may be determined from the formula

$$A = \frac{0.3208q}{V} \tag{14-35}$$

where A = internal area of pipe, in.^{2}
q = maximum flow, gpm
V = velocity of oil, ft per sec

A velocity of from 2 to 4 ft per sec is recommended for intake or suction lines. Higher velocities are usually used for pressure lines. It is suggested that a velocity of from 7 to 15 ft per sec be selected.

Hydraulic Controls. There are an almost infinite number of means available for controlling the action of hydraulic systems. Space limitations make it necessary that we mention only a few of the principal types. The designer of hydraulic systems will, of course, have available a number of manufacturers' publications from which he can select the type of control needed.

A large group of valves may be classified as *pressure controls.* These include pressure-relief valves; back-pressure valves, which are somewhat

Table 14-5. Internal Diameters, Areas, and Safe Working Pressures (Factor of Safety = 6) for Pipe and Tubing*

Specification	Quantity	Nominal pipe size or outside diameter of tubing							
		½	⅝	¾	⅞	1	1¼	1½	2
Standard weight pipe	Diameter, in.	0.62	...	0.82	...	1.05	1.38	1.61	2.07
	Area, $in.^2$	0.304	...	0.533	...	0.864	1.495	2.036	3.355
	Pressure, psi	1,731	...	1,434	...	1,348	1,124	1,017	864
Extra-strong pipe	Diameter, in.	0.546	...	0.742	...	0.957	1.278	1.500	1.939
	Area, $in.^2$	0.234	...	0.433	...	0.719	1.283	1.767	2.953
	Pressure, psi	2,333	...	1,955	...	1,815	1,533	1,403	1,223
Double extra-strong pipe	Diameter, in.	0.252	...	0.434	...	0.599	0.896	1.100	1.939
	Area, $in.^2$	0.050	...	0.148	...	0.282	0.630	0.950	1.774
	Pressure, psi	4,667	...	3,911	...	3,629	3,068	2,807	2,650
0.035 wall tubing	Diameter, in.	0.430	0.555	0.680	0.805	0.930	1.180	1.430	1.930
	Area, $in.^2$	0.145	0.241	0.363	0.508	0.679	1.093	1.606	2.925
	Pressure, psi	1,120	895	750	640	560	450	370	275
0.065 wall tubing	Diameter, in.	0.370	0.495	0.620	0.745	0.870	1.120	1.370	1.870
	Area, $in.^2$	0.107	0.192	0.301	0.435	0.594	0.985	1.474	2.746
	Pressure, psi	2,080	1,670	1,390	1,180	1,040	830	695	520
0.080 wall tubing	Diameter, in.	0.340	0.465	0.590	0.715	0.840	1.090	1.340	1.840
	Area, $in.^2$	0.090	0.169	0.273	0.401	0.554	0.933	1.410	2.659
	Pressure, psi	2,560	2,050	1,700	1,460	1,280	1,030	855	640
0.095 wall tubing	Diameter, in.	0.310	0.435	0.560	0.685	0.810	1.060	1.310	1.810
	Area, $in.^2$	0.075	0.148	0.246	0.368	0.515	0.882	1.347	2.573
	Pressure, psi	3,040	2,430	2,030	1,740	1,530	1,210	1,020	760

* Courtesy of Vickers, Inc.

similar to check valves; and valves to obtain a particular sequence of operation, to unload or divide the load in a particular circuit, and to reduce the pressure. The valves in this class are usually spring-loaded in order to achieve the desired effect. In general, pressure controls are used to determine the pressure in any part of the circuit and sometimes to unload the pumps during a portion of the cycle.

A second group of valves are called *directional controls*. They may be operated manually, mechanically, hydraulically, or electrically. They are used to direct the flow of oil to particular portions of the hydraulic circuit and may be either two-, three-, or four-way types. Pilot valves are frequently used to operate these valves, by giving them a hydraulic assist, because sometimes the forces required for their operation may become quite large. Several controls may be embodied in a single unit in order to operate them with a single actuating element.

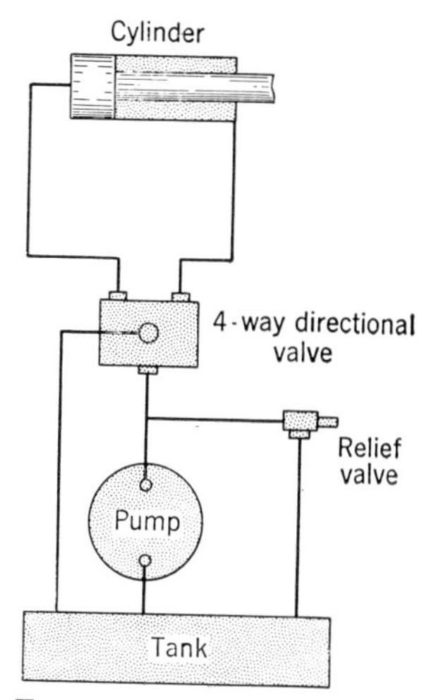

FIG. 14-18. An elementary hydraulic circuit. (*Reproduced from Walter Ernst, "Oil Hydraulic Power and Its Industrial Applications," p. 268, McGraw-Hill Book Company, Inc., New York, 1949, by permission of the author and publisher.*)

Volume controls include throttle valves, metering valves, and flow dividers. They are used with either constant- or variable-delivery-pump circuits. Frequently they are operated automatically in order to obtain several velocities in the hydraulic cycle of operation.

Hydraulic Circuits. Space limitations will not permit a complete discussion of hydraulic circuits. We shall, however, discuss the building of a circuit in four steps. This, together with the preceding discussion, should give an idea of the range of circuitry which is possible.

Figure 14-18 shows a circuit for operating a double-acting cylinder. The pump may be either a constant-delivery or a variable-delivery pump with a suitable control. The pump draws oil from a tank from which it may be directed either to a relief valve or to a four-way directional-control valve. The four-way valve may be controlled manually or automatically. The valve directs the flow of oil from the pump to either side of the cylinder. The oil discharged from the cylinder is directed back to the tank by the directional control.

Sometimes hydraulic cylinders are mounted vertically. In this case, provision must be made to hold the piston at any position, because the weight of the piston, piston rod, and attached equipment might otherwise be sufficient to cause gravity drop. It may be held at any position by employing a back-pressure valve, as shown in Fig. 14-19. This valve is adjusted slightly greater than the pressure required to hold the weight. With this arrangement, even if the directional valve is held in the neutral position, the piston will remain at any preset position.

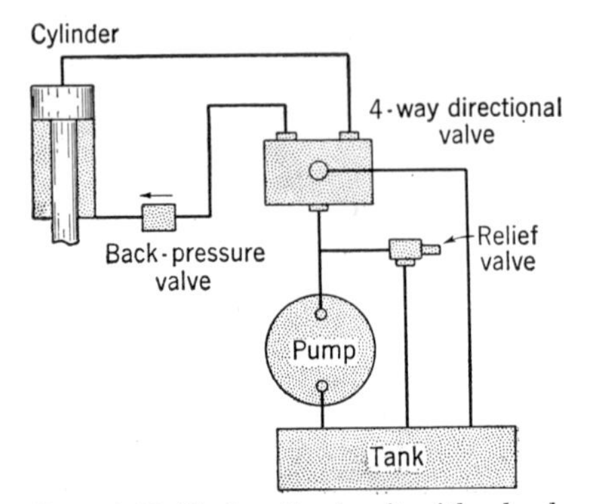

FIG. 14-19. Hydraulic circuit with a back-pressure valve. (*Reproduced from Walter Ernst, "Oil Hydraulic Power and Its Industrial Applications," p. 269, McGraw-Hill Book Company, Inc., New York, 1949, by permission of the author and publisher.*)

Figures 14-18 and 14-19 show that the area for retraction of the piston is smaller than the working area. This means that during retraction the amount of oil discharged from the head end is greater than the pump output. There are two solutions to this problem. One is to use larger piping for the head end. Since this might require very large pipe sizes, a better solution would be to install an unloading valve in the head end. This is shown in Fig. 14-20. The unloading valve is operated by a pilot line which amounts to a "hydraulic assist." This circuit makes it possible for retraction to take place at a high speed.

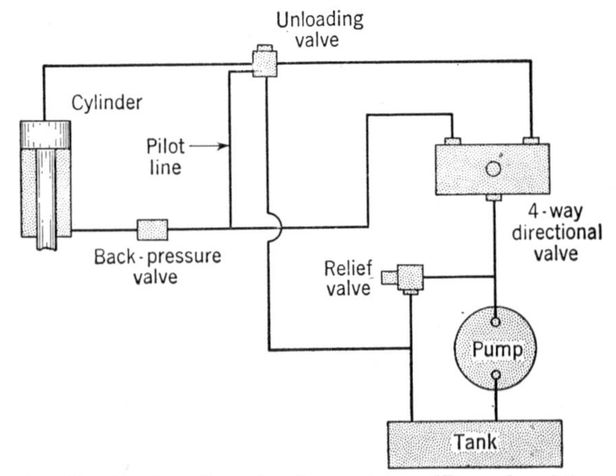

FIG. 14-20. Hydraulic circuit with unloading valve. (*Reproduced from Walter Ernst, "Oil Hydraulic Power and Its Industrial Applications," p. 269, McGraw-Hill Book Company, Inc., New York, 1949, by permission of the author and publisher.*)

In some cases it is desirable to cause the piston to advance at a high speed for a portion of the stroke and then to perform the balance of the work at a slow speed and high pressure. One method of accomplishing this is to use a large-capacity low-pressure pump for the rapid portion of the advance and a low-capacity high-pressure pump for the slow portion of the advance. Such an arrangement is illustrated in Fig. 14-21. An unloading valve and a check valve are inserted between the low-pressure pump and the directional valve. The pumps are in parallel. The check

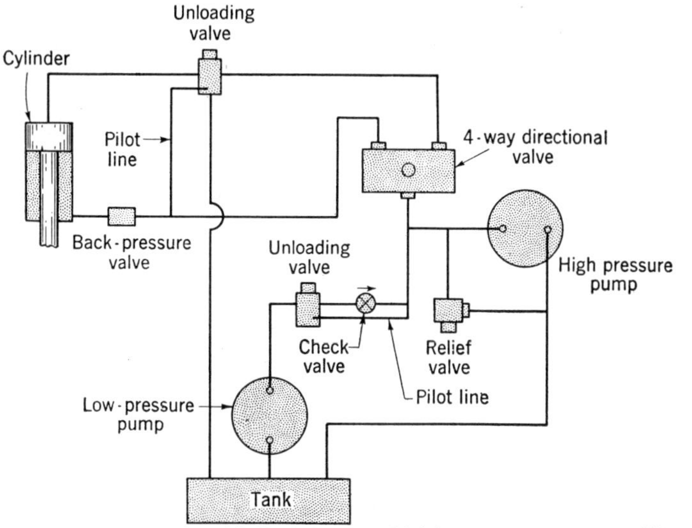

FIG. 14-21. Hydraulic circuit with both low- and high-pressure pumps. (*Reproduced from Walter Ernst, "Oil Hydraulic Power and Its Industrial Applications," p.* 270, *McGraw-Hill Book Company, Inc., New York,* 1949, *by permission of the author and publisher.*)

valve prevents the high-pressure pump from discharging through the low-pressure pump. When the pressure reaches the maximum value of the low pressure, a pilot line causes the unloading valve to open, and the full capacity of the low-pressure pump is delivered to the cylinder. The remaining portion of the circuit is the same as previously described.

BIBLIOGRAPHY

"ASME Handbook, Metals Engineering—Design," McGraw-Hill Book Company, Inc., New York, 1953.

Beitler, Samuel R., and E. J. Lindahl: "Hydraulic Machinery," Irwin-Farnham Publishing Company, Chicago, 1947.

Conway, H. G.: "Fluid Pressure Mechanisms," Pitman Publishing Corporation, New York, 1949.

Ernst, Walter: "Oil Hydraulic Power and Its Industrial Applications," McGraw-Hill Book Company, Inc., New York, 1949.

Roark, Raymond J.: "Formulas for Stress and Strain," 3d ed., McGraw-Hill Book Company, Inc., New York, 1954.

Seely, Fred B.: "Advanced Mechanics of Materials," John Wiley & Sons, Inc., New York, 1947.

Timoshenko, S.: "Strength of Materials," pt. II, D. Van Nostrand Company, Inc., New York, 1941.

PROBLEMS

14-1. A cylinder is 1 in. ID × 2 in. OD and is subjected to an internal pressure of 20,000 psi. Determine the tangential stress at the inner and outer surfaces.

14-2. Find the tangential stress at the inner and outer surfaces of the cylinder in Prob. 14-1 if the external pressure is 20,000 psi and the internal pressure is zero.

*__14-3.__ A steel tire 3/8 in. thick is to be shrunk over a cast-iron rim 16 in. in diameter and 1 in. thick. Calculate the inside diameter to which the tire must be bored in order to induce a tangential stress of 20,000 psi in the tire.

*__14-4.__ Determine the stress distribution in the assembly of Example 14-1 (Sec. 14-3) if it is subjected to an internal pressure of 5,000 psi.

14-5. Find the maximum stress in a 10-in. circular saw if it runs idle at 7,200 rpm. The saw is 14-gauge (0.0747-in.) and is used on a 3/4-in. arbor. (Assume the thickness is uniform.)

14-6. The maximum recommended speed for a 12-in. abrasive grinding wheel is 2,069 rpm. Assume the material is isotropic, use a bore of 1 in., $\mu = 0.24$, and a density of 0.12 lb per in.^{3}, and find the maximum tensile stress at this speed.

14-7. An abrasive cutoff wheel is 6 in. in diameter, 1/16 in. thick, and has a 1-in hole. It weighs 6 oz and is designed to run at 10,000 rpm. Assume the material is isotropic, $\mu = 0.20$, and determine the maximum stress at the design speed.

14-8. A flywheel has a mean rim diameter of 56 in. and varies in speed from 260 to 240 rpm. If the energy fluctuation is 5,000 ft-lb, find (*a*) the coefficient of speed fluctuation and (*b*) the weight of the rim.

14-9. A single-crank geared blanking press has a stroke of 8 in. and a rated capacity of 35 tons. The crankshaft has a speed of 90 rpm and is geared to the flywheel shaft at a 6:1 ratio. Use a frictional allowance of 16 per cent, and assume the full load is delivered during 15 per cent of the stroke. (*a*) Calculate the maximum energy fluctuation. (*b*) Find the rim weight for a mean rim diameter of 48 in. and a 10 per cent slowdown.

*__14-10.__ The following data apply to a stationary diesel engine: four cylinders, four-stroke cycle, 90 hp, 900 rpm. Using a mean rim diameter of 16 in., determine a satisfactory rim weight.

*__14-11.__ An Elgin outboard motor is two-stroke-cycle, 1.25-hp, single-cylinder, and runs at 4,000 rpm. Assume the propeller contributes 30 per cent of the necessary flywheel effect, that the mean diameter of the flywheel is 6 in., and that the shaft size is 3/4 in. Design the flywheel. Make a sketch showing all dimensions.

*__14-12.__ A diesel engine is 16-cylinder, 90° V, four-stroke-cycle, and delivers 1,600 hp at 800 rpm. The engine is to drive a d-c electric generator. The shaft diameter is 6 in. The mean flywheel diameter is 24 in. Make a complete design of the flywheel.

*__14-13.__ The following data apply to the hydraulic circuit of Fig. 14-18: cylinder, 4-in. bore, 16-in. stroke, 1½-in.-diameter piston rod; pressure, 1,000 psi; piston speed, 60 fpm both ways. Specify the pipe sizes and the capacity of the valves and pump. Find the hydraulic horsepower.

*__14-14.__ Repeat Prob. 14-13 for the circuit of Fig. 14-19.

*__14-15.__ The following data apply to the hydraulic circuit of Fig. 14-20: cylinder, 6-in. bore, 24-in. stroke, 2¼-in.-diameter piston rod; pressure, 1,000 psi; piston speed, 10 fpm advance, 60 fpm retract. Specify the pipe sizes, the valve capacity, and the capacity and horsepower of the pump required.

APPENDIX

TABLE A-1. PHYSICAL CONSTANTS OF MATERIALS*

Material	Modulus of elasticity E, psi	Modulus of rigidity G, psi	Poisson's ratio	Density lb per in.^{3}
Aluminum (all alloys)	10.3×10^6	3.8×10^6	0.334	0.098
Beryllium copper	18×10^6	7.0×10^6	0.285	0.297
Carbon steel	28.5×10^6	11×10^6	0.292	0.282
Cast iron, gray	14.5×10^6	6×10^6	0.211	0.260
Inconel	31.0×10^6	11×10^6	0.290	0.307
Magnesium	6.5×10^6	2.4×10^6	0.350	0.065
Molybdenum	48.0×10^6	17×10^6	0.307	0.368
Monel metal	26.0×10^6	9.5×10^6	0.320	0.319
Nickel silver	18.5×10^6	7.0×10^6	0.322	0.316
Nickel steel	28.5×10^6	11×10^6	0.291	0.280
Phosphor bronze	16.1×10^6	6.0×10^6	0.349	0.295
Stainless steel (18-8)	27.6×10^6	10.6×10^6	0.305	0.280
Titanium (pure)	15.0×10^6	....	.....	0.162

* The values given are the average values and depend upon the method of processing and the alloying elements.

Table A-2. Shear, Moment, and Deflection Formulas for Beams*

Loading, support, and reference number	Reactions R_1 and R_2, vertical shear V	Bending moment M, maximum bending moment	Deflection y and maximum deflection
1. Cantilever, end load 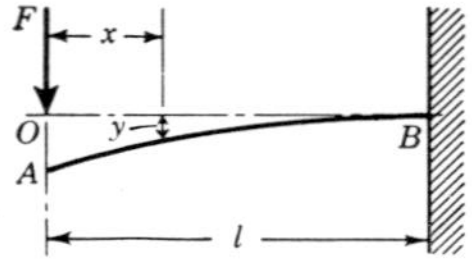 F, x, y, O, A, B, l	$R_2 = +F$ $V = -F$	$M = -Fx$ Max $M = -Fl$ at B	$y = -\frac{1}{6}\frac{F}{EI}(x^3 - 3l^2x + 2l^3)$ Max $y = -\frac{1}{3}\frac{Fl^3}{EI}$ at A
2. Cantilever, intermediate load 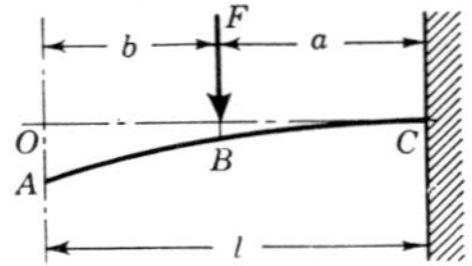 b, F, a, O, A, B, C, l	$R_2 = +F$ A to B: $V = 0$ B to C: $V = -F$	A to B: $M = 0$ B to C: $M = -F(x - b)$ Max $M = -Fa$ at C	A to B: $y = -\frac{1}{6}\frac{F}{EI}(-a^3 + 3a^2l - 3a^2x)$ B to C: $y = -\frac{1}{6}\frac{F}{EI}[(x - b)^3 - 3a^2(x - b) + 2a^3]$ Max $y = -\frac{1}{6}\frac{F}{EI}(3a^2l - a^3)$
3. Cantilever, uniform load 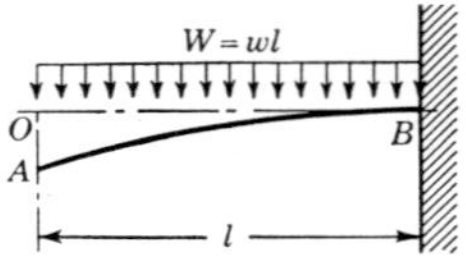 W = wl, O, A, B, l	$R_2 = +W$ $V = -\frac{W}{l}x$	$M = -\frac{1}{2}\frac{W}{l}x^2$ Max $M = -\frac{1}{2}Wl$ at B	$y = -\frac{1}{24}\frac{W}{EIl}(x^4 - 4l^3x + 3l^4)$ Max $y = -\frac{1}{8}\frac{Wl^3}{EI}$
4 End supports, center load 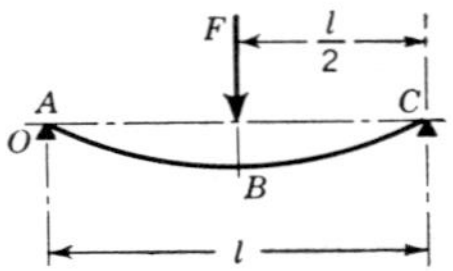 F, l/2, A, O, B, C, l	$R_1 = +\frac{1}{2}F$ $R_2 = +\frac{1}{2}F$ A to B: $V = +\frac{1}{2}F$ B to C: $V = -\frac{1}{2}F$	A to B: $M = +\frac{1}{2}Fx$ B to C: $M = +\frac{1}{2}F(l - x)$ Max $M = +\frac{1}{4}Fl$ at B	A to B: $y = -\frac{1}{48}\frac{F}{EI}(3l^2x - 4x^3)$ Max $y = -\frac{1}{48}\frac{Fl^3}{EI}$ at B

Loading	Reactions and shear	Bending moment	Deflection
5. End supports, intermediate load 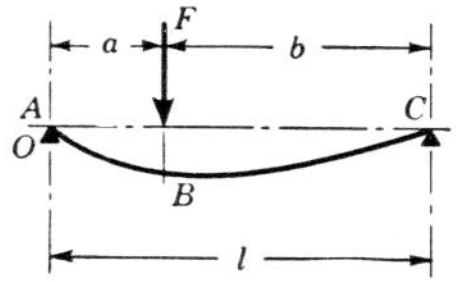	$R_1 = +F\frac{b}{l}$ $R_2 = +F\frac{a}{l}$ A to B: $V = +F\frac{b}{l}$ B to C: $V = -F\frac{a}{l}$	A to B: $M = +F\frac{b}{l}x$ B to C: $M = +F\frac{a}{l}(l - x)$ Max $M = +F\frac{ab}{l}$ at B	A to B: $y = -\frac{Fbx}{6EIl}[2l(l - x) - b^2 - (l - x)^2]$ B to C: $y = -\frac{Fa(l - x)}{6EIl}[2lb - b^2 - (l - x)^2]$ Max $y = -\frac{Fab}{27EIl}(a + 2b)\sqrt{3a(a + 2b)}$ at $x = \sqrt{\frac{1}{3}a(a + 2b)}$ when $a > b$
6. End supports, uniform load 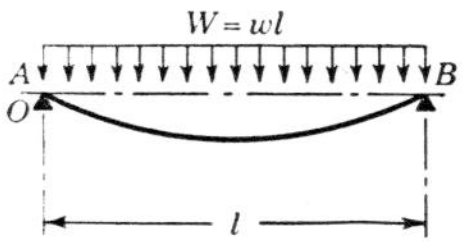	$R_1 = +\frac{1}{2}W$ $R_2 = +\frac{1}{2}W$ $V = \frac{1}{2}W\left(1 - \frac{2x}{l}\right)$	$M = \frac{1}{2}W\left(x - \frac{x^2}{l}\right)$ Max $M = +\frac{1}{8}Wl$ at $x = \frac{1}{2}l$	$y = -\frac{1}{24}\frac{Wx}{EIl}(l^3 - 2lx^2 + x^3)$ Max $y = -\frac{5}{384}\frac{Wl^3}{EI}$ at $x = \frac{1}{2}l$
7. One end fixed, one end supported, center load 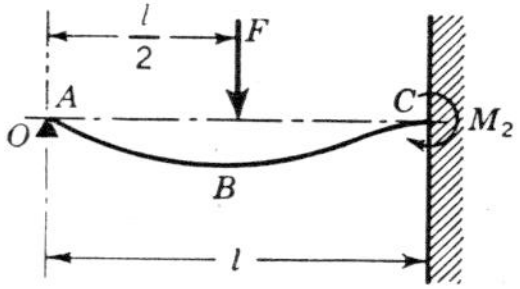	$R_1 = \frac{5}{16}F$ $R_2 = \frac{11}{16}F$ $M_2 = \frac{3}{16}Fl$ A to B: $V = +\frac{5}{16}F$ B to C: $V = -\frac{11}{16}F$	A to B: $M = \frac{5}{16}Fx$ B to C: $M = F(\frac{1}{2}l - \frac{11}{16}x)$ Max $+ M = \frac{5}{32}Fl$ at B Max $- M = -\frac{3}{16}Fl$ at C	A to B: $y = \frac{1}{96}\frac{F}{EI}(5x^3 - 3l^2x)$ B to C: $y = \frac{1}{96}\frac{F}{EI}\left[5x^3 - 16\left(x - \frac{l}{2}\right)^3 - 3l^2x\right]$ Max $y = -0.00932\frac{Fl^3}{EI}$ at $x = 0.4472l$
8. One end fixed, one end supported, uniform load 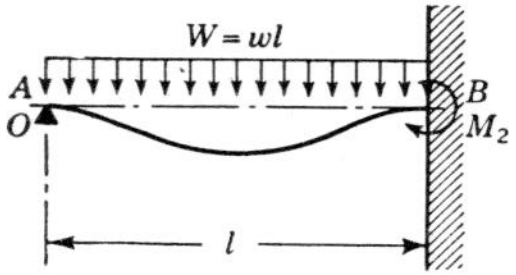	$R_1 = \frac{3}{8}W$ $R_2 = \frac{5}{8}W$ $M_2 = \frac{1}{8}Wl$ $V = W\left(\frac{3}{8} - \frac{x}{l}\right)$	$M = W\left(\frac{3}{8}x - \frac{1}{2}\frac{x^2}{l}\right)$ Max $+ M = \frac{9}{128}Wl$ at $x = \frac{3}{8}l$ Max $- M = -\frac{1}{8}Wl$ at B	$y = \frac{1}{48}\frac{W}{EIl}(3lx^3 - 2x^4 - l^3x)$ Max $y = -0.0054\frac{Wl^3}{EI}$ at $x = 0.4215l$

TABLE A-2. SHEAR, MOMENT, AND DEFLECTION FORMULAS FOR BEAMS* (*Continued*)

Loading, support, and reference number	Reactions R_1 and R_2, vertical shear V	Bending moment M, maximum bending moment	Deflection y and maximum deflection
9. Both ends fixed, center load $\frac{l}{2}$, F, M_1, O, A, B, C, M_2, l	$R_1 = \frac{1}{2}F \qquad R_2 = \frac{1}{2}F$ $M_1 = \frac{1}{8}Fl \qquad M_2 = \frac{1}{8}Fl$ A to B: $V = +\frac{1}{2}F$ B to C: $V = -\frac{1}{2}F$	A to B: $M = \frac{1}{8}F(4x - l)$ B to C: $M = \frac{1}{8}F(3l - 4x)$ Max $+ M = \frac{1}{8}Fl$ at B Max $- M = -\frac{1}{8}Fl$ at A and C	A to B: $y = -\frac{1}{48}\frac{F}{EI}(3lx^2 - 4x^3)$ Max $y = -\frac{1}{192}\frac{Fl^3}{EI}$ at B
10. Both ends fixed, intermediate load a, b, F, M_1, O, A, B, C, M_2, l	$R_1 = \frac{Fb^2}{l^3}(3a + b)$ $R_2 = \frac{Fa^2}{l^3}(3b - a)$ $M_1 = F\frac{ab^2}{l^2} \qquad M_2 = F\frac{a^2b}{l^2}$ A to B: $V = R_1$ B to C: $V = R_1 - F$	A to B: $M = -F\frac{ab^2}{l^2} + R_1x$ B to C: $M = -F\frac{ab^2}{l^2} + R_1x - F(x - a)$ Max $+ M = -F\frac{ab^2}{l^2} + R_1a$ at B Max $- M = -M_1$ when $a < b$ Max $- M = -M_2$ when $a > b$	A to B: $y = \frac{1}{6}\frac{Fb^2x^2}{EIl^3}(3ax + bx - 3al)$ B to C: $y = \frac{1}{6}\frac{Fa^2(l - x)^2}{EIl^3}[(3b + a)(l - x) - 3bl]$ Max $y = -\frac{2}{3}\frac{F}{EI}\frac{a^3b^2}{(3a + b)^2}$ at $x = \frac{2al}{3a + b}$ if $a > b$ Max $y = -\frac{2}{3}\frac{F}{EI}\frac{a^2b^3}{(3b + a)^2}$ at $x = l - \frac{2bl}{3b + a}$ if $a < b$
11. Both ends fixed, uniform load $W = wl$, M_1, O, A, B, M_2, l	$R_1 = \frac{1}{2}W \qquad R_2 = \frac{1}{2}W$ $M_1 = \frac{1}{12}Wl \qquad M_2 = \frac{1}{12}Wl$ $V = \frac{1}{2}W\left(1 - \frac{2x}{l}\right)$	$M = \frac{1}{2}W\left(x - \frac{x^2}{l} - \frac{1}{6}l\right)$ Max $+ M = \frac{1}{24}Wl$ at $x = \frac{1}{2}l$ Max $- M = -\frac{1}{12}Wl$ at A and B	$y = \frac{1}{24}\frac{Wx^2}{EIl}(2lx - l^2 - x^2)$ Max $y = -\frac{1}{384}\frac{Wl^3}{EI}$ at $x = \frac{1}{2}l$

* By permission from Raymond J. Roark, "Formulas for Stress and Strain," 3d ed., pp. 100–108, McGraw-Hill Book Company, Inc., New York, 1954.

TABLE A-3. TENSILE PROPERTIES OF MATERIALS*

Material	Size	Condition	Yield strength, kpsi	Tensile strength, kpsi	Elongation in 2 in., %	Reduction area, %	Brinell hardness, Bhn
Low-carbon steel	1-in. round	Hot-rolled	46	63	38	62	126
		Cold-drawn	65	77	20	60	156
AISI C1015 steel	1-in. round	Hot-rolled	45.5	61	39	61	126
		Cold-drawn	62	74	24	57	143
AISI C1018 steel	1-in. round	Hot-rolled	48	69	38	62	143
		Cold-drawn	70	82	20	57	163
		Casehardened (core properties)	56	92	27	48	197
AISI C1019 steel	1-in. round	Hot-rolled	51	71	37	60	149
		Cold-drawn	72	84	20	56	170
AISI C1020 steel	1-in. round	Hot-rolled	43	65	36	59	143
	1-in. round	Cold-drawn	66	78	20	55	156
	1 1/16-in. round	Annealed	41	62	40	69	112
	5/8-in. round	Cold-drawn	80	85	17	60	156
	2-in. round	Cold-drawn	79	80	14	50	163
AISI B1112 steel	1-in. round	Cold-drawn	71	82.5	15	43	170
AISI B1113 steel	1-in. round	Cold-drawn	72	83.5	14	40	170
AISI C1117 steel	1-in. round	Hot-rolled	44.3	70.6	33	63	137
		Cold-drawn	66	78	20	55	156
AISI C1213 steel	1-in. round	Cold-drawn	68	76	18	53	156
Rycase steel	1-in. round	Hot-rolled	44.3	70.6	33	63	137
		Cold-drawn	74	84	21	52	170
		Casehardened (core properties)	59.3	96.5	23	53	192
AISI C1035 steel	1-in. round	Hot-rolled	54	85	30	53	183
		Cold-drawn	79	92	25	50	201

Table A-3. Tensile Properties of Materials* (*Continued*)

Material	Size	Condition	Yield strength, kpsi	Tensile strength, kpsi	Elongation in 2 in., %	Reduction area, %	Brinell hardness, Bhn
AISI C1035 steel	1-in. round	Drawn 800°F	81	110	18	51	220
		Drawn 1000°F	72	103	23	59	201
		Drawn 1200°F	62	91	27	66	180
AISI C1040 steel	1-in. round	Hot-rolled	58	91	27	50	201
		Cold-drawn	88	100	17	42	207
		Drawn 1000°F	86	113	23	62	235
AISI C1042 steel	1-in. round	Hot-rolled	59	93	26	50	201
		Cold-drawn	89	102	16	40	207
		Drawn 1000°F	90	116	22	60	235
AISI C1045 steel	1-in. round	Hot-rolled	59	98	24	45	212
		Cold-drawn	90	103	14	40	217
		Drawn 600°F	114	149	8	33	312
		Drawn 800°F	104	145	14	44	290
	2-in. round	Drawn 800°F	66	108	15	45	216
	4-in. round	Drawn 800°F	63	102	16	46	200
	6-in. round	Drawn 800°F	63	102	16	46	200
	1-in. round	Drawn 1000°F	89	120	19	52	240
	1-in. round	Drawn 1200°F	73	104	24	60	208
AISI C1095 steel	1-in. round	Hot-rolled	83	142	8	18	293
		Drawn 800°F	138	200	12	37	388
AISI C1137 steel	1-in. round	Hot-rolled	57	92	27	61	192
		Cold-drawn	90	105	15	38	207
		Drawn 1000°F	88	112	21	56	255
AISI C1141 steel	1-in. round	Hot-rolled	59	97	25	52	201
		Cold-drawn	93	110	14	40	223
		Drawn 1000°F	100	126	19	54	277

Rytense AA steel	1-in. round	Hot-rolled	60	97	25	51	201
		Cold-drawn	93	110	14	40	223
AISI 2015 steel	1 3/16-in. round	Hot-rolled	44	64	34	66	130
	0.762-in. round	Cold-drawn	79.6	84.3	17	60	168
AISI 2317 steel	1-in. round	Hot-rolled	56	85	29	60	163
		Cold-drawn	75	95	25	58	197
		Casehardened (core properties)	107	137	22	52	285
AISI 2320 steel	1 1/16-in. round	Hot-rolled	62.9	93.6	23	44	170
	1 11/32-in. round	Hot-rolled	63	86	27	65	183
	1 9/16-in. round	Hot-rolled	57.3	80.4	29	61	163
	5/8-in. round	Cold-drawn	114	120	13	50	220
	1 9/32-in. round	Cold-drawn	99.8	104	15	57	223
	1 1/2-in. round	Cold-drawn	91.4	97	16	55	207
AISI 2330 steel	1-in. round	Hot-rolled	68	105	21	50	207
		Cold-drawn	119	124	12	43	223
		Drawn 400°F	195	221	11	40	425
		Drawn 600°F	171	196	14	49	382
		Drawn 800°F	131	160	18	56	327
		Drawn 1000°F	97	127	23	61	268
		Drawn 1200°F	70	108	27	64	222
AISI 2340 steel	1-in. round	Drawn 800°F	164	178	23	53	368
AISI 2345 steel	1-in. round	Drawn 800°F	177	188	20	51	388
AISI 2350 steel	1-in. round	Drawn 800°F	180	194	17	50	402
AISI 3115 steel	1-in. round	Hot-rolled	60	76	32	69	156
		Cold-drawn	78.3	87	25	62	163
AISI 3120 steel	1-in. round	Drawn 600°F	145	162	12	45	320
		Drawn 1000°F	91	112	22	68	222
AISI 3130 steel	1-in. round	Drawn 600°F	178	210	10	37	404
		Drawn 1000°F	120	137	20	62	276

TABLE A-3. TENSILE PROPERTIES OF MATERIALS* (*Continued*)

Material	Size	Condition	Yield strength, kpsi	Tensile strength, kpsi	Elongation in 2 in., %	Reduction area, %	Brinell hardness, Bhn
AISI 3140 steel	1-in. round	Hot-rolled, annealed	64	96	26	56	197
		Cold-drawn	91.3	104	17	48	212
	½-in. round	Drawn 800°F	162	194	14	52	400
	1-in. round	Drawn 800°F	157	188	15	50	376
	2-in. round	Drawn 800°F	128	147	15	47	296
	4-in. round	Drawn 800°F	106	136	16	45	276
	½-in. round	Drawn 1200°F	97	115	20	64	236
	4-in. round	Drawn 1200°F	69	100	25	60	196
AISI 3145 steel	1-in. round	Drawn 800°F	164	195	12	47	380
AISI 3150 steel	1-in. round	Drawn 800°F	171	202	12	44	396
AISI 3240 steel	1-in. round	Drawn 600°F	211	237	10	40	466
AISI 3250 steel	1-in. round	Drawn 600°F	214	243	9	37	477
AISI 3340 steel	1-in. round	Drawn 800°F	183	211	13	47	394
AISI 3435 steel	1-in. round	Drawn 800°F	160	184	15	55	362
AISI 4130 steel	1-in. round	Hot-rolled and annealed	60	90	30	45	183
	1-in. round	Cold-drawn and annealed	87	98	21	52	201
	1-in. round	Drawn 1000°F	133	146	17	60	293
	¼-in. sheet	Drawn 1000°F	138	152	12	...	302
AISI 4140 steel	1-in. round	Hot-rolled and annealed	63	90	27	58	187
	1-in. round	Cold-drawn	90	102	18	50	223
	1-in. round	Drawn 1000°F	131	153	16	45	302
AISI TS4140 steel	1-in. round	Drawn 1000°F	133	158	16	43	311
AISI 4340 steel	1-in. round	Hot-rolled and annealed	69	101	21	45	207
	1-in. round	Cold-drawn	99	111	16	42	223
	1-in. round	Drawn 600°F	234	260	12	43	498
	1-in. round	Drawn 1000°F	160	187	15	57	377

AISI 4620 steel	1-in. round	Drawn 800°F	94	130	23	66	256
AISI 4640 steel	1-in. round	Drawn 800°F	170	187	13	54	378
AISI 4650 steel	1-in. round	Drawn 800°F	179	198	13	49	410
AISI E52100 steel	1-in. round	Hot-rolled and annealed	81	100	25	57	192
AISI E6150 steel	1-in. round	Hot-rolled and annealed	58	91	22	53	183
AISI 8620 steel	1-in. round	Drawn 400°F	112	140	17	52	282
	1-in. round	Drawn 800°F	98	122	22	63	246
	1-in. round	Drawn 1200°F	77	98	26	70	194
AISI 8630 steel	1-in. round	Drawn 800°F	142	162	14	54	316
AISI 8742 steel	1-in. round	Drawn 600°F	220	246	12	39	492
	1-in. round	Drawn 1000°F	144	168	15	53	336
	2-in. round	Drawn 1000°F	118	142	17	55	288
	4-in. round	Drawn 1000°F	107	131	18	56	264
AISI 9255 steel	1-in. round	Hot-rolled and annealed	78	115	22	45	223
	1-in. round	Drawn 1000°F	160	180	15	32	352
AISI 9442 steel	1-in. round	Drawn 800°F	180	201	12	43	404
AISI 9840 steel	1-in. round	Drawn 800°F	199	218	12	47	436
1100-O† (2S)	½-in. round	Wrought	5	13	45	...	23
1100-H12 (2S)	½-in. round	Wrought	14	15.5	25	...	28
1100-H14 (2S)	½-in. round	Wrought	16	18	20	...	32
1100-H16 (2S)	½-in. round	Wrought	19	21	17	...	38
1100-H18 (2S)	½-in. round	Wrought	22	24	15	...	44
3003-O (3S)	½-in. round	Wrought	6	16	40	...	28
3003-H12 (3S)	½-in. round	Wrought	17	19	20	...	35
3003-H14 (3S)	½-in. round	Wrought	20	22	16	...	40
3003-H16 (3S)	½-in. round	Wrought	24	26	14	...	47
3003-H18 (3S)	½-in. round	Wrought	27	29	10	...	55
3004-O (4S)	½-in. round	Wrought	10	26	25	...	45
3004-H32 (4S)	½-in. round	Wrought	22	31	17	...	52
3004-H34 (4S)	½-in. round	Wrought	27	34	12	...	63
3004-H36 (4S)	½-in. round	Wrought	31	37	9	...	70

TABLE A-3. TENSILE PROPERTIES OF MATERIALS* (*Continued*)

Material	Size	Condition	Yield strength, kpsi	Tensile strength, kpsi	Elongation in 2 in., %	Reduction area, %	Brinell hardness, Bhn
3004-H38 (4S)	½-in. round	Wrought	34	40	6	...	77
2011-T3 (11S)	½-in. round	Wrought	48	55	15	...	95
2011-T8 (11S)	½-in. round	Wrought	45	59	12	...	100
2014-O (14S)	½-in. round	Wrought	14	27	18	...	45
2014-T4 (14S)	½-in. round	Wrought	40	62	20	...	105
2014-T6 (14S)	½-in. round	Wrought	60	70	13	...	135
2017-O (17S)	½-in. round	Wrought	10	26	22	...	45
2017-T4 (17S)	½-in. round	Wrought	24	43	22	...	105
2117-T4 (A17S)	½-in. round	Wrought	24	43	27	...	70
2018-T61 (18S)	½-in. round	Wrought	46	61	12	...	120
2218-T72 (B18S)	½-in. round	Wrought	37	48	11	...	95
2024-O (24S)	½-in. round	Wrought	11	27	22	...	47
2024-T3 (24S)	1/16-in. sheet	Wrought	50	70	16	...	120
2024-T4 (24S)	1/16-in. sheet	Wrought	48	68	20	...	120
2024-T36 (24S)	1/16-in. sheet	Wrought	57	73	13	...	130
2025-T6 (25S)	½-in. round	Wrought	37	58	19	...	110
4032-T6 (32S)	½-in. round	Wrought	46	55	9	...	120
5350-O (C50S)	1/16-in. sheet	Wrought	8	20	28	...	35
5350-H32 (C50S)	1/16-in. sheet	Wrought	20.5	24.5	10	...	45
5350-H34 (C50S)	1/16-in. sheet	Wrought	24	27.5	9	...	50
5350-H36 (C50S)	1/16-in. sheet	Wrought	26	29	8	...	55
5350-H38 (C50S)	1/16-in. sheet	Wrought	29	31.5	7	...	63
6151-T6 (A51S)	½-in. round	Wrought	43	48	17	...	100
5052-O (52S)	½-in. round	Wrought	13	28	30	...	45
5052-H32 (52S)	½-in. round	Wrought	27	34	18	...	62
5052-H34 (52S)	½-in. round	Wrought	31	37	14	...	67

5052-H36 (52S)	½-in. round	Wrought	34	39	10	...	74
5052-H38 (52S)	½-in. round	Wrought	36	41	8	...	85
5056-O (56S)	½-in. round	Wrought	22	42	35		
5056-H18 (56S)	½-in. round	Wrought	59	63	10		
5056-H38 (56S)	½-in. round	Wrought	50	60	15		
6061-O (61S)	½-in. round	Wrought	8	18	30	...	30
6061-T4 (61S)	½-in. round	Wrought	21	35	25	...	65
6061-T6 (61S)	½-in. round	Wrought	40	45	17	...	95
6062-O (62S)	½-in. round	Wrought	6.5	17	30	...	28
6062-T4 (62S)	½-in. round	Wrought	21	35	25	...	65
6062-T6 (62S)	½-in. round	Wrought	40	45	17	...	95
6063-T5 (63S)	1/16-in. sheet	Wrought	25	30	12	...	65
6063-T6 (63S)	1/16-in. sheet	Wrought	30	35	12	...	73
7075-O (75S)	½-in. round	Wrought	15	33	16	...	60
7075-T6 (75S)	½-in. round	Wrought	72	82	11	...	150
43 aluminum	½-in. round	Sand-cast	9	19	6	...	40
108 aluminum	½-in. round	Sand-cast	14	21	2.5	...	51
112 aluminum	½-in. round	Sand-cast	15	24	1.5	...	70
113 aluminum	½-in. round	Sand-cast	15	24	1.5	...	70
122-T2 aluminum	½-in. round	Sand-cast	20	27	1.0	...	80
122-T61 aluminum	½-in. round	Sand-cast	30	40	...	...	115
142-T21 aluminum	½-in. round	Sand-cast	18	27	1.0	...	70
142-T571 aluminum	½-in. round	Sand-cast	28	32	0.5	...	85
142-T77 aluminum	½-in. round	Sand-cast	25	28	2.0	...	75
195-T6 aluminum	½-in. round	Sand-cast	24	36	5	...	75
195-T62 aluminum	½-in. round	Sand-cast	30	40	2	...	95
212 aluminum	½-in. round	Sand-cast	14	23	2	...	65
214 aluminum	½-in. round	Sand-cast	12	25	9	...	50
220-T4 aluminum	½-in. round	Sand-cast	25	46	14	...	75
319 aluminum	½-in. round	Sand-cast	18	27	2	...	70
319-T6 aluminum	½-in. round	Sand-cast	24	36	2	...	80

TABLE A-3. TENSILE PROPERTIES OF MATERIALS* (*Continued*)

Material	Size	Condition	Yield strength, kpsi	Tensile strength, kpsi	Elongation in 2 in., %	Reduction area, %	Brinell hardness, Bhn
355-T6 aluminum	½-in. round	Sand-cast	25	35	2.5	...	80
355-T7 aluminum	½-in. round	Sand-cast	36	38	0.5	...	85
356-T51 aluminum	½-in. round	Sand-cast	20	25	2	...	60
356-T6 aluminum	½-in. round	Sand-cast	24	33	4	...	70
356-T7 aluminum	½-in. round	Sand-cast	30	34	2	...	75
356-T71 aluminum	½-in. round	Sand-cast	21	28	4.5	...	60
ASTM B16-29 brass	...	Cold-drawn (free cutting)	50	65	12		
ASTM B21-29 brass	...	Cold-drawn (naval)	40	62	25		
ASTM B15-18 brass	...	Forged (naval)	28	54	35		
Electrolytic copper	...	Cold-drawn	...	53	5		
ASTM B30-36 phosphor bronze	...	Cast	15	27	7	...	47
ASTM B62-36 red bronze	...	Cast	17	27	12	...	60
ASTM B80-47T magnesium	...	Sand-cast	14	25	2	...	65
ASTM B107-48T magnesium	...	Extruded bars	28	37	7	...	42
ASTM B217-48T magnesium	...	Extruded tubing	23	34	7	...	41
ASTM B91-45T magnesium	...	Forged	26	42	10	...	55
AISI 301 stainless steel	⅞-in. round	Wrought (annealed)	40	105	55	70	
AISI 302 stainless steel	⅞-in. round	Wrought (annealed)	35	90	60	70	150
AISI 303 stainless steel	⅞-in. round	Wrought (annealed)	35	90	50	55	160
AISI 304 stainless steel	⅞-in. round	Wrought (annealed)	30	85	60	70	150

* The values shown are from a variety of sources and are believed to be representative. There are so many variables which affect the properties of materials, however, that the approximate nature of these values must be clearly recognized. Unless a detailed study of the particular material chosen is made, the values shown must not be used to specify the minimum requirements of a material.

† New Aluminum Association designation system for wrought aluminum alloys. The old numbering system is included in parentheses for reference purposes.

TABLE A-4. PROPERTIES OF GRAY CAST IRON

Property	ASTM number					
	20	25	30	35	40	50
Tensile strength, psi	20,000	25,000	30,000	35,000	40,000	50,000
Compressive strength, psi	80,000	90,000	100,000	110,000	125,000	145,000
Brinell hardness, Bhn	110	140	170	200	230	250
Endurance limit, psi	8,000–10,000	10,000–12,000	12,000–15,000	14,000–16,000	16,000–20,000	20,000–24,000
Modulus of elasticity, psi	11,000,000	12,000,000	13,000,000	14,000,000	15,000,000	18,000,000
Torsional modulus, psi	4,000,000	4,500,000	5,000,000	5,500,000	6,000,000	7,000,000

TABLE A-5. TYPICAL PROPERTIES OF CAST CARBON STEELS

Composition, per cent					Yield point, kpsi	Tensile strength, kpsi	Elongation in 2 in., %	Reduction area, %	Brinell hardness, Bhn	Treatment
C	Mn	Si	P	S						
0.11	0.60	0.40	0.03	0.03	26	59	13	30	126	As cast
					35	60	30	60	116	Annealed 1650°F
0.19	0.62	0.42	0.03	0.05	47	76	15	26	...	1625°F water-quenched; drawn 200°F
0.30	0.79	0.33	0.03	0.03	36	75	20	29	156	As cast
					42	76	25	32	143	Annealed
					100	130	9	18	250	1650°F water-quenched; drawn 500°F
0.34	0.96	0.19	0.06	0.02	51	87	18	21	...	As cast
0.40	0.63	0.30	0.06	0.07	51	87	17	20	182	1740°F air-cooled; drawn 930°F
0.48	0.68	0.41	0.02	0.01	39	83	23	27	...	As cast
					52	88	25	42	...	1650°F water-quenched; drawn 1250°F
0.53	0.79	0.25	0.03	0.04	35	87	6	4	213	As cast
					35	79	5	5	200	Annealed 1290°F
					50	99	16	18	208	Annealed 1510°F
0.86	0.90	0.27	0.02	0.03	43	71	1.5	0.5	255	As cast
					51	108	4	3.5	253	Annealed 1470°F

TABLE A-6. TYPICAL PROPERTIES OF THE COPPER-BASE ALLOYS

Alloy name	Form	Temper	Yield strength (0.5% offset), kpsi	Tensile strength, kpsi	Elongation in 2 in., %	Rockwell hardness	Composition, %			
							Cu	Zn	Pb	Sn
Gilding brass	Sheet	Hard	50	56	5	64B	95	5		
	Sheet	Soft	10	34	45	46F	95	5		
Commercial bronze	Sheet	Hard	54	61	5	70B	90	10		
	Sheet	Soft	10	37	45	53F	90	10		
	Rod	Hard	55	60	20	60B	90	10		
	Rod	Soft	10	40	50	55F	90	10		
Red brass	Sheet	Hard	57	70	5	77B	85	15		
	Sheet	Soft	12	40	47	59F	85	15		
	Rod	Hard	52	57	23	75B	85	15		
	Rod	Soft	10	40	55	55F	85	15		
	Tube	Hard	58	70	8	75B	85	15		
Cartridge brass	Sheet	Hard	63	76	8	82B	70	30		
	Sheet	Soft	15	47	62	64F	70	30		
	Rod	Hard	52	70	30	80B	70	30		
	Rod	Soft	16	48	65	65F	70	30		
Yellow brass	Sheet	Hard	60	74	8	80B	65	35		
	Sheet	Soft	15	47	62	64F	65	35		
	Rod	Hard	45	60	25	80B	65	35		
	Rod	Soft	16	48	65	65F	65	35		
Muntz metal	Sheet	Hard	60	80	10	85B	60	40		
	Sheet	Soft	21	54	45	80F	60	40		
	Rod	Hard	55	75	20	80B	60	40		
	Rod	Soft	21	54	50	80F	60	40		
	Tube	Hard	55	74	10	80B	60	40		
	Tube	Soft	23	56	50	82F	60	40		
Low-leaded brass	Tube	Hard	60	75	7	80B	67	32½	½	
	Tube	Soft	15	47	60	64F	67	32½	½	
High-leaded brass	Sheet	Hard	60	74	7	80B	64	34	2	
	Sheet	Soft	17	49	52	68F	64	34	2	
Free-cutting brass	Rod	Hard	45	58	25	78B	61½	35½	3	
	Rod	Soft	18	49	53	68F	61½	35½	3	
Admiralty	Sheet	Hard	70	85	5	90B	71	28	...	1
	Sheet	Soft	18	50	55	25B	71	28	...	1
	Tube	Hard	80	100	3	95B	71	28	...	1
	Tube	Soft	22	53	65	75F	71	28	...	1
Naval brass	Sheet	Hard	70	90	5	90B	60	39¼	...	¾
	Rod	Hard	53	75	20	82B	60	39¼	...	¾
	Tube	Hard	66	88	18	95B	60	39¼	...	¾
Phosphor bronze	Sheet	Hard	75	81	10	87B	95	...	...	5
	Sheet	Soft	19	47	64	73F	95	...	...	5
	Rod	Hard	58	70	25	78B	95	...	...	5
	Sheet	Hard	68	93	10	93B	92	...	...	8
Beryllium (2¼%)	Rod	Hard	75	115	5	98B	97			
	Rod	Soft	25	60	50	77B	97			
	Sheet	Hard	145	180	2	....	97			
Aluminum (5%)	Tube	Hard	...	70	25	80B	95			

TABLE A-7. PROPERTIES OF SECTIONS

A = area, in.^{2}
I = moment of inertia, in.^{4}
J = polar moment of inertia, in.^{4}
I/c = section modulus, in.^{3}
r = radius of gyration, in.
$\bar{y}$ = centroidal distance, in.

Rectangle		
h, b, $\bar{y}$	$A = bh$ $I = \frac{bh^3}{12}$ $\frac{I}{c} = \frac{bh^2}{6}$	$r = 0.289h$ $\bar{y} = \frac{h}{2}$
Triangle		
h, b, $\bar{y}$	$A = \frac{bh}{2}$ $I = \frac{bh^3}{36}$ $\frac{I}{c} = \frac{bh^2}{24}$	$r = 0.236h$ $\bar{y} = \frac{h}{3}$
Circle		
d	$A = \frac{\pi d^2}{4}$ $I = \frac{\pi d^4}{64}$ $\frac{I}{c} = \frac{\pi d^3}{32}$	$J = \frac{\pi d^4}{32}$ $r = \frac{d}{4}$ $\bar{y} = \frac{d}{2}$
Hollow Circle		
d, d_i	$A = \frac{\pi}{4}(d^2 - d_i^2)$ $I = \frac{\pi}{64}(d^4 - d_i^4)$ $\frac{I}{c} = \frac{\pi}{32d}(d^4 - d_i^4)$	$J = \frac{\pi}{32}(d^4 - d_i^4)$ $r = \sqrt{\frac{d^2 + d_i^2}{16}}$ $\bar{y} = \frac{d}{2}$

TABLE A-8. PROPERTIES OF STRUCTURAL SHAPES—EQUAL ANGLES

W_a = weight per foot of aluminum sections, lb
W_s = weight per foot of steel sections, lb
A = area, in.^{2}
I = moment of inertia, in.^{4}
r = radius of gyration, in.
y = centroidal distance, in.
I/c = section modulus, in.^{3}

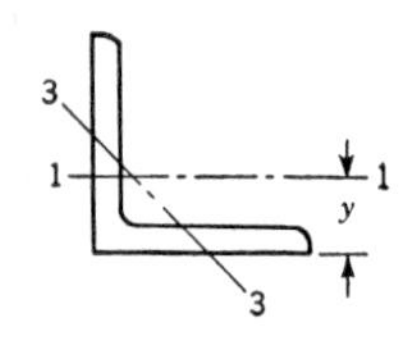

Size	W_a	W_s	A	I_{1-1}	r_{1-1}	I/c_{1-1}	y	I_{3-3}	r_{3-3}
1 × 1 × ⅛	0.28	0.80	0.23	0.02	0.30	0.03	0.30	0.008	0.19
1 × 1 × ¼	0.53	1.49	0.44	0.04	0.29	0.05	0.34	0.016	0.19
1½ × 1½ × ⅛	0.44	1.23	0.36	0.07	0.45	0.07	0.41	0.031	0.29
1½ × 1½ × ¼	0.83	2.34	0.69	0.14	0.44	0.13	0.46	0.057	0.29
2 × 2 × ⅛	0.59	1.65	0.49	0.18	0.61	0.13	0.53	0.08	0.40
2 × 2 × ¼	1.14	3.19	0.94	0.34	0.60	0.24	0.58	0.14	0.39
2 × 2 × ⅜	1.65	4.70	1.37	0.47	0.59	0.35	0.63	0.20	0.39
2½ × 2½ × ¼	1.45	4.1	1.19	0.69	0.76	0.39	0.71	0.29	0.49
2½ × 2½ × ⅜	2.11	5.9	1.74	0.98	0.75	0.56	0.76	0.41	0.48
3 × 3 × ¼	1.73	4.9	1.43	1.18	0.91	0.54	0.82	0.49	0.58
3 × 3 × ⅜	2.55	7.2	2.10	1.70	0.90	0.80	0.87	0.70	0.58
3 × 3 × ½	3.32	9.4	2.74	2.16	0.89	1.04	0.92	0.91	0.58
3½ × 3½ × ¼	2.05	4.9	1.69	1.93	1.07	0.76	0.94	0.80	0.69
3½ × 3½ × ⅜	3.01	7.2	2.49	2.79	1.06	1.11	1.00	1.15	0.68
3½ × 3½ × ½	3.94	11.1	3.25	3.56	1.05	1.45	1.05	1.49	0.68
4 × 4 × ¼	2.35	6.6	1.94	2.94	1.23	1.00	1.07	1.21	0.79
4 × 4 × ⅜	3.46	9.8	2.86	4.26	1.22	1.48	1.12	1.75	0.78
4 × 4 × ½	4.54	12.8	3.75	5.46	1.21	1.93	1.17	2.26	0.78
4 × 4 × ⅝	5.58	15.7	4.61	6.56	1.19	2.36	1.22	2.76	0.77
6 × 6 × ⅜	5.27	14.9	4.35	14.85	1.85	3.38	1.60	6.07	1.18
6 × 6 × ½	6.95	19.6	5.74	19.38	1.84	4.46	1.66	7.92	1.17
6 × 6 × ⅝	8.59	24.2	7.10	23.64	1.82	5.51	1.71	9.70	1.17
6 × 6 × ¾	10.20	28.7	8.43	27.64	1.81	6.52	1.76	11.43	1.16

Table A-9. Properties of Structural Shapes—Unequal Angles

W_a = weight per foot of aluminum sections, lb
W_s = weight per foot of steel sections, lb
A = area, in.^{2}
I = moment of inertia, in.^{4}
r = radius of gyration, in.
x and y = respective centroidal distances, in.
I/c = section modulus, in.^{3}

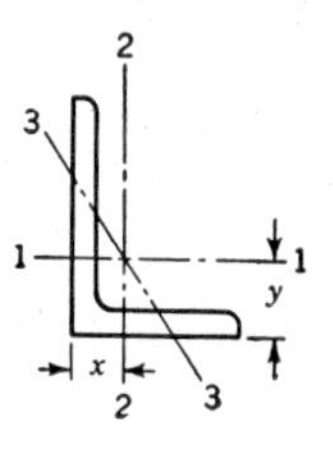

Size	W_a	W_s	A	I_{1-1}	r_{1-1}	I/c_{1-1}	y	I_{2-2}	r_{2-2}	I/c_{2-2}	x	I_{3-3}	r_{3-3}
2 × 1½ × ⅛ . .	0.51	1.44	0.42	0.17	0.63	0.12	0.60	0.08	0.44	0.07	0.36	0.04	0.32
2 × 1½ × ¼ . .	0.98	2.77	0.81	0.31	0.62	0.23	0.66	0.15	0.43	0.14	0.41	0.08	0.32
3 × 2 × 3⁄16 . . .	1.10	3.07	0.91	0.82	0.95	0.40	0.94	0.29	0.56	0.19	0.46	0.17	0.43
3 × 2½ × ¼ . .	1.58	4.5	1.31	1.12	0.92	0.53	0.89	0.70	0.73	0.38	0.64	0.35	0.52
3 × 2½ × ⅜ . .	2.32	6.6	1.92	1.60	0.91	0.78	0.94	1.00	0.72	0.55	0.69	0.51	0.51
3 × 2½ × ½ . .	3.02	9.4	2.49	2.03	0.90	1.01	0.99	1.26	0.71	0.72	0.74	0.65	0.51
4 × 3 × ¼	2.05	5.8	1.69	2.68	1.26	0.96	1.21	1.29	0.87	0.56	0.72	0.70	0.64
4 × 3 × ½	3.94	11.1	3.25	4.96	1.24	1.85	1.31	2.36	0.85	1.08	0.82	1.30	0.63
6 × 4 × ⅜	4.36	12.3	3.60	13.02	1.90	3.17	1.90	4.63	1.13	1.50	0.91	2.67	0.86
6 × 4 × ½	5.74	16.2	4.74	16.95	1.89	4.19	1.96	6.01	1.13	1.98	0.97	3.47	0.86

TABLE A-10. PROPERTIES OF STRUCTURAL SHAPES—CHANNELS

W_a = weight per foot of aluminum sections, lb
W_s = weight per foot of steel sections, lb
A = area, in.^{2}
I = moment of inertia, in.^{4}
r = radius of gyration, in.
x = centroidal distance, in.
I/c = section modulus, in.^{3}

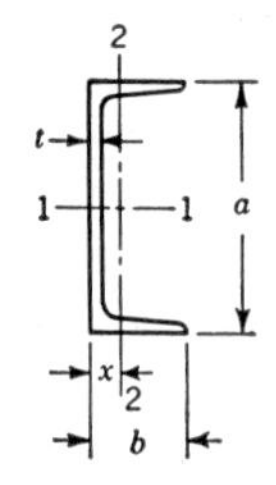

a	b	t	A	W_a	W_s	$I_{1\text{-}1}$	$r_{1\text{-}1}$	$I/c_{1\text{-}1}$	$I_{2\text{-}2}$	$r_{2\text{-}2}$	$I/c_{2\text{-}2}$	x
3	1.410	0.170	1.21	1.46	4.1	1.66	1.17	1.10	0.20	0.40	0.20	0.44
3	1.498	0.258	1.47	1.78	5.0	1.85	1.12	1.24	0.25	0.41	0.23	0.44
3	1.596	0.356	1.76	2.13	6.0	2.07	1.08	1.38	0.31	0.42	0.27	0.46
4	1.580	0.180	1.57	1.90	5.4	3.83	1.56	1.92	0.32	0.45	0.28	0.46
4	1.720	0.320	2.13	2.58	7.25	4.58	1.47	2.29	0.43	0.45	0.34	0.46
5	1.750	0.190	1.97	2.38	6.7	7.49	1.95	3.00	0.48	0.49	0.38	0.48
5	1.885	0.325	2.64	3.20	9.0	8.90	1.83	3.56	0.63	0.49	0.45	0.48
6	1.920	0.200	2.40	2.91	8.2	13.12	2.34	4.37	0.69	0.54	0.49	0.51
6	2.034	0.314	3.09	3.73	10.5	15.18	2.22	5.06	0.87	0.53	0.56	0.50
6	2.157	0.437	3.82	4.63	13.0	17.39	2.13	5.80	1.05	0.52	0.64	0.51
7	2.090	0.210	2.87	3.47	9.8	21.27	2.72	6.08	0.97	0.58	0.63	0.54
7	2.194	0.314	3.60	4.36	12.25	24.24	2.60	6.93	1.17	0.57	0.70	0.52
7	2.299	0.419	4.33	5.24	14.75	27.24	2.51	7.78	1.38	0.56	0.78	0.53
8	2.260	0.220	3.36	4.10	11.5	32.30	3.10	8.10	1.30	0.63	0.79	0.58
8	2.343	0.303	4.04	4.89	13.75	36.11	2.99	9.03	1.53	0.61	0.85	0.55
8	2.527	0.487	5.51	6.67	18.75	43.96	2.82	10.99	1.98	0.60	1.01	0.57
9	2.430	0.230	3.91	4.74	13.4	47.68	3.49	10.60	1.75	0.67	0.96	0.60
9	2.485	0.285	4.41	5.34	15.0	51.02	3.40	11.34	1.93	0.66	1.01	0.59
9	2.648	0.448	5.88	7.11	20.0	60.92	3.22	13.54	2.42	0.64	1.17	0.58
10	2.600	0.240	4.49	5.43	15.3	67.37	3.87	13.47	2.28	0.71	1.16	0.63
10	2.739	0.379	5.88	7.11	20.0	78.95	3.66	15.79	2.81	0.69	1.32	0.61
10	2.886	0.526	7.35	8.89	25.0	91.20	3.52	18.24	3.36	0.68	1.48	0.62
10	3.033	0.673	8.82	10.67	30.0	103.45	3.43	20.69	3.95	0.67	1.66	0.65
12	3.047	0.387	7.35	8.89	25.0	144.37	4.43	24.06	4.47	0.78	1.89	0.67
12	3.170	0.510	8.82	10.67	30.0	162.08	4.29	27.01	5.14	0.76	2.06	0.67

TABLE A-11. DECIMAL EQUIVALENTS OF WIRE AND SHEET-METAL GAUGES*

Name of gauge:	American or Brown & Sharpe	Birmingham or Stubs iron wire	United States Standard	Manufacturers Standard†	Steel wire or Washburn & Moen	Music wire	Stubs steel wire	Twist drill
Principal use:	Nonferrous sheet, wire, and rod	Tubing, ferrous strip, flat wire, and spring steel	Ferrous sheet and plate, 480 lb per ft³	Ferrous sheet	Ferrous wire except music wire	Music wire	Steel drill rod	Twist drills and drill steel
7/0	......	.....	0.500	......	0.4900			
6/0	0.5800	.....	0.46875	......	0.4615	0.004		
5/0	0.5165	.....	0.4375	......	0.4305	0.005		
4/0	0.4600	0.454	0.40625	......	0.3938	0.006		
3/0	0.4096	0.425	0.375	......	0.3625	0.007		
2/0	0.3648	0.380	0.34375	......	0.3310	0.008		
0	0.3249	0.340	0.3125	......	0.3065	0.009		
1	0.2893	0.300	0.28125	......	0.2830	0.010	0.227	0.2280
2	0.2576	0.284	0.265625	......	0.2625	0.011	0.219	0.2210
3	0.2294	0.259	0.25	0.2391	0.2437	0.012	0.212	0.2130
4	0.2043	0.238	0.234375	0.2242	0.2253	0.013	0.207	0.2090
5	0.1819	0.220	0.21875	0.2092	0.2070	0.014	0.204	0.2055
6	0.1620	0.203	0.203125	0.1943	0.1920	0.016	0.201	0.2040
7	0.1443	0.180	0.1875	0.1793	0.1770	0.018	0.199	0.2010
8	0.1285	0.165	0.171875	0.1644	0.1620	0.020	0.197	0.1990
9	0.1144	0.148	0.15625	0.1495	0.1483	0.022	0.194	0.1960
10	0.1019	0.134	0.140625	0.1345	0.1350	0.024	0.191	0.1935
11	0.09074	0.120	0.125	0.1196	0.1205	0.026	0.188	0.1910
12	0.08081	0.109	0.109357	0.1046	0.1055	0.029	0.185	0.1890
13	0.07196	0.095	0.09375	0.0897	0.0915	0.031	0.182	0.1850
14	0.06408	0.083	0.078125	0.0747	0.0800	0.033	0.180	0.1820
15	0.05707	0.072	0.0703125	0.0673	0.0720	0.035	0.178	0.1800
16	0.05082	0.065	0.0625	0.0598	0.0625	0.037	0.175	0.1770
17	0.04526	0.058	0.05625	0.0538	0.0540	0.039	0.172	0.1730
18	0.04030	0.049	0.05	0.0478	0.0475	0.041	0.168	0.1695
19	0.03589	0.042	0.04375	0.0418	0.0410	0.043	0.164	0.1660
20	0.03196	0.035	0.0375	0.0359	0.0348	0.045	0.161	0.1610
21	0.02846	0.032	0.034375	0.0329	0.03175	0.047	0.157	0.1590
22	0.02535	0.028	0.03125	0.0299	0.0286	0.049	0.155	0.1570
23	0.02257	0.025	0.028125	0.0269	0.0258	0.051	0.153	0.1540
24	0.02010	0.022	0.025	0.0239	0.0230	0.055	0.151	0.1520
25	0.01790	0.020	0.021875	0.0209	0.0204	0.059	0.148	0.1495

TABLE A-11. DECIMAL EQUIVALENTS OF WIRE AND SHEET-METAL GAUGES*
(*Continued*)

Name of gauge:	American or Brown & Sharpe	Birmingham or Stubs iron wire	United States Standard	Manufacturers Standard†	Steel wire or Washburn & Moen	Music wire	Stubs steel wire	Twist drill
Principal use:	Nonferrous sheet, wire, and rod	Tubing, ferrous strip, flat wire, and spring steel	Ferrous sheet and plate, 480 lb per ft³	Ferrous sheet	Ferrous wire except music wire	Music wire	Steel drill rod	Twist drills and drill steel
26	0.01594	0.018	0.01875	0.0179	0.0181	0.063	0.146	0.1470
27	0.01420	0.016	0.0171875	0.0164	0.0173	0.067	0.143	0.1440
28	0.01264	0.014	0.015625	0.0149	0.0162	0.071	0.139	0.1405
29	0.01126	0.013	0.0140625	0.0135	0.0150	0.075	0.134	0.1360
30	0.01003	0.012	0.0125	0.0120	0.0140	0.080	0.127	0.1285
31	0.008928	0.010	0.0109375	0.0105	0.0132	0.085	0.120	0.1200
32	0.007950	0.009	0.01015625	0.0097	0.0128	0.090	0.115	0.1160
33	0.007080	0.008	0.009375	0.0090	0.0118	0.095	0.112	0.1130
34	0.006305	0.007	0.00859375	0.0082	0.0104	...	0.110	0.1110
35	0.005615	0.005	0.0078125	0.0075	0.0095	...	0.108	0.1100
36	0.005000	0.004	0.00703125	0.0067	0.0090	...	0.106	0.1065
37	0.004453	...	0.006640625	0.0064	0.0085	...	0.103	0.1040
38	0.003965	...	0.00625	0.0060	0.0080	...	0.101	0.1015
39	0.003531	...	...	...	0.0075	...	0.099	0.0995
40	0.003145	...	...	...	0.0070	...	0.097	0.0980

* Reproduced by courtesy of the Reynolds Metal Company. Specify sheet, wire, and plate by stating the gauge number, the gauge name, and the decimal equivalent in parentheses.

† Reflects present average unit weights of sheet steel.

INDEX

Accuracy of gear teeth, 334, 345, 346
Acme thread, 183
Addendum, 316
  gears, bevel, 387
    helical, 371, 372
    spiral, 396
    spur, 323–327
    worm, 383
  meaning, 318
Admiralty metal, 141
AISI (American Iron and Steel Institute) numbering system for steel, 117
Allowance, 305
Alloying elements, 126, 127
  of aluminum, 137, 138
  of copper, 140–142
  of steels, 132, 133
Alloys of steels, 132
Alternating stress, 100
Aluminum alloys, aging, 138
  designation, 117, 118
  heat-treatment, 138
  temper, 118
Aluminum bronze, 142
American Iron and Steel Institute (AISI), 117
American Petroleum Institute (API), 273
American Society for Testing Materials (ASTM), 116
Angle, of action, 319
  of approach, 319
  of contact of belts, 437
  of recess, 319
Angular-contact ball bearing, 249
Angular deflection, 49
Annealing, 130
Arc length of bearings, 291
Arc welding, 207–215
Arms of spur gears, 360
Assumptions, basic, 8
  design, 163
  effects of, 163

Babbitt, 308
Back cone of bevel gear, 386
Bainite, 131
Ball bearings (*see* Bearings)
Band brake, 413
  analysis, 414
  heat capacity, 420
Barth, Carl G., 332
Barth equation, 333
Base circle, construction, 317
  in gears, 315
Beam strength of gear, bevel, 387–389
  helical, 372, 373
  spur, 337–342
  worm, 384
Beams, bending, 23–31, 51–58, 62–66
  cantilever, 63
  curved, 72–75
  deflection, 51–57, 75
    of indeterminate, 56
Bearing, characteristic number, 283
  definition, 270
  fitted, 278
  full, 278
  journal (*see* Bearings)
  length-diameter ratio, 298
  plain, 270
  ring-oiled, 309
  sleeve (*see* Bearings, journal)
Bearing area, projected, 275
Bearing clearances, 278, 286, 303–306
Bearing-design decisions, 282, 309
Bearing loads, load-correction factor, 257, 258, 261, 289
  values, 302
Bearing metals, 308
Bearing pressure, 31, 32, 195, 275, 302
Bearings, 247–312
  antifriction, 247–269
    design, 247
    friction in, 251, 252
    Hertz stresses, 252
    life expectancy, 253
    lubrication, 264
    mountings, 266, 267
    preloading, 267
    sealed, 249
    seals, 265

Bearings, antifriction, shielded, 249
  arc length, 291
  ball, 247–259, 264–267
    angular-contact, 249
    average life, 257
    dimensions, 255
    double row, 249
    friction coefficient, 252
    nomenclature, 248
    ratings, 256
    speed factors, 258
    types, 248, 249
  journal, 270–312
    design factors, 282
    dimensions, 303
    effective length, 298
    formulas, 293
    friction, 288
    frictional coefficients, 275, 277, 285, 297
    grooves, 294, 307
    heat dissipation, 300
    hydrodynamic theory, 279–281
    life, 302, 305, 308
    loads for, 302
    materials, 308
    minimum film thickness, 286
    nomenclature, 278
    partial, 277
    pressure distribution, 276
    pressure-fed, 294
      analysis, 297
      theory, 294–297
    side flow, 289
    tolerances, 304, 305
    types, 306
  needle, 251
  New Departure, 248
  oil flow through, 288–292, 297–300
  oil temperature of, 293, 297, 300, 301, 304, 305
  oilless, 270, 309
  optimum, 306
  preloading, 267
  pressure distribution, 290
  roller, 249–251, 259–267
    dimensions, 263
    induced thrust, 261
    life factors, 261
    nomenclature, 260
    ratings, 263
    speed factors, 261
    tapered (*see* Tapered roller bearings)
    Timken, 259
    types, 250
  self-aligning, 249, 250
Bearings, thrust (*see* Thrust bearing)
  (*See also* Bearing)
Belleville springs, 236, 237
Belt thickness, 438
Belts, characteristics, 433
  contact angles, 437
  flat (*see* Flat belts)
  lengths, 437
  tensile strength, 438
  tension, 437, 438
Bending, of beams, 23–31, 51–58, 62–66
  of gear teeth, 337–342
Bending moment, 23
Bending stress, 23–31
Beryllium bronze, 142
Bevel gears (*see* Gears)
Bolted connections, failure, 195
Bolting, torque required, 190
Bolts, loads on, 187
  materials, 190
  preloading, 186, 202
    advantages, 188
    methods, 189
  properties, 190
  shear loading, 188
  stiffness constant, 186
  tension, 186–192
  torque values, 191
  (*See also* Screw threads)
Boundary lubrication, 272
Boyd, John, 282*n*.
Brake shoes, actuating forces required, 407
  external types, 412
  forces on, 407
  internal, 408
  pressure distribution, 407
  torque capacity, 408
Brakes, band-type, 414
  energy requirements, 419, 420
  frictional materials for, 417, 418
    characteristics, 417
  heat dissipation, 420
  rim-type, 404
  self-energizing, 406
  (*See also* Clutches)
Braking torque, 408, 409, 414, 416
Brass composition, 140
Brinell hardness, 96
Brittle materials, 96
  failure, 106, 110, 112
Brittleness, meaning, 94
Bronze composition, 140
Buckingham, Earle, 332
Buckingham equation, 344
Buckling, of columns, 67
  of springs, 227

Bushings, 306
Buttjoint, welded, 208

Cable, hoisting, 454
Cantilever beam, 63
Carbon steel, 128, 129
Carburizing, 131
Cartridge brass, 140
Casehardening, 131
Cast iron, alloy, 137
  designation, 117
  ductile, 137
  gray, 135
  malleable, 136
  nodular, 137
  white, 136
Castigliano theorem, 63, 64
Casting, centrifugal, 121
  die, 121
  permanent-mold, 121
  sand, 118
  steel, 119
Cementite, 129
Center of gravity, 197, 212
Center distance, belt drive, 437
  chain drive, 450
  worm gears, 382
Centipoise, definition, 273
Centrifugal effect in belts, 438
Centrifugal force, 358, 473
Chain, roller (*see* Roller chain)
Charpy test, 113
Circle of stress, 19
Circular pitch, 317
  normal, 368
Clearance, of bearing, 275
  of gear teeth, 346
Clearance fit, 304
Clutch-design decisions, 424
Clutch selection, 425
Clutch shoes, pressure distribution, 407
Clutches, axial, 415
  friction materials, 417, 418
  kinetic energy capacity, 419, 420
  magnetic fluid, 422
  overload-release type, 403
  overrunning types, 421
  positive contact, characteristics, 402
  rating factors, 425
  rim types, 403
  rules for analysis, 404
  self-energization, 406
  (*See also* Brakes)
Coarse-grained steel, 130
Coefficient, of fluctuation for flywheel, 479
Coefficient, of friction, 405
    for ball bearings, 252
    for brakes, 418
    for flat belts, 440
    for journal bearings, 275, 277, 285, 297
    for screws, 184
    for worm gears, 380
  of thermal expansion, values, 79
Cold drawing, meaning, 124
Cold finishing, 124
Cold heading, 124
Cold working, 124
Collar bearings, friction, 184
Columns, buckling, 67
  critical loads, 67, 68
  definition, 66
  with eccentric load, 70
  end conditions, 68, 72
  Euler formula, 68
  failure, 67
  J. B. Johnson formula, 71
  parabolic formula, 71
  secant formula, 70
  slenderness ratio, 66
  stability, 66
Combined stress, 17–22
Composite gears, 323
Compression springs, 229
Compression stress, 16
  contact, 31, 32
  surface, 31
  ultimate, 92
  yield, 92
Computations, form, 165–169
Concentration of stress (*see* Stress concentration)
Cone distance, 386
Connections, bolted, loads, 187
  riveted, failure, 195
Constant angular velocity, condition for, 314
Constitution of steel, 129
Contact ratio of gears, values, 320
Contact stresses, 31
  in gear teeth, 350–353
Controls, hydraulic, 485
Cooling curves, 126
Cooling rate, 130
Copper alloys, 140
Corrosion, 108
Cost of machine, items, 150
Couplings, 402
  eddy-current types, 421
  fluid, 422, 423
    variable-fill type, 424
Creation, definition, 5

Creep of metals, 115
Critical load for columns, 67, 68
Critical speed, 77
  of springs, 239
Crossed-helical gears (*see* Gears)
Curved beam, 72
  deflection, 75
  stresses, 74
Cyaniding, 131
Cylinders, hydraulic, 485
  thick-walled, 463
    stress distribution, 466
    stresses, 463–466
  thin-walled, 462

Damping in vibration, 77
Decarburization, 107
Decisions, general, 13
Dedendum, 316
  meaning of, 318
Deflection, beams, 51–57
  Belleville springs, 237
  curved beams, 75
  helical spring, 227
  leaf spring, 243
  shaft, 54
  torsional, 49
Deformation, 48
  angular, 48
  in bolted connection, 187
Design factors, 156
  general, 14
  stiffness, 14
  strength, 14, 157
Design form, 165
Diagrams, equilibrium, 125
  Mohr's circle, 19
  stress-strain, 91
  torque-twist, 93
Diametral pitch, 317, 318
Die casting, 121
Direct shear stress, 92
  in beams, 28
  in bolts, 197
  in helical springs, 224
  in welds, 212
Disk clutch, 415–417
Disks, stresses in, 473–476
Distortion-energy theory, 112
Ductile material, 94
Ductility, meaning, 94
Dudley, Darle W., 335
Duraluminum, 138
Dynamic load for gears, bevel, 389–393
    helical, 372–375
    spur, 332, 334, 342–350

Eccentric loads, in bending, 26
  in bolted joints, 196
  in columns, 70
  in riveted joints, 196
  in welds, 209, 212
Eccentricity of journal bearings, 278
Eccentricity ratio, in bearings, 277
  for columns, 71
Efficiency, of power screws, 183
  of pumps, 482, 483
  of spur gears, 354
  of worm gears, 385
Elastic constants, of connected parts, 187
  effect on bolt load, 188
  effect of relative stiffnesses, 202
  relation between, 50
Elastic limit, definition, 90
  Johnson's apparent, 91
Elastic stability of columns, 67
Elasticity, definition, 49
  modulus, 49
Electric-resistance welding, 214
Electric-strain-gauge method, 9
Elevated temperature, effect of, on
      elongation, 115
    on impact, 113
    on strength, 115
Elongation percentage, 94
Empiricism, definition, 9
  discussion, 445–447
End-fixity coefficient for columns, 68, 72
Ends of springs, 228, 229, 235
Endurance limit, 100
  bolt materials, 188, 189
  effect of surface finish, 107
  gear teeth, 342
  methods to raise, 108, 188
  range of stress, 231
  spring materials, 231
  versus tensile strength, 106
  values, 106, 107
Energy-absorption measurements, 95
Energy fluctuation, values of coefficient, 479
Energy loads, 58
Energy method for finding displacements, 66
Energy storage, flywheels, 477
  springs, 239–243
Equilibrium, stable, 66
  unstable, 66
Equilibrium diagram for steel, 129
Equivalent load, antifriction bearings, 257, 259
Error in gear teeth, 346
Euler formula, 68
Eutectic alloy, 127

Eutectic temperature, 127
Eutectoid, 129
Expansion coefficient, 79
Extension springs, 227
Extrusion, 123

Face width of gear, 313, 372, 383, 386
Factor of safety, definition, 16, 158
  design, 158
  selection, 159
  true, 158
  values, 160, 213, 456
Failure, fatigue, 98
    brittle materials, 106
    theories, 109
      Hencky-von Mises, 112
    torsional fatigue, 106
Fatigue, of antifriction bearings, 253
  meaning, 98
Fatigue failure (*see* Failure, fatigue)
Fatigue strength, 99
  effect on, of decarburization, 107
    of surface condition, 107
  improvement, 108
  variation, 106
Fellows gear shaper, 326
Ferrite, 129
Fillet of gear tooth, 313, 319, 323-327
Fillet weld, 208
Film thickness of bearings, 304, 305
Fine-grained steel, 133
Fitted bearing, 278
Flanders, Ralph E., 333
Flat belts, capacity, 438
  center distances, 436
  construction, 433
  correction factor, for center distance, 439
    load, 439–440
    for pulley diameter, 439
    for service conditions, 440
  failure, 436
  friction, 440
  pulley sizes, 435, 436
  ratings, 438
  selection, 436
Flat spring, 238
Flexible shafts, 456
  construction, 457
Fluctuating load, 100
  on bolts, 203, 204
  on brittle materials, 106
  on ductile materials, 106
  on gears, 335, 343
  on springs, 230
Fluctuation coefficient, 479
Fluid coupling, 422–424
Fluid lubrication (*see* Lubrication)
Flywheels, 476
  energy storage, 477
  purpose, 476
Force, bending, 23
  shearing, definition, 23
Forging, 123
Form factor, 337, 338
Friction, ball bearings, 252
  brakes, 418
  coefficients, 184, 252, 380, 418, 440
  collar bearing, 184
  dry, 271
  flat belts, 440
  plain bearings, 275, 293
  screws, 184
  theory, 271
  worm gears, 385
Full-depth gears, 323–326
Fundamental law of toothed gearing, 315

Gas welding, 214
Gaskets, 202
Gear blanks, stresses, 359
Gear-design decisions, 335
Gear materials, endurance limits, 342
Gear teeth, acceleration loads, 344
  accuracy, 334, 345, 346
  bending, 337–342
  construction, 318
  contact stresses, 350–353
  dynamic forces on, 343
  dynamic loads on, 344
  error in, 346
  fillet, 313, 319, 323–327
  finishing, 323
  generation, 320, 321
  Hertz stresses, 351
  hobbing, 322
  loads, 331
  milling, 321
  shaping, 321
  sizes, 318
  stress-concentration factors, 339, 340
  stress distribution, 340
  surface stresses, 350
Gear-tooth systems, Fellows Gear Shaper Company stub, 326
  14½° composite, 323
  14½° full depth, 324
  for nonmetallic gears, 328
  20° full depth, 324
    for small pinions, 325
  20° involute fine pitch, 327
  20° stub involute, 326

Gears, angle, of action, 319
of approach, 319
of recess, 319
angular-velocity ratio, 316
beam strength (*see* Beam strength of gear)
bevel, 385–391
addendum, 387
back cone, 386
beam strength, 388
Lewis equation, 388
loads on, 393, 394
dynamic, 389, 390
nomenclature, 386
outboard mounting, 391
overhanging, 387
pitch angles, 386
straight, 385
strength, 387
virtual number of teeth, 387
cast-iron, properties, 355
center distances for small pinions, 326
clearance, 318
composite, 323
conjugate action, 314
crossed-helical, contact, 375
efficiency, 379
friction, 380
hand relations, 376
load-stress factors, 378
pitch diameter, 375
power loss, 380
rotation, 376
strength, 377
thrust relations, 376
tooth loads, 379
tooth proportions, 376
velocity, 379
definition, 313
deformation factors, 346
design factors, 331
dynamic loads, 332
error in action, 346
fabrication, 358
face width, 313, 372, 383, 386
forces on, 329
form factors, 338
grinding, 323
helical, contact, 367
description, 367
hand relations, 369
loads, 369
dynamic, 373
wear, 374
strength, 372
tooth proportions, 371, 372
velocity factors, 373
Gears, helical, virtual number of teeth, 369
helix angle, 368, 372
herringbone, 367
hypoid, 394
interference, 319
internal, 353
law, 315
length of contact, 320
line of action, 314
load-stress factors, 352
materials, 354–356
nonmetallic, 328, 356
pitch, 315
selection, 336
power losses, 354
pressure angle (*see* Pressure angle)
pressure line, 317
rack cutter for, 322
spiral bevel, 394
addendum, 396
loads, 397
dynamic, 396
wear, 396
strength, 395, 396
tooth proportions, 395
spur (*see* Spur gears)
tooth proportions for small pinions, 325
transmitted load, 331
undercutting, 320
velocity factors, 341
wear loads, 353
worm, 381
center distance, 382
efficiency, 385
face width, 383
form factors, 384
friction coefficient, 380
lead angle, 381, 383
load-stress factors, 385
materials, 384
nomenclature, 382
pressure angles, 383
strength, 384
wear loads, 385
Zerol bevel, 394
Generating line, 317
Geometric factor (*see* Stress-concentration factors)
Goodman law, 101
Graphical integration, procedure, 52–55
Graphite, spheroidal, 137
Gray iron, 135
Grease lubrication, 265
Grinding of gears, 323
Grooves in bearings, 307

Hard-drawn spring wire, 240–242
Hardness, case, 131
  conversion table, 97
  versus endurance limit, 108
  versus ultimate strength, 98
Heading, 124
Heat dissipation, bearings, 289, 293, 297–301
  brakes, 420
  clutches, 420
  coefficient, 300, 301, 354
  gears, 354
Heat-transfer coefficient, 420
Heat-treatment, 129
Helical gears (*see* Gears)
Helical springs, 223
  (*See also* Springs)
Helix angle, helical gear, 367
  threads, 182
  worm gear, 381
Hencky-von Mises theory of failure, 112
Herringbone gears, 367
Hertz stresses, 31
High temperature, creep at, 116
  effect of, on elongation, 115
    on strength, 115
Hobbing of gear teeth, 322
Hoisting cable, 454
  (*See also* Rope, wire)
Hooke's law, 90
  statement, 49
Horsepower equations, 23, 329
Hot rolling, 122
Hydraulic circuits, 487–489
Hydraulic machines, advantages, 481
Hydraulic pumps, types, 481
Hydrodynamic theory, 279
  (*See also* Lubrication)
Hypoeutectoid steels, 129
Hypoid gears, 394

Impact, in bolts, 204, 205
  effect of temperature, 113
  of elastic bodies, 60
  in gears, 343
  stresses due to, 60
Impact loads, 58, 60
  definition, 112
Impact strength, 113
Impact value, 113
Imperfect lubrication, 272
  (*See also* Lubrication)
Indeterminate problems, 50, 56–58, 63–66
Index, spring, 224
  toughness, 96
Initial tension, in belts, 437
  in bolts, 186–192
  in gaskets, 202
  in springs, 228
Instability, elastic, 67
Interference of gear teeth, 320
Internal gears, 353
Internal shoe brake (*see* Brakes)
Invention, steps, 153
Investment casting, 121
Involute, 315
Iron, cast, 135
  ductile, 136
  gray, 135
  malleable, 136
  white, 136
  wrought, 128
Izod test, 113

J. B. Johnson formula, 71
Journal bearings (*see* Bearings)

Keys, 205–207
Kinematic viscosity, 273

Lap joints, 208
Lasche, Oscar, 334
Law of gearing, 315
Lay of wire rope, 452
Lead of screw, 182
Lead angle of worm, 383
Leaf spring, 236
Ledeburite, 128
Length of contact in gears, 320
Length-diameter ratio of bearing, 298
Lewis, Wilfred, 332
Lewis equation, 332, 341
Lewis form factor, 337
Limit load for wear of gears, 390
  helical, 374, 377
  spur, 350
  worm, 385
Line, of action of gears, 317
  of centers of bearings, 278
Linear-expansion coefficient, 79
Linear pitch, 381
Liquidus, 125
Load-correction factor, 445–447
  bearings, 257, 258, 261, 289
  flat belts, 439, 440
  roller chain, 450, 451
  V belts, 444
Loads on gear teeth, 331
  (*See also* Gears)
Low temperature, effect on strength, 113

Lower yield point in steel, 91
Lubricants, choice, 302
  selection, 301
  specific gravity, 273, 274
Lubrication, ball bearings, 264, 265
  boundary, 272
  complete, 271
  fluid, 271
  grease, antifriction bearings, 265
  hydrodynamic, 271
  imperfect, 272
  partial, 272
  perfect, 271, 276
  principle of, 270
  purpose, 271
  requirements, 271
  stability, 277
  stable, 277
  thick-film, definition, 271
  thin-film, 271
  unstable, 277
  (*See also* Bearings)

Machine design, definition 4, 148
  kinds, 148
  study, 4
Machine designer's responsibility, 1, 10, 155, 156
Machine specifications, 148
Magnesium properties, 139
Magnetic couplings, 422
Malleability, meaning, 94
Malleable iron, 136
Manila rope, 452
Manjoine, M. J., 114
Martensite, tempered, 131
Materials, belts, 438
  brakes, 418
  clutches, 418
  gears, 346, 352, 354–356, 378, 384
  numbering systems, 117, 118
  plain bearings, 308
  prices, 173
  properties at high temperatures, 115
  screws, 190
  springs, 231, 240–242
  uses, 161
  welds, 214
  (*See also* specific materials)
Marx, Guido H., 333
Maximum-shear theory, 111
Maximum-stress theory, 109
Mean (average) stress, 100
Mechanical properties, 89–97
  chart, 132
  test specimen, 90
Milling cutter for gear teeth, 321
Mises-Hencky theory of failure, 112
Modified Goodman diagram, 101
Modulus, elasticity, 49
  resilience, 95
  rigidity, 49
  rupture, 93
  toughness, 95
Mohr's circle, 19
Moment, bending, definition, 23
Moore, H. F., 106
Motors, hydraulic reciprocating, 485
  rotary hydraulic, 484
Mounting of antifriction bearings, 266, 267
Muntz metal, 141
Music wire, 243

Naval brass, 141
Necking, 90
Needle bearings, 251
Neutral axis, 24
Neutral plane, 24
Newton's law of viscous flow, 272
Nitriding, 131
Nodular cast iron, 137
Nominal stress, 33
Nonmetallic gears, 328, 356
Normal circular pitch, 368
Normal pitch, 368
Normal stress, 24
Normalizing, 130
Notch-sensitivity index, 109
Numbering systems for materials, 117, 118
Nuts, strength, 192
  stress distribution, 192
Nylon, 356

Offset for yield strength, 91
Oil flow through bearings, 288–292, 297–300
Oil-flow variable, 285
  values, chart, 287
Oil grooves, 307
Oil supply, bearings, 294
Oil temperature of bearings, 293, 297, 300, 301, 304, 305
Oil tempered spring wire, 240
Oilless bearings, 270, 309
Oils, viscosities, 274, 284
  (*See also* Lubricants)
Optimum bearings, 306
Overhanging bevel gears, 387
Overrunning clutch, 421

Overload-release clutch, 403
Oxyacetylene welding, 214

Parabolic formula, 71
Partial bearing, 277
Patenting, definition, 243
Pearlite, 129
Percentage elongation, 94
Permanent-mold casting, 121
Petroff's law, 275
Phosphor bronze, 142, 385
Pinion cutter, 321
Piping, sizes, 485
  specifications, 486
  working pressures, 486
Pitch, axial, 368
  circular, 317
    normal, 368
    transverse, 367
  definition, 317
  diametral, 317
    normal, 368
  of gears, 315
  units, 317
Pitch angle, bevel gears, 386
Pitch circle in gears, 315
Pitch cone, 386
Pitting, 350
Pivoted shoe brake, 405
Plate clutch, 415
Plates, with concentrated loads, 471
  with fixed edges, 471
  loaded uniformly, 470
  stresses, 470–473
Plating, effect on fatigue strength, 107
Poise, definition, 273
Poisson's ratio, 50
Powder metallurgy process, 121
Power screws, coefficient of friction, 184
  design, 186
  dimensions, 182
  efficiency, 183
Preloading of bearings, 267
Pressure angle, in gears, bevel, 371
    definition, 317
    helical, 371
    worm, 383
  normal, in gears, 368
Pressure distribution in bearings, 290
Pressure line in gears, 317
Pressure vessels, 462, 463
Principal stresses, 18, 109
Processes, cost, 169
  (*See also* Materials)
Proof load, definition, 190
Properties of materials at high
    temperatures, 115
  (*See also* Materials)
Proportional limit, definition, 90
Pumps, hydraulic gear, 481
  hydraulic vane, 482
  radial plunger, 484

Quantity in relation to cost, 171
Quenching, 130

Rack cutter for gears, 322
Raimondi, Albert A., 282*n.*
Range of stress, 231
Rate of spring, 223
Rated capacity, ball bearings, 256
  flat belts, 438
  roller bearings, 263
  roller chains, 449
  V belts, 443
  wire rope, 454
Reduction in area, significance, 94
Reinforcing in welds, 208
Residual stress (*see* Stresses)
Resilience, meaning, 95
Resistance welding, 214
Reyn, definition, 272
Reynolds, Osborne, 272, 279
Rigidity, 14, 48
Ring-oiled bearing, 309
Riveted joints, 193
Rivets, shear loading, 193–195
Rockwell hardness, 96
Roll threading, 124
Roller bearings (*see* Bearings)
Roller chain, 447
  angle of articulation, 448
  capacity, 449
  dimensions, 447
  length, 450
  life, 450
  load-correction factor, 450, 451
  lubrication, 451
  nomenclature, 448
  ratings, 449
  selection, 450
  service factors, 451
  sprockets, 449
  strength, 447
  velocity, 449
Rope, cotton, 452
  manila, 452
  wire, 452
    construction, 452, 453
    designation, 453

Rope, wire, factors of safety, 456
lay of, 452
life, 455
ratings, 454
standard sizes, 454
strength, 454
stresses, 453–455
Rotating-beam fatigue test, 100
Rotating disks, 473
stresses, 475, 476

S-N diagram, 99
for antifriction bearings, 253
SAE (Society of Automotive Engineers) numbering system for steel, 117
Safety factor, 16, 158
Sand-casting, 118
Saybolt Universal viscosity, 273
Scale of spring, 223
Scleroscope hardness, 96
Screw threads, Acme, 181
modified square, 181
number per inch, 182
pitch, 182
stresses, 185
Unified, 183
Screws, efficiency, 183
friction coefficient, 184
torque requirements, 183
(*See also* Bolts)
Seals, commercial, 265
felt, 265
labyrinth, 265
Secant formula, 70
Self-aligning bearings, 249, 250
Self-energizing, 406
Self-lubricated bearings, 309
Sensitivity to stress concentration, 109
Service factor, bearings, 260
belts, 440, 444
brakes, 425
clutches, 425
roller chains, 451
Shafts, bearing reactions, 10, 25–28
bending force, 23
bending moment, 23
in combined torsion and bending, 20–22
critical speeds, 75–77
deflection, 51–58
design, 167–169
in pure bending, 23
stiffness, 51–58
in torsion, 22, 23, 48
Shear, in bolts, 193–201
direct, 92
force, 16, 28
Shear, primary, 197
Shear center, meaning, 26
Shearing strain, 48
Shearing stress, 17
definition, 16
maximum combined, 111
in springs, 223–226
torsional, 22
Sheaves, V belt, 441
wire rope, 454
Shell molding, 120
Shock loads, 112, 113
Shot peening, 108, 231
Shrink fits, 467
stresses due to, 468
Side flow, bearings, 289
correction factor, 288–290
Silicon bronze, 141
Sintering, 121
Slaymaker, Robert R., 294*n.*
Sleeve bearings (*see* Bearings, journal)
Slenderness ratio, 66
Society of Automotive Engineers, (SAE), 116, 117
Soderberg, C. R., 102
Soderberg law, 102
Solidus, 125
Sommerfeld number, 283
Specific gravity of lubricants, 273, 274
Specifications, form, 149
of machine, 149
Speed-fluctuation coefficient, 477
Spherical roller bearing, 250
Spheroidized graphite, 137
Spinning, 124
Spiral gears, 394–398
Splines, 205
Spring index, definition, 224
values, 225
Spring scale, 223
Springs, active coils, 229
Belleville, 237
cantilever, 238
close-wound, 228
compression, ends, 229
constant, 223, 227
critical speed, 239
dead coils, 229
deflection, 227, 235
extension, 227
fatigue strength, 231
flat, 238
helical, 223
leaf, 236, 243
materials, 231, 240–242
rate, 223
shot peening, 231

Springs, special section, 225
  tension, 228
  torsion, 235
  Wahl correction factor, 224
Sprockets, 448
Spur gears, 313
  arms, 360
  bead, 357
  hubs, 356
  materials, 354
  nomenclature, 313
  pitch, 318
  rim, 359
  welded construction, 358
  (*See also* Gears)
Square threads, 181
  efficiency, 183
  force analysis, 182, 183
  pitch, 182
Stainless steels, 117, 135
Stamping, 124
Steel castings, 119
Steels, alloy, 132, 133
  carbon, 128, 129
  cast, 133
  chemical composition, 128
  chromium, 132
  chromium nickel, 135
  coarse-grained, 130
  cold-drawn, 124
  constitution, 129
  cost, 173
  creep, 116
  effect on, of carbon, 131
    of temperature, 113, 115
  fine-grained, 133
  hardening, 130
  heat-treatment, 129
  hot-rolled, 122
  hypereutectoid, 129
  manganese, 133
  molybdenum, 133
  nickel, 132
  numbering systems, 117
  properties, cast carbon, 134
  quenching, 130
  silicon, 133
  stainless, 135
    numbering systems, 117
  tensile strength, 132
  transformation, 129
  tungsten, 133
  uses, 161
  vanadium, 133
  yield point, 91
Stiffness coefficient, bolts, 202
  definition, 186
Straight bevel gears, 385
  (*See also* Gears)
Strain, biaxial, 51
  definition, 48
  shearing, 48
Strain energy, in bending, 62
  compressive, 58, 59
  tensile, 58, 59
  torsional, 61
Strain-rate values, 114
Strains, thermal, 78
Strength, definition, 89, 157
  in direct shear, values, 93
  effect on, of strain rate, 114
    of temperature, 115
  fatigue (*see* Fatigue strength)
  gears (*see* Gears)
  machine member, 157
  material, 157
  nuts, 192
  roller chain, 447
  tensile (*see* Tensile strength)
  torsional, ultimate, 93
  ultimate, 91
  yield, 91
Stress, alternating, 100
  bearing, 195
  bending, definition, 24
  circle of, 19
  compressive (*see* Compression stress)
  design, 158
  direction, 18
  endurance range, 230, 231
  longitudinal, 462
  nominal, 90
    definition, 33
  normal, 24
  residual (*see* Stresses)
  shearing (*see* Shearing stress)
  tangential, 462
  tensile, definition, 16
  torsional, distribution, 94
  true, 90
  working, 158
Stress concentration, charts, 34–38
  fatigue, 104, 108, 109
  meaning, 32
  reduction, 40
Stress-concentration factors, bolts, 202
  gear teeth, 339, 340
  springs, 224–226
    torsion, 235
  welds, 213
Stress range, 101
Stress-strain diagram, 91
  for bolt materials, 191

Stresses, bearings (*see* Bearings)
  bending, 23
  biaxial, 111
  in columns, 68
  combined, 17–22
    equations, 18
    meaning, 17
  contact, 31
  curved beams, 73
  cylinders, 463
    (*See also* Cylinders)
  fluctuating, 100
    in springs, 230
  gear teeth (*see* Gear teeth)
  normal, in bending, 24
    definition, 18
  nuts, 192
  pipe, 462
  planes, 18
  principal, definition, 18
    normal, 109
  pulsating, 100
  radial, 463
  repeating, 100
  residual, 108, 130
    causes, 131
    in springs, 229
    in welds, 207, 208
  reversed, 100
  screw-thread, 185
  shear, 27
  superposition, 30
  thermal, 77, 78
    definition, 78
  in thin-walled cylinders, 462
  torsional, definition, 22
  in welds, 210, 211, 213
Stub teeth, 326
Superposition, for deflections, 55
  of stresses, 30

Tapered roller bearing, 260
  capacity, 263
  selection, 259
  thrust, 264
Temper carbon, 136
Temperature, effect on steel, 115, 116
Tempering, purpose, 131
Tensile strength, 91
  belts, 438
  bolt materials, 191
  roller chain, 447
  spring materials, 240–242
  steel, 132
  wire rope, 454
Tension springs, 227
Tension test, 91
Testing, compressive, 92
  creep, 116
  direct shear, 92
  fatigue strength, 99
  hardness, 96
  impact, 113
  notched bar, 113
  rotating beam, 100
  tensile, 90
  torsional, 93
Theories of failure, 109
  maximum-shear, 111
  maximum-stress, 109, 110
  von Mises-Hencky, 112
Thermal expansion, 79
Thick cylinders (*see* Cylinders)
Thick-film lubrication, 271
Thin-film lubrication, 271
Thin-wall pressure vessel, 462
Thread angle, 183
Threads (*see* Screw threads)
Thrust bearing, 264
  ball, 249, 264
  collar, 184
  plain, 308
  roller, 250
  segmented, 307
Tightening torque, bolts, 191
Timing belts, 435
Timken Engineering Journal, 260
Timken roller bearings, 259
Tolerances, costs, 172
Tooth thickness, 323–327
Torque, 22
  brake, 409
  clutch, 409
  from horsepower, 23
Torque converters, 422
Torsion springs, 235
Toughness, determination, 95, 96
  meaning, 95
Toughness index number, 96
Tower, Beauchamp, 279
Tubing specifications, 486
Two-dimensional stress, 17–22

Ultimate strength, 91
Undercutting in gears, 320
Understressing, 108
Unified threads, 183
Unsymmetric sections in bending, 26
Upper yield point in steel, 91

Wahl, A. M., 224
Wahl correction factor, 224

Wear, clutches, 416
  gears, 353, 374, 385, 396
Weldability, 214
Welded gear blanks, 358
Welded joints, 207
Welds, factors of safety, 213
  stresses, 210, 211, 213
White cast iron, 136
Whitworth threads, 202
  (*See also* Screw threads)
Whole-depth tooth (*see* Gear-tooth systems)
Width of face of gear, 313
Wire rope (*see* Rope)
Working stress, 158
Worm (*see* Gears, worm)
Wrought iron, 128

Yellow brass, 140
Yield point, 91
Yield strength, 91
  torsional, 93
  (*See also* Materials)

Zerol gears, 394